048

ANIMAL AGENTS AND VECTORS OF HUMAN DISEASE

By

Ernest Carroll Faust, A.B., M.A., Ph.D.

*Emeritus Professor of Parasitology, Department of Tropical Medicine and Public Health,
The Tulane University of Louisiana, New Orleans, La.; Emeritus Professor, Facultad
de Medicina, Universidad del Valle, Cali, Colombia; Honorary Professor, Facultad
de Medicina, Universidad de Chile and Universidad Nacional, Bogotá,
Colombia; Member, Expert Panel on Parasitic Diseases, World Health
Organization; Member, Committee on Revision, U.S. Pharmacopeia,
1950–1960,*

Paul Chester Beaver, A.B., M.S., Ph.D.

*The William Vincent Professor of Tropical Diseases and Hygiene, and Head, Division of
Parasitology, Department of Tropical Medicine and Public Health, The Tulane
University of Louisiana, New Orleans, La.; Member, Commission on Parasitic
Diseases, Armed Forces Epidemiological Board, Editor American Journal of
Tropical Medicine and Hygiene,*

and

Rodney Clifton Jung, B.S., M.D., M.S., Ph.D.

*Associate Professor of Tropical Medicine and Head, Division of Tropical Medicine,
Department of Tropical Medicine and Public Health, The Tulane University of
Louisiana, New Orleans, La.; Senior Visiting Physician, The Charity Hospital
of Louisiana, New Orleans; Consultant in Tropical Medicine, U.S. Veterans
Administration and of the U.S. Public Health Service Hospital,
New Orleans, La.*

Second Edition, Thoroughly Revised
195 Text Figures, 10 Plates, Including Six in Color

LEA & FEBIGER

Philadelphia

Preface

DURING the seven years which have elapsed since the publication of the first edition of this volume medical parasitology has progressed along a broad front, including increased knowledge of those animals which are themselves human parasites and those which are vectors to man of pathogenic microörganisms. More and more there is an appreciation of the need to understand that parasite-host relationships are the result of many variable factors, involving the metabolism of the parasite itself, the compatibility of man and other animals to serve as hosts for a given strain of the parasite, and the community in which both parasite and host occur. A particular combination of these variables will determine the degree of human exposure, the adjustment of the parasite or microörganism which it as vector transmits to man as host, and the welfare of the human community. Elucidation of these factors one by one will provide a guide for control of the infection by therapeutic procedures, by environmental sanitation, and by education in personal and group hygiene.

This volume is intended to serve as a *textbook in medical parasitology,* and is not designed as an exhaustive manual; yet it is more than a syllabus. For the medical or college student, the laboratory diagnostician or public health worker who desires to obtain more extensive information on a particular topic, a list of selected references will be found at the end of each chapter.

This second edition constitutes a thorough revision. Some chapters have been rewritten in their entirety, others have been measurably modified to include recent facts. Some tables included in the first edition and not regarded as essential for the scope of this volume have been omitted. A considerable number of new illustrations have been added or have been substituted for less satisfactory ones.

The authors have undertaken this revision as a cooperative project and are in agreement with reference to the major objectives and relative amount of emphasis placed on each subject. Although the senior author has assumed responsibility for the overall editorial policy, the other authors have contributed important portions of the new volume. Grateful acknowledgement is extended to all persons who have assisted by helpful suggestion and criticism in the development of this edition, and particularly are the authors indebted to Lea & Febiger for their advice and cooperation in its preparation and publication.

ERNEST CARROLL FAUST
PAUL C. BEAVER
RODNEY C. JUNG

NEW ORLEANS, LOUISIANA

(3)

Contents

Important General References
to the Literature

ASH, J E., and SPITZ, S. 1945. *Pathology of Tropical Diseases. An Atlas*, 350 pp. W. B. Saunders Co., Philadelphia.

BELDING, D. L. 1952. *Textbook of Clinical Parasitology*, 1130 pp, Appleton-Century-Crofts, New York.

BROWN, H. W. 1961. Parasitology, Parasitic Diseases and Medicine. Presidential Address. J. Parasitol., *47*, 1–9.

BRUMPT, E. 1949. *Précis de Parasitologie*, 6th ed. Vols. I and II, 2138 pp., Masson & Cie., Paris.

CHANDLER, A. C., and READ, C. P. 1961. *Introduction to Parasitology*, 10th ed., 822 pp., John Wiley & Sons, Inc., New York.

FAUST, E. C. 1949. *Human Helminthology*, 3rd ed., 744 pp., Lea & Febiger, Philadelphia.

FAUST, E. C., and RUSSELL, P. F. 1957. Craig and Faust's *Clinical Parasitology*, 6th ed., 1078 pp., Lea & Febiger, Philadelphia.

HERMS, W. B., and JAMES, M. T. 1961. *Medical Entomology*, 5th ed., 615 pp., The Macmillan Co., New York.

HULL, T. G. 1962. *Diseases Transmitted from Animals to Man.*, 5th ed., (In Press). Charles C Thomas, Springfield, Ill.

HUNTER, G. W., III, FRYE, W. W., and SWARTZWELDER, J. C. 1960. *Manual of Tropical Medicine*, 3rd ed., 892 pp., W. B. Saunders Co., Philadelphia.

KUDO, R. R. 1954. *Protozoology*, 6th ed., 966 pp., Charles C Thomas, Springfield, Ill.

MANWELL, R. D. 1961. *Introduction to Protozoology*, 675 pp., St. Martin's Press, New York.

MARKELL, E. K., and VOGE, MARIETTA. 1958. *Diagnostic Medical Parasitology*, 276 pp., W. B. Saunders Co., Philadelphia.

MATHESON, R. 1950. *Medical Entomology*, 2nd ed., 612 pp., Comstock Publ. Co., Ithaca, N.Y.

NOBLE, E. R., and NOBLE, G. A. 1961. *Parasitology. The Biology of Animal Parasites*, 767 pp., Lea & Febiger, Philadelphia.

SPENCER, F. M., and MONROE, L. 1961. *The Color Atlas of Intestinal Parasites*, 142 pp., Charles C Thomas, Springfield, Ill.

WHITLOCK, J. H. 1960. *Diagnosis of Veterinary Parasitisms*, 236 pp., Lea & Febiger, Philadelphia.

Animal Agents and Vectors of Human Disease

SECTION I

General Principles and Orientation

Chapter 1

Introduction. Parasite-Host-Community

THE PHENOMENA OF PARASITISM

AMONG the evolutionary processes which have been under way during countless millenia perhaps the most interesting are the adaptations to a parasitic mode of life. Many illustrations are found among the lower groups in the Plant Kingdom, including the viruses, rickettsiæ, bacteria, fungi and spirochetes. Even more important from the standpoint of evolutionary changes are the parasites belonging to the Animal Kingdom, because they have originated from so many phylogenetic stems, from the simplest one-celled organisms to man himself. Yet parasitism varies widely with respect to the degree of adaptation, including morphological simplification and physiological readjustments which have resulted from a dependent relationship (Baer, 1951; Cameron, 1956).

A *parasite* is an organism which has found and utilizes a source of shelter and provision for its metabolic needs on, or in some other organism, the *host*, which is usually larger than itself. In some instances this association is helpful both to parasite and host: this is *mutualism*, as illustrated by the protozoan fauna in the digestive tract of the termites and wood roaches. The parasite may benefit without detectable damage to the host, as is the case of *Entamœba coli*, a common inhabitant of the large intestine of man. This relationship is termed *commensalism*. The designation *parasitism* possibly suggests that the parasite is harmful to its host, but the successful parasite has reached a delicate equilibrium with its host so that each tolerates the other well. If the balance is upset the host may spontaneously evacuate or destroy the parasite, or, on the other extreme, the association may be so detrimental to the host that the latter succumbs to the infection and the parasite may likewise be destroyed. In contrast to the parasite

(7)

there is the *predator*, an animal usually larger than its victim or prey, which is consumed whole or in part as a source of food.

Many parasites have closely related free-living kindred, as, for example, the amebæ, flagellate and ciliate protozoans, and the nematodes. Other groups have become exclusively parasitic, for example, the hematozoa, the nematode group of the filariæ, the tapeworms and digenetic trematodes. The agents of malaria, the leishmaniæ and trypanosomes, as well as the filariæ, have lost all vestiges of a former free-living existence. Yet a majority of the parasitic nematodes, the tapeworms and digenetic trematodes have retained at least one residual stage of their earlier ways of life. Depending on its surroundings, the nematode *Strongyloides stercoralis* still exhibits a wide range of possibilities from development exclusively within the host (internal autoinfection) to exclusive free-living propagation.

Most insects and other arthropods which obtain blood or tissue juices from vertebrates are in contact with these sources of food for very limited periods, but some ticks remain on their host during their entire active life. Lice, the chigoe flea, and several crustaceans (the parasitic copepods, the branchiurid *Argulus* and the barnacle *Sacculina*) are parasitic for all or a considerable part of their life.

Organisms which live on or within the skin of their hosts are *ectoparasites*. In animal parasitology this relationship is an *infestation*. Most parasitic arthropods belong to this category. Parasites of the digestive tract, extra-intestinal organs and tissues, and those which are intra-cellular within the host, are referred to as *endoparasites* and produce *infection*, irrespective of their size.

In earlier decades parasitism was commonly regarded as a degenerate form of life. This is now known to be an inaccurate appraisal. Because the parasite has achieved a relatively secure ecological niche, typically with an abundant food supply, it has gradually lost those morphological features no longer useful for its survival, but it has developed physiological and biochemical adaptations needed for its new associations (Stauber, 1960). It has at times changed its metabolic pathways to conform to an anaërobic environment, and it has elaborated anti-enzymes to counteract the harmful by-products of the host (Bueding, 1949; Smyth, 1947). The use of labeled isotopes is a valuable tool in the elucidation of these processes.

To assure itself of continued existence, the endoparasite has developed means for reaching and entering its host as well as maintenance of its position within the host once it had arrived (Cameron, 1956). In order to guarantee that some of its progeny will survive and reach the next host, it has elaborated enormously its reproductive potential. Considering the complexity of the life cycles of many parasites, their chances of miscarriage in transfer of a particular stage of the parasite from one susceptible host to another, it is a matter of wonder that so many thousands of species of parasites have succeeded in their evolutionary transformation from a free-living to a parasitic mode of life, and in consequence have been able to maintain themselves satisfactorily in their new environment.

Parasitism in the Animal Kingdom has evolved as a polyphyletic phenomenon at various times in past ages, partly as a method of survival following the accidental ingestion of the parasite-to-be by the host-to-be, or after its entry into the skin (no doubt initially through a cutaneous abrasion). After a multitude of trials and almost as many failures, a few successes were achieved. This transformation from a free-living to a parasitic existence, like all other evolutionary events, has been and still is a continuing dynamic process, gradually focusing on the more successful adaptations and eliminating those less advantageous (Villee, Walker and Smith, 1958). Coprozoic flagellates and rhabitid nematodes, which are at times recovered from human excreta, probably represent some of the many organisms in the early stages of adaptation to parasitism, while *Trypanosoma rangeli*, a parasite of the triatomid bug *Rhodnius prolixus*, is apparently just becoming adapted to secondary mammalian hosts.

It is not difficult to understand how free-living aquatic animals, having been fortuitously introduced into the digestive tract of a metazoön living in the same environment, gradually became adapted to the new *milieu*. Perhaps in the beginning only one in a million succeeded but later, with physiological modifications, the parasite-host relationship became easier to accomplish and more secure. Even then transfer to a new host remained hazardous. Within their adopted hosts some of the parasites elaborated enzymes which allowed them to penetrate into, and multiply in the intestinal wall, thus achieving a more intimate tissue relationship with the host. The coccidia, like most species of parasitic amebæ, must have been originally lumen dwellers in their host's intestine, then perhaps for greater security lodged in the glandular crypts, secreted newly developed digestive enzymes, and penetrated into the wall, as *Entamœba histolytica* is often able to do in the human large intestine. Probably the malaria parasites, too, had their earliest parasitic life in the intestinal canal of their present-day vertebrate host, and later penetrated into the intestinal wall, where they multiplied. From this site their progeny reached the blood stream and they proceeded to enter and multiply in the red blood corpuscles. If this line of reasoning is correct, the mosquito came into the picture somewhat later as alternate host of the malaria parasites when the mosquito took blood from the infected vertebrate, serving first as a mechanical vector, then as an incubator, and finally as the essential host for the sexual phase of the life cycle.

Another type of complication in the life cycle which has been developed by the parasite is illustrated by the roundworm *Ascaris lumbricoides*, which as an adult is typically a lumen parasite of the small intestine. Once the infective-stage egg gets into the human mouth as a contamination from the outside world and is swallowed, hatching occurs in the duodenum and the larva undertakes a required journey to the lungs, where it molts twice, with growth each time, then migrates *via* the air passages and upper part of the digestive tract to the small intestine, where it develops into the adult worm. The hookworms, *Strongyloides*, and the blood flukes (*schistosomes*) actively enter the human body by the cutaneous route, with required migration to the lungs before proceeding to the sites where they mature. Appropriate species of insect intermediate hosts introduce the infective stage of the leishmaniæ, trypanosomes and filariæ into the skin, to initiate infection in the human or other susceptible vertebrate host. These and many other complexities have been developed as useful adaptations by the parasites.

Once an organism has become committed to parasitism, with rare exceptions the situation is irreversible. The parasite can no longer choose freedom. Not only has it lost certain of its original morphological features essential for free-living existence, but more importantly its physiological and biochemical changes have fitted it only for parasitism. Parasites have lost their ability to synthesize certain substances which are provided in adequate amount by their hosts (Bueding, 1949). Many of these modifications are genetic in nature. Descriptive information of such phenomena is considerable but knowledge of the exact mechanisms is very scanty.

THE HOST, THE INFECTED INDIVIDUAL

The host is the organism which harbors the parasite. Read (1958) has remarked: "For the establishment of parasitism, the environmental characteristics in or on a host must be compatible with the life requirements of the parasite . . . if the initial events of establishment involve multiple physical or chemical stimuli leading to the alteration of behavioral or other physiological characteristics of the parasite, it may be expected that the duration and sequence of these environmental stimuli may be important in promoting or preventing establishment of parasitism."

In many instances the parasite is able to colonize in a wide range of hosts. Possibly an example of the widest host compatibility is found in the heterophyid trematodes, some species of which are known to parasitize all birds and mammals which eat infected raw fish. Likewise mammals which consume vegetation on which the encysted larvæ of the liver flukes *Fasciola hepatica* and *F. gigantica* have become attached are subject to infection. In contrast, many parasites are limited to a single optimum host, for example the human hookworms *Ancylostoma duodenale* and *Necator americanus*, and the pinworm *Enterobius vermicularis*. *Ascaris lumbricoides* of man and pig is essentially indistinguishable morphologically, but it is probably not often that man becomes infected with the porcine strain in spite of frequent exposure. These and other examples indicate that in many host-parasite relationships there is an associated host specificity (Talmage, 1959). Increasing evidence suggests that the major factor involved in this specificity is immunological, resulting from delicate biochemical adjustments between certain hosts and certain parasites, adjustments which have developed gradually through the ages (Stauber, 1960). Much can be learned in this area from an intensive study of antibodies, their nature, diversity, cross reactions and the immune tolerance which they produce.

As in other evolutionary processes, so in host-parasite relationships geographical contiguity or isolation has played an important role. The human blood flukes belonging to the genus *Schistosoma* provide an interesting example. *S. japonicum* is widely distributed throughout the Orient, *S. hæmatobium* from India throughout Africa to Portugal, and *S. mansoni* from Arabia throughout Africa and, due to its introduction within recent centuries, also in several foci of tropical America. It has been demonstrated that there are notable host incompatibilities in strains of the same species of these blood flukes from different geographical areas.

Transmitters of parasites are their *vectors*. If the transmitter is not essential in the life cycle, it is a *mechanical vector*; if it is essential, it is a *biological vector*. A *reservoir host* is an animal species on which the parasite depends for its survival in nature and thus serves as a source of infection for other susceptible hosts, including man. *Zoönosis* is the term applied to a disease of animals which may be transmitted to man as well as to each other. Susceptible human beings at times become infected with the mature or larval stage of the parasite directly or indirectly from the animal source. This may be a common or an incidental occurrence. Arthropod-transmitted (*i.e.*, arbor) viruses, rickettsiæ, bacteria and spirochetes for the most part do not often parasitize man but there are notable exceptions, *viz.*, urban yellow fever and dengue (virus origin), louse-borne typhus fever (rickettsiosis), urban plague (bacterial origin), and louse-borne relapsing fever (spirochetosis). Chagas' disease, due to *Trypanosoma cruzi*, the leishmaniases, African trypanosomiases and even malaria, all of which today are prevalent in man, probably originated exclusively as animal diseases. Blood-fluke infection in China, Japan and the Philippines, caused by *Schistosoma japonicum*, is today for the most part a human disease, but in Formosa man is refractory to the autochthonous strain of this etiologic agent, which parasitizes domestic and wild mammals. The cat ascarid *Toxocara felis* has been reported occasionally as an intestinal parasite of man. The related dog ascarid *T. canis* and the tropical dog hookworm *Ancylostoma braziliense* initiate infection in man but during the required migration to the lungs their larval stages wander through host tissues, causing extra-intestinal lesions.

Not only are there differences in susceptibility of hosts of different species to a particular parasite or its products, but there are differences in susceptibility among different individuals of the same host species. For example, when an insect introduces a droplet of its saliva into the skin of some individuals there is essentially no reaction, while in other persons there are severe local and systemic consequences. Moreover, following colonization of animal parasites within the human body some persons exhibit essentially no effects while others become acutely ill. The Negro is as susceptible as are other racial groups to tertain malaria but he tolerates the infection much better than persons of other races. Likewise native populations which are repeatedly exposed to infection with *Entamœba histolytica* may be essentially asymptomatic carriers, whereas newcomers to the endemic area who are exposed to the same strains of this ameba at times develop severe amebic colitis.

In some parasitic diseases an original exposure may stimulate sufficient antibody reaction to the foreign antigen to confer lasting immunity. A good illustration is cutaneous leishmaniasis produced by *Leishmania tropica*. In other instances, such as malaria, trichinosis, ascariasis, hookworm infections, filariasis and schistosomiasis, an original infection stimulates humoral and tissue responses which provide a variable degree of host refractoriness to superinfection, especially if the parasite is of the same strain as that to which the individual was earlier exposed. Such immunological responses are most notable when the parasite has a required route of migration through the body of the host.

THE PARASITE AND ITS ENVIRONMENT

The information presented thusfar has concerned the parasite and its immediate environment, *viz.*, the host to which it has become adapted in its transformation to a parasitic life. The host is the ecological niche, but the host and the parasite which it harbors live in a larger environment, the community. This macrocosm consists not only of a variable number of susceptible hosts but also of other animals and plants in competition with one another. All of these organisms are subject to climatic conditions, such as temperature, rainfall, abundance or scarcity of food, and over-crowding. Favorable or unfavorable factors which affect the host likewise affect the parasite, its ability to survive and to gain transfer from one host to the next.

When man or domestic animals of economic importance are the hosts, certain aspects of the parastic-host-community relationship which are not solely academic in nature come into focus. This is especially true when the parasite is harmful to the individual and hence to the community. In tropical Africa tsetse flies serve not only as biological vectors for trypanosomes which produce disease in man but are biological vectors of these and other species of pathogenic trypanosomes which infect cattle and thus endanger the major food supply of millions of native Africans. Here the economic picture greatly complicates the problem of human trypanosomiasis, resulting in human malnutrition. This and many other instances illustrate how parasitosis in domestic animals may endanger human well-being, and in consequence may reduce tolerance to the diseases to which man is exposed.

CLASSIFICATION OF ANIMAL PARASITES AND VECTORS

Three groups of animals are of major importance in medical parasitology, *viz.*, the protozoa, helminths and arthropods. These organisms are classified according to the Rules of Zoological Nomenclature (International Commission on Zoological Nomenclature, 1926, 1961). Within the ANIMAL KINGDOM there are first the larger divisions, Phylum and Subphylum, then successive lesser divisions consisting of Classes, Orders and Families down to Genus and Species (Pease, 1949). All of these names must be of Greek or Latin origin, or have a classical termination.

A *species* designates a population, the members of which have essentially the same genetic characters and are capable of continued reproduction of their kind, but usually can not interbreed with individuals of other species (Mayr, 1957). A *genus* is a group of closely related species.

The scientific designation of a species is a combination of the genus and species names, *viz.*, for the domestic dog, *Canis* (genus), *familiaris* (species). This is referred to as *binomial nomenclature*, which originated in the tenth edition of Linnæus' *Systema Naturæ* (1758). The genus name is always a noun, while the species name may be an adjective agreeing in gender and number with the noun, a noun in apposition with the genus name or a noun in the genitive case. Examples of these three categories are: *Entamœba histolytica*, *Giardia lamblia* and *Plasmodium malariæ*. Proper usage requires that the scientific binomial be printed in *Italics*; the genus name begins with a capital letter, while the species name, including the first letter, is in lower case, even if the name originates from a proper noun, such as a person or country. For additional information on the Rules of Zoölogical Nomenclature and their application, the reader is referred to Faust and Russell's *Clinical Parasitology*, 6th. ed., (1957), pages 39–48.

The Protozoa

The protozoa are animals which consist of a single cell that performs all of the functions of animal life. They all belong to the PHYLUM *Protozoa*, which contains the following four subphyla:

Subphylum MASTIGOPHORA (the flagellates), each member of which possesses relatively long filamentous processes of ectoplasm, the *flagella*, which are the locomotor organs. Many species are free-living, others are parasitic. The flagellates which parasitize man belong to two groups, those in the digestive and genital tracts, and those which parasitize the blood and tissues.

Subphylum SARCODINA, in which the members are characterized by having finger-like ectoplasmic organelles called *pseudopodia*, which serve in procurement of food and for locomotion. Many species are free-living but some are parasitic, including six species of amebæ (FAMILY Endamœbidæ) which live in the digestive tract of man.

Subphylum CILIOPHORA (the ciliates), the members of which possess numerous short thread-like ectoplasmic extensions, the *cilia*, which serve in locomotion. Many species are free-living, others are parasitic, including *Balantidium coli*, an intestinal parasite of man.

Subphylum SPOROZOA, the members of which are typically not provided with special organelles for locomotion, but which, unlike the other subphyla, have an alternation of asexual and sexual generations in their life cycle. All members of this group are parasites. Species which parasitize man includes the coccidia, malaria parasites and *Sarcocystis*.

The Helminths

The helminths are metazoa which belong to five separate phyla, the Platyhelminthes, Acanthocephala, Nematoda, Nematomorpha and Annelida.

PHYLUM **Platyhelminthes** (flatworms), containing organisms which are bilaterally symmetrical, usually flattened dorso-ventrally, with three body layers. They lack a body cavity as well as true segmentation, and have a bilateral excretory system ending internally in "flame cells." The Class Turbellaria, which is almost exclusively free-living, has a ciliated epithelium. Two classes are exclusively parasitic, *viz.*, the Trematoda and the Cestoidea.

Class TREMATODA (trematodes or flukes), the members of which are single-unit, usually hermaphroditic worms lacking ciliated epithelium except in the larva hatched from the egg. The digenetic trematodes have three or more consecutive stages in their life cycle. Many species parasitize man.

Class CESTOIDEA (tapeworms), hermaphroditic worms, most species of which constitute a chain consisting of a scolex (head), neck and a variable number of sexually complete units arising from the neck (region of growth) and becoming mature more distally. Several species parasitize man.

PHYLUM **Acanthocephala** (thorny-headed worms), containing forms which are exclusively parasitic; consisting of a non-segmented body and an anterior proboscis usually armed with spines; sexes separate; they require an arthropod intermediate host. Two species are potential parasites of man.

PHYLUM **Nematoda** (true roundworms), containing bilaterally symmetrical, unsegmented, elongated, cylindroidal worms, with a complete digestive tract and body cavity not lined with mesothelium (schizocele); the sexes are usually separate. Many species are free-living, others parasitic. A considerable number are important human parasites.

PHYLUM **Nematomorpha** ("hair snakes"), containing bilaterally symmetrical, unsegmented, elongated, cylindroidal worms, with atrophied digestive tract in the adults, and true body cavity; sexes separate; developing from larva to maturity in hemocele of insects; adults free in water. Many species are accidental or spurious parasites of man.

PHYLUM **Annelida,** consisting of worms which are bilaterally symmetrical and have true segmentation (metamerism) but lack true appendages. Members of the Class HIRUDINEA (leeches), at times accidental parasites of man.

The Arthropods

PHYLUM **Arthropoda.** This very extensive group comprises bilaterally symmetrical metazoa, with true segmentation, jointed appendages and a chitinous exoskeleton which may be impregnated with lime. The sexes are typically separate. Most arthropods are free-living, but many species have adaptations for sucking blood, others are ectoparasites, and several are venomous. Still others serve as essential hosts in the life cycle of protozoan and helminth parasites.

Class EUCRUSTACEA, containing several species which are necessary intermediate hosts of helminth parasites of man.

Class ARACHNIDA, containing two orders, each with several venomous species harmful to man, *viz.,* Scorpiones (scorpions) and Araneæ (spiders); likewise the Acari (ticks and mites), some of which are essential vectors of disease-producing organisms as well as annoying ectoparasites of man.

Class INSECTA, containing the Anoplura (sucking lice), Heteroptera (true bugs), Diptera (flies), Siphonaptera (fleas), Coleoptera (beetles), Hymenoptera (bees, wasps, ants, etc.), Lepidoptera (moths and butterflies), etc. Many insects are required biological vectors of human parasites, others are mechanical vectors, and still others are venomous or annoying human pests.

In addition to the three groups outlined above the PHYLUM **Mollusca** (snails and lamellibranchs) contains many species which are required intermediate hosts of trematodes that cause widespread human disease.

More detailed information on these various parasites and vectors will be found in subsequent chapters in the text dealing with the respective organisms.

PATHOGENESIS AND SYMPTOMATOLOGY

PARASITES which produce injury to their hosts are *pathogens* and the development of this damage is *pathogenesis*. The degree of injury to the hosts depends on a variety of factors, including the virulence of the agent (*i.e.*, its intrinsic pathogenicity), the amount of the inoculum and the rapidity with which it may multiply in host tissues, the site of inoculation, whether the exposure is single or repeated, the tolerance or resistance of the host for the particular strain of the agent, and the general threshold of resistance of the host. The type of damage produced may be primarily mechanical, lytic (digestive), intoxicative or allergenic in nature, or the lesion produced by the parasite may open a way for bacteria and other secondary pathogens to enter the tissues (Faust and Russell, 1957).

The reaction of the host has a distinct bearing on the immediate and subsequent effects of the pathogen (Anderson *et al.*, 1953; Ash and Spitz, 1945; Gould, 1945; Maegraith *et al.*, 1951; Most *et al.*, 1950; Rhoads *et al.*, 1934). In some parasitoses the host may be essentially unresponsive, as in an uncomplicated intestinal infection with *Entamœba histolytica*. In other instances the host may elaborate specific antibodies in an attempt to counteract the antigens introduced by the foreign agent, or may attempt to wall off the invader or its products by cellular infiltration into the affected area. The host response may be essentially local at the site of injury or it may include systemic humoral or cellular changes, or a histamine-like reaction.

The *symptoms* are the manifestations of the pathological processes resulting from the effects of the pathogenic agent. The physician starts with the patient's complaint and by experience and careful analysis attempts to ascertain the cause of the illness.

DIAGNOSIS AND TREATMENT

With very few exceptions laboratory diagnosis is essential for a definitive diagnosis of parasitic diseases (Markell and Voge, 1958). Three Plates are provided in this section to assist the student in his development of an overall picture of the most common parasite objects and artifacts in the excreta seen under the light microscope. Plate I includes the vegetative and cystic stages of the intestinal protozoa and their close relatives. Plate II shows the eggs and larvæ of the important helminths observed in the feces, urine and sputum. Plate III provides illustrations of a variety of objects found in the feces which may be mistaken for parasites.

The objectives of treatment of disease are four-fold, *viz.*, to alleviate pain and other severe manifestations of disease, to remove the cause of the symptoms, to institute therapy against associated causes of the disease syndrome, and to provide chemotherapeutic prophylaxis. All of these objectives are employed in the field of parasitic infections. At times supportive and alleviative therapy is desirable preceding or associated with specific therapy, as in acute amebic dysentery and severe hookworm disease. In some types of parasitosis, as hydatid cyst and cysticercosis, no chemotherapy is available but surgical removal of the parasite may be curative or at least remedial. In many parasitoses there are today specific chemotherapeutics which are relatively well tolerated and serve to eliminate the infections in a high percentage of cases (See Table 7, p. 416).

Many drugs are effective because they function as antimetabolites. (Antimetabolites resemble certain essential metabolites, such as vitamins and hormones.) By combining with a specific enzyme or other metabolic agent the antimetabolite interferes with normal metabolic activity, creating a deficiency of the natural metabolite. For example, the antibiotic erythromycin inhibits synthesis of proteins in protozoan cells and is a specific in intestinal amebic infection (Woolley, 1959). The trivalent antimonials interfere with a single step in the glycolytic pathway of the blood flukes and hence are specifically valuable in treating the disease which they produce (Bueding and Swartzwelder, 1957). The antimalarials quinine, chloroquine and quinacrine directly inhibit RNA exchange and DNA synthesis, while pyrimethamine inhibits DNA synthesis (Schellenberg and Coatney, 1959).

Likewise, insect toxicants, when brought in contact with harmful arthropods, function as antimetabolites in a variety of ways, including inhibition of activity of acetylcholinesterase and other enzymes (Winteringham and Lewis, 1959).

Chemoprophylaxis is the use of drugs over a period when persons are liable to exposure to infectious organisms. Quinacrine, chloroquine, amodiaquin, chlorguanide and pyrimethamine, when taken prophylactically, prevent development of *falciparum* malaria but not of the other three types of human malaria, which they suppress temporarily but do not usually prevent or eradicate. Similarly, diamidine drugs are considered to be prophylactically valuable in areas of African trypanosomiasis. There is some clinical evidence that prophylactic administration of diiodohydroxyquin (Diodoquin) and bismuth glycoarsanilate may prevent amebic infection from developing in persons in an endemic area (Beaver *et al.*, 1956).

EPIDEMIOLOGY

EPIDEMIOLOGY is the science concerned with the propagation of human disease. It is the natural history of the disease, including not only infection in man but in other animals and agents which serve as reservoirs and vectors (Scott, 1943; Simmons *et al.*, 1944, 1951; Strode, 1951). If the disease maintains itself in a human community it is *endemic*; if there is high prevalence it is *hyperendemic*; if it appears only occasionally it is *sporadic*, and if it develops as a sharp outbreak it is *epidemic*. Comparable terms for diseases in animals are *enzoötic, hyperenzoötic, sporadic* and *epi-zoötic* respectively.

Parasitic diseases may be grouped epidemiologically as follows:

1. *Filth-borne or contaminative,* as in the case of the intestinal protozoa (McCoy *et al.,* 1936; Kuntz and Lawless, 1958), some of the intestinal helminths, sarcoptic mange and louse infestation.
2. *Infection contracted from soil or water,* with exposure through ingestion of the infective stage, as the eggs of *Ascaris* and *Trichuris* (Cort, 1931; Weiner *et al.,* 1959); or through the skin, as the infective larvæ of hook-worms or blood flukes (Faust and Meleney, 1924).
3. *Food-borne infections* contracted (*a*) from raw or inadequately processed flesh containing the larval stage of the parasite, *viz., Trichinella* in pork, fish tapeworm in fresh-water fish, or (*b*) from ingestion of encysted larvæ on aquatic plants, *viz.,* sheep liver-fluke.
4. *Arthropod-borne infections:* (*a*) In which the arthropod is an essential intermediate host and vector between man and man, *viz., Anopheles* and malaria, tsetse flies and African trypanosomiasis, or (*b*) in which the arthropod is a mechanical vector, *viz.,* filth flies and enteric diseases.
5. *Infestation by arthropods,* which may be specific, semispecific or accidental, depending on the degree of adaptation of the arthropod for the host.
6. *Arthropod venenation,* including a wide range, from mild allergy to fatal venenation or hypersensitization (not a parasitosis but conveniently included in this outline).

CONTROL AND PREVENTION

Since parasitic diseases involve the individual, the community in which he lives, and larger geo-political areas, the control and preventive problems involve all of these entities.

The Individual.—In the parasitized individual, chemotherapy, when available, should be employed to eradicate the infection, not only to relieve his suffering but also to prevent others in the community from contracting the infection. Yet this in itself can rarely control the disease. The individual and his associates must be educated in methods of personal hygiene and provided with means for taking precautions against exposure, whether due to person-to-person contact, environmental contamination or vector transmission of the infection.

The Community.—Here the services of public health come into the picture as the important functioning operation, to assist the community in obtaining safe water supplies (Newton, 1950), sanitary disposal of human excreta, and measures directed against arthropod vectors (Henderson, 1957) and molluscan intermediate hosts, in order to break the life-cycles of many disease-producing organisms, and thus reduce the hazards of individual and group exposures (Andrews, 1959). At times mass chemotherapy may be a valuable adjuvant, as in areas of endemic malaria and filariasis, in preventing insects from acquiring and later transmitting the disease (Kessel, 1957).

Equally important is the need to improve the nutritional standards of

2

the community. The malnutrition of entire communities in extensive underprivileged areas of the world, and particularly in younger children lowers the threshold of resistance to parasitic diseases, as Platt (1957) has ably argued. A diet almost exclusively carbohydrate, with deficiency in proteins, fats, vitamins and essential minerals, is the rule in most of these populations. Removal of this deficiency will require not only the production of more and better quality foods, but education to overcome food preferences or prejudices which have existed for decades or centuries. Here the public health officials must develop their program in close cooperation with agricultural agencies.

National and International Aspects.—Parasitic and other infectious diseases know no national boundaries. For this reason the Health Section of The League of Nations was established several decades ago to obtain epidemiological information on communicable diseases. The Panamerican Sanitary Bureau (Soper, 1958) provided an even earlier demonstration of the value of international cooperation in the field of public health, while more recently The World Health Organization has attacked these problems on a global scale (Beye, 1960).

Whatever may be the size of the community or larger population group, an unavoidable aspect is the economic one (Wolman, 1953). The methods of control or attempted eradication of a parasitic disease must be practical and within the financial ability of the group or its sponsors. Hence it is necessary to employ the most practical methods, in order to obtain the greatest degree of control compatible with developing knowledge, the mores and economic status of the community (Yekutiel, 1960).

SUMMARY

1. Adaptation to parasitism constitutes one of the most interesting evolutionary processes in biology. Adjustment from a free-living mode of life to a parasitic existence has been accompanied by morphological simplification, physiological and metabolic changes, and development of means for transfer from one host to the next.

2. For success in its new environment in an appropriate host, the parasite must develop a host-parasite relationship which is compatible with its own existence and that of the host. Some parasites are host-group adapted, others host-species adapted, resulting from delicate biochemical adjustments. Geographical contiguity or isolation plays an important role in this relationship.

3. The transmitter of a parasite from one host to the next is a *vector*. The host on which the parasite depends for survival is the *reservoir*. In many human parasitoses domestic or wild animals are the reservoirs. Man may be an essential or incidental host.

4. Both the parasite and the host live in a macrocosm, the community. Factors affecting the host also affect the parasite. Survival of both depends to a considerable degree on ability of the host to obtain adequate nourishment. Parasitic diseases of domestic animals on which man depends for food may create a serious imbalance by reducing tolerance to diseases to which man is exposed.

5. Classification of animal parasites follows the Rules of Zoölogical Nomenclature. The major groups in which human parasites occur are the Protozoa (one-celled organisms), the Platyhelminthes (trematodes and tapeworms), the Nematoda (true roundworms) and the Arthropoda (insects and their allies).
6. Parasites which cause injury to their hosts are *pathogens*. The damage produced may be mechanical, digestive, intoxicative or allergenic. The host's reaction may be essentially nil, may consist of local or generalized cellular response, or elaboration of specific antibodies.
7. Diagnosis of parasitic diseases is dependent on demonstration of the parasite. Treatment of many parasitoses is relatively specific, often using an antimetabolite which interferes with the normal metabolism of the parasite. In some instances suppressive or prophylactic drug therapy is successful.
8. Epidemiological classification of parasitic infections includes the following categories: (1) filth-borne or contaminative, (2) infections contracted directly from soil or water, (3) food-borne, (4) arthropod-borne, (5) infestation by arthropods, and (6) arthropod venenation. Adequate understanding of the natural history of parasitoses requires knowledge of the life cycles of the etiological agents, their presence in vectors and reservoirs, and their prevalence in a community.
9. Control of parasitic diseases involves the individual, the community in which he lives, and the larger geo-political areas, with the objective of preventing the survival and dissemination of the etiological agents.

REFERENCES

The Phenomena of Parasitism

BAER, J. G. 1951. *Ecology of Animal Parasites.*, 224 pp., University of Illinois Press, Urbana.
BUEDING, E. 1949. Metabolism of Parasitic Helminths. Physiol. Rev., *29*, 195–218.
CAMERON, T. W. M. 1956. *Parasites and Parasitism*, 322 pp., John Wiley & Sons, Inc. New York.
READ, C. P. 1958. Status of Behavioral and Physiological "Resistance." The Rice Inst. Pamphlet, *45* (1), 36–54.
SMYTH, J. D. 1947. The Physiology of Tapeworms. Biol. Rev., *22*, 214–238.
STAUBER, L. A. (Editor). 1960. *Host Influence on Parasite Physiology*, 96 pp. Rutgers Univ. Press.
TALMAGE, D. W. 1959. Immunological Specificity. Science, *129*, 1643–1649.
VILLEE, C. A., WALKER, W. F., JR., and SMITH, F. E. 1958. *General Zoölogy*, 877 pp., W. B. Saunders Co., Philadelphia and London.

Classification

INTERNATIONAL COMMISSION ON ZOOLOGICAL NOMENCLATURE. 1926. Rules and Regulations. Proc. Biol. Soc., Washington, D.C., *39*, 75–104.
1961. *International Code of Zoölogical Nomenclature*, 176 pp., Intern'l Trust for Zool. Nomencl., London.
MAYR, E. (Editor). 1957. *The Species Problem*, A Symposium Presented at the Atlanta Meeting of the American Association for the Advancement of Science, December 28–29, 1955, 395 pp., Publ. No. 50, Am. Assn. Adv. Sci., Washington D.C.
PEASE, A. S. (Editor). 1949. Zoölogical Names, A List of Phyla, Classes and Orders. 24 pp., Durham (N. Carolina).

Pathogenicity and Symptomatology

ANDERSON, H. H., BOSTICK, W. L , and JOHNSTONE, H. G. 1953. *Amebiasis, Pathology, Diagnosis and Chemotherapy*, 431 pp., Charles C Thomas, Publisher, Springfield, Illinois.

ASH, J. E., and SPITZ, S. 1945. *Pathology of Tropical Diseases. An Atlas*, 350 pp., W. B. Saunders Co., Philadelphia and London.

FAUST, E. C., and RUSSELL, P. F. 1957. *Craig and Faust's Clinical Parasitology*, 6th. ed., 1078 pp., Lea & Febiger, Philadelphia.

GOULD, S. E. 1945. *Trichinosis*, 356 pp., Charles C Thomas, Publisher, Springfield, Illinois.

MAEGRAITH, B., JONES, E., and ANDREWS, W. H. H. 1951. Pathological Processes in Malaria: Progress Report. Trans. R. Soc. Trop. Med. & Hyg., *45*, 15–42.

MOST, H., KANE, C. A., *et al.* 1950. Schistosomiasis Japonica in American Military Personnel: Clinical Study of 600 Cases During First Year after Infection. Am. J. Trop. Med., *30*, 239–299.

RHOADS, C. P., *et al.* 1934. Hookworm Anemia. Am. J. Hyg., *20*, 291–306.

Diagnosis and Treatment

BEAVER, P. C., *et al.* 1956. Experimental Chemoprophylaxis of Amebiasis, Am. J. Trop. Med. & Hyg., *5*, 1015–1021.

BUEDING, E., and SWARTZWELDER, C. 1957. Anthelmintics. Pharmacol. Rev., *9(3)*, 329–365.

MARKELL, E. K., and VOGE, M. 1958. *Diagnostic Medical Parasitology*, 276 pp., W. B. Saunders Co., Philadelphia and London.

SCHELLENBERG, K. A., and COATNEY, G. R. 1959. The Mode of Action of Antimalarial Drugs. J. Parasitol., *45* (sec. 2), 54.

WINTERINGHAM, F. P. W., and LEWIS, S. E. 1959. On the Mode of Action of Insecticides. Ann. Rev. Entomol., *4*, 303–318.

WOOLLEY, D. W. 1959. Antimetabolites. Science, *129*, 615–621.

Epidemiology

CORT, W. W. 1931. Recent Investigations on the Epidemiology of Human Ascariasis. J. Parasitol., *17*, 121–144.

FAUST, E. C., and MELENEY, H. E. 1924. *Studies on Schistosomiasis Japonica*, 339 pp., Am. J. Hyg., Monogr. Ser. No. 3.

KUNTZ, R. E., and LAWLESS, D. K. 1958. Acquisition of Intestinal Protozoa and Helminths by Young Children in a Typical Village of Lower Egypt. Am. J. Trop. Med. & Hyg., *7*, 353–357.

McCOY, G. W., *et al.* 1936. *Epidemic Amebic Dysentery*, 187 pp., Nat'l. Inst. Health Bull. No. 166, Washington, D.C.

SCOTT, H. H. 1943. The Influence of the Slave Trade in the Spread of Tropical Disease. Trans. R. Soc. Trop. Med. & Hyg., *37*, 169–188.

SIMMONS, J. S., *et al.* 1944. *Global Epidemiology. A Geography of Disease and Sanitation*. Vol I, India and the Far East; The Pacific Area, 504 pp., J. B. Lippincott Co., Philadelphia. 1951. Vol. II, Africa and the Adjacent Islands, 652 pp., J. B. Lippincott Co., Philadelphia.

STRODE, G. K. (Editor). 1951. *Yellow Fever*, 710 pp., McGraw-Hill, New York.

WEINER, D., BROOKE, M. M., and WITKOW, A. 1959. Investigation of Parasitic Infections in the Central Area of Philadelphia. Am. J. Trop. Med. & Hyg., *8*, 625–629.

Control and Prevention

ANDREWS, J. M. 1959. El control residual de las enfermedades transmisibles. Bol. Ofic. San. Panam., *46*, 203–212.

BEYE, H. K. 1960. International Organizations and Filariasis Control. Jour. Malariol. *14*, 503–508.

HENDERSON, J. M. 1957. A Practical Philosophy of Vector Control in the U.S.A. Am. J. Trop. Med. & Hyg., *6*, 595–597.

KESSEL, J. F.   1957.   Disabling Effects and Control of Filariasis. Am. J. Trop. Med. &
  Hyg., *6*, 402–414.
NEWTON, W. L.   1950.   Water Treatment Measures in Control of Amebiasis. Am. J.
  Trop. Med., *30*, 135–138.
PLATT, B. S.   1957.   Protein Malnutrition and Infection. Am. J. Trop. Med. & Hyg.,
  6, 773–779.
SOPER, F. L.   1958.   Quadriennial Report of the Director of the Panamerican Sanitary
  Bureau, Regional Office of the World Health Organization 1954–1957, and the
  1957 Annual Report. 238 pp., PASB, Washington, D.C.
WOLMAN, A.   1953.   Financing Sanitary Works in the Tropics. Am. J. Trop. Med. &
  Hyg., *2*, 557–564.
YEKUTIEL, P.   1960.   Problems of Epidemiology in Malaria Eradication. Bull. Wld.
  Hlth. Org., *22*, 669–683.

PLATE I

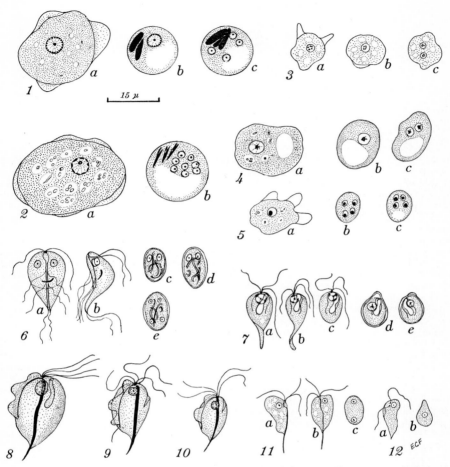

15 μ

Trophozoites and Cysts of the More Common Amebæ and Flagellate Protozoa of the Digestive Tract (Iron-hematoxylin Staining). All Drawn to Scale. (Original.)

(Legend on opposite page.)

(*Legend for Plate II*)

Eggs and Larvæ of the More Common Helminth Parasites of Man. Diagnostic chart of the characteristic eggs and larvæ of the more common helminths parasitizing man. *A, Ascaris lumbricoides* (giant intestinal roundworm), unsegmented fertile egg, usually with bile-stained outer shell, passed in feces; *B, A. lumbricoides,* infertile egg, usually with bile-stained outer shell, passed in feces; *C, Enterobius vermicularis* (pinworm or seatworm), with completely developed larva, usually deposited by the mother worm on the perianal or perineal skin; *D, Ancylostoma duodenale* ("Old World hookworm") or *Necator americanus* ("American hookworm"), early cleavage stage, passed in semiformed feces; *E, A. duodenale* ("Old World hookworm") or *N. americanus* ("American hookworm"), with completely developed first-stage (rhabditoid) larva, passed in constipated stool or developed in feces that have stood twenty-four to forty-eight hours in the laboratory; *F, A. duodenale* ("Old World hookworm") or *N. americanus* ("American hookworm"), anterior extremity of hatched rhabditoid larva, showing long, narrow, buccal cavity (contrast with anterior end of *G*); *G, Strongyloides stercoralis* (threadworm), rhabditoid larva passed in feces or obtained by duodenal drainage, showing very short buccal cavity (contrast with *F*); *H, Trichostrongylus,* characteristic morula-stage egg passed in feces; *I, Trichuris trichiura (Trichocephalus trichiurus* or whipworm), with unsegmented ovum, usually with bile-stained outer shell, passed in feces; *J, Taenia saginata* (beef tapeworm) or *T. solium* (pork tapeworm), with fully embryonated oncosphere, with dark brown outer shell passed in feces; *K, Hymenolepis nana* (dwarf tapeworm), with fully embryonated oncosphere, passed in feces; *L, Hymenolepis diminuta* (rat tapeworm), with fully embryonated oncosphere, passed in feces; *M, Diphyllobothrium latum* (fish tapeworm), characteristically unembryonated as passed in feces; *N, Diphyllobothrium mansoni, D. erinacei, D. houghtoni* et al. of subgenus *Spirometra,* characteristically unembryonated, as passed in feces of definitive host; *O, Dipylidium caninum* (double-pored dog tapeworm), mother egg capsule containing several fully embryonated oncospheres, as passed in feces or expressed from disintegrating gravid proglottid; *P, Fasciolopsis buski* (giant intestinal fluke) or *Fasciola hepatica* (sheep liver fluke), unembryonated, as passed in feces or obtained by duodenal and/or biliary drainage; *Q, Dicrocœlium dendriticum,* with developed miracidium, passed in feces or obtained by duodenal or biliary drainage; *R, Heterophyes heterophyes,* with developed miracidium, passed in feces; *S, Metagonimus yokogawai,* with developed miracidium, passed in feces; *T, Opisthorchis felineus,* with developed miracidium, passed in feces or obtained by duodenal or biliary drainage; *U, Clonorchis sinensis* (Chinese liver fluke), with developed miracidium, passed in feces or obtained by duodenal or biliary drainage; *V, Paragonimus westermani* (Oriental lung fluke), unembryonated, recovered from sputum or swallowed and passed in feces; *W, Gastrodiscoides hominis,* unembryonated, passed in feces; *X, Schistosoma hæmatobium* (vesical blood fluke), with developed miracidium, passed in urine or at times in feces; *Y, Schistosoma mansoni* (Manson's blood fluke), with developed miracidium, passed in feces; *Z, Schistosoma japonicum* (Oriental blood fluke), with developed miracidium, passed in feces.

R, S, T, and *U,* × 666; all other figures, × 333. (From Faust's *Human Helminthology,* Lea & Febiger, Philadelphia.)

PLATE II

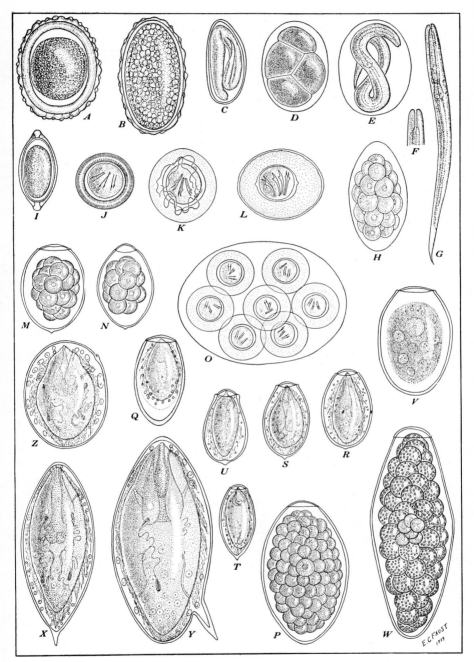

Eggs and Larvæ of the More Common Helminth Parasites of Man.

(*Legend on opposite page.*)

(Legend for Plate III.)

Objects in the Feces at Times Causing Confusion in Parasitologic Diagnosis.

1.—Precyst of *Entamœba histolytica,* for comparison with cellular exudate;
2.—macrophage;
3.—neutrophilic polymorphonuclear leukocyte;
4.—squamous epithelial cell from aspirate of the rectum;
5.—plasma cell from aspirate of the rectum;
6.—Blastocystis;
7.—yeast cells;
8.—units from septate mycelium of *Monilia;*
9,10.—conidia respectively of the fungi *Alternaria* and *Helminthosporium;*
11.—Charcot-Leyden crystals;
12.—cholesterol crystals;
13.—partly digested particle of casein;
14.—air bubble;
15.—oil droplet;
16a,16b.—diatoms;
17.—pollen grains (*a*, pine; *b*, African violet; *c*, hibiscus; *d*, broom sage; *e*, ragweed; *f*, timothy grass);
18.—plant hair;
19.—fragment of cotton fiber;
20.—mammalian hair;
21–32.—plant remnants (*21*, beef or pork muscle; *22*, crab meat; *23*, fish; *24*, wheat grain; *25*, corn kernel; *26*, string beans; *27*, conducting tubules of fibrovascular bundle; *28*, Irish potato starch grain; *29*, rice starch; *30*, plantain starch; *31*, sweet potato starch; *32*, woody cell wall). *1–12,* × 1125; *16a,* × 700; *16b,* × 200; *17–20,* × ca. 300; *21–27,* × ca. 240; *28–31,* × ca. 750; *32,* × 200. (Original, Faust.)

PLATE III

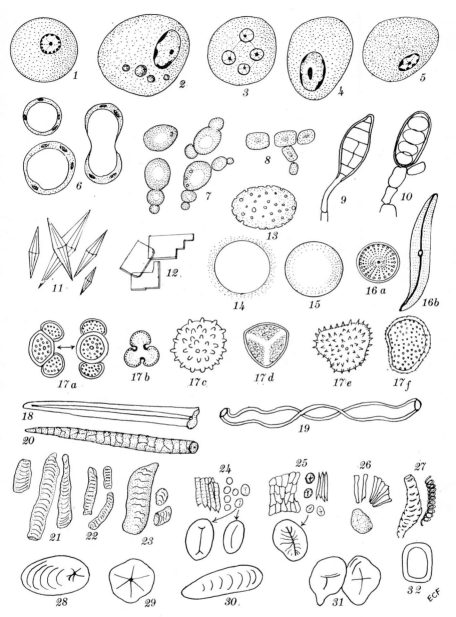

Objects in the Feces at Times Causing Confusion in Parasitologic Diagnosis.

(*Legend on opposite page.*)

SECTION II
Protozoan Agents of Human Disease

Chapter 2
Introduction to the Protozoa

THE protozoa are single-celled animals which belong to the Phylum PROTOZOA. Each cell-unit performs all of the necessary functions of life. Many thousands of species of protozoa have been described, a majority of which are free-living; yet many representatives of the Subphyla Mastigophora, Sarcodina and Ciliophora are parasitic during all or a major part of their life and all species of the Subphylum Sporozoa are exclusively parasitic.

MORPHOLOGY AND BIOLOGY

Although the size and structure of the protozoa vary greatly, yet, in so far as is known, all of them possess mitochondria, Golgi apparatus, microsomes and an endoplastic reticulum, just as do the individual cells of a metazoön (Hall, 1953; Kudo, 1954). The size of the species in different groups ranges from forms visible to the naked eye to others which require high-power magnification with the light microscope in order to observe and identify them. The morphology of the protozoa is as variable as their size but is relatively the same in species of the same group. Some are practically spherical or regularly ovoidal in contour, some have a bilateral symmetry and others possess a torsion along their longitudinal axis. Still others like the naked Sarcodina have no consistent contour during their trophozoite stage because of the constant change in movement of their protoplasm.

All protozoa possess certain morphological features which can be readily observed. The most essential is the *nucleus*, which contains the chromosomes that regulate growth, reproduction, and are responsible for the genetic characters of the species. Among the parasitic protozoa the number of chromosomes may vary in different families of the same Class but is relatively constant in closely related species of the same genus, as for example in *Giardia*, *Trichomonas*, *Entamœba* (Kudo, 1954, Table 5, pp. 167–169), and in *Plasmodium* (Wolcott, 1957). In the alveolar type of nucleus, such as is characteristic of the intestinal amebæ of man, there is a *karyosome* or nucleolus, which is situated in a relatively viscous nucleoplasm. The nucleoplasm is bounded by a distinct membrane which may possess minute pores connecting it with the *endoplasm*, the inner portion of the cytoplasm. This latter consists of moderately dense, finely granular protoplasm and functions in the digestion of food taken into the organism. Here also food reserves in the form of *glycogen* and *chromatoidal bodies* may be accumulated in the trophic stage. Surrounding the endoplasm is a less dense portion of the cytoplasm, the *ectoplasm*, which serves as a locomotor organelle as well as for obtaining and ingesting food, for respiration, for discharge of wastes, and which may also have a protective function (Hall, 1953; Kudo, 1954). The limiting cell membrane, the *plasma membrane*, controls the intake of food and discharge of waste products, and maintains normal concentration of the plasma. Typically the endoplasm contains food vacuoles. Certain parasitic protozoa such as species of *Balantidium* also have contractile vacuoles that preserve normal osmotic pressure. Specialized structures which are characteristic of the different groups of parasitic protozoa will be considered in subsequent chapters of this section.

Very considerable adaptation has been developed among the parasitic protozoa with respect to their immediate environment, their microclimate, including temperature at different stages in the parasite's life cycle, anaërobic metabolism, hydrogen-ion concentration, available food, and in some species a variety of hosts or multiple habitats within the same host (Lwoff, 1951; Hutner and Lwoff, 1955). Striking examples are found in the adaptation of the malaria parasites, leishmaniæ and trypanosomes from a mammal to an alternate required insect host in the life cycle (Cameron, 1956). While much has been discovered in controlled laboratory experiments with reference to the metabolic activities of several parasitic protozoa, there are many unsolved problems in this field of host-protozoön relationship.

LIFE CYCLES AND REPRODUCTION

The life cycle of the parasitic protozoa may be very simple, consisting only of a trophic stage in a single host, in which propagation is by asexual mitotic binary division, so that each of the daughter cells receives qualitatively the aliquot of the chromosome material. This type of propagation is illustrated by *Entamœba gingivalis* and *Dientamœba fragilis*, as well as by the flagellate species *Trichomonas tenax*, *T. hominis* and *T. vaginalis*, which parasitize man. Somewhat more advanced in their cycles are *Entamœba histolytica*, *E. coli*, *Endolimax nana* and *Iodamœba bütschlii*, which have an encysted resting stage that provides a better chance for transfer from one host to the next. Moreover, in the case of *E. histolytica*, *E. coli* and *Endolimax nana* there is multiplication of the nuclei during the encysted stage. Asexual binary division in the examples cited and in many other protozoa is continued indefinitely without need for, or the intervention of a sexual stage. In so far as is known, no sexual process occurs in these amebæ and flagellates, and possibly not in *Toxoplasma* (Jacobs, 1956). In contrast, the ciliate *Balantidium coli* occasionally undergoes conjugation, while an essential part of the life cycle of the coccidia and malaria parasites is the sexual phase called gametogony, followed by sporogony.

In the amebæ there is no characteristic plane of binary division. In the flagellates division is along a longitudinal axis, and in the ciliates it is transverse. In the flagellates the trophic nucleus functions in the ordinary processes of metabolism and growth; a second organelle-apparatus, the *kinetoplast*, is primarily responsible for binary division. In *Balantidium coli* the macronucleus performs the first-named function, and the micronucleus is responsible for the second. Asexual multiplication of the malaria parasites and their relatives, with the production of several to many daughter cells, appears to be a precocious telescoping of binary division.

A type of life cycle in which two successive hosts are presently required is a delicately adjusted sequence, in which one of the hosts is undoubtedly a secondary adaptation. Where blood-sucking insects are hosts and biological vectors, as in the life cycle of the leishmaniæ, trypanosomes and plasmodia, not only does this adaptation provide a moderately secure mechanism for transfer from one vertebrate host to the next, but likewise it furnishes an additional opportunity for multiplication of progeny, hence a better chance for some of the offspring to reach the vertebrate host.

CLASSIFICATION OF THE PROTOZOA

An outline classification of the animal parasites has been provided in Section I (pp. 13 and 14). A somewhat more complete classification of the parasitic protozoa is presented here.

Phylum: PROTOZOA.—One-celled organisms.
    Subphylum: MASTIGOPHORA (Flagellates), having one or more elongated thread-like extensions of the ectoplasm.
        Class: *ZOOMASTIGOPHOREA*, lacking chromatophores, hence dependent on holozoic or parasitic methods of nutrition. (*All parasitic flagellates* belong to this group.)
    Subphylum: SARCODINA, with locomotion and procurement of food by temporary extensions of the ectoplasm.
        Class: *RHIZOPODEA*, with root-like, thread-like or finger-like temporary extensions of the ectoplasm. (*Amebæ* and related groups.)
    Subphylum: CILIOPHORA, having numerous short thread-like extensions of the ectoplasm, the cilia; containing two types of nuclei, a macronucleus and a micronucleus; multiplication commonly by transverse binary division.
        Class: *CILIATEA* (Ciliates), with cilia present in both trophic and encysted stage. (*Balantidium coli.*)
    Subphylum: SPOROZOA, typically without special organelles for locomotion; life cycle consisting of alternation of asexual and sexual generations.
        Class: *TELOSPORIDEA*, with sexual spore simple, producing one to many sporozoites.
            Subclass: COCCIDIA (*Coccidians*), requiring only one host for both asexual and sexual phases of the life cycle.
            Subclass: HÆMOSPORIDIA (*Malaria parasites and their relatives*), with alternation of two required hosts in the life cycle; parasitic

within fixed tissue cells and red blood corpuscles of the vertebrate host.

Class: *SARCOSPORIDEA* (*Sarcosporidians*), characterized by multiple spores developed in cysts in striated muscles of higher vertebrates. (*Sarcocystis*.)

PROTOZOAN SPECIES OF UNCERTAIN CLASSIFICATION:

Toxoplasma gondii.

Pneumocystis carinii.

SUMMARY

1. Protozoa are single-celled animals which perform all of the necessary functions of life.
2. Protozoa vary remarkably in size, shape and morphology, but all species possess a nucleus, an endoplasm and an ectoplasm with a limiting cell membrane.
3. Parasitic protozoa have developed special adaptations to their immediate host environment, including variation in temperature, anaërobic metabolism, hydrogen-ion concentration, available food, and transfer from one host to the next.
4. A few protozoan species have only a trophozoite stage; closely related species also have an encysted stage. Asexual mitotic binary division is characteristic for all protozoa, but some ciliates at times undergo conjugation and all sporozoans employ both asexual and sexual reproduction.
5. The protozoa which parasitize man belong to the following subdivisions of the Phylum Protozoa: Mastigophora (flagellates), Sarcodina (including the amebæ), Ciliophora (ciliates), Sporozoa (coccidians, malaria parasites and *Sarcocystis*), and, of uncertain relationship, *Toxoplasma* and *Pneumocystis*.

REFERENCES

CAMERON, T. W. M. 1956. Protozoa, in *Parasites and Parasitism*, pp. 19–62, John Wiley & Sons, Inc., New York; Methuen & Co. Ltd., London.

HALL, R. P. 1953. *Protozoölogy*, 682 pp., Prentice-Hall, Inc., New York.

HUTNER, S. H., and LWOFF, A. (Editors). 1955. *Biochemistry and Physiology of Protozoa*, Vol. II, 388 pp., Academic Press, Inc., New York.

JACOBS, L. 1956. Propagation, Morphology, and Biology of Toxoplasma. Ann. N.Y. Acad. Sci., *64*, 154–179.

KUDO, R. R. 1954. *Protozoölogy*, 4th ed., 966 pp., Charles C Thomas, Springfield.

LWOFF, A. (Editor). 1951. *Biochemistry and Physiology of Protozoa*, Vol. I, 434 pp., Academic Press, Inc., New York.

WOLCOTT, G. B. 1957. Chromosome Studies in the Genus *Plasmodium*. J. Protozoöl. *4*, 48–51.

Chapter 3

The Flagellate Protozoa (Mastigophora)

THESE protozoa are distinguished by possessing in their trophozoite stage one to several long, thread-like extensions of the ectoplasm, the *flagella* (singular, *flagellum*), each of which arises from an *axoneme*, which is associated with a *kinetoplast*. Flagella, axonemes and kinetoplast constitute the *neuromotor apparatus*, of which the former two are the motor component and the latter, consisting of *blepharoplast* and *parabasal body*, the energizing portion.

Many flagellates are free-living; others are parasitic in certain plants; several live in the intestines of arthropods, many in the digestive tract of vertebrate hosts, a few in the genital tract of certain vertebrates, and several have become parasites in the blood and tissues of vertebrate hosts.

The flagellate protozoa which parasitize man are conveniently studied under two main topics based on the relationship of these organisms to host tissues, *viz.*, (1) Flagellates of the Digestive Tract and Genital Organs, and (2) Flagellates of the Blood and Tissues.

FLAGELLATES OF THE DIGESTIVE TRACT AND GENITAL ORGANS

All of these species are typically lumen parasites. Those more commonly occurring in man are host specific. Others appear to be accidentally associated with the intestinal tract and are coprozoites (feces feeders) which are perhaps just beginning to become adjusted to a parasitic environment. Although none of the members of this group are tissue invaders, at times *Giardia lamblia* in the duodenum and *Trichomonas vaginalis* in the vagina erode the epithelial lining of their respective organs and evoke symptoms.

Giardia lamblia Stiles, 1915.—This flagellate parasite is probably restricted to the human small intestine. It has a cosmopolitan distribution but is common only in warm climates.

Morphology, Biology and Life Cycle.—*G. lamblia* has a trophozoite and a cystic stage. The *trophozoite* (Fig. 1a, b) is a delicate but very active organism, measuring 9.5 to 21 microns in length by 5 to 15 microns in width and only about 2 to 5 microns thick. When seen from the ventral aspect the trophozoite appears broadly rounded anteriorly and tapering to a point posteriorly; when viewed in profile it is relatively thin and in its anterior half is curved ventrally, forming an adhesive disc. There are *4 pairs of long flagella*, all arising from a complex system of *axonemes* connected with *paired blepharoplasts*. Approximately in the center of the trophozoite there is a deeply staining, short, rod-shaped organelle which is believed to be the *parabasal body*. In the anterior portion of the body there are *two ovoidal nuclei*, each with a central *karyosome*, one nucleus lying on each side of the mid-line. By means of the 8 flagella *Giardia* is able to move very actively, and by applying its

3

cup-shaped anterior ventral disc it becomes firmly attached to epithelial surfaces. Multiplication is by longitudinal binary fission.

The *cyst* (Fig. 1*c,d,e*) is ovoidal, measuring 8 to 12 microns in length by 6 to 10 microns in breadth. In preparation for encystment the flagella are retracted into their respective axonemal components which now appear as stiffly curved fibrils situated in parallel pairs. Meanwhile the protoplasm is condensed into an ovoidal mass and a thin hyaline membrane is secreted around the organism. At first the cyst contains only one pair of nuclei but in the ripe cyst (Fig. 1*e*) four are present.

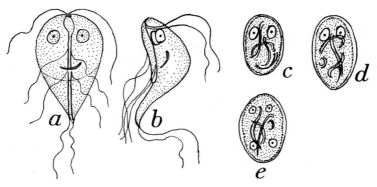

Fig. 1.—*Giardia lamblia.* *a*, trophozoite, ventral view, and *b*, profile view; *c*, *d*, immature cysts; *e*, mature cyst. × 1600. (Original, Faust.)

The primary habitat of the trophozoites is the intestinal crypts at the duodenal level, where myriads of the active organisms may be present. Smaller numbers are found at lower levels of the intestine, and at times likewise in the common duct and gall bladder. The stage commonly recovered in the feces is the cyst; trophozoites are seen in the stool only when it is frankly diarrheic or following saline catharsis.

Pathogenicity and Symptomatology.—A great majority of persons harboring *G. lamblia* are asymptomatic but some have symptoms referable to the duodenum and a few to the gall bladder, in which the only plausible etiology is the infection with *Giardia.* Although this flagellate does not invade tissues, it apparently occasionally produces irritation of the duodenal wall, and may even simulate a sprue syndrome (Servino *et al.*, 1960). The most common symptoms in these cases are epigastric or right upper quadrant pain and a persistent diarrhea, but occasionally this infection may cause a celiac syndrome (Cortner, 1959).

Diagnosis and Treatment.—Diagnosis is usually based on recovery of typical cysts, less frequently trophozoites in the stools. The cysts are easily concentrated by the zinc sulfate flotation technic (see TECHNICAL AIDS, page 428). Trophozoites may also be obtained by duodenal aspiration. In at least 90 per cent of cases the infection is eradicated following quinacrine (Atabrine) therapy (See Table 7, p. 416).

Epidemiology.—Infection with *Giardia lamblia* results from ingestion of viable cysts of this organism from previous human sources, *i.e.*, evacuated human stools. Giardiasis is most common in warm moist climates throughout the world and particularly in children who are closely associated with one another, as in children's asylums and large families. Exposure is probably most frequent from finger contact with perianal skin and soiled underpants. In heavily infected groups infection begins in early infancy and is built up to a peak incidence during the years of adolescence. Thereafter it rapidly declines to about one-third or one-fourth of the maximum, which tends to be maintained in later years.

Control.—This can be accomplished only by training children and adults to develop cleaner habits of personal and group hygiene.

Chilomastix mesnili (Wenyon, 1910) Alexeieff, 1912.—This is a common protozoön of the human intestinal tract; it has a cosmopolitan distribution but is more prevalent in warm than in cool climates. It has both a trophozoite and a cystic stage. Infection is acquired from swallowing viable cysts contaminating food, drink or from fingers introduced into the mouth.

The actively moving trophozoite (Fig. 2*a,b*) is rounded anteriorly and is spirally twisted posteriorly to a tapering end. It measures up to 20 microns in length when in progressive forward movement but only about 6 microns when it is relatively quiescent and the posterior end is contracted and rounded (Fig. 2*c*); its greatest breadth is about 5 to 7 microns. In the anterior rounded portion there is a distinct longitudinal cleft, the *cytostome*. Arising from a small group of *blepharoplasts* just within the anterior pole there are *2 short and one long flagella*, likewise *a delicate*

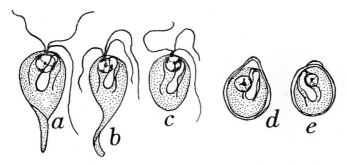

Fig. 2.—*Chilomastix mesnili. a, b, c,* trophozoites; *d, e,* cysts. × 1600. (Original, Faust.)

flagellum which lies within the cytostome and 2 stiffer *curved fibrils*, one on each side of the cytostome. The conspicuous spherical *nucleus*, situated in the mid-line immediately behind the blepharoplasts, has a small central *karyosome* and chromatin plaques lining the nuclear membrane. *Chilomastix mesnili* moves forward with a jerky movement in a spiralled path. Multiplication is by longitudinal binary fission.

The *cyst* (Fig. 2*d,e*) is lemon-shaped, measures 7 to 10 microns in length by 4.5 to 6 microns in breadth, has a relatively thick hyaline wall and the characteristic internal features of the trophozoite, *viz.*, cytostome, curved fibrils and nucleus. The fully mature cyst has 2 nuclei.

The natural habitat of *C. mesnili* is the lumen of the anterior portion of the large intestine of man. In unformed stools a majority of the evacuated organisms are motile trophozoites, which, however, may encyst in a semi-liquid medium. Usually only cysts are seen in formed stools.

C. mesnili is not pathogenic, hence the only significance attached to its presence in the intestine is that ingested material has been contaminated with human excreta.

Species of Trichomonas.—These flagellates have the following common characteristics in their trophozoite stage (Figs. 3, 4, 5): a rounded anterior and a somewhat pointed posterior end; a semi-rigid translucent rod-like *axostyle* which arises near the median anterior pole and extends through the entire body, protruding as a rather sharp spike through the posterior tip of protoplasm; a small *cytostome* on one side of the anterior end; a spherical or subspherical *nucleus* in the mid-line near the anterior pole, a *blepharoplast* between the nucleus and the anterior margin of the organism, from which arise 3 to 5 *free flagella* and an additional *marginal flagellum* on an *undulating membrane*, which spirals down the side of the body. Multiplication is by longitudinal binary fission. Only trophozoites are described for those species that parasitize man.

Three distinct species of *Trichomonas* are adapted to the human host and none of these has been demonstrated as a normal parasite of other hosts except perhaps certain monkeys. The species which occur in man are: *T. hominis, T. tenax* and *T. vaginalis.* Although they closely resemble one another they are morphologically different, develop in different locations and are reciprocally not transplantable.

Trichomonas hominis (Davaine, 1860) Leuckart, 1879.—This trichomonad has a cosmopolitan distribution. It inhabits the lumen of the cecum. It is small, pear-shaped (Fig. 3), and measures 7 to 15 microns in length and about 4 to 7 microns in breadth. There are 3 to 5 *free flagella* (usually 4). Its *undulating membrane* has a characteristic movement which arises at the anterior attachment end and proceeds in successive waves to the posterior end of the membrane. The distal end of

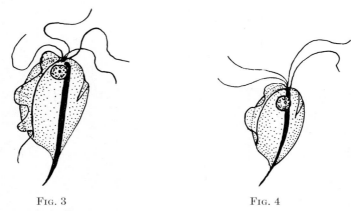

Fig. 3   Fig. 4

FIG. 3.—*Trichomonas hominis* from a diarrheic stool. × 1600. (Original, Faust.)

FIG. 4.—*Trichomonas tenax* from gingival scrapings. × 1600. (Original, Faust.)

the flagellum on the margin of the undulating membrane extends a short distance behind the posterior termination of the membrane. There is a spherical *nucleus* near the anterior pole. At times the organism exhibits pseudopodial prolongations of its cytoplasm, and might be mistaken for a very active ameba were it not for the undulations of its membrane and the *axostyle* which protrudes a short distance through the posterior extremity. It feeds on mucus, bacteria, and red blood cells if they are present in the lumen of the large intestine.

There is no proof that *T. hominis* is pathogenic. Since it has only a trophozoite stage, it is presumably acquired in a rounded-up unencysted stage and is probably able to survive passage through the stomach and anterior portion of the small intestine only if it is ingested in a menstruum of buffered semi-liquid food, or when there is no free hydrochloric acid in the gastric secretions. In formed stools this organism is extremely difficult to identify, although it may be present as an inactive rounded object. It is most commonly diagnosed in warm weather, particularly if the stools are unformed and contain considerable mucus. It is not clinically important. Furthermore, there is no evidence that active *T. hominis* escaping from the anus is able to colonize in the female genital tract.

Trichomonas tenax (O. F. Müller, 1773) Dobell, 1939.—This trichomonad is probably a cosmopolitan parasite of man, although relatively few surveys have been conducted to determine its geographic distribution. The active organism (Fig. 4) has 4 anterior *free flagella* of equal length, a relatively short *undulating membrane*, a slender *axostyle* which protrudes a considerable distance beyond the posterior end of the body, and a subspherical *nucleus*. On the average *T. tenax* is smaller then *T. hominis*. The normal habitat is the mouth, particularly in diseased gums, in tartar around the teeth and in carious teeth. It is not pathogenic but its presence indicates very poor dental and oral hygiene.

Trichomonas vaginalis Donné, 1837.—This trichomonad is a cosmopolitan parasite of man. The active organism (Fig. 5) is frequently but not always consider-

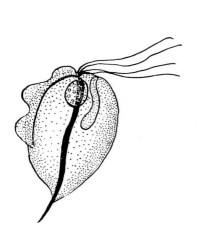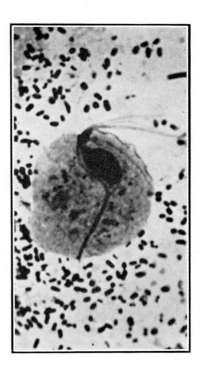

Fig. 5.—*Trichomonas vaginalis*. (Left, × 1600, original, Faust; right, × 2000, after Prof. O. Jírovec, Charles Univ., Prague, courtesy of Melantrich, publisher; in Faust and Russell's *Clinical Parasitology*, Lea & Febiger, Philadelphia.)

ably larger than *T. hominis* and *T. tenax*, reaching maximum measurements of 27 microns in length and 18 microns in breadth. There are 4 anterior *free flagella* of equal length, a fifth flagellum on the margin of the relatively short *undulating membrane* but not extending beyond the posterior limit of the membrane, a long delicate *axostyle* protruding a considerable distance beyond the posterior tip of the organism, a large ovoidal *nucleus* and a large sausage-shaped *parabasal body*. This flagellate is found only in the trophozoite stage and mutiplies by longitudinal binary fission.

T. vaginalis is a frequent inhabitant of the human vagina and of the male genital tract (probably localized in the prostate gland), and is commonly found in the urine of infected subjects. Different strains vary remarkably in virulence (Reardon and Jacobs, 1958). In the United States it is much more common in Negroes than in white women, most prevalent between 30 and 49 years of age, and is more often associated with *T. tenax* than not (P<.001) (Burch, Rees and Reardon, 1959). Transmission of the infection is accomplished principally through sexual intercourse, although there is the possibility that it may at times be transferred from female to female through a contaminated toilet seat, a common vaginal douche or from grossly contaminated clothing. The organism survives from one to a few hours on dry fomites (Kessel and Thompson, 1950).

T. vaginalis infection in the male is often asymptomatic although at times it is associated with a nonspecific urethritis. In the female the propagation of this organism in the vagina may be symptomless, it may produce a characteristic type of vaginitis or it may be complicated by bacterial, fungous or spirochetal infection. There is definite evidence that at times *T. vaginalis* is at least an important contributor to a distinct type of vaginitis characterized by leukorrhea, pruritus vaginæ and vulvæ, burning of the vagina and vulva, and chafing of the vulva. The *p*H of the vaginal discharge in these symptomatic infections is typically alkaline as

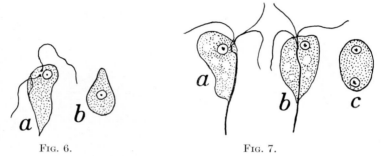

FIG. 6.   FIG. 7.

FIG. 6.—*Retortamonas intestinalis.* *a*, trophozoite; *b*, cyst × 1600. (Original, Faust).
FIG. 7.—*Enteromonas hominis.* *a,b*, trophozoites; *c*, cyst. × 1600. (Original, Faust.)

distinguished from the slightly acid condition of the normal vagina. The symptoms vary from mild to almost intolerable pruritus but the disease is more annoying than disabling (Trussell, 1947).

Diagnosis of *T. vaginalis* infection is based on recovery of the organism in the urine, prostatic, or urethral discharges in the male, the urine and vaginal discharge or mucosal scrapings of the vagina in the female. This infection in the male is frequently terminated by oral administration of diiodohydroxyquin, while symptomatic infection in the female requires both oral and topical therapy (See Table 7, p. 416). Control of *Trichomonas* vaginitis is a difficult problem but at least all married males found infected during urologic examination should be advised of the hazard of transmitting the infection to their wives during sexual intercourse and should be given specific treatment.

Occasional Flagellate Parasites of the Human Intestine.—From time to time other species of harmless flagellate parasites of the large intestine of man are found in uncontaminated stools. These include *Retortamonas intestinalis* Wenyon and O'Connor, 1917 (Fig. 6*a,b*); *R. sinensis* Faust and Wassell, 1921; *Enteromonas hominis* da Fonseca, 1951 (Fig. 7*a,b*); *E. hervei* Lamy, Marshal and Chevrier, 1948, and possible other species. Moreover, coprozoic flagellates such as *Bodo caudatus* (Dujardin, 1841) Stein, 1878 and *Spiromonas angusta* (Dujardin, 1841) Kent, 1880 may at times be ingested and pass through the intestinal tract uninjured, or may be present in contaminated specimen containers or in water employed to make fecal films.

Table 1.—Characteristic Stages of Species of Leishmania and Trypanosoma in Man and in the Insect Host

Stage of the Parasite	Leishmania	Leptomonas	Crithidia	Trypanosoma
	A	B	C	D
Name of Parasite				
Leishmania tropica	Intracellular in macrophages of skin and subcu- taneous tissue	In midgut and later in probos- cis of sand-fly (Phlebotomus); transfer stage to man	Lacking	Lacking
Leishmania braziliensis	Intracellular in macrophages of skin; may be carried to muco- cutaneous junc- tions	In midgut and later in probos- cis of sand-fly (Phlebotomus); transfer stage to man	Lacking	Lacking
Leishmania donovani	Intracellular in macrophages; predominantly in liver, spleen, bone marrow and lymph nodes	In midgut and later in probos- cis of sand-fly (Phlebotomus); transfer stage to man	Lacking	Lacking
Trypanosoma rhodesiense	Lacking	Lacking	In salivary glands of tsetse-fly (Glossina)	In proboscis of tsetse-fly; trans- fer stage to man; first in blood stream, then in lymph nodes
Trypanosoma gambiense	Lacking	Lacking	In salivary glands of tsetse-fly (Glos- sina)	In proboscis of tsetse-fly; trans- fer stage to man; first in blood stream, then in lymph nodes, later in central nervous system
Trypanosoma cruzi	Intracellular in macrophages, es- pecially in skin, lymph nodes, liver and spleen; also in myocar- dium, brain and endocrine glands	Transitional stage only	In midgut of triatomid bug	In feces of triat- omid bug; trans- fer stage to man; present in blood stream only dur- ing acute attacks

FLAGELLATE PROTOZOA OF THE BLOOD AND TISSUES

Seven species of flagellate protozoa inhabit the blood stream and tissues of man, *viz.*, *Leishmania tropica*, *L. braziliensis*, *L. donovani*, *Trypanosoma rhodesiense*, *T. gambiense*, *T. cruzi* and *T. rangeli*. All of these organisms require two hosts in their life cycle, man or other appropriate mammal on the one hand, and a blood-sucking insect on the other. For the species of *Leishmania* the insect is a sandfly (*Phlebotomus*); for *T. rhodesiense* and *T. gambiense*, a tsetse fly (*Glossina*), and for *T. cruzi* and *T. rangeli*, a triatomid bug.

In infections with species of *Leishmania* as well as *T. gambiense* and *T. rhodesiense* the organisms multiply as flagellates in the midgut of the insect, then migrate forward to the insect's proboscis. In *T. cruzi* the parasites pass through the posterior part of the digestive tract and are evacuated in liquid feces at the time the bug feeds. They then enter the skin or mucous membrane at or near the site where the bug punctures the host's epithelium.

The sequence of stages of *T. rangeli* in the insect host differs considerably from that of the other three human trypanosomes (see page 60).

The essential features in the life cycle of the species of *Leishmania* and the first three species of *Trypanosoma* which infect man are compared in Table 1.

THE LEISHMANIA PARASITES OF MAN

The genus *Leishmania* is named in honor of William Leishman, who discovered the species (*L. donovani*) which causes kala-azar. In man and reservoir hosts (dogs, rodents, etc.) the organism is a parasite in the cytoplasm of a macrophage cell in which it obtains nourishment and multiplies by binary division, soon causing the death of the host cell.

When a sand-fly "bites" an infected person or a reservoir host, it sucks up parasitized macrophages or temporarily free parasites circulating in the peripheral blood or tissue juices. Soon after the leishmaniæ reach the midgut of the fly they transform into the flagellated leptomonas form, which then proceeds to divide rapidly. If conditions are favorable, the number of leptomonads is increased tremendously and in 3 to 5 days many of them have migrated up through the esophagus and pharynx into the delicate hypopharyngeal tube in the sand-fly's proboscis. They are now in a position to be injected into the skin of the next individual when the sand-fly prepares to take another blood meal.

The life cycle of species of *Leishmania* is illustrated in Figure 8.

In the Americas the protean clinical manifestations of leishmaniasis in man and in reservoir mammals frequently intergrade, so that it is at times difficult to distinguish between a strictly cutaneous type and a mucocutaneous type, likewise between the visceral type in man and the cutaneous expression of the same organism in dogs and foxes (Garnham and Lewis, 1959; Deane, 1956). For this reason the three species which parasitize man may be regarded as a *Leishmania* complex.

The geographical distribution of the three species of *Leishmania* is shown in Figure 9.

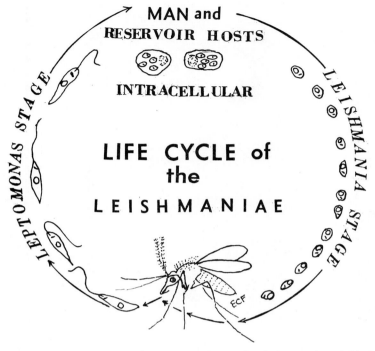

FIG. 8.—Diagrammatic representation of the life cycle of the species of *Leishmania* which parasitize man. (Original, Faust.)

Leishmania tropica (Wright, 1903) Lühe, 1906

(Causing cutaneous leishmaniasis, locally known as Oriental sore, Delhi boil, Bagdad boil, Aleppo button, Jericho boil, etc.)

Historical Notes.—This organism was probably seen by Cunningham in 1885, was described by Borovsky in 1898, and was redescribed and named by Wright in 1903. French workers in North Africa (Sergent *et al.*, 1921) and Adler and Theodor (1926) in Palestine provided experimental evidence that *Phlebotomus papatasii* is the important transmitter of *L. tropica* in the Mediterranean area, while Adler and Ber (1941) produced 28 typical "sores" in 5 human volunteers bitten by infected *P. papatasii*.

Morphology and Biology of L. tropica.—In the mammalian host *Leishmania tropica* lives within the cytoplasm of the large phagocytic monocytes. Here it multiplies by binary fission and soon destroys the host cell. It is a small ovoidal body (Fig. 10) about 2 to 3 microns in length and 1.0 to 1.5 microns in breadth. When sections or smears of the ulcer are stained by Giemsa's or Wright's technic, the cytoplasm of the leishmania stains light azure-blue, the subspherical nucleus a madder red and the short rod-shaped parabasal body, which characteristically lies at an oblique angle to the longer axis of the cell, a deep reddish violet. Nearby there is a minute,

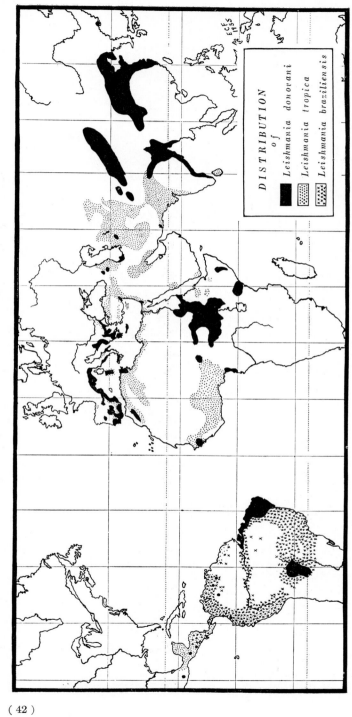

FIG. 9.—World distribution of leishmania infections. (Original, Faust, in Faust and Russell's *Clinical Parasitology*, Lea & Febiger, Philadelphia.)

DISTRIBUTION
of
Leishmania donovani
Leishmania tropica
Leishmania braziliensis

densely staining granule, the kinetoplast, which is at the inner end of the axoneme. There is no free flagellum. In the sand-fly the leptomonad stage (Fig. 11) is narrowly to broadly spindle-shaped, has an ovoidal nucleus near the equatorial plane, a short rod-shaped parabasal body near the anterior end, and a free flagellum which is usually somewhat longer than the body of the organism.

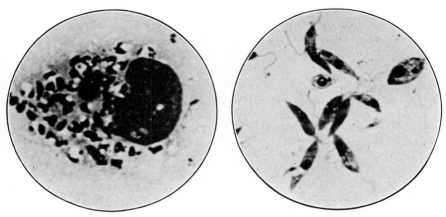

FIG. 10   FIG. 11

FIG. 10.—*Leishmania tropica.* Smear from cutaneous lesion of Armenian patient with Oriental sore diagnosed by Dr. J. H. Wright in Boston, 1903. On right, large mononuclear cell, with nucleus and many leishmaniæ on left about to burst out of the cell membrane. The cytoplasm of the parasites is lightly stained, the nucleus and adjacent parabasal body are densely stained. × 1800. (Photomicrograph from collection of Armed Forces Institute of Pathology, in Faust and Russell's *Clinical Parasitology,* Lea & Febiger, Philadelphia.)

FIG. 11.—*Leishmania tropica.* Leptomonas form of the parasite from blood-agar culture. This same morphologic form occurs in the midgut of the sand-fly. × 1800. (Photomicrograph of preparation by Craig from collection of Armed Forces Institute of Pathology, in Faust and Russell's *Clinical Parasitology,* Lea & Febiger, Philadelphia.)

Pathogenesis and Symptomatology.—Tissue reaction is initiated with the introduction of the leptomonas stage of the parasite into the dermis. A wandering histiocyte in the vicinity picks up the parasite, which rapidly transforms into the leishmania stage, multiplies, and destroys the macrophage. Soon there is a dense concentration of macrophages in the invaded area, all of which are liable to infection and destruction. The center of the lesions then becomes necrotic and the margins containing parasitized macrophages may become infiltrated with giant and plasma cells.

The lesion appears first as a macule, then a papule with a slightly raised center covered by a thin blister-like layer of epidermis. The lesion now breaks down with discharge of a small amount of clear or purulent exudate. At its crater-like base in the dermis a granulating layer is formed and the margin becomes indurated by infiltration of fibroblasts (Fig. 12). If not secondarily infected, the ulcer may dry up and the leishmaniæ slowly disappear, so that within about 9 months or less there is only a slightly raised, depigmented scar at the site. A wet form is also found in steppes and deserts.

Characteristically there is one ulcer for each infected sand-fly "bite," developing at or near the point of inoculation on the exposed skin.

According to Napier (1946), the *incubation period* may be as short as 2 weeks or as long as 3 years and usually fluctuates between 2 and 6 months. In uncomplicated cases, there are no systemic manifestations and since the

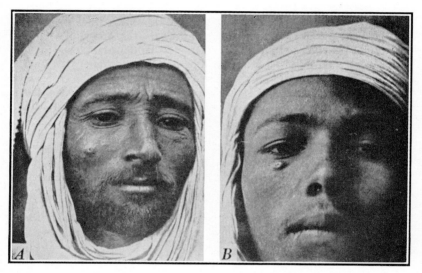

FIG. 12.—Lesions of cutaneous leishmaniasis. *A*, early stage following breaking down of the papule; *B*, slightly more advanced stage when the margin has become more raised and indurated and a granulating floor has developed in the center. (After Sergent *et al.*, in Arch. Inst. Pasteur d'Algerie, from Faust and Russell's *Clinical Parasitology*, Lea & Febiger, Philadelphia.)

infection is typically self-limiting the patients seldom seek medical assistance. However, the common occurrence of pyogenic complications causes not only painful, disfiguring, local ulcers but neutrophilic leukocytosis and fever, at times a bacterial septicemia.

Diagnosis.—Clinically the uncomplicated lesion may be mistaken for a variety of infections of the skin, hence demonstration of the parasite is essential. As soon as the ulcer opens, material scraped from the margin of the crater may be smeared onto a clean microscopic slide and stained by Giemsa's or Wright's technic. The leishmania stage of the parasite will be found within macrophages or spread out from ruptured macrophages. (See TECHNICAL AIDS, pp. 445 and 448.)

Treatment.—One or a small number of clean ulcers may be treated with injections of stibophen (Fuadin), 2 per cent berberine bisulfate or glucantime at the site of each lesion. Each sore is treated in turn, the infiltration in each being repeated every three or four days. For multiple ulcers these drugs should be administered intramuscularly twice weekly for 8 weeks. Secondary bacterial infection of the ulcer, when present, should be eliminated by treatment with antibiotics or sulfonamides before the leishmanicidal drug is employed (see Table 7, p. 416).

Epidemiology.—Cutaneous leishmaniasis (see map, Fig. 9) has an extensive distribution from western and northwestern India and West Pakistan into the countries bordering on the Mediterranean Sea. It also occurs in several foci in tropical Africa. Cutaneous leishmaniasis is found in relatively barren, sandy, arid regions where there is considerable moisture at the time the sand-fly vectors are breeding.

Like the other species of *Leishmania*, *L. tropica* requires two hosts to complete its life cycle, *viz.*, man, dogs or wild rodents, and an appropriate species of sand-fly. The sand-fly obtains the parasite either from the human or reservoir host and after incubation of several days is able to inoculate the leishmaniæ into new hosts. There are distinct biological races of this species which differ in their infectivity for different species of *Phlebotomus* (Adler, 1958).

The vectors most widely distributed in the endemic-enzoötic zones are *P. papatasii* and *P. sergenti*. The stable-fly (*Stomoxys calcitrans*) may transmit the organism from an open ulcer to clean skin by mechanical transfer, while close contact provides opportunity for direct person-to-person transmission.

Control.—Chemotherapy is not practical for mass control but immunization by injection of a pure culture of *L. tropica* into a covered area of the skin will provide lasting immunity (Berberian, 1939). Dog reservoirs should be destroyed. Residual DDT sprayed around the doors, windows and on the inside walls of human habitations and adjacent buldings is very effective in killing the adults and thus preventing extension of the infection (Hertig and Fisher, 1945).

Leishmania braziliensis Vianna, 1911

(Causing American leishmaniasis, espundia, uta, úlcera de los chicleros, pian bois, or muco-cutaneous leishmaniasis)

Historical Notes.—This mutilating type of leishmaniasis was prevalent among natives in the high Andean valleys of Peru at the time the first Spanish explorers entered the country (Weiss, 1943). In 1909 Lindenberg, in São Paulo, Brazil, isolated the organisms from cutaneous ulcers and two years later Carini (1911) recovered typical leishmania forms from cutaneous and naso-pharyngeal tissues in Brazil. Vianna (1911) gave the organism its specific name.

Morphology and Biology of Leishmania braziliensis.—The size and other morphologic characters of this organism within macrophages of man or reservoir hosts and in the sand-fly are indistinguishable from those of *L. tropica* and *L. donovani* (Figs. 10, 11).

Pathogenesis and Symptomatology.—The primary lesion is formed in the same manner as in leishmaniasis tropica and is similar in appearance.

The first macroscopic evidence of the lesion is a macule, which transforms into a slightly elevated pustule (Fig. 13), then opens at the center to discharge semi-liquid necrotic material. At times the base of the crater may become covered with a granulating layer and the ulcer gradually dry up. More frequently the ulcer remains open, with an oozing, glistening surface. In Venezuela (pian bois) the lesion may be florid, with widely scattered plaques, does not cause mucocutaneous involvement, and the leishmaniæ may at times be recovered from peripheral blood (Garnham, 1960). If the inoculation by the sand-fly is on the margin of the ear or the ear lobe (Yucatan), the parasites usually erode the skin and underlying cartilage, leaving a mutilated auricle which may have a smooth or granulomatous surface.

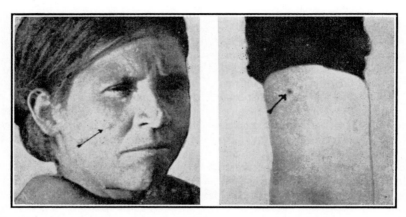

Fig. 13.—Initial primary lesions of muco-cutaneous leishmaniasis. (Photographs courtesy of Drs. Pessôa and Barretto, from *Leishmaniose Tegumentar Americana*, in Faust and Russell's *Clinical Parasitology*, Lea & Febiger, Philadelphia.)

The relatively unique feature of *L. braziliensis* infection in some areas is a tendency for the organisms to migrate to secondary foci at or near muco-cutaneous junctions, particularly the nasal septum. These lesions may be ulcerative, indurative or granulomatous. Blocking of lymphatic capillaries leads to necrosis and extensive destruction of soft and underlying hard tissues, producing extensive erosive mutilation of the nares, and at times of the naso-pharynx, larynx and palatine bones (Fig. 14). Granulomatous disfigurement of the nose, lips and cheeks (Fig. 15) is common. These secondary lesions are typically complicated by bacterial invasion.

The *symptoms* in muco-cutaneous leishmaniasis result from the primary lesion in the skin and from the metastatic lesions. The *incubation period* until the primary lesion develops varies from a few days to several weeks. The early stage of the primary sore is essentially symptomless but following the opening of the ulcer and its enlargement the raw surface is tender and is easily contaminated. Bacterial invasion of the sore produces systemic reaction, with fever and neutrophilic leukocytosis. With muco-cutaneous involvement there are moderate to intense pain in the involved areas, anemia, relative monocytosis and malaise. The condition may persist for years.

Diagnosis.—As in other types of leishmaniasis, accurate diagnosis requires demonstration of the organism in smears or biopsied specimens from the lesion. As soon as bacteria invade the lesion they tend to overgrow the leishmaniæ so that the latter are difficult to discover. South American blastomycosis of the face, which has a similar geographic distribution, is distinguished with difficulty on clinical grounds alone. Cultures and serologic tests are at times diagnostically helpful. (See TECHNICAL AIDS, pp. 445 and 448.)

Treatment.—The treatment of the uncomplicated primary lesion is similar to that for cutaneous leishmaniasis (See Table 7, 416). The open

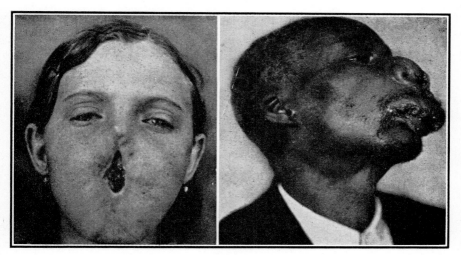

FIG. 14   FIG. 15

FIG. 14.—Extensive erosion of hard and soft tissues of upper jaw, hard palate and nares, with partial healing, resulting from metastatic implantation of *Leishmania braziliensis* in the nasal septum. (Photograph, courtesy of Dr. M. Barretto, São Paulo, Brazil, in Faust and Russell's *Clinical Parasitology*, Lea & Febiger, Philadelphia.)

FIG. 15.—Granulomatous lesions of nares, lips and underlying tissues in metastatic *L. braziliensis* infection. (Photograph, courtesy of Dr. M. Barretto, São Paulo, Brazil, in Faust and Russell's *Clinical Parasitology*, Lea & Febiger, Philadelphia.)

sore and the metastatic lesions are much more difficult to manage and require months or years of persistent treatment with antibiotics in association with antimonial preparations. Even though the leishmaniæ temporarily disappear, Pessôa and Barretto (1948) found that the condition tends to relapse in a few months.

Epidemiology.—Infection with *Leishmania braziliensis* extends from northeastern Argentina through the countries of Continental America as far north as Yucatan. (See map, Fig. 9). In practically all of these regions of endemicity the disease is restricted to sylvatic areas. The highest prevalence is characteristically among young adult males, although all ages and both sexes on first exposure are equally susceptible.

Man is the common definitive host, but natural infection occurs in dogs, likewise sylvatic rodents.

Several species of *Phlebotomus* have been incriminated as likely transmitters, *viz.*, on the basis of natural infection and their common association with infected human cases; yet complete life cycle transmission of *L. braziliensis* has apparently never been accomplished under carefully controlled conditions.

Control.—Since the disease is not contracted in the villages, residual DDT-spraying of homes is not a major weapon. However, area power dusting with DDT, along with residual spraying of dwellings, has been shown to be successful in destroying the adult flies.

Leishmania donovani (Laveran and Mesnil, 1903) Ross, 1903

(Causing visceral leishmaniasis, commonly referred to as kala-azar)

Historical Notes.—In 1900, William Leishman first demonstrated the agent of kala-azar in smears from the spleen of an English soldier who died of a fever near Calcutta, India. In 1903, Charles Donovan found the same organism in smears from splenic puncture of a person with the disease in Madras, India. Ross created the genus *Leishmania* in honor of the original discoverer. Leonard Rogers (1904) first cultured the leishmania and demonstrated that it had a flagellate stage. It was not until 1942 that Swaminath, Shortt and Anderson were able to demonstrate natural transmission to 5 of 5 human volunteers by "bites" of infected *Phlebotomus argentipes*.

Morphology and Biology of Leishmania donovani.—In its leishmania and leptomonas forms *L. donovani* is indistingusihable in size or other morphological characters from *L. tropica* (Figs. 10, 11) and *L. braziliensis*. In its host tissue relations in man and most susceptible laboratory animals, however, *L. donovani* has a predilection for the reticulo-endothelial cells of the liver, spleen, bone marrow and visceral lymph nodes, and its primary colonization in the skin is usually inapparent. In the dog the conspicuous lesions are in the skin, so that in this reservoir host cutaneous leishmaniasis due to infection with *L. tropica* and kala-azar caused by *L. donovani* are difficult to distinguish. Rarely cutaneous leishmania lesions are associated with the visceral infection in man (P.E.C. Manson-Bahr, 1959).

Pathogenesis and Symptomatology.—The leptomonad stage of the parasite is introduced into the outer dermis by an infected sand-fly. In China, India, and the Mediterranean endemic area the primary lesion is inapparent. In the U.S.S.R., Mirzorian (1941) found that one or more minute papules the size of a pinhead appear on the exposed skin some time before *Leishmania donovani* infection can be otherwise demonstrated in infants. After first colonizing in the dermis of man some of the increasing progeny gain access to the blood stream or lymphatics and are transported to the viscera, where they are trapped by fixed tissue macrophages and begin to multiply rapidly.

As the number of leishmaniæ becomes greatly augmented, there is intense phagocytic activity and a remarkable increase in the number of macrophages, increasing neutropenia and anemia. The decrease in neutrophils provides greatly reduced defense against pathogenic bacteria and the increasing anemia reduces the threshold of resistance to intercurrent diseases.

Although the leishmaniæ are found in all soft tissues of the body, they are particularly abundant in those rich in reticulo-endothelial cells (Napier, 1946). Hence the fundamental histopathology results from this parasite-host cell relationship.

The *liver* is enlarged and firm but somewhat friable, with increase in size and number of the Kupffer cells. The *spleen* is likewise greatly enlarged. The *bone marrow* exhibits pathologic activity in production of macrophages, many of which are parasitized, and in decreased erythropoietic function. Congestion in the smaller blood vessels results in multiple hemorrhages, particularly from mucous membranes.

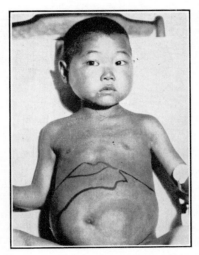

Fig. 16.—Chinese child acutely ill with kala-azar. Note enlarged liver, tremendously enlarged spleen and edema of face. (Photo, Peking Union Medical College Hospital.)

The *incubation period* varies from 10 days to many months (Napier, 1946). The *onset* may be sudden, with acute manifestations, but the usual case develops insidiously, on the average about 90 days following exposure.

A typical acute case has fever of an undulant type fluctuating daily from 36.7 to 40° C. (90 to 104° F.), and may exhibit a double rise of temperature every 24 hours, but without pronounced headache or mental lethargy. The appetite is usually good. Loss of weight may be partly masked by edema of the face, trunk and feet. The abdomen is protuberant and both the liver and spleen can be palpated far below the costal margin. In spite of the engorged liver there is no periportal cirrhosis, hence no ascites (Fig. 16). Bleeding typically occurs from the gums, lips and nares, and hemorrhage from the intestinal mucosa.

4

The blood picture is that of a moderate erythropenia (averaging about 3,000,000 r.b.c./cmm.), an absolute monocytosis and neutropenia, occasionally complete agranulocytosis.

Complications usually observed in kala-azar are principally diarrhea or dysentery, and especially bronchopneumonia.

Diagnosis.—In an endemic area typical cases may be diagnosed on clinical grounds with a fair degree of accuracy. However, since the patient who is seriously ill usually requires hospitalization for complications, there is ample time to obtain laboratory confirmation.

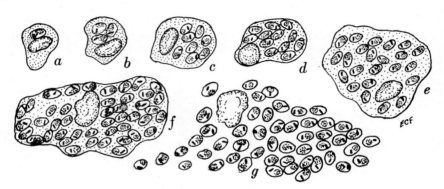

FIG. 17.—*Leishmania donovani*, showing successive stages *a–f* in multiplication of the leishmania in a macrophage and *g*, final rupture of host cell. × 1000. (Original, Faust.)

Suggestive laboratory evidence short of specific demonstration of the etiologic agent consists in a positive aldehyde test, indicating an excess of serum globulin, with a depression in serum albumin and increase in gamma globulin.

For complete assurance that the patient is suffering from kala-azar the organism itself must be demonstrated by biopsy, preferably a bone marrow specimen from the iliac crest, employing the van den Bergh technic. (See "Technical Aids," page 435.)

Treatment.—Supportive treatment and good nursing care are needed in most cases, particularly those with a complication of bronchopneumonia, severe diarrhea, dysentery, or cancrum oris. The advent of the sulfa drugs and especially the antibiotics has greatly reduced the hazards of these complications.

Specific Treatment.—Two types of drugs are employed in the treatment of kala-azar, antimonials and diamidines.

Antimonials.—Of the pentavalent antimonials ethyl stibamine (*Neostibosan*), methylglucamine antimoniate (*Glucantime*) and sodium antimony gluconate (*Solustibosan*) have been the most useful. Methylglucamine antimoniate and sodium antimony gluconate may be administered intramuscularly, which is a distinct advantage in mass treatment in clinics. With the latter drug, however, relapses are common (See Table 7, p. 416).

The Diamidines.—These drugs, including stilbamidine, hydroxystilbamidine and pentamidine, are employed routinely in the Sudan in the treatment of kala-azar, since this particular strain of *L. donovani* does not respond satisfactorily to antimony therapy. Likewise, in India, China and in the Mediterranean endemic area cases refractory to antimony are usually benefitted by diamidine therapy.

In India, a sequela to antimony treatment is known as post-treatment kala-azar dermal leishmaniasis, in which a verrucous condition develops in the skin. Histologically these excrescences contain leishmaniæ in focal concentrations of macrophages. This post-treatment phenomenon is interpreted as an indication of inadequate antimony treatment of the visceral lesions, with a residuum of leishmaniæ which have been driven to the skin where they continue to propagate.

Epidemiology.—Kala-azar is endemic in many regions of Asia, Africa, Europe, South America and Central America. (See map, Fig. 9, p. 42.) These include much of northern China, eastern India and Turkestan; the Sudan, many foci around the Mediterranean Sea, and northern Argentina and eastern Brazil, likewise minor foci elsewhere in South and Central America.

In most of these areas, the infection is endemic or hyperendemic but on occasion it may become epidemic. In Mediterranean countries and China it is primarily a disease of infants and young children. In India and South America, young adults are most frequently infected. In the Sudan, a particularly fulminating type is observed, commonly in young adults. Previous infection confers considerable immunity.

In North China, Bagdad and the Mediterranean areas of endemicity dogs are common reservoir hosts; dogs and foxes have been found naturally infected in Brazil. Lesions caused by *L. donovani* in dogs are primarily cutaneous, so that the sand-fly has direct access to infected macrophages (Berberian, 1959).

Kala-azar is essentially a domestic disease in villages and communities near urban centers, where moisture is temporarily abundant for growth of rank vegetation in which the sand-flies breed. A new crop of human kala-azar cases may be anticipated about 3 months after the breeding season of the sand-fly transmitters.

Control.—With the demonstration that residual spraying of DDT in and around human habitations is both highly efficacious and economical in sand-fly control (Hertig, 1949), this measure has replaced all others as the main weapon of attack on kala-azar.

In areas where dogs constitute a constant source of infection for the sand-flies, campaigns to destroy all street dogs and others with obvious skin lesions will effectively reduce this reservoir of the disease.

TRYPANOSOME PARASITES OF MAN

Many species of trypanosomes parasitize fishes, amphibians, reptiles, birds and mammals. Leeches serve as intermediate hosts and biological vectors for the trypanosomes of aquatic vertebrates, and arthropods as the transmitters of the trypanosomes of non-aquatic hosts. Blood-sucking flies are the vectors for most species of this latter group but there are a few notable exceptions. *Trypanosoma lewisi* utilizes rat fleas (*Nosopsyllus fasciatus et al.*), *T. cruzi* is transmitted by triatomid bugs, and *T. equiperdum*, the species causing dourine in horses and mules, has become adapted to direct transmission from vertebrate to vertebrate through coitus. Blood-sucking arthropods may also mechanically transmit several species of trypanosomes through contamination of their proboscis with the organisms at the time of an interrupted blood meal.

Some species of trypanosomes apparently live in their natural vertebrate hosts without causing evident tissue damage. Others cause variable degrees of tissue pathology. The three species of trypanosomes which commonly parasitize man, *viz.*, *Trypanosoma rhodesiense*, *T. gambiense* and *T. cruzi*, are all pathogenic for the human host and not infrequently their infection has a fatal outcome.

Since *T. rhodesiense* and *T. gambiense*, like *T. brucei*, their relative in game animals, differ from *T. cruzi* in their life cycle, method of transmission and tissue relationship to the mammalian host, the former two will be considered separately from *T. cruzi*.

Trypanosome Parasites of Man Having Proboscis Emergence from the Vector

Trypanosoma rhodesiense, *T. gambiense* and certain other trypanosomes which infect game and domestic animals utilize *Glossina* (tsetse flies) as biological vectors (Davey, 1958). Multiplication of the trypanosomes occurs within the digestive tract of the tsetse fly and emergence of the organisms takes place through the hypopharyngeal tube within the proboscis; but the sites and morphologic stages of development vary depending on the species of trypanosome.

In *T. brucei*, *T. rhodesiense* and *T. gambiense* the trypanosome forms which are sucked into the labial cavity from the mammalian host pass directly through the proventriculus into the midgut, where multiplication occurs in an elongated trypanosome stage. Thereafter the organisms migrate back through the proventriculus and buccal cavity up the hypopharynx into the salivary glands, where a second multiplication occurs. These forms are crithidial, with a posterior nucleus, but they later transform into infective-stage trypanosomes, which accumulate in the salivary-gland ducts.

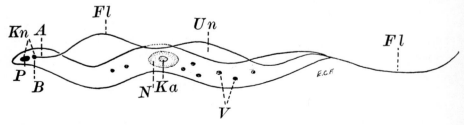

Fig. 18.—Diagram illustrating the morphology of a typical trypanosome. *Kn*, kinetoplast; *P*, parabasal body; *B*, blepharoplast; *A*, axoneme; *Fl*, flagellum; *Un*, undulating membrane; *N*, nucleus; *Ka*, karyosome; *V*, volutin granules. (From Faust and Russell's *Clinical Parasitology*, Lea & Febiger, Philadelphia.)

In these species the hypopharynx is utilized only for transit and not for multiplication or metamorphosis of the parasites.

In the mammalian host *T. brucei, T. rhodesiense* and *T. gambiense* are trypanosome forms (Fig. 18) circulating primarily in the blood stream, where they multiply by longitudinal binary division. In case the host-parasite adaptation is good, they produce no extensive humoral or tissue damage. This is illustrated by *T. brucei* in African game animals. *T. rhodesiense* is a mutant of *T. brucei* which has recently become adapted to man. Here the adjustment is extremely poor, and the parasite typically produces an overwhelming infection with fatal consequences to the victim. It is also likely that *T. gambiense* was originally derived from a parent stock of *T. brucei* but at a much earlier period than *T. rhodesiense*, so that the adjustment to the human host has been somewhat more satisfactory and the disease process is usually less fulminating than in *T. rhodesiense* infection.

The life cycle of the *T. brucei-rhodesiense-gambiense* complex is diagrammatically shown in Figure 19.

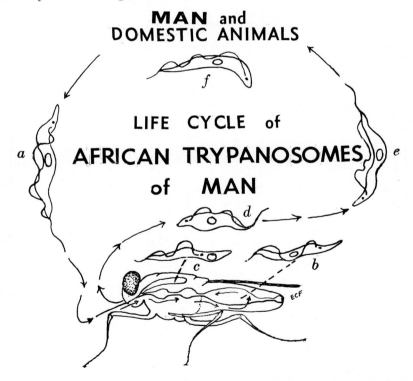

Fig. 19.—Diagram illustrating the life cycle of the *Trypanosoma brucei-rhodesiense-gambiense* complex in the tsetse fly, in mammals and man. *a*, trypanosome stage from mammalian host sucked up by fly; *b*, multiplication of trypanosome stage in fly's midgut; *c*, multiplication of crithidial stage in salivary glands, followed by transformation into metacyclic trypanosome stage; *d*, metacyclic trypanosomes introduced by fly into mammal; *e*, intercellular trypanosome stage in mammal; *f*, trypansome stage in bloodstream of mammal. (Original, Faust).

Trypanosoma rhodesiense Stephens and Fantham, 1910
(Causing Rhodesian trypanosomiasis)

Historical Notes.—This hemoflagellate was discovered by Stephens and Fantham in 1909 (1910) in the blood of a patient in Rhodesia who had symptoms suggestive of a fulminating early stage of African "sleeping sickness." Three years later Kinghorn and Yorke (1912) demonstrated that it is transmitted to man by the tsetse fly, *Glossina morsitans.*

Morphology, Biology and Life Cycle.—Wenyon (1926) refered to *T. rhodesiense* as "the human strain of *Trypanosoma brucei,*" and all subsequent work is consistent with this view. Morphologically the infective trypanosome stage of these two species can not be distinguished, nor can it be differentiated from this stage of *T. gambiense* (Fig. 21, compare with Fig. 22).

When a tsetse fly takes a blood meal containing *T. rhodesiense* from animal reservoirs or man, the trypanosomes reach the midgut, then migrate to the salivary glands and reach the infective stage (Wenyon, 1926). The whole development within the fly averages approximately 14 days. When

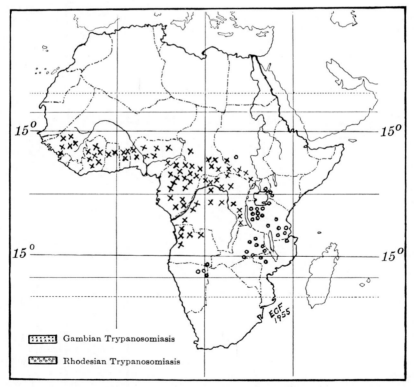

Fig. 20.—Map of Africa showing distribution of Rhodesian and Gambian trypanosomiasis. (From Faust and Russell's *Clinical Parasitology*, Lea & Febiger, Philadelphia.)

the infective-stage trypanosomes are introduced into the human host, they survive and multiply only in case they belong to the strain adapted to man.

Pathogenesis and Symptomatology.—On introduction into the human skin from the proboscis of an infected tsetse fly, *T. rhodesiense* first lodges in the local tissues where the trypanosomes set up an interstitial inflammatory reaction. This usually subsides within a week or two as the trypanosomes gain entry to the circulating blood, where they multiply. Then they enter the lymph nodes, where a second focus of inflammation occurs, with hyperplasia of the endothelial lining of the blood sinuses and perivascular infiltration of leukocytes, due to toxic metabolites of the trypanosomes. This process is rapid, fulminating and usually causes death of the patient

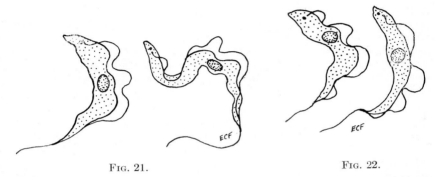

Fig. 21.   Fig. 22.

Fig. 21.—*Trypanosoma rhodesiense.* Stages seen in peripheral blood of man. × 1600 (Original, Faust.)

Fig. 22.—*Trypanosoma gambiense.* Stages seen in peripheral blood of man, morphologically indistinguishable from *T. rhodesiense.* × 1600. (Original, Faust.)

in a few months. Only rarely does the victim survive long enough for the trypanosomes to invade the central nervous system and produce lesions characteristic of the third stage of *T. gambiense* infection (so-called "sleeping sickness").

Following an incubation period of 1 to 2 weeks, the patient suffers from febrile paroxysms, which frequently recur, with edema, extreme weakness, rapid loss of weight and myocarditis as the cardinal symptoms. Death supervenes within a year in untreated cases.

Diagnosis.—During febrile episodes the trypanosomes appear in circulating blood; at other times specific diagnosis must be based on recovery of the organisms from lymph node aspirates.

Treatment.—Until recent years the only drug which has been found to be effective in Rhodesian trypanosomiasis is *suramin* and this is valuable only during the early stage of the disease. Patients with late infections, recognized principally by increased cells and protein in the cerebrospinal fluid, should be treated with a diamidine or melarsen oxide (Mel B) intravenously, which will often produce cure (See Table 7, p. 416).

Epidemiology.— *T. rhodesiense* has a geographic distribution limited to the upland savannas of East Africa. (See map, Fig. 20).

Rhodesian trypanosomiasis results from the "bite" of the infected tsetse fly, which is usually *Glossina morsitans,* both sexes of which are blood suckers and transmitters. Less commonly *G. swynnertoni* and rarely *G. palpalis, G. pallidipes* and *G. brevipalpis* serve as vectors. These flies breed in relatively dry habitats, preferring warm to cold environmental temperatures.

Small numbers of persons are infected with *T. rhodesiense* compared with *T. gambiense* but the usually fatal course of the Rhodesian disease serves to emphasize its importance. It occurs typically in sporadic form but epidemics at times develop.

Control.—This involves primarily setting up a barrier between human beings and infected tsetse flies. Fairburn (1943) recommended the following procedures: (1) remove people from forested or heavy bush regions (especially around lakes) to open country; (2) clear out brush between settlements, and (3) settle individual families in uninfected territory. Reclamation of land from tsetse fly and resettlement of the population requires pasture land for excess cattle on which the natives rely for their basic food (Ford, 1958). Attempts to eradicate the disease by destruction of infected game animals have not succeeded.

Trypanosoma gambiense Dutton, 1902

(Causing Gambian trypanosomiasis or African "sleeping sickness")

Historical Notes.—In 1901 Forde saw a trypanosome in the blood of a European in Gambia, West Africa. The next year Dutton proposed the name by which this organism has since been designated. In 1903 Castellani found trypanosomes in the cerebro-spinal fluid of patients in Uganda suffering from "sleeping sickness." The same year Bruce and Nabarro (1903) discovered that the organism was transmitted from man to man by a tsetse fly, *Glossina palpalis.*

Morphology, Biology and Life Cycle.—Like *T. brucei* and *T. rhodesiense, T. gambiense* varies remarkably in size and shape in its trypanosome stage from delicate spindle-shaped with a free flagellum to broad and stumpy forms with or without a free flagellum (range of measurements: 14–33 microns long by 1.5–3.5 microns in breadth) (See Fig. 22).

In the tsetse fly the organisms multiply in the midgut as delicate, elongated trypanosomes. After the 15th day they migrate back through the esophagus, pharynx and labial cavity, then up to the salivary glands. Here they transform into broad crithidial forms, divide many times and revert to the slender trypanosome type. They pass down the salivary ducts about the 20th day and are ready to be introduced into the next victim when the tsetse fly takes a blood meal.

Pathogenesis and Symptomatology.—At the site of inoculation in the skin the trypanosomes provoke an interstitial inflammation which gradually subsides in 1 to 2 weeks. Meanwhile they gain access to the blood stream and initiate a rather heavy parasitemia. Although they never invade the cytoplasm of cells, their toxic metabolites produce proliferative and necrotic damage to all cells with which they come in contact, including particularly the endothelial lining of the smaller blood vessels. The parasites come more and more to lodge in lymph nodes, and later the arachnoid spaces of the central nervous system and then the brain substance. Thus, following the initial lesion in the skin, three progressive stages of tissue relationship occur, *viz.*, parasitemia, lymphadenitis and central nervous system involvement. A remarkable variation exists in the virulence of this species, from low grade to exalted pathogenicity resembling that of *T. rhodesiense* (Fairbairn, 1958).

Symptoms.—The primary dermal lesion is seen in European patients, rarely if ever in native Africans. Within 6 to 14 days (the *incubation period*) the trypanosomes appear in circulating blood. In natives, this is

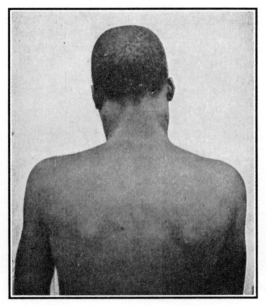

Fig. 23.—Enlargement of the lymph nodes of the posterior cervical triangle (Winterbottom's sign) during the active fulminating stage of Rhodesian and Gambian trypanosomiasis. (After Koch, from *Stitt's Diagnosis, Prevention and Treatment of Tropical Diseases*, courtesy, The Blakiston Co., in Faust and Russell's *Clinical Parasitology*, Lea & Febiger, Philadelphia.)

characteristically a symptomless stage. But as soon as the parasites invade lymph nodes, causing painful enlargement, there is a febrile attack of about a week's duration, then an apyrectic period, typically followed by one or more bouts of fever. The trypanosomes are found in the blood only during the febrile episodes. The most pronounced lymphadenitis occurs in the posterior cervical triangle (Winterbottom's sign, see Fig. 23), but the axillary lymph nodes and those of the groin are also frequently enlarged, as well as the spleen and liver. At this stage, the patient complains of headache, arthritic pain, weakness of the legs and cramps. Later dyspnea, precordial pain, disturbed vision, delayed sensation to pain, anemia and extreme weakness are apt to appear. At times, there is spontaneous improvement in the symptoms followed by another acute febrile attack. Again, the patient may die during this stage of the disease from fulminating toxemia as in Rhodesian trypanosomiasis.

The syndrome resulting from invasion of the central nervous systems is commonly referred to as "sleeping sickness" but this designation suggests only one of the more advanced neurological symptoms. Sleepiness occurs and becomes so pronounced that the patient falls asleep while eating or even standing (Fig. 24). In the more advanced stage the patient sleeps

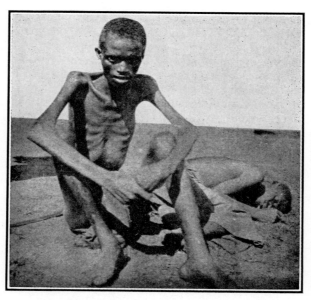

Fig. 24.—Sleeping sickness (terminal) stage of Gambian trypanosomiasis. The patient sitting on the ground illustrates the extreme emaciation and mental apathy, while the patient lying down typifies the tendency to fall asleep. (Photograph of patients from the Belgian Congo, courtesy of Dr. E. R. Kellersberger, in Faust and Russell's *Clinical Parasitology,* Lea & Febiger, Philadelphia.)

continuously, emaciation becomes extreme, convulsions occur, then profound coma and finally death, which frequently results from intercurrent infection.

Diagnosis.—A presumptive diagnosis should always be supplemented by demonstration of the trypanosome in blood, tissue fluid aspirated from enlarged lymph nodes, bone marrow biopsy or spinal fluid. Since the trypanosomes rapidly disintegrate following their removal from the tissues, it is necessary that the microscopic preparation be fixed and stained immediately. (See "Technical Aids," page 435.)

Treatment.—This should be undertaken at the earliest possible moment following proof that the disease is Gambian trypanosomiasis, since delay reduces the chances of recovery. The drugs most valuable in treatment are tryparsamide and certain other arsenicals, suramin sodium, and diamidine compounds.

Tryparsamide has been the most widely used and helpful drug in Gambian trypanosomiasis. It must be administered by vein, once or twice weekly, with larger dosage for the more advanced condition. When optic neuritis develops, treatment with this, or any other arsenical must be terminated immediately. Melarsen oxide (Mel B) is valuable in the later stages of the disease.

Suramin (Bayer 205) is very effective in the febrile-lymphadenitis stage but valueless after the parasites have invaded the central nervous system. It is administered by vein, once weekly in 1-Gm. doses for 10 weeks.

Diamidines, particularly *pentamidine* and *propamidine*, are specifically valuable during the earlier stage of the infection and may be substituted for tryparsamide if optic neuritis develops. (See Table 7, p. 417).

Epidemiology.—Gambian trypanosomiasis is widely distributed through the central half of Africa (Fig. 20). In recent years this infection on the north shore of Lake Victoria has been replaced by the Rhodesian type (Robertson and Baker, 1958). In some of these countries the infection rate is low, in other areas extremely high.

The amount of infection is determined by the number of *Glossina palpalis* (or at times other species of tsetse flies) which have an opportunity to "bite" patients infected with *T. gambiense*. All of the endemic territory is in rain-forests, where there are luxuriant vegetation and moist ground in which the flies breed (Morris, 1959).

Age, sex, race and occupation have no relation to susceptibility to Gambian trypanosomiasis, although they may favor exposure. Infection may also be transmitted by sexual intercourse.

The principal mammalian host of *T. gambiense* is man himself. However, domestic animals are highly susceptible to infection. There is no proof that wild game animals serve as reservoirs.

Control.—The following measures have been found practical in reducing the incidence of Gambian trypanosomiasis in endemic areas: (1) discovery, isolation and specific treatment of all human cases, including mildly symptomatic and asymptomic carriers in the area; (2) protection of persons from *Glossina* "bite"; (3) quarantine of persons coming from infected into uninfected territory; (4) campaigns to destroy the breeding and resting places of the tsetse flies; (5) at times the removal of inhabitants from hyperendemic areas, and (6) administration of prophylactic doses of *suramin*, every 3 months, or *propamidine*, once every 5 or 6 months, to individuals liable to exposure. Domestic mammals which acquire the disease not only serve as reservoirs but infected cattle become emaciated and hence the principal human food supply is greatly depleted. No eminently satisfactory prophylactic has yet been developed against Gambian or other type of trypanosomiasis in these animals, although spraying of dieldrin on tsetse habitats in Kenya promises some control of cattle trypanosomiasis.

Remarkable reduction in the incidence of Gambian trypanosomiasis has been obtained since mass diagnosis and treatment of the human population in endemic areas was undertaken on an extensive scale.

Trypanosoma rangeli Téjera, 1920

In 1920, Téjera found unusual crithidial and trypanosome stages of a flagellate in the gut of *Rhodnius prolixus*, the principal vector of *T. cruzi* in Venezuela. The organisms differed from similar stages of *T. cruzi*, so that Téjera gave it the name *T. rangeli*. In 1942, Medina obtained this same organism by xeno-diagnosis from two patients in Venezuela. The next year DeLeón and Montenegro, in Guatemala (DeLeón, 1949) apparently found the same trypanosome in triatomid bugs and in the peripheral blood of four children. More recently Pifano *et al.* (1949) found a high incidence of *T. rangeli* in *R. prolixus* in the Yaracuy River Valley, Venezuela. It has been reported from Brazil (State of Pará), French Guiana, El Salvador, and possibly from Chile, in *R. prolixus* and other species of triatomid bugs, as well as in *Cebus* and *Ateles* monkeys, opossums and rodents.

This trypanosome occurs likewise in Panama, in the Ariari and Magdalena river valleys, and possibly elsewhere in Colombia. In human blood films the flagellate is trypanosome in form, averages 31 microns in length, with a relatively broad undulating membrane and a free flagellum rarely more than half the length of the body. The ovoidal nucleus is situated somewhat anterior to the equatorial plane and the small, round blepharoplast is subterminal. Human infection, either alone or associated with *T. cruzi*, is relatively high in these areas, where *Cebus fatuellus* and dogs are also naturally infected. The organism shows trypanosome division stages in mammalian blood. Groot (1952) demonstrated that in experimentally infected *Rhodnius prolixus* there is first a developmental phase in the midgut. Later, some of the organisms migrate into the hemolymph and forward to the salivary glands, where they complete their development and then descend into the proboscis, through which they are introduced into the mammalian host. No intracellular leishmania stage has been demonstrated, and no clinical manifestations developed in two human volunteers in whom the course of the infection was carefully followed.

Trypanosome Parasite of Man Having Posterior Emergence from the Vector
Trypanosoma cruzi Chagas, 1909

(Causing Chagas disease or American trypanosomiasis)

Historical Notes.—In 1909 Carlos Chagas discovered a flagellate in the hindgut of a blood-sucking bug, *Panstrongylus megistus*. He allowed infected bugs to feed on a *Callithrix* monkey free of blood parasites and some days later found a trypanosome in the animal's circulating blood. Because of the unique morphology of the flagellate, Chagas named it *Trypanosoma cruzi*. Chagas then searched for the natural host. In bug-infested homes in the area he discovered the trypanosome first in the blood of a cat, then in that of a child with facial edema who was suffering from fever, anemia, splenomegaly and lymphadenitis. Soon many chronic cases with the same clinical manifestations were found to be due to infection with this parasite.

Morphology, Biology and Life Cycle.—Two stages of *T. cruzi*, *viz.*, trypanosome and leishmania, are found in the mammalian host, and two, *viz.*, crithidia and trypanosome, in the insect host. (See Table 1, page 39.) While the infected bug is taking a blood meal it discharges excrement containing the metacyclic trypanosome stage of the parasite, which is rubbed into the site, or possibly at times actively invades mucous membranes. Almost immediately the trypanosomes are engulfed by nearby macrophages, in which the organisms rapidly transform into a leishmania stage, multiply by binary fission, cause disintegration of the macrophage and then invade and multiply within other macrophages. After 4 or 5 days some of the parasites from the primary focus get into the blood stream, in which they are transformed into a trypanosome stage, but in this stage they

Chagas' Disease in Man

Chagas' Disease in Reservoir Hosts

Fig. 25.—Map showing distribution of *Trypanosoma cruzi* infection (Chagas' disease). Not shown on this map are foci of animal infection in Louisiana, Georgia and Maryland. (From Faust and Russell's *Clinical Parasitology*, Lea & Febiger, Philadelphia.)

never divide. *Via* the circulating blood *T. cruzi* is carried to the viscera, where the organisms lodge and invade the cytoplasm of the cells, transforming again into leishmaniæ and multiplying. Thus, within the mammalian host the extra-cellular trypanosome stage is a very temporary one, found only in the blood stream, while the intra-cellular leishmania stage is the essential one. In this respect *T. cruzi* differs fundamentally from *T. brucei*, *T. rhodesiense*, *T. gambiense*, *T. rangeli* and most other trypanosomes.

In the blood of man and reservoir hosts or susceptible laboratory animals *T. cruzi* is a typical trypanosome (Fig. 27*a*), delicately spindle-shaped, about 20 microns in length, with relatively few curves to its narrow undulating membrane and a short free flagellum, or considerably shorter, broader, more or less C-shaped, with or without a free flagellum. In its intra-cellular

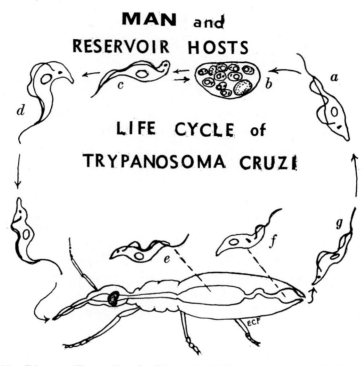

FIG. 26.—Diagram illustrating the life cycle of *Trypanosoma cruzi* in the vector (triatomid bug), in wild and domestic mammals and in man. *a*, trypanosome stage in mammalian bloodstream; *b*, leishmania stage in histiocytes; *c*, trypanosome stage in bloodstream derived from intracellular leishmaniæ; *d*, trypanosome stage sucked up by bug; *e*, trypanosome stage in midgut, transforming into *f*, crithidial stage in hindgut; *g*, metacyclic trypanosomes derived from crithidiæ, excreted in bug's feces, infective for mammal. (Original, Faust.)

phase *T. cruzi* is a typical leishmania, ovoidal in shape, 1.5 to 5 microns in longer diameter, with a large nucleus and a deeply staining parabasal body (Fig. 27*d*–*g*). In reticulo-endothelial cells *T. cruzi* can not be easily distingusihed from species of *Leishmania*; but only *T. cruzi* invades myocardial and neuroglia cells as a leishmania-type organism.

The organism is sucked up by the triatomid bug as a free flagellate or as an intra-cellular leishmania within a macrophage. In the midgut of the bug the organism becomes flagellated and binary multiplication occurs. It does not migrate forward but proceeds to the hindgut, where it transforms into the metacyclic trypanosome form infective again for the vertebrate host. Once a triatomid bug has become parasitized with *T. cruzi*, it will retain the infection for months or years.

Pathogenesis and Symptomatology.—The site of inoculation of *T. cruzi* into the mammalian host may be anywhere on exposed skin or on a mucous membrane. Multiplication of the organisms which have been engulfed by nearby macrophages and their entry into other macrophages produce a

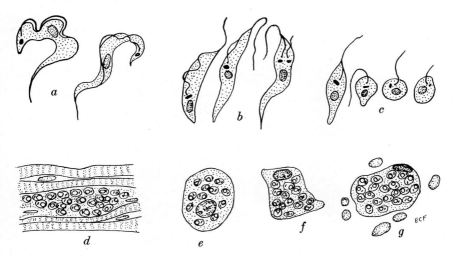

Fig. 27.—Stages of *Trypanosoma cruzi* in the mammalian host. *a*, typical trypanosomes in peripheral blood; *b*, transitional crithidial forms; *c*, transitional leptomonas forms; *d*, leishmania form in myocardium; *e, f, g*, leishmania form in macrophages of liver, spleen and glial cell of brain. × 1600. (Original Faust.)

small granuloma (*chagoma*) which obstructs lymph flow. This is the primary, usually apparent lesion, the expression of which is probably at times intensified by sensitization from the salivary secretions introduced into the site by the infected bug (Lumbreras, Flores and Escallón, 1959).

Four or five days later progeny get into the blood stream and circulate as typical trypanosomes. Meanwhile some of them become lodged in reticulo-endothelial tissues, myocardium, endocrine glands and the glia cells of the brain. Here they multiply as leishmania forms, destroying the host cells. Reticulo-endothelial activity and increase in the number of fixed macrophage cells cause splenomegaly, hepatomegaly, adenopathy and engorgement of bone marrow, reminiscent of kala-azar (page 49). Colonies of the parasites which develop in myocardium produce insidious destruction of heart muscle (Laranja *et al.*, 1956), and those which are located in the brain cells cause extensive neuropathologic changes.

Symptoms in Chagas' disease are associated in sequence with the primary lesion, the parasitemia and the more chronic pathology due to development of the protozoön in the several visceral organs. Frequently the primary site is at the outer canthus of one eye, with unilateral palpebral edema (*Romaña's* sign), at times causing a swelling of the entire side of the face (Fig. 28). During the primary parasitemia of about 12 to 30 days, there is fever, a marked toxic condition suggesting typhoid fever, tachycardia and in children at times fatal termination. If the patient survives this acute stage, or if it is by-passed, the symptoms of the chronic disease depend on the localization of the parasites, *viz.*, cardiac, meningo-encephalitic, suprarenal, etc. This stage may last for years with gradual increase in the chronic manifestations, but with febrile exacerbations and parasitemia supervening from time to time.

Diagnosis.—During febrile periods diagnosis may be made by demonstrating the typical trypanosome stage of *T. cruzi* in blood films. Aspiration

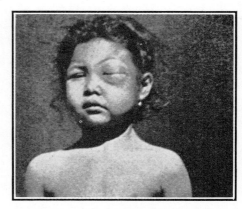

Fig. 28.—Photograph of Brazilian child suffering from acute stage of Chagas' disease. Note the unilateral palpebral edema (Romaña's sign) which is relatively characteristic of this disease. (Photograph by Dr. C. Romaña, in Faust and Russell's *Clinical Parasitology*, Lea & Febiger, Philadelphia.)

of spleen, liver, lymph nodes or bone marrow will frequently reveal the leishmania form of the organism in fixed macrophages. Complement fixation of patient's blood serum, employing pure antigen obtained from cultured organisms, is a very satisfactory method. A procedure commonly employed in endemic areas is *xeno-diagnosis*. A clean triatomid bug is allowed to "bite" the suspected Chagas'-disease patient. If the patient has Chagas' disease, the bug's fecal discharge 10 days later may contain active stages of the parasite.

Treatment.—Symptomatic relief is all that is available, although primaquine may be useful in terminating the acute stage of the disease (personal communication, Dr. Pedreira de Freitas, 1960).

Epidemiology.—*Trypanosoma cruzi* is probably confined to the Western Hemisphere. In blood-sucking (triatomid) bugs and in reservoir hosts this trypanosome is found from central Chile, northern Argentina and Uruguay on the south to the southwest and south of the United States on the north; in man it has been demonstrated as a natural infection as far north as

Corpus Christi, Texas (See Fig. 25). It is prevalent in the human population principally in dry areas of marginal agriculture, where the homes built of adobe and usually with thatched roofs provide abundant opportunity for the bugs to breed in cracks and crevices of the walls and for them to sally forth from their hiding places to feed on their victims. In some localities 40 to 50% or more of the inhabitants are infected. Congenital transmission has been demonstrated in human infections in Chile, with asymptomatic mothers and fulminating disease in the new-born (Howard et al., 1957).

Many species of triatomid bugs have been found naturally infected with *T. cruzi*. In addition to *Panstrongylus megistus* the most common of these are *Triatoma infestans* in the southern part of the infected area and *Rhodnius prolixus* in northern South America. At times, the percentage of infected bugs in an endemic area may be as high as 75 to 95%.

Many domestic and wild mammals are reservoirs of this infection. These include dogs, cats, pigs, armadillos, bats, ferrets, foxes, opossums, wild rodents, anteaters, squirrels and monkeys. Human beings constitute only one of a multitude of mammalian host species susceptible to the infection.

T. cruzi is occasionally transmitted by blood transfusion. Congenital transmission may occur (Rubio et al., 1961).

Control.—The task of control is a formidable one. This is particularly true for human beings since there is no drug which serves as a therapeutic agent either for curative or prophylactic purposes. However, residual spraying of the inside walls and roofs with a kerosene-detergent emulsion of Gammexane (gamma isomer of benzene hexachloride) once or twice yearly will keep the habitation free of the bugs and thus minimize human exposure. Concerted anti-vector programs throughout endemic areas will greatly reduce the infection as a human disease.

SUMMARY

1. The common intestinal flagellate parasites of man are: *Giardia lamblia* (duodenum and jejunum), *Trichomonas tenax* (mouth), *T. hominis* and *Chilomastix mesnili* (cecum). *T. vaginalis* is found in the male and female urogential organs. *T. tenax*, *T. hominis* and *Chilomastix mesnili* are non-pathogenic.
2. *Giardia lamblia* has world-wide distribution but is more prevalent in warm climates, particularly in children. Cysts passed in the feces constitute the transfer stage. Usually giardiasis is asymptomatic but occasionally it may produce persistent diarrhea. Patients may usually be freed of their infection with quinacrine. Control requires improvement in personal and group hygiene.
3. *Trichomonas vaginalis* is cosmopolitan. It is commonly transmitted by sexual intercourse. In the male, infection is often symptomless; in the female, it may produce vaginitis with a characteristic discharge.
4. Flagellate protozoa of the blood and tissues of vertebrate hosts typically develop in a blood-sucking invertebrate which transmits the infection to the vertebrate. The blood and tissue flagellates which parasitize

5

man and other mammals belong to *Leishmania, viz., L. tropica, L. braziliensis* and *L. donovani,* and *Trypanosoma, viz., T. rhodesiense, T. gambiense, T. rangeli* and *T. cruzi.*

5. All species of *Leishmania* utilize sand-flies (*Phlebotomus*) as inter-mediate hosts. When injected into the skin of the definitive host by the sand-fly, the flagellates are engulfed by wandering macrophages, transform into the leishmania stage, propagate by binary fission, destroy the host cell and are engulfed by other macrophages in which they continue to develop.

6. *Leishmania tropica,* in the more arid regions of the Eastern Hemisphere, causes cutaneous leishmaniasis, in which a relatively small ulcer is produced at the site of each inoculation. Infection confers permanent immunity. Man, dogs and rodents constitute the susceptible verte-brate hosts.

7. *Leishmania braziliensis,* which has an extensive distribution in the sylvatic regions of tropical America, causes muco-cutaneous leish-maniasis. The primary lesion resembles that of cutaneous leish-maniasis. Some strains have a proclivity to metastasize to muco-cu-taneous junctions, particularly in the vicinity of the nares. Here a deep, disfiguring, erosive process develops. Dogs are reservoir hosts in some endemic areas, sylvatic rodents in other regions.

8. *Leishmania donovani,* with large areas of endemicity in northern China, eastern India, the Mediterranean countries, the Sudan and several foci in continental Latin America, produces visceral leishmaniasis (kala-azar). This involves the entire reticulo-endothelium, especially spleen, liver, bone marrow and visceral lymph nodes, causing increase in macrophages with comparable reduction in neutrophils and red blood cells. Intercurrent infections produce pathologic changes in the tissues of the respiratory and digestive tracts. In China, Iraq, the Mediter-ranean countries and tropical America dogs are important reservoirs, also foxes in Brazil.

9. Diagnosis of all types of leishmaniasis is most satisfactorily made by demonstration of the parasite within infected macrophages. Except for the Sudanese variety of kala-azar, all types of leishmaniasis are usually amenable to antimony therapy. Modern control is concerned with death of the adult sand-fly transmitter by use of residual DDT sprayed on the walls of human habitations, likewise destruction of infected dogs or other reservoirs.

10. *Trypanosoma rhodesiense* and *T. gambiense* are African in their dis-tribution (*T. rhodesiense* in upland savannas of east Africa, *T. gambiense* in the rain-forest areas of west and central Africa). These species utilize tsetse flies (*Glossina*) as intermediate hosts and transmitters. Infection is through the "bite" of the fly. These organisms get into circulating blood and multiply. In lymph nodes they set up inter-stitial inflammation and necrosis. In *T. rhodesiense* infection the disease is so fulminating that patients characteristically die early, but in *T. gambiense* infection the parasites tend to invade the central nervous system, where necrotic damage causes a wide variety of nervous disorders, including "sleeping sickness."

11. African trypanosomiasis is diagnosed by recovery of the trypanosomes in the blood during periods of parasitemia, later in tissue fluids aspirated from lymph nodes, and, in *T. gambiense* infection, from the spinal fluid after invasion of the central nervous system. Treatment of Rhodesian trypanosomiasis is effective only during the early stage. Gambian infection is treated with tryparsamide or other arsenicals, suramin and diamidines. Control consists in clearing extensive areas around human habitations to prevent transmission to man by tsetse fly "bites", or in removing the human population to non-infected areas.

12. *Trypanosoma rangeli*, discovered in man, dogs and monkeys in tropical forest areas in Venezuela, Panama, Colombia and Guatemala, as well as in other countries of South and Central America, is transmitted by triatomid bugs, primarily *Rhodnius prolixus*, which introduce the parasite through its proboscis into the mammal. It is not known to invade tissue cells and appears to produce no symptoms in the human subject.

13. *Trypanosoma cruzi* occurs in the tropics and subtropics of continental America. It utilizes triatomid bugs as transmitters. The parasites are discharged in small drops of liquid feces at the time the bug is taking a blood meal. Some of the organisms from the primary skin colony get into the blood stream, in which they are morphologically typical trypanosomes, although they do not divide in this stage. Later they lodge in liver, spleen, lymph nodes, myocardium, central nervous tissue or other organs, where they invade the fixed cells and multiply as leishmaniæ, with destruction of the parasitized cells.

14. *Trypanosoma cruzi* infection (Chagas' disease) is diagnosed by recovery of the trypanosome from blood during febrile episodes, or the leishmania stage from invaded cells, likewise by complement fixation or xeno-diagnosis. There is no specific treatment. Human exposure can be greatly diminished by residual spraying of benzene hexachloride (Gammexane) inside homes, to kill the bugs which infest the dwellings.

REFERENCES

BERBERIAN, D. A. 1959. Relationship of Mediterranean Kala-azar to Canine Kala-azar. Trans. R. Soc. Trop. Med. & Hyg., *53*, 364–365.

BURCH, T. A., REES, C. W., and REARDON, L. V. 1959. Epidemiological Studies in Human Trichomoniasis. Am. J. Trop. Med. & Hyg., *8*, 312–318.

CORTNER, J. A. 1959. Giardiasis, a Cause of Celiac Syndrome. Am. J. Diseases Children, *98*, 311–316.

DAVEY, D. G. 1958. Human and Animal Trypanosomiasis in Africa. Am. J. Trop. Med. & Hyg., *7*, 547–553.

DEANE, L. DE MELLO. 1956. *Leishmaniose Visceral* no Brasil. Estudio sôbre reservatórios e transmissores realizados no Estado de Ceará. Serviço Nac. Educ. Sanitar, Rio de Janeiro (Brasil), 162 pp.

GARNHAM, P. C. C., and LEWIS, D. J. 1959. Parasites of British Honduras with Special Reference to Leishmaniasis. Trans. R. Soc. Trop. Med. & Hyg., *53*, 12–40.

GROOT, H. 1954. Estudios sobre los trypanosomas humanos (*T. rangeli* y *T. ariarii*). An. Soc. Biol. Bogotá, *6*, 109–126.

HERTIG, M., and FISHER, R. A. 1945. Control of Sandflies with DDT. Bull. U.S. Army Med. Dept., No. 88, 97–101.

HOARE, C. A. 1955. The Epidemiological Role of Animal Reservoirs in Human Leishmaniasis and Trypanosomiasis. Veterin. Rev. & Annot., I (Pt. II), 62–68.

HOWARD, J. E., RIOS, C., EBENSPERGER, I., and OLIVOS, P. 1957. Enfermedad de Chagas congénita. Bol. Chileno de Parasitol., *12*, 42–45.

JÍROVEC, O., and PETER, R. 1955. Zum Problem der Trichomoniasis Vaginalis. Prophylaxe. Zeitschr. f. Mikrobiol., Hyg., u. Sozialhyg., (Jena), *1*, 285–291.

KESSEL, J. G., and THOMPSON, C. F. 1950. Survival of *T. vaginalis* in Vaginal Discharge. Proc. Soc. Exp. Biol. & Med., *74*, 755–758.

LUMBRERAS, H., FLORES, W., and ESCALLÓN, A. 1959. Allergische Reaktionen auf Stiche von Reduviiden und ihre Bedeutung bei der Chagaskrankheit. Zeitschr. Tropenmed. u. Parasitol., *10*, 6–19.

LARANJA, F. S., DIAS, E., NOBREGA, G., and MIRANDA, A. 1956. Chagas' Disease: a Clinical, Epidemiologic and Pathologic Study. Circulation (New York), *14*, 1035–1060.

MANSON-BAHR, P. E. C. 1959. East African Kala-azar with Special Reference to the Pathology, Prophylaxis and Treatment. Trans. R. Soc. Trop. Med. & Hyg., *53*, 123–136.

MORRIS, K. R. S. 1959. The Epidemiology of Sleeping Sickness in East Africa. Part I. A. Sleeping Sickness Outbreak in Uganda in 1957. Trans. R. Soc. Trop. Med. & Hyg., *53*, 384–393.

NOBLE, E. R. 1955. The Morphology and Life Cycles of Trypanosomes. Q. Rev. Biol., *30*, 1–28.

PESSÔA, S. B., and BARRETTO, M. O. 1948. *Leishmaniose Tegumentar Americana*. Rio de Janeiro, Brasil, 527 pp.

ROBERTSON, D. H. H., and BAKER, J. R. 1958. Human Trypanosomiasis in South-East Uganda. I. A Study of the Epidemiology and Present Virulence of the Disease. Trans. R. Soc. Med. & Hyg., *52*, 337–348.

ROMAÑA, C. 1954. Panorama epidemiológico de la enfermedad de Chagas en la Argentina a través de investigaciones sistemáticas. An. Inst. de Med. Regional, Tucumán, *4*, 27–33.

RUBIO, M., GALECIO, R. and HOWARD, J. 1961. Dos casos de enfermedad de Chagas congénita. Bol. Chileno Parasitol., *16*, 15–18.

SERVINO, V., MONACO, G., TALLARICO, P., and DeLUCA, D. 1960. Osservazioni clinico-terapeutiche su alcini casi di sindrome spruiforme in sogetti affeti da giardaisi cronica. Parassitol., *2*, 296–299.

TRUSSELL, R. E. 1947. *Trichomonas Vaginalis and Trichomoniasis*. Charles C Thomas, Springfield, 277 pp.

VEGHELYI, P. 1940. Giardiasis. Am. J. Dis. Child., *59*, 793–804.

WENRICH, D. H. 1944. Comparative Morphology of the Trichomonad Flagellates of Man. Am. J. Trop. Med., *24*, 39–51.

WOODY, N. C., and WOODY, H. B. 1955. American Trypanosomiasis (Chagas' Disease). First Indigenous Case in the United States. J. Am. Med. Assn., *159*, 476–477.

Chapter 4

The Amebae

GENERAL DESCRIPTION

THE name "ameba" refers to a large number of protozoa belonging to several genera of the Subphylum SARCODINA, Class Rhizopodea, the members of which move by means of cytoplasmic extensions that are projected and retracted in response to external stimuli. Many species of amebæ are free-living while others are parasitic, typically in the digestive tract of invertebrates and vertebrates.

All amebæ possess a *trophozoite* stage, during which they multiply by binary division. This method of reproduction continues as long as environmental conditions are favorable. Many species also have an encysted stage, which is more resistant than the trophozoite to unfavorable conditions, and in the case of the parasitic amebæ provides a better opportunity for transfer from one host to the next. In preparation for encystation the ameba discharges undigested foods, rounds up to form the *precyst*, then secretes a tough membrane to become the *cyst*. A few species exhibit a maturing process of the cyst, whereby the nucleus divides one or more times. Among the parasitic forms the cyst is voided in the host's feces; excystation in nature occurs only after the mature cyst has been taken into the mouth of the appropriate host, has passed through the stomach and the cyst membrane has been acted on by the host's intestinal juices. Thereupon the ameba becomes active, a small fissure is produced in the cyst membrane and the metacyst escapes from its confined quarters. This stage then divides into the number of trophozoites corresponding to the number of nuclei in the mature cyst. The minute *metacystic trophozoites* then take in nourishment, growing into the typical trophozoites, which divide repeatedly and establish themselves in the host's digestive tract. No sexual reproduction has been demonstrated for any species of ameba. The life cycle of *Entamœba histolytica*, is represented diagrammatically in Figure 29.

The parasitic amebæ belong to the Family Endamœbidæ, the members of which typically lack contractile vacuoles. Generic classification is based principally on nuclear structure. This clearly distinguishes the genus *Endamœba* (*viz.*, *Endamœba blattæ* and other species in the cockroach and termites) from *Entamœba*, *Endolimax*, *Iodamœba* and *Dientamœba*, which have representatives parasitizing man (Kirby, 1951; Kudo, 1954).

Entamœba moshkovskii, which resembles *E. histolytica* in most morphological characters, has been found only in sewage, and attempts to demonstrate that it is fundamentally an intestinal parasite have thusfar been unsuccessful. Another close relative of *E. histolytica*, *E. invadens*, a natural intestinal parasite of reptiles, produces epizoötics in snakes in captivity. *Entamœba polecki,* a natural parasite of the hog, on rare occasions has been diagnosed from human feces. In nature monkeys, less frequently dogs, harbor the six species of amebæ which parasitize man, *viz.,* *Entamœba histolytica, E. coli* and *E. gingivalis, Endolimax nana, Iodamœba bütschlii* and *Dientamœba fragilis.*

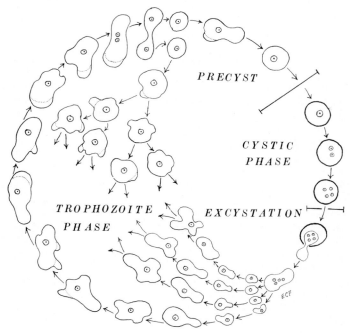

Fig. 29.—Diagram illustrating the life cycle stages of *Entamœba histolytica.* (Original, Faust.)

ENTAMOEBA HISTOLYTICA

Historical Notes.—Trophozoites of *Entamœba histolytica* were discovered and described by Lösch in 1875 from the dysenteric stools of a patient in St. Petersburg, Russia. Although Lösch was able to produce amebic dysentery in an experimental dog following intra-rectal introduction of the dysenteric human menstruum, he failed to recognize the significance of his findings. However, within the next two decades the pathogenicity of this organism was amply demonstrated by investigators in Egypt, Prague and Baltimore, following which the cystic stage was described, while Walker and Sellards in Manila (1913) clearly differentiated *E. histolytica* as a pathogen from *E. coli* as a harmless commensal. Meanwhile Schaudinn (1903) named this ameba *Entamœba histolytica.* Several other species names have been assigned to this protozoön, of which the only one presently deserving consideration is *E. hartmanni,* a designation employed by von Prowazek in 1912 for a small race of *Entamœba* without demonstrated pathogenicity. Recent experimental studies have been focused primarily on the metabolic activities of *E. histolytica*, its ability to utilize various food elements in its environment and its potential ability to invade tissues.

Considerable information has been accumulated concerning racial size in *E. histolytica* (Sapero, Hakansson and Loutitt, 1942; Burrows, 1957, 1959; Faust, 1958; Freedman and Elsdon-Dew, 1959). Two racial groups have been distinguished, one with cysts having a mean diameter less than 10 microns and one with a mean of more than 10 microns; and under favorable circumstances it is possible to demonstrate minute morphological differences within the nucleus and cytoplasm of these two races (Burrows, 1957; Faust, 1958). There is suggestive evidence that the fluorescent antibody technic may be able to determine whether there are antigenically different strains in the *E. histolytica* complex (CDC Report of Activities, 1958, page 43). Most European and some American workers are inclined to consider the small-race *E. histolytica* as a separate species, referred to as *E. hartmanni*, and reserve the name *histolytica* for the *Entamœba* of

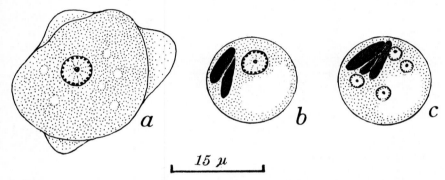

FIG. 30.—*Entamœba histolytica.* *a*, trophozoite, *b*, immature cyst, *c*, ripe cyst. × 1600. (Original, Faust.)

larger racial size which has a proven pathogenic potential. Yet at times the large race is avirulent (Hoare, 1958), while much earlier Kessel (1928) demonstrated pathogenicity in kittens for a small-race *histolytica* from asymptomatic human carriers. In the present state of confusion perhaps a satisfactory solution is to refer to the two racial types as *E. histolytica* var. *histolytica* for the large race and *E. histolytica* var. *hartmanni* for the small race (Faust, 1961), in the meanwhile having an "open" mind on this question of a small race and its appropriate designation.

Morphology, Biology and Life Cycle.— *E. histolytica* exhibits four distinct stages in its life cycle, *viz.*, trophozoite, precyst, cyst and metacyst (See (Fig. 29). The stages recognized in the feces are the trophozoites and cysts; the latter are not present in the tissues.

The *trophozoite* (Fig. 30*a*) in its natural habitat in the large intestine and in extra-intestinal foci varies from 8 to 60 microns in diameter, a size difference often related to its metabolic activity, depending on the immediate environmental conditions.

The active trophozoite has a finely granular, somewhat viscous endoplasm and a limpid ectoplasm which has a grayish, glassy-green tinge when observed under the microscope. The pseudopodia are broadly finger-like. During temporary progressive movement in one direction a single pseudopodium characteristically takes the lead, drawing the entire organism after it.

The *nucleus* is spherical; its diameter is one-fifth to one-third as large as the diameter of the quiescent ameba. It is surrounded by a delicate nuclear membrane, which is studded on its inner surface with minute granules having a chromatin-staining reaction. In the center of the nucleus there is a single dense, bead-like chromatin body, the *karyosome* or nucleolus. Immediately around the karyosome there is an essentially clear halo, and extending radially between this and the nuclear membrane there are several to many delicate achromatic (linin) fibrils, in the midst of a moderately dense nucleoplasm.

E. histolytica is primarily, if not exclusively anaërobic in its metabolism. In appropriate culture media it grows and multiples best at a temperature of about 37° C., under reduced oxygen tension. In the test tube it requires certain types of associated bacteria or other microörganisms for growth and multiplication, and this is apparently likewise a requisite while it is a lumen parasite in the mucosal crypts of the large intestine, utilizing mucus as its principal source of nourishment. However, there is no proof that invasion of the tissues by the ameba requires associated enteric bacteria, while it has been shown that as soon as it becomes established as a tissue parasite, it is able to develop normally in a bacteriologically sterile environment. Tissue invasion is accomplished by lytic and physical means. Mægraith and associates (1959) have demonstrated tryptic and mucopolysaccharide enzyme activity of trophozoites in contact with human and guinea pig cecal epithelium, likewise the presence of hyaluronidase in cultured amebæ (1960). Lytic digestion of host cells provides food for the ameba and allows it and its progeny to advance into the tissues. At times the trophozoite is seen lying between cells, suggesting that invasion may also be accomplished in part by forceful penetration.

Colonization in the host occurs as a result of frequently repeated binary division. In this way it may produce superficial or deep ulceration of the intestinal wall, and may develop extensive secondary colonies in the liver and other extra-intestinal sites. Although this ameba is able to digest red blood corpuscles, these are apparently not required as food (Fig. 31).

Encystation does not occur while E. histolytica is within the tissues, but only after the trophozoites have been extruded into the intestinal lumen. Usually during this process diffuse glycogen within the protoplasm of the trophozoite becomes concentrated in a mass often having hazy margins; chromatic material (the *chromatoidals*) is concentrated into bars, rods or grape-like clusters in the cytoplasm of the cyst. Except for moderate reduction in size, the nucleus of the uninucleate cyst is morphologically identical with that of the trophozoite. Either before the stool is passed or soon thereafter the nucleus of the cyst divides into two, then each of the two daughter nuclei divides once again, so that the mature cyst typically has four nuclei (Fig. 30 *c*).

Viable cysts of *E. histolytica* in the external environment are soon killed by drying, bacterial putrefaction of the medium, hypertonicity, direct sunlight and heat. On being swallowed, viable cysts pass unchanged through the stomach into the small intestine. When they reach a level where the *p*H of the digestive juices is neutral or slightly alkaline, excystation occurs. First the encysted ameba becomes activated, stretches the cyst wall, which splits open at a weak place, and the ameba slowly squeezes its way out of the wall. The 4-nucleate metacyst almost immediately undergoes cytoplasmic division, so that 4 little metacystic trophozoites are formed. These feed, grow to normal size and are ready to start a new cycle (see Fig. 29).

Pathogenesis and Symptomatology.—*Pathogenesis.*—Infection with *Entamœba histolytica* implies colonization. The rapidity with which colonization occurs and the depth of penetration of the intestinal wall depend to a

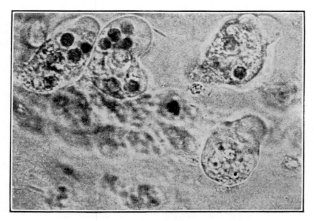

Fig. 31.—Trophozoites of *Entamœba histolytica* in dysenteric stool, unstained preparation, showing ingested red blood corpuscles. (From Medical Museum Collection, Armed Forces Institute of Pathology, in Faust and Russell's *Clinical Parasitology*, Lea & Febiger, Philadelphia.)

considerable extent on the pathogenic capacity of the particular strain of *E. histolytica* at the time of exposure, whether or not the mucosal surface is intact, and probably also on the general resistance of the host to infection. Trophozoites of *E. histolytica* may lodge in the crypts of the large intestine, feeding on mucus and colonizing, but likelihood of lytic digestion of the intestinal epithelium and superficial tissue invasion is considerable.

The earliest opportunity for *E. histolytica* to colonize in the intestine is at the cecal level (Fig. 32). If this does not occur then primary infection may develop at a lower level of the large intestine. The characteristic lesion produced as the ameba enters the wall is superficially a minute cavity resulting from lytic necrosis of the mucosa (Fig. 33). The increasing colony of amebæ usually proceeds in a narrow channel down to the base of the mucosa where the lesion enlarges somewhat as the amebæ reach the more resistant muscularis mucosæ. The invading organisms may not readily penetrate this layer and will thus be confined to the epithelial layer. Moreover, repair may take place as rapidly as lytic necrosis occurs so that no extensive functional damage is produced; likewise the repair process may reëstablish the normal mucosa and thus the amebæ will be confined to the lumen. Recent observations suggest that a disease-free carrier condition may be common (Faust and Read, 1959), while spontaneous loss of this infection may take place as early as 3 weeks after it has been acquired (Beaver *et al.*, 1956).

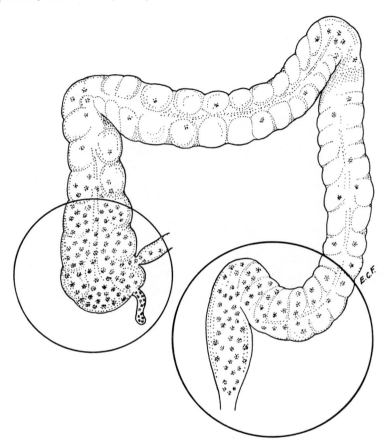

Fig. 32.—Diagram illustrating the relative numbers of accumulated amebic lesions in the large intestine. The most frequently invaded level is the cecal area and the second most common site, the sigmoido-rectal area. (After Faust, Transactions and Studies, College of Physicians of Philadelphia.)

In many cases, the amebæ gradually erode a passage through the muscularis mucosæ into the submucosa, where they are able to spread out radially into the surrounding tissues. If this primary lesion is not complicated by accompanying bacteria there is essentially no tissue reaction to the amebic invasion.

From the submucosa the amebæ may proceed into the muscular coats and may even erode a passage into the serosa, in which case they are likely to cause perforation. They may effect an entry into the mesenteric venules or lymphatics and be carried into the liver and other extra-intestinal organs. All soft extra-intestinal tissues are subject to infection, although the lesions develop most frequently in the liver. *Wherever the amebic lesion develops outside the intestinal tract, it is without exception secondary to one or more lesions in the large intestine.*

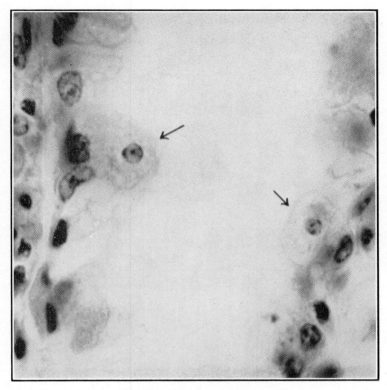

Fig. 33.—Photomicrograph of section of large intestine, showing early primary invasion of the mucosa by trophozoites of *Entamœba histolytica.* Two amebæ are indicated by arrows. Note early lytic necrosis of epithelial cells on the surface and between the glands; likewise essential lack of host-cell reaction. × 470. (After James and Getz, in Craig's *Amebiasis and Amebic Dysentery,* courtesy of Charles C Thomas, Springfield, Ill.)

As the infection progresses, additional sites of invasion are likely to develop, although on the average the cecal and then the sigmoido-rectal areas are those in which a majority of the lesions are found (Fig. 32).

From the surface, the early uncomplicated amebic lesions are minute openings surrounded by a slightly raised yellowish ring and leading into a deeper enlargement in the submucosa, with tunneled connections between two or more lesions. They are separated from one another by undamaged mucosa, and show no remarkable evidence of inflammatory reaction.

Sooner or later the subsurface enlargement cuts off the arteriolar blood supply to the overlying layers and the surface sloughs off, leaving shaggy overhanging edges. As the lesion becomes chronic round cell infiltration occurs, probably in response to secondary bacterial infection; the tissues

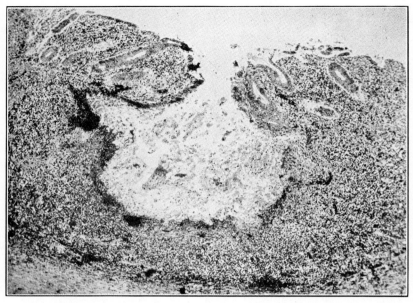

Fig. 34.—Chronic amebic ulcer of the colon involving the mucosa and submucosa. Extensive infiltration of the border of the lesion by neutrophils and fibrocytes suggests secondary bacterial invasion. (From Medical Museum Collection, Armed Forces Institute of Pathology, in Craig's *Amebiasis and Amebic Dysentery,* courtesy of Charles C Thomas, Springfield, Ill.)

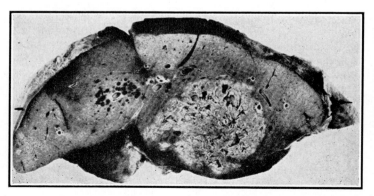

Fig 35 —Section through an advanced amebic abscess of the liver × ½. (Photograph, Medical Museum Collection, Armed Forces Institute of Pathology, in Faust and Russell's *Clinical Parasitology,* Lea & Febiger, Philadelphia.

become infiltrated with neutrophilic leukocytes and fibroblasts, which tend to form a wall around the margin of the ulcer; and the overhanging edges become thickened (Fig. 34).

The extra-intestinal amebic lesion at first consists of a small focus where one or more amebæ have become lodged in a vascular embolus and have proceeded to colonize, producing necrosis of the nearby host cells. In the liver, there is a tendency for these lesions to be multiple, but later one or at most a very few may become enlarged to develop into the so-called "amebic liver abscess" (Fig. 35). Although these lesions are usually bacteriologically sterile, the amount of tissue necrosis produced by the amebæ characteristically stimulates some local and systemic leukocytosis. The absence of fibrosis in amebic liver abscess may be due to the fibrolytic capacity of this ameba (Jarumilinta and Mægraith, 1961).

Symptomatology.—The incubation period has been reported as varying from a few days (Walker and Sellards 1913) to three months or even a year (Craig, 1944), but in instances of very short incubation the presence of other types of enteric infection has not been adequately ruled out. In most cases it is impossible to determine the interval between exposure and the first symptoms. The onset may be insidious, with vague abdominal discomfort or soft stools for a variable period, or sudden, with precipitate development of dysentery or acute abdominal pain. In a high percentage of cases of hepatic amebiasis there is no previous history of the primary infection in the colon.

The clinical types of amebiasis may be classified as follows:

I. *Intestinal:*
   A. Dysenteric.
   B. Non-dysenteric.
      1. Symptoms consisting primarily of abdominal pain and tenderness.
      2. Bouts of diarrhea alternating with longer periods of constipation, with or without abdominal pain and tenderness.
      3. Asymptomatic.

II. *Extra-intestinal:*
   A. Deep, including hepatic, pleuro-pulmonary, cerebral and other visceral sites.
   B. Cutaneous, mostly perianal or perineal.

An examination of this classification reveals an unusual amount of latitude in the clinical types of amebiasis, both with respect to the locations of the lesions and the intensity or mildness of the symptoms. In some cases the symptoms are much more severe than the extent of the lesions would seem to indicate; on the other hand, relatively mild symptoms may mask extensive organic disease. Except in epidemics a majority of amebic infections will be chronic or asymptomatic. In chronic infections of the colon one must consider that a considerable proportion of the damage, and hence of the symptoms, may result from secondary bacterial invasion of the amebic ulcers. Moreover, it must always be remembered that amebiasis may be only one of two or more concurrent disease processes, as,

Table 2.—Differential Morphologic Characters Between Entamoeba Histolytica and the Other Intestinal Amebæ of Man

	Entamœba histolytica	Entamœba coli	Endolimax nana	Iodamœba bütschlii	Dientamœba fragilis
		"Vegetative" or Trophozoite Stage. Unstained			
Size in microns	8 to 60μ	15 to 50μ	6 to 15μ	8 to 20μ	5 to 12μ
Motility	Active; progressive and directional	Sluggish; rarely progressive and directional	Sluggishly progressive	Sluggishly progressive	Active and progressive
Pseudopodia	Finger shaped; hyaline and glass-like; rapidly extruded	Shorter and more blunt; more granular; slowly extruded	Blunt and hyaline; very rapidly extruded	Blunt and hyaline; slowly extruded	Blunt and leaf-like; hyaline
Inclusions	Red blood corpuscles; no bacteria in fresh specimens	Bacteria and other material; no blood corpuscles	Bacteria; no blood corpuscles	Bacteria; no blood corpuscles	Bacteria; no blood corpuscles
		"Vegetative" or Trophozoite Stage. Iron Hematoxylin Stain			
Nucleus	Invisible usually	Visible rarely	Visible rarely	Invisible	Invisible
Nuclear membrane	Delicate; inner surface has single layer of minute chromatin dots	Thicker; inner surface lined with coarse chromatin dots	Intermediate in thickness; chromatin seldom present on inner surface	Thick; chromatin dots may be present on inner surface	Very delicate; no chromatin dots on inner surface
Karyosome	Minute and in center of nucleus	Much larger and eccentrically situated	Large and may be in center or to one side of center of nucleus	Large and granular, in center of nucleus or somewhat eccentrically placed	Large and composed of definite chromatin granules lying in a dimly stained matrix
Intranuclear chromatin	No chromatin between karyosome and nuclear membrane	Chromatin grains between karyosome and nuclear membrane	No chromatin between karyosome and nuclear membrane	....	No chromatin between karyosome and nuclear membrane
Inclusions	Red blood corpuscles; no bacteria unless degenerated	No red blood corpuscles; many bacteria and other material	No red blood corpuscles; many bacteria	No red blood corpuscles; bacteria	No red blood corpuscles; bacteria

Cystic Stage. Iodine Smear Preparations

	3.5 to 20μ	10 to 33μ	5 to 14μ	5 to 20μ	
Size in microns	3.5 to 20μ	10 to 33μ	5 to 14μ	5 to 20μ	No cysts have been demonstrated
Shape	Usually spherical	Usually spherical	Spherical, ovoidal or ellipsoidal	Irregular	
Cytoplasm	Bright greenish-yellow	Yellowish-brown	Pale green with numerous refractile vacuoles	Yellowish-green	
Glycogen mass	Diffuse and reddish-brown	Dark brown and indefinite central mass with indistinct border	Usually absent, brownish and either diffuse or defined	Usually present, dark brown and sharply outlined	
Nuclei	1 to 4; minute central karyosome very refractive; nuclear membrane beaded and refractive	1 to 8 or more; nuclear membrane refractive and granular; karyosome eccentric	1 to 4; indistinct	Indistinct; one usually present	

Cystic Stage. Iron Hematoxylin Stain

Size in microns	6 to 20μ	10 to 33μ	5 to 14μ	5 to 20μ	No cysts have been found
Shape	Usually spherical	Spherical	Ovoidal or ellipsoidal	Irregular	
Cytoplasm	Alveolar, often vacuolated	Granular and vacuolated	Vacuolated with chromatin granules	Vacuolated, large glycogen vacuole usually present	
Chromatoidal bodies	Bar, oval or thick rod-like masses with rounded ends	Filamentous, thread-like or splinter-like with square or pointed ends	Small, spherical or baciliform, often in a vacuole	Usually absent; when present small round or granular	
Nuclei	1 to 4; delicate membrane lined with minute chromatin granules; karyosome minute central dot	1 to 8 or more; thick nuclear membrane lined with large dots of chromatin or irregular masses; karyosome eccentrically placed and large	1 to 4; nuclear membrane indistinct; karyosome in a single or divided mass on or near nuclear membrane	1, rarely 2; nuclear membrane very thin, often indistinct; karyosome placed centrally or laterally and surrounded by large granules	

for example, amebic colitis associated with shigellosis, salmonellosis, carcinoma, appendicitis of bacterial etiology, cholecystitis, peptic ulcer or idiopathic chronic ulcerative colitis. Furthermore, at times one or more amebic granulomas (*amebomas*) develop in the wall of the colon or rectum (Faust, 1954).

The patient with amebic dysentery will usually have tenesmus and sometimes will be troubled with abdominal cramps. Nevertheless he ordinarily appears relatively well in spite of the gradual debilitation which occurs if the dysentery persists. He does not suffer the acute systemic intoxication seen in bacillary dysentery.

The abdominal pain and tenderness in intestinal amebiasis, whether dysenteric or not, is mostly in the lower quadrants of the abdomen, especially on the right. Clinically, cecal amebiasis is sometimes mistaken for appendicitis.

The symptoms of extra-intestinal amebiasis depend on the localization of the infection. The most common form of extra-intestinal amebiasis, hepatic abscess, usually presents with fever, an enlarged tender liver, bulging and fixation of the right leaf of the diaphragm, and frequently serous effusion of the right pleura.

Pulmonary amebiasis is usually a consequence of rupture of an hepatic abscess into the chest cavity, the lung, and thence into a bronchus. The patient therefore presents with signs of pneumonia and expectoration of characteristic liver-colored pus passing through the broncho-hepatic fistula.

Amebiasis of the skin is invariably the result of damaged skin frequently brought in contact with amebic trophozoites. It is thus seen most commonly in the perineum secondary to amebic dysentery or on the abdomen at the mouth of a fistulous tract from the colon or an hepatic abscess.

Diagnosis.—Intestinal amebiasis cannot be diagnosed on clinical grounds alone. Diagnosis, therefore, must depend upon microscopic examination of the feces, either by direct microscopic search for the amebæ, by *in vitro* cultivation of the organisms in the feces or aspirates, or by their recognition in stained sections of tissue obtained at biopsy or autopsy. Methods of examination of the feces are described in the section on TECHNICAL AIDS (pages 424 to 426), and the distinguishing morphologic differences between *E. histolytica* and the other intestinal amebæ of man are summarized in Table 2 (p. 78–79).

Saline purgation is sometimes valuable since it may allow detection of trophozoites at times when formed stools are consistently negative for cysts. If saline purgation is clinically contraindicated, a high retention enema with lukewarm physiologic salt solution will provide similar material. The main advantage of these direct methods of obtaining material from the bowel is that fresh specimens can conveniently be made available to the laboratory.

Proctoscopic and other aspirates should be examined promptly in unstained direct-film preparations. Proctoscopic aspirates from ulcers of the colon invariably contain a variety of tissue cells which may readily be mistaken for amebæ. Although cysts may be present in such material, there is no evidence that cysts are formed in the tissues; a report of cysts from the mucosa is therefore an indication of mistaken identification. No other medium constitutes as prolific a source of mis-diagnosis as the procto-scopic aspirate. When the specimen is obtained from an hepatic, pul-monary or other extra-intestinal abscess, recovery of amebæ may be assisted by enzymatic digestion as described in the section on *Technical Aids.*

Culture technics are unsuitable for routine diagnosis, as amebæ usually can not be grown in the test tube when direct microscopic examination has proven fruitless.

If examination is to be made for amebæ in the tissues, biopsies and autopsy material may be processed according to approved technics, but after the sections have been cut and stained by conventional hematoxylin-and-eosin methods they should be superstained with Best's carmine. Amebic trophozoites in the tissues will be stained a strawberry pink, due to diffuse glycogen in their cytoplasm. This staining reaction may be relied upon for histopathologic diagnosis of *E. histolytica.*

Complement fixation and other serodiagnostic tests have been tried by various workers but have not proved suitable for routine use.

Treatment.—The method of treating amebiasis varies with the clinical types as outlined on page 77 and described below.

Intestinal Amebiasis

Amebic Dysentery.—The management of amebic dysentery depends on its severity. Bed rest may be required if the patient is passing very frequent bloody stools. Blood or physiologic solutions may be given intravenously if the patient is very anemic or dehydrated, but in uncom-plicated amebic dysentery this is rarely necessary. Abdominal cramps or tenesmus may be relieved by hypodermic administration of opiates, if severe, or if milder, by such demulcent preparations as bismuth subcar-bonate or kaolin. Usually none of the above measures is required and the physician will depend on more specific anti-amebic or anti-bacterial therapy.

The primary objective in treatment is to check the dysentery as rapidly as possible. This is not only to provide relief of discomfort but also to improve the chances of later eradicating the amebic infection, since most of the amebicidal drugs are less effective in the presence of dysentery.

At present the choice of drugs in amebic dysentery is between emetine hydrochloride and a broad spectrum antibiotic. Both types of agent are extremely effective in checking amebic dysentery, but only the tetracycline antibiotics also produce a high rate of parasitologic cure (Powell, Wilmot and Elsdon-Dew, 1958).

In addition to emetine, which combats the dysentery, another amebicidal drug such as diidohydroxyquin or glycobiarsol should be given to eradicate the amebic infection. If a tetracycline antibiotic is given, this alone will suffice but parasitologic cure rate will be increased by concurrent adminis-tration of another drug (See Table 7, p. 417).

Non-dysenteric, Symptomatic.—Several drugs provide high parasitologic cure rates in non-dysenteric intestinal amebiasis. These may function by affecting the amebæ directly, or indirectly by removing bacteria necessary for the survival of the protozoön at the mucosal surface. The selection of a drug is made, as above, with consideration of economy, toxicity and efficacy. Among those commonly employed are glycobiarsol and diido-hydroxyquin (Sodeman and Beaver, 1952) (See Table 7, p. 417).

Asymptomatic.—The physician's first decision here is whether to treat the patient or not. While in the United States it is generally recommended that all cases of intestinal amebiasis be treated, this recommendation is not accepted in all parts of the world. In some countries the prevalence of intestinal amebiasis is very high, but the incidence of manifest disease is low. In such situations, routine treatment of all infections would be impracticable, as it would be costly and would accomplish little. In other countries such as Britain the prevalence of amebiasis is low and infections of domestic origin rarely cause disease of clinical grade. Here too, treatment of autochthonous infections is commonly foregone with no apparent ill effect. On the other hand, in the United States where the prevalence of intestinal amebiasis today is relatively low, amebic disease, sometimes serious, is seen more frequently. Until further evidence to the contrary has been produced, any infection with *E. histolytica* should be regarded as potentially pathogenic.

It is advisable, when feasible, to give individuals who are being treated for intestinal amebiasis a course of chloroquine as a prophylactic against hepatic abscess.

Extra-Intestinal Amebiasis

Specific therapy for amebic liver abscess consists of the administration of emetine, or chloroquine, or both. Although emetine is more toxic it is considered to be more effective than chloroquine. In the case of large abscesses aspiration of pus in addition to drug therapy may be necessary for cure. Other forms of deep extra-intestinal amebiasis are treated similarly.

Amebiasis cutis will respond to local therapy with topical antibiotics and treatment of the primary amebic disease, which is either amebic liver abscess or amebic dysentery (See Table 7, page 417).

Epidemiology.— *E. histolytica* is known to be a parasite of man in all areas of the world where careful coprologic examinations have been conducted. Due to greater opportunity for exposure the infection is usually more prevalent and produces more severe symptoms in warm climates, but in mental hospitals, prisons, children's homes and other communities in cooler climates with poor personal and group hygiene the incidence is high compared with that of the general population of the same localities.

Persons of all races and ages, and of both sexes appear to be equally susceptible to infection and differences in distribution can be explained on the basis of differences in exposure. Infants are not as commonly infected as older children and young adults characteristically show a higher incidence than older persons.

Amebiasis is usually endemic, but epidemics of serious proportions have developed in recent years as a result of gross contamination of water with viable cysts of this ameba.

Methods of Transmission of E. histolytica.—The following are probably the most important: person-to-person contact, water, foodhandlers and filth flies. Person-to-person contamination has been demonstrated to be the most likely method in children's homes, mental hospitals, rural populations in a temperate climate, from foodhandlers, and from gross negligence in personal hygiene and unpotable water supplies throughout many tropical communities.

Food is an important vehicle for the transmission of *E. histolytica* in most countries only in so far as it is handled by persons who are cyst passers and whose hands are contaminated with the cysts.

Filth flies which breed in human excreta have been repeatedly demonstrated to ingest cysts of *E. histolytica* and later deposit them in a viable state in their vomit drops and fecal dejecta (Pipkin, 1949). Cockroaches are also highly suspect as mechanical vectors of amebic cysts.

*Animal Reservoirs.—*Many species of monkeys are natural hosts of strains of *E. histolytica* which are infective for man. Dogs and rats have likewise been found infected but the number of these cases is entirely too small to account for the incidence in man. The evidence supports the conclusion that man is primarily the source of his own infection.

*The Inoculum.—*The viable cyst of *E. histolytica* is the usual and probably the only type of inoculum which produces infection in man.

*Exposure.—*Exposure occurs by the oral route. Single light exposure may be inconsequential but repeated exposure may eventually allow colonization of the amebæ in the large bowel. Wherever a heavy inoculum is taken into the mouth the chance of a "take" is greatly enhanced, particularly if the strain of ameba is highly pathogenic. Natives in hyperendemic areas typically develop a tolerance to the autochthonous strains of *E. histolytica*, while newcomers to the region are usually susceptible and rather rapidly develop severe symptoms (Faust, 1958).

Control.— Control of amebiasis must be undertaken as a public health problem. Presence of *E. histolytica* in a patient, whether in an active or carrier condition, and in each community at large, must be detected by reliable diagnostic procedures, so that its total incidence in the population and especially its high frequency in any particular group in the community are matters of official record in the vital statistics of the local and national health agencies.

The cause for endemic, hyperendemic or epidemic amebiasis in a population is to be found in its epidemiologic pattern, *viz.*, how the agent is maintained and propagated. Therefore, careful study must be made to determine whether water, food handlers, person-to-person contact, filth flies, or possibly reservoir hosts are the responsible factors. Then practical methods must be set up to rectify the difficulties.

In mental hospitals in cool or warm climates, as well as in restricted communities in temperate and tropical climates, chemotherapeutic prophylaxis has been demonstrated to be a valuable practical plan to control amebiasis (Berberian, Dennis and Korns, 1952; Sodeman and Beaver, 1952; Hoekenga, 1952; Brooke *et al.*, 1958).

OTHER AMEBÆ OF THE DIGESTIVE TRACT

Entamœba gingivalis (Gros, 1849) Smith and Barrett, 1915.—This ameba is cosmopolitan in its distribution. It is a parasite of the mouth of man and other animals, including several species of monkeys, dogs and cats, and is most commonly found as a phagocyte in diseased gums and tonsils. Only the trophozoite stage has been described; the only plausible method of transmission is through droplet spraying of saliva or during more intimate oral contact of one person with another while kissing.

E. gingivalis (Fig. 36) measures 5 to 35 microns in diameter depending on its metabolic activity. In most respects it closely resembles *E. histolytica*, with a few to several finger-like pseudopodia, finely granular endoplasm and clear ectoplasm, but it apparently does not exhibit true progressive locomotion. The nucleus contains a small karyosome which is central or slightly eccentric in position and is surrounded by a thin halo. There are likewise numerous lenticular chromatin granules lying against the under surface of the nuclear membrane. Delicate achromatic fibrils extend from the center to the margin of the nucleus.

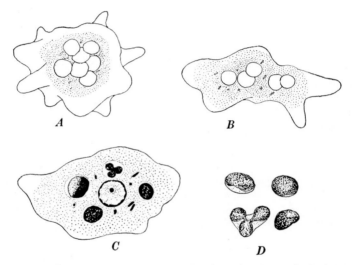

Fig. 36.—*Entamœba gingivalis.* Active trophozoites from gingival scrapings of individual having pyorrhea alveolaris. *A, B,* unstained living organisms; *C,* hematoxylin-stained specimen; *D,* characteristic nuclear débris of host cells in vacuoles of the ameba. × 1000. (After Faust, in Faust and Russell's *Clinical Parasitology,* Lea & Febiger, Philadelphia.)

Entamœba coli (Grassi, 1879) Hickson, 1909.—This ameba has a world-wide distribution and is usually the most common amebic parasite of man. Although it is a harmless commensal of the lumen of the cecum and lower levels of the large intestine, its presence is concrete evidence that the host has ingested fecal material.

All typical life-cycle stages are found in *E. coli, viz.,* trophozoite, precyst, cyst and metacystic stages. The *trophozoite* (Fig. 37*a*) measures 15 to 50 microns in diameter. It is a sluggish, quite viscous protoplast. The pseudopodia are broad, short, and do not typically extend any considerable distance from the main mass of protoplasm. This ameba does not exhibit progressive locomotion. The cytoplasm is dense and the non-granular ectoplasm is frequently poorly delimited from the coarsely granular endoplasm, while the nucleus is rarely distinguishable in the living organism. In stained preparations it is observed as a dense rounded mass, with a relatively large karyosome eccentrically placed and surrounded by a delicate halo.

On the inner surface of the nuclear membrane there are coarse lenticular or plaque-like concentrates of chromatin. Bacteria and other enteric microbes, which are seen within food vacuoles, constitute the food of *E. coli*, although in a dysenteric menstruum this ameba will ingest red blood cells.

Encystation occurs in a less dehydrated fecal medium than in the case of *E. histolytica*, so that trophozoites of *E. coli* are rarely seen in the stool except when it is frankly diarrheic. The cyst (10 to 33 microns in diameter) is usually larger than that of *E. histolytica*. When first formed the *cyst* has a single nucleus but as it matures it passes through successive stages with 2 to 8 nuclei (Fig. 37b), occasionally reaching the extraordinary number of 16 to 32 or more. The cytoplasm of the cyst is densely granular and is free of undigested inclusions seen in the trophozoite. However, there are usually one or more dense masses of glycogen with foggy edges and sharp-ended chromatoidal splinters.

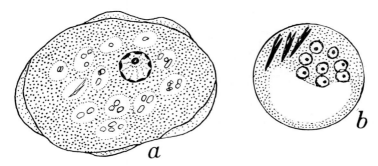

Fig. 37.—*Entamœba coli.* *a*, trophozoite, *b*, ripe cyst. × 1600. (Original, Faust.)

There is no clinical indication for treatment of persons harboring *Entamœba coli*, since it is non-pathogenic.

Endolimax nana (Wenyon and O'Connor, 1917) Brug, 1918.—This species is world-wide in distribution and is frequently found in as high a frequency in any population as is *Entamœba coli*. It is a commensal in the lumen of the cecum and lower levels of the large intestine and produces no lesions, but like *E. coli* its presence indicates that polluted material has been ingested.

As the species name *nana* (*i.e.*, dwarf) suggests, this ameba is small compared with *E. histolytica* and *E. coli*, although large strains of *E. nana* may actually be larger than small-sized *E. histolytica*. The *trophozoite* (Fig. 38a) measures 8 to 10 or more microns in diameter. The endoplasm is finely granular with numerous minute vacuoles, so that it has a foggy appearance. In contrast, the ectoplasm, with one or more short finger-like pseudopodia when the organism displays activity, is hyaline and almost transparent. The nucleus is ovoidal or subspherical. There is a relatively large karyosome, consisting of a mass of one or more granules, commonly eccentric in position, and anchored to the inner surface of the nuclear membrane by a few short fibrils.

In preparation for encystation *E. nana* discards all undigested inclusions and consolidates into an ovoidal or subspherical mass. A delicate cyst wall is then secreted. The mature cyst contains four nuclei (Fig. 38b,c). Masses of glycogen with a hazy margin may obscure the nuclei. Chromatoidal bodies, if present in the cytoplasm, are coccoid or short curved rods.

Iodamœba bütschlii (von Prowazek, 1911) Dobell, 1919.—This ameba is probably cosmopolitan in distribution but it is seldom as common as *E. histolytica*, *E. coli* and *Endolimax nana*. It is a harmless commensal living in the lumen of the large

intestine. The trophozoite (Fig. 39a) is sluggish, with little evidence of pseudopodial extension, and the thin layer of ectoplasm is not easily distinguished from
the endoplasm except that the latter is denser and has a more viscous, granular
composition. This trophozoite has a diameter of 8 to 20 microns. The nucleus is
spherical, has a rather thick membrane, a karyosome which is central or somewhat
eccentric in position and contains an inner chromatic granule surrounded by
achromatic globules, all anchored to the nuclear membrane by radial filaments.
Minute chromatin granules have also been described as lining the nuclear membrane.
In addition to food-containing vacuoles this ameba is unique in its trophozoite stage
in having in its cytoplasm one or two distinct rounded masses of glycogen. When
the organism encysts it discharges undigested material, becomes somewhat condensed and secretes a cyst wall. The cyst (Fig. 39b,c) is irregularly rounded, measures 5 to 18 microns in diameter, and usually contains only one nucleus (although
two nuclei have been observed).

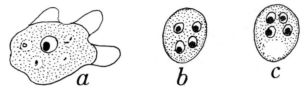

Fig. 38.—*Endolimax nana.* a, trophozoite, b, c, ripe cysts. × 1600. (Original, Faust.)

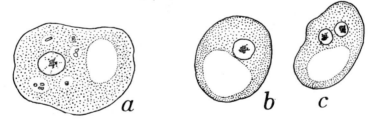

Fig. 39.—*Iodamœba bütschlii.* a, trophozoite, b, c, cysts. × 1600. (Original, Faust.)

The clearly outlined glycogen mass which stains a deep mahogany brown with
iodine readily differentiates *I. bütschlii* from the other intestinal amebæ.

Dientamœba fragilis Jepps and Dobell, 1918.—This ameba has been described
from many parts of the world but its minute size (usually 5 to 12 microns) and the
fact that it exists only in the trophozoite stage have frequently caused it to be overlooked in coprologic examinations except when iron-hematoxylin preparations have
been made and carefully searched under the oil-immersion objective. This organism
is not a tissue invader but it lives typically in the mucosal crypts in intimate contact with the epithelium, at levels all the way from the cecum to the rectum.
Although bacteria may be seen in its food vacuoles it seems probable that *D.
fragilis* prefers mucus as its source of nourishment. The trophozoite (Fig. 40) is a
delicate protoplast, with clear ectoplasm having very active lobulate hyaline pseudopodia and finely granular endoplasm. The nucleus is provided with a very thin
spherical membrane that is sometimes not distinguishable even with good iron-
hematoxylin staining. In its center there are four or more chromatin granules
embedded in an achromatic matrix, with a few radiating fibrils extending to the

nuclear membrane. Although uninucleate trophozoites are relatively common, there are often two nuclei, situated close together or widely separated.

Dientamœba fragilis is recovered both from formed and unformed stools but only when there are elements of mucus to which the organism adheres. Since encystation does not occur, transmission must be accomplished in the trophozoite stage.

Several investigators have attributed pathogenicity to *D. fragilis* which has been the only identified organism associated with certain cases of anorexia, nausea, vomiting, low-grade fever, abdominal discomfort and diarrhea. It is possible that

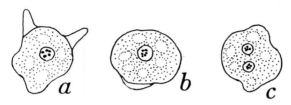

FIG. 40.—*Dientamœba fragilis, a, b, c,* trophozoites, × 1600. (Original, Faust.)

D. fragilis at times produces a mild colitis comparable to the mucous duodenitis which may result from infection with *Giardia lamblia.* At times it may be desirable to prescribe anti-amebic treatment as recommended for *Entamœba histolytica.*

Coprozoic Amebæ.—The following free-living, coprozoic amebæ have been reported from time to time in specimens of human feces submitted for examination: *Dimastigamœba gruberi, Hartmanella hyalina, Sappinia diploides, Vahlkampfia lobospinosa* and *V. punctata.* (Consult Wenyon's *Protozoölogy,* 1926 or Kudo's *Protozoölogy,* 1954 for detailed description of these species.)

SUMMARY

1. All amebæ have an active trophozoite stage. The trophozoite multiplies by binary fission. Many amebæ also have a cystic stage, which in some species provides survival. In parasitic amebæ the cyst serves principally as a transfer stage to a new host. When viable amebic cysts are taken into the mouth and swallowed by susceptible hosts, opportunity is provided for the amebæ to establish a new infection.
2. Man is parasitized by: *Entamœba histolytica* (large intestine); *E. gingivalis* (mouth); *E. coli* (cecum); *Endolimax nana* (cecum); *Iodamœba bütschlii* (cecum), and *Dientamœba fragilis* (large intestine). All of these species except *E. gingivalis* and *D. fragilis* have a cystic stage.
3. The only tissue-invading ameba of man is *Entamœba histolytica.* It is world-wide in its distribution but is more prevalent in warm than in cold climates. Two races are recognized, a larger one with a mean cyst diameter of 10 microns or more and a smaller one having a measurement of less than 10 microns. Infection with either race may produce a carrier state in the human host, suggesting lumen infection or only superficial erosion of the intestinal mucosa. Many strains manifest capacity to invade the wall of the large intestine, first and most frequently at the cecal level, secondly in the sigmoido-rectal area. The principal mechanism of invasion is lytic necrosis. The lesions are char-

acterized by minute points of entry into the mucosa, colonization in this layer and extensive enlargement after penetration into the submucosa. *E. histolytica* may also invade and produce lesions in extra-intestinal foci, especially the liver. All extra-intestinal amebic lesions are secondary to earlier ones established in the large intestine.

4. The symptoms in amebiasis are remarkably variable, including, on the one hand, acute fulminating dysentery, exhausting diarrhea, appendicitis syndrome, and abscess of the liver, lungs or brain, and, on the other hand, asymptomic infection.

5. Diagnosis of amebiasis by clinical procedures is tentative and requires laboratory confirmation. Accurate laboratory diagnosis is the reliable basis for therapeutic procedures.

6. Treatment of amebiasis may usually be satisfactorily carried out with several relatively specific anti-amebic drugs.

7. Control of amebiasis requires correction of the factors responsible for endemicity or epidemicity of the infection.

REFERENCES

The Amebæ

BEAVER, P. C., *et al.* 1956. Experimental Chemoprophylaxis of Amebiasis. Am. J. Trop. Med. & Hyg., *5*, 1015–1021.

BERBERIAN, D. A., DENNIS, E. W., and KORNS, R. F. 1952. Drug Prophylaxis of Amebiasis. J. Am. Med. Assn., *148*, 700–704.

BROOKE, M. M. 1958. Amebiasis. Methods in Laboratory Diagnosis. 67 pp. Communicable Disease Center, Atlanta, Georgia.

BROOKE, M. M. *et al.* 1958. Mass Therapy in Attempted Control of Amebiasis in a Mental Institution. Pub. Health Repts., *73*, 499–510.

BURROWS, R. B. 1957. *Endamœba hartmanni.* Am. J. Hyg., *65*, 172–188.

CRAIG, C. F. 1944. *The Etiology, Diagnosis and Treatment of Amebiasis.* 332 pp., Williams & Wilkins Co., Baltimore.

FAUST, E. C. 1954. *Amebiasis.* 154 pp., Charles C Thomas, Publisher, Springfield, Illinois.

————. 1958. Parasitologic Surveys in Cali, Departamento del Valle, Colombia. I. Incidence and Morphologic Characteristics of Strains of *Entamœba histolytica.* Am. J. Trop. Med. & Hyg., *7*, 4–15.

————. 1961. The Multiple Facets of *Entamœba histolytica* Infection. Int'l Rev. Trop. Med., *1*, 43–76.

FAUST, E. C. and READ, T. R. 1959. Parasitologic Surveys in Cali, Departmento del Valle, Colombia. V. Capacity of *Entamœba histolytica* of Human Origin to Utilize Different Types of Starches in Its Metabolism. Am. J. Trop. Med. & Hyg., *8*, 293–303.

FREEDMAN, L., and ELSDON-DEW, R. 1959. Size as a Criterion of Species in the Human Intestinal Amebæ. Am. J. Trop. Med. & Hyg., *8*, 327–330.

HOARE, C. A. 1958. The Enigma of Host-Parasite Relations in Amebiasis. The Rice Inst. Pamphlet, *45* (1), 23–35.

HOEKENGA, M. 1952. The Prophylaxis of Malaria and Amebiasis with Milibis-Aralen. J. Lab. & Clin. Med., *39*, 267–270.

JARUMILINTA, R. and MAEGRAITH, B. G. 1961. Fibrinolytic Activity of *Entamœba histolytica.* Trans. R. Soc. Trop. Med. & Hyg., *54*, 9.

KESSEL, J. F. 1928. Amœbiasis in Kittens Infected with Amœbæ from Acute and "Carrier" Human Cases and with the Tetranucleate Amœbæ of the Monkey and of the Pig. Am. J. Hyg., *8*, 311–355.

KIRBY, H. 1951. *"Entamœba coli"* versus *"Endamœba coli."* Bull. Zool. Nomenclature, *2*, 9–10, 243–281.

KUDO, R. R.   1954.   *Protozoölogy*, 4th. ed., 966 pp., Charles C Thomas, Publisher, Springfield, Illinois.

MAEGRAITH, B. G., HARINASUTA, C., and DEEGAN, T.   1959.   Digestion of Human Gut Epithelium by *Entamœba histolytica*. Trans. R. Soc. Trop. Med. & Hyg., *52*, 1–2.

POWELL, S. J., WILMOT, A. J., and ELSDON-DEW, R.   1958.   A Comparison of Erythromycin, Spiramycin and Novobiocin in the Treatment of Acute Amebic Dysentery. J. Trop. Med. & Hyg., *61*, 67–70.

PIPKIN, A. C.   1949.   Experimental Studies on the Rôle of Filth Flies in the Transmission of *Endamœba histolytica*. Am .J. Hyg., *49*, 255–275.

SAPERO, J. J., HAKANSSON, E. G., and LOUTITT, C. M.   1942.   The Occurrence of Two Significantly Distinct Races of *Endamœba histolytica*. Am. J. Trop. Med., *22*, 191–208.

SODEMAN, W. A., and BEAVER, P. C.   1952.   A Study of the Therapeutic Effects of Some Amebacidal Drugs. Am. J. Med., *12*, 440–446.

WALKER, E. L., and SELLARDS, A. W.   1913.   Experimental Entamœbic Dysentery Philippine J. Sci. (B), *8*, 253–331.

Chapter 5

The Ciliate Protozoa

THE ciliate protozoa constitute a very large number of species belonging to the Subphylum Ciliophora, Class Ciliatea, characterized by having numerous short ectoplasmic threads or *cilia*, which are present both in the trophozoite and encysted stage.

Many ciliates exist as free-living infusoria and possibly even a larger number are parasites of the digestive tract of insects (*viz.*, termites and wood roaches) and vertebrates, particularly herbivorous mammals such as horses, cattle, sheep and goats. Near the anterior end of the body there is a conical mouth, the *cytostome*, and at the opposite end an anal opening, the *cytopyge*. There are two types of nuclei, a larger, less dense *macronucleus* and nearby a small, dense *micronucleus* (or at times more than one). Multiplication is by transverse binary fission, with division of the cytoplasm following that of the nuclei. Many species also undergo conjugation, during which exchange of nuclei occurs. The only ciliate which is a *bona fide* parasite of man is *Balantidium coli*.

Balantidium coli (Malmsten, 1857) Stein, 1862.—This protozoön has a cosmopolitan distribution in hogs and is a common parasite of several species of monkeys. In man it is found mostly in warm climates, although human infections have also been reported from almost every country in the Northern and Southern Hemispheres outside the warm areas.

Morphology, Biology and Life Cycle.—The organism has two stages, the trophozoite and the cyst. The trophozoite (Fig. 41*A*) is the largest of the protozoa parasitizing man. It is ovoidal, greenish-gray, covered with short cilia which are constantly in motion during life, and has a vigorous forward movement as it plows through even relatively thick liquid feces. It varies considerably in size (50 to 100 microns in length by 40 to 70 microns in breadth). The anterior end is somewhat conical and the posterior end broadly rounded. To one side of the anterior tip there is a funnel-shaped *peristome*, which leads into the *cytostome*. A minute cytopyge is situated at the opposite end. One, and at times two large *pulsating vacuoles* are found within the cytoplasm (Fig. 41). The body is covered with a relatively tough pellicle. Somewhat posterior to the equator of the organism there is an elongated kidney-shaped *macronucleus* and lying within the concave side of the macronucleus a minute *micronucleus*.

The natural habitat of *Balantidium coli* is the cecal level of the large intestine but the parasite also occurs at all lower levels. It feeds on host cells, bacteria and other nutritious substances in the tissues or lumen of the large bowel.

Asexual reproduction consists of transverse binary fission, in which the micronucleus first divides mitotically, then the macronucleus amitotically, followed by the cytoplasm, resulting in two daughter organisms. Although conjugation has been observed in *B. coli*, this is not a common occurrence and apparently is not essential for its propagation.

The cyst (Fig. 41*B*) is the resting and transfer stage. Encystation takes place with dehydration of the feces, either before or following evacuation from the large intestine (Svensson, 1955).

Pathogenicity and Symptomatology.—In the hog, there is little if any evidence that *Balantidium coli* produces deep invasion of the intestinal wall, although there may be superficial erosion of the mucosa. In monkeys,

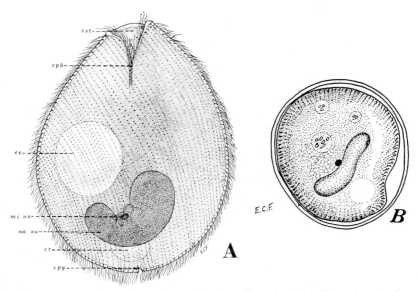

Fig. 41.—*Balantidium coli.*, *A*, trophozoite, *B*, cyst. × 750. *cph*, cytopharynx, within cytostome; *cpy*, cytopyge; *cst*, cytostome; *cv*, contractile or pulsating vacuole; *ma nu*, macronucleus; *mi nu*, micronucleus. (A, original, *B*, from Faust and Russell's *Clinical Parasitology*, Lea & Febiger, Philadelphia.)

the mucosal layer may be penetrated, with extensive submucosal destruction, and in man similar tissue damage occurs. Since *Balantidium coli* is a much larger, sturdier organism than *Entamœba histolytica*, it produces a bigger opening in the intestinal mucosa as it enters the wall. Moreover, its penetration seems to be accomplished more by boring action than by lysis, although it produces hyaluronidase (Tempelis and Lysenko, 1957). Once established in the tissues it usually has no difficulty in penetrating through the muscularis mucosæ into the submucosa, where it spreads out radially, causing rapid destruction of the tissues (Fig. 43); but unlike *E. histolytica* it rarely invades the muscular coats and it has seldom been found in extra-intestinal tissues. While balantidial lesions may develop at any level of the large intestine, they most commonly occur in the cecal and sigmoid-rectal regions. Rarely this infection occurs in the vagina (Isaza Mejía, 1955).

The symptoms in balantidiasis vary from fulminating, sometimes fatal dysentery or profuse diarrhea to an essentially asymptomatic carrier state. In this respect they parallel the broad spectrum of symptoms in amebic colitis.

Diagnosis and Treatment.—Diagnosis is made on recovery of the characteristic trophozoites or cysts of *Balantidium coli* in the stool. (See Figs. 41 and 42). Care must be taken that the stool and the water or physiologic saline solution employed in making fecal films for microscopic diagnosis of this infection are not contaminated with free-living infusoria, otherwise these ciliates may be mistaken for *B. coli.*

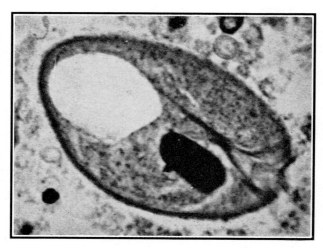

Fig. 42.—*Balantidium coli.* Trophozoite in a diarrheic stool. × 600. (Photomicrograph by Drs. James and Getz, in Medical Museum Collection, Armed Forces Institute of Pathology; from Faust and Russell's *Clinical Parasitology,* Lea & Febiger, Philadelphia.)

Relatively little attention has been paid to specific treatment of balantidiasis. Clinical and experimental tests with carbarsone and tetracycline antibiotics have demonstrated that these drugs are effective in relieving the symptoms, and in some cases they produce eradication of the organism (See Table 7, page 417.)

Frequently balantidiasis may coexist with a debilitating disease such as malnutrition or one like trichuriasis which is injurious to the colon. The balantidial infection may disappear spontaneously following the correction of such contributory factors.

Epidemiology.—Exposure occurs from swallowing viable cysts of *B. coli.* The number of actual human infections with this parasite is few indeed compared with the opportunities for acquiring the infection from animal reservoirs. Probably man is relatively refractory to infection with the strains from these hosts, so that human infection develops only occasionally from this type of exposure. In contrast, once an infection has become established in man and the organism is adapted to the human intestine, it can be more easily transmitted from person to person, particularly in tropical communities and mental hospitals where personal and group hygiene is remarkably poor.

Control.—Since balantidiasis is very common in hogs and human infection from this source is so infrequent, control of this potential source of exposure is not primarily indicated. In contrast, exposure from human sources requires attention. Possibly the most practical method of attack is to discover all human cases in foci of moderate to heavy endemicity and treat all infected persons simultaneously with effective drugs.

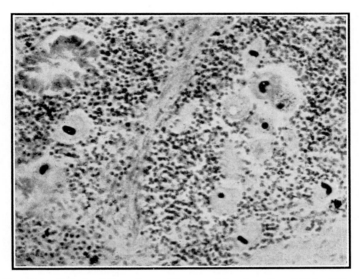

Fig. 43.—Balantidiasis of the colon, with several trophozoites of *Balantidium coli*, in the submucosa. Note extensive inflammatory reaction around the organisms. (Photomicrograph by Drs. James and Getz, in Medical Museum Collection, Armed Forces Institue of Pathology; from Faust and Russell's *Clinical Parasitology*, Lea & Febiger, Philadelphia.)

SUMMARY

Infection of the large intestine of hogs, monkeys and man with *Balatidium coli* is acquired from ingesting the cysts. Man appears to be relatively refractory to infection from animal reservoirs but once *B. coli* becomes established as a human parasite it may produce extensive ulcers in the mucosa and submucosa of the large intestine. *B. coli* rarely produces lesions in extra-intestinal locations. The symptoms in human balantidiasis range from fulminating dysentery and prostrating diarrhea to an essentially asymptomatic condition. Very little study has been given to specific treatment. Treatment of all diagnosed human infections in a community should serve as an effective control measure.

REFERENCES

HOEKENGA, M. T. 1953. Terramycin Treatment of Balantidiasis in Honduras. Am. J. Trop. Med. & Hyg., *2*, 271–273.

ISAZA MEJÍA, G.   1955.   Balantidiasis Vaginal. Antioquia Méd. (Colombia), *5*, 488–491.

SVENSSON, R.   1955.   On the Resistance to Heating and Cooling of *Balantidium coli* in Culture and Some Observations Regarding Conjugation. Exp. Parasitol., *4*, 502–525.

TEMPELIS, C. H., and LYSENKO, M. G.   1957.   The Production of Hyaluronidase by *Balantidium coli*. Exp. Parasitol., *6*, 31–36.

YOUNG, M. D.   1950.   Attempts to Transmit Human *Balantidium coli*. Am. J. Trop. Med., *30*, 70–71.

YOUNG, M. D., and BURROWS, R. B.   1943.   Carbarsone Treatment for *Balantidium coli* Infections. Pub. Health Repts., *58*, 1272–1273.

Chapter 6

The Coccidia, Malaria Parasites and the Sarcosporidea

THESE protozoa are members of the Subphylum SPOROZOA, an exclusively parasitic group which typically requires alternation of asexual and sexual generations in the life cycle. The species which parasitize man belong to the Class Telosporidea, which includes the coccidia and the malaria parasites, and the Class Sarcosporidea, to which the species *Sarcocystis lindemanni* belongs.

THE COCCIDIA

The members of this subclass employ only one host for both asexual and sexual phases of their life cycle. The species which commonly parasitize man and domestic animals belong to two genera, *Isospora* and *Eimeria*. Like other closely related genera, these coccidians have similar, independent gametocytes (isogametocytes) and the male gametocyte produces multiple gametes, following which an oöcyst is formed from fertilization of a female gamete by a male gamete. The oöcyst in species of *Isospora* produces 2 internal sporocysts, each with 4 sporozoites; that of species of *Eimeria* produces 4 internal sporocysts, each with 2 sporozoites. Only two species of coccidia are known to parasitize man, *viz.*, *Isospora belli* and *I. hominis*.

Although the life cycle of these two species has not been elucidated, that of *I. canis* in the dog and *I. felis* in the cat is well established (Wenyon, 1923; Hitchcock, 1955). The infective stage is the *sporozoite*, produced in units of four's within each of the two sporocysts developed in the oöcyst, the stage evacuated in the host's feces. When ripe oöcysts get into the mouth and are swallowed, they pass through the stomach into the small intestine. On becoming free of the oöcyst and sporocyst membranes, the sporozoites enter the intestinal epithelium, where they transform into *trophozoites*. The trophozoites grow, developing into *schizonts*, and each schizont produces internally several *merozoites*. These asexual daughter cells enter other epithelial cells, with repetition of asexual multiplication. Eventually some of the merozoites transform into *male* and *female gametocytes*. Each male gametocyte produces a number of *male gametes* and each female gametocyte transforms into a single *female gamete*. Male and female gametes unite to produce the *zygote* or fertilized egg. A resistant cell wall is secreted around the spherical zygote, which is now the *oöcyst*. In *Isospora* the enclosed cell divides into two equal units, the *sporocysts*. Within each sporocyst four curved sausage-shaped sporozoites are developed. The complete cycle is diagrammatically illustrated in Figure 44.

Isospora belli Wenyon, 1923 and **I. hominis** (Rivolta, 1878) Dobell, 1919.

Morphology, Biology and Life Cycle.—Although Wenyon (1923) distinguished two species of *Isospora* parasitizing man, until recently there

(95)

has not been unanimous opinion in favor of this view. Only the oöcysts and their end products are known, as observed in the diarrheic feces of infected individuals. In fresh stools those of *I. belli* are found typically in an unsegmented condition (Fig. 45, *A1*) and ripen after their discharge from the intestine. They are elongate-ovoidal in shape, measuring from 18 to 40 microns in length by 8 to 19 microns in breadth. One end is more rounded, the other somewhat narrower. The oöcyst wall consists of two layers, is smooth, hyaline and is highly resistant to desiccation and other unfavorable environmental conditions. At times a minute micropyle can be distinguished at the narrower end. Within the wall of the early-stage

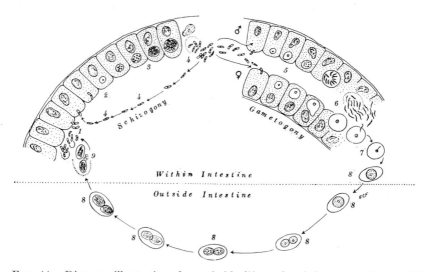

Fig. 44.—Diagram illustrating the probable life cycle of *Isospora belli*, coccidian parasite of man. *1*, sporozoites entering intestinal mucosa; *2*, young trophozoite in mucosal cell; *3*, development of schizont; *4*, merozoites freed of parent membrane; *5*, gametocytes, male (above) and female (below), developed from merozoites; *6*, gametes; *7*, union of gametes to form zygote; *8*, maturing stages of oöcyst; *9*, sporocysts freed of oöcyst wall. (Original, Faust.)

oöcyst there is a single spherical granular mass of protoplasm, with a central denser nuclear mass. When the fecal specimen is kept in the laboratory at 25° to 30° C. for several hours the protoplasmic mass divides into two equal masses, the immature sporocysts (Fig. 45, *A2*). Within 18 to 36 hours four falciform sporozoites, each with a minute central nucleus, are formed inside of each spore (Fig. 45, *A3*). A number of highly refractive granules are seen at one end within each sporocyst membrane.

Typically the oöcysts of *I. hominis* have ripened before they are evacuated from the intestine and the oöcyst wall has been sloughed off or only a residual portion remains around the sporocysts, which may be attached to one another side-by-side (Fig. 45B *1,2*) or completely separate (Fig. 45B, *3*). In contrast to the thin sporocyst wall of *I. belli*, that of *I. hominis* is as thick as the oöcyst wall of *I. belli*. The sporocysts of *I. hominis* are regularly ovoidal, measure 10 to 16 microns in length by 7.5 to 12 microns in breadth; each contains four sausage-shaped sporozoites, which are appreciably longer and thicker than those of *I. belli*, and likewise each has a clump of residual refractory granules.

Based on comparison with *I. canis* and *I. felis,* and on clinical evidence, it seems likely that *I. belli* and *I. hominis* invade the mucosa of the small intestine (and cecum), where they obtain nourishment for asexual and sexual development. The fact that the immature oöcysts of *I. belli* and ripe sporocysts of *I. hominis* are evacuated in the feces possibly suggests that the former species is either a tissue parasite at a lower level of the intestine or is more superficially located in the intestinal wall than is

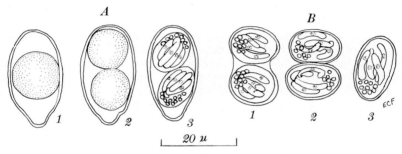

Fig. 45.—Oöcysts of the two species of *Isospora* parasitizing man. *A*, *Isospora belli: 1*, immature oöcyst passed in the feces; *2*, ripening oöcyst with two sporocysts; *3*, ripe oöcyst, with four sporozoites in each sporocyst. *B*, *I. hominis: 1, 2, 3*, types of sporocysts from ripe oöcysts passed in the feces. (Original, Faust.)

I. hominis. Piekarski (1954) believes that the more mature condition of the oöcysts of *I. hominis* indicates that this species inhabits subepithelial tissues, while Elsdon-Dew and Freedman (1953) consider that it resides at a higher level of the intestine than does *I. belli*; yet Orrego *et al.* (1959) obtained oöcysts of *I. belli* from duodenal aspiration. In two experimental human infections Matsubayashi and Nozawa (1948) found a new generation of oöcysts of *I. belli* in the stools ten days after feeding ripe oöcysts of human origin.

Pathogenicity and Symptomatology.—The invasion and destruction of intestinal mucosa by these coccidia is responsible for mucous diarrhea, low-grade fever, chills, anorexia and nausea which are often characteristic of this disease (Jeffery, 1958). These symptoms may be mild and transient, lasting for less than a month, or severe and exhausting (Jarpa *et al.*, 1960); less frequently they may become chronic, with periodic exascerbation of acute symptoms.

Diagnosis.—This is made by discovery of the immature oöcyst of *I. belli* or the mature sporocysts of *I. hominis* in freshly discharged feces, often of a diarrheic type. These parasite objects are transparent and are likely to be overlooked in direct fecal films, especially since only a few are present in the average infection. Concentration by the zinc sulfate centri-

7

fugal flotation technic (see Technical Aids, p. 428) will often demonstrate the respective diagnostic objects when direct fecal films are negative. In mild cases they may be found only once in successive stool specimens from the patient. Frequently Charcot-Leyden crystals are present in positive specimens (Faust *et al.*, 1961).

Treatment.—There is no satisfactory chemotherapy. In the average case, rest and a bland diet are sufficient to allow spontaneous elimination of the parasites. Bismuth salicylate is helpful in terminating the diarrhea (Routh, McCroan and Hames, 1955).

Epidemiology.—*I. belli* and *I. hominis* are widely distributed but are more prevalent in warm than in cool climates. Isolated cases have been reported from many countries but more frequent diagnoses have been made by workers in the Southwest Pacific, Natal, S. Africa, São Paulo State, Brazil, Santiago, Chile, and by the senior author and his co-workers in Cali, Colombia (Faust *et al.*, 1961). In general, these infections appear sporadically, are of short duration, are more common in children under ten years of age than in adults, may be familial in occurrence, and occasionally appear epidemically in groups subject to gross exposure from contaminated persons, soil, food or drink. During 1957–1959 the senior author and his associates diagnosed 28 cases of *I. belli* and 12 of *I. hominis* from clinic and private cases in Cali, Colombia. Five hundred twenty eight stools from dogs in this area in 1957 revealed the following percentage of infection with coccidia: *I. belli*, 0.37; *I. hominis*, 24.6; *I. canis*, 3.4; *I. felis*, 0.57. In this study dogs, like human beings, maintained infection with *I. belli* and *I. hominis* for only a limited time. While there is no definite evidence that dogs constitute a reservoir for human infection, no other host source has been discovered. Poor environmental sanitation and poor personal hygiene provide abundant opportunity for human exposure from the infested *milieu* containing the highly resistant oöcysts.

Control.—This can be accomplished only by improvement in sanitary and hygienic conditions.

Species of Eimeria *as Spurious Parasites of Man*

From time to time oöcysts of species of *Eimeria* have been diagnosed in human feces. Dobell (1919) mistakenly considered them to be genuine parasites of the human intestine and named them *Eimeria wenyoni*, *E. oxyspora* and *E. snijdersi*. Thomson and Robertson (1926) demonstrated that these coccidia are parasites of sardines and other fish and that they are only in transit through the intestine of persons who consume the fish. They can be readily distinguished from the oöcysts of human *Isospora*, since those of *Eimeria* contain four sporocysts, each with two sporozoites, and those of *Isospora* two sporocysts, each with four sporozoites.

THE MALARIA PARASITES

The malaria parasites are species of Sporozoa belonging to the Order **Hæmosporidea** (hemosporidia). Their life cycle, like that of the coccidia, includes an asexual phase (*schizogony*) alternating with a sexual one (*gametogony* followed by *sporogony*). However, the hemosporidia require two hosts, an intermediate one in which the asexual phase develops and mother sex cells (*gametocytes*) are produced, and a definitive one in which the sex cells become mature *gametes*. Following maturation the male (*microgamete*) unites with the female (*macrogamete*) to form a *zygote*, which then becomes encysted (*oöcyst*) and produces a considerable number of sexual spores (*sporozoites*). The sporozoites, when introduced into the intermediate host, develop into the asexual stage. There are two separate transfer stages, the gametocyte and the sporozoite. The asexual phase of the cycle (*schizogony*) is found only in vertebrate hosts, while maturation and union of sex cells followed by production of sporozoites takes place only in blood-sucking invertebrates, which are mostly arthropods and predominantly mosquitoes.

In many species of malaria parasites of birds the earliest asexual stages occur in the fixed cells of the reticulo-endothelial system and the endothelial lining cells of the blood capillaries, after which some of the asexual daughter cells (*merozoites*) invade red blood cells and initiate erythrocytic infection. The malaria parasites in monkeys and man establish their first foci exclusively in the non-phagocytic cells of the liver before the parasites are released into the circulating blood and begin to parasitize red blood cells (Shortt and Garnham, 1948; Shortt *et al.*, 1951; Garnham, 1951; Jeffery *et al.*, 1952).

Sporozoites of the malaria parasites inoculated into man by an infected *Anopheles* mosquito disappear from circulating blood within approximately 30 minutes and no parasites can be found in red blood cells for several days. Thereafter they appear in increasing numbers in circulating red cells (*parasitemia*). Pre-erythrocytic development corresponds approximately to the clinical incubation period.

THE MALARIA PARASITES OF MAN

The Genus Plasmodium.—All malaria parasites belong to the genus *Plasmodium*, in which much of the asexual development takes place in red blood cells, with the production of so-called "malaria pigment," which is deposited within the body of the parasite. The growing asexual parasite (*trophozoite*) utilizes the globin part of the hemoglobin and retains the iron component as hematin.

Historical Notes.—The clinical manifestations of malaria were recorded in ancient Chinese and Indian medical classics, and the ravages of malaria were severe during the later days of the Roman Empire. Yet it was not until 1880 that Alphonse Laveran, in Algeria, first demonstrated the parasites within red blood corpuscles in fresh wet microscopic films.

By 1894 Patrick Manson was firmly convinced that malaria was mosquito-transmitted and persuaded Surgeon Ronald Ross of the Indian Medical Service to test this theory experimentally. He first completed the mosquito phase of the cycle by employing the parasites of avian malaria in "grey mosquitos," *viz.*, *Culex fatigans* (1898). Sometime later in West Africa he was able to demonstrate similar development of the human parasites in *Anopheles gambiæ* and *A. funestus*. During 1898–1899 Bignami, Bastianelli and Grassi in Italy also worked out the complete mosquito phase of human plasmodia in *Anopheles maculipennis*. A field test by

British investigators demonstrated conclusively that malaria is contracted through the bites of infected mosquitoes (Manson, 1900).

Meanwhile Golgi (1886) first accurately described the tertian parasite and Grassi and Feletti (1890) assigned the names *vivax* to this species and *malariæ* to the quartan parasite, while Welch (1897), in Baltimore, named the species with crescent-shaped gametocytes *falciparum*. Stephens (1922) described and named the fourth malaria parasite of man, *viz.*, *P. ovale*.

The full life cycle of human malaria parasites is illustrated in the accompanying diagram (Fig. 46).

Malaria Parasites in the Human Host. —This includes asexual development in fixed tissue cells and in the erythrocytes, and early gametogony.

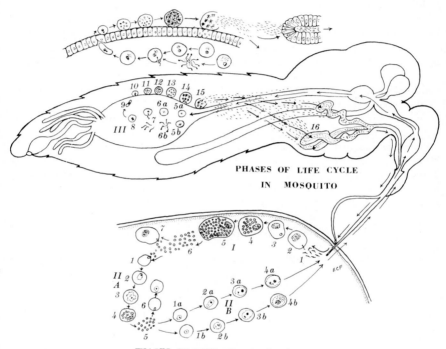

PHASES OF LIFE CYCLE

IN MOSQUITO

PHASES OF LIFE CYCLE IN MAN

FIG. 46.—The life cycle of the malarial parasite in man and female *Anopheles* mosquito.—**I. Preërythrocytic Phase.** Asexual multiplication (schizogony) in the parenchyma cells of the liver (*I, 2–6*), derived from sporozoites (*I, 1*) introduced into man by the infected mosquito. Second preërythrocytic schizogony (*I, 7*) derived from first-generation merozoites (*1, 6*). **II. Erythrocytic Phases.** *Merozoites* from preërythrocytic schizonts invade red blood cells, producing trophozoites (*A, 1–5*) leading to replicative schizogony (*A, 6*); *Gametocytes* (*B, 1a–4a*, female, and *1b–4b* male). **III. Mosquito Phases.** Gametocytes, sucked up from peripheral blood of man, reach the mosquito's midgut (*5a, 5b*), where they mature into female and male *gametes* (*6a, 6b*). One male gamete enters a female gamete (*7*), producing a fertilized cell, or *zygote* (*8*), which becomes the motile *oökinete* (*9*) and migrates through the stomach wall to become encysted (*oöcyst*) on the hemocelic side. The oöcyst grows (*10–14*), producing a large number of *sprorozoites*. When mature, the oöcyst bursts (*15*), releasing the sporozoites, many of which reach the salivary glands (*16*), pass down the salivary ducts to the hypopharynx to be introduced into man when the mosquito takes its next blood meal. (Enlarged detail of III 5-16 shown above outline of mosquito.) (Original, Faust.)

Pre-erythrocytic Development.—Inoculation of the human subject occurs when an infected female *Anopheles* mosquito injects a droplet of saliva containing sporozoites of human plasmodia into cutaneous blood vessels preparatory to taking a blood meal. For a few minutes these sporozoites circulate in the blood stream but within a half hour they have disappeared (Fairley, 1945). The first colonization takes place in fixed tissue cells in the liver.

In human volunteers inoculated with large numbers of sporozoites of *Plasmodium vivax* (Shortt and Garnham, 1948), *P. falciparum* (Shortt *et al.*, 1951; Jeffrey *et al.*, 1952), *P. ovale* (Garnham *et al.*, 1954), and *P.*

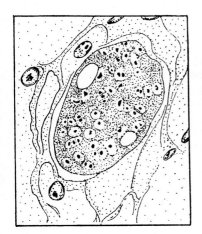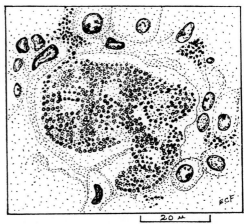

FIG. 47.—Preërythrocytic stages of *Plasmodium vivax* in parenchyma cells of liver of human volunteer on seventh day after sporozoite inoculation. On left, immature schizont; on right ripe schizont containing thousands of merozoites which are breaking out of the parasitized parenchyma cell. (Black and white drawing from color reproduction by Shortt and Garnham, 1948, Transaction of the Royal Society of Tropical Medicine and Hygiene, with kind permission of the authors and publisher.)

malariæ in chimpanzees (Bray, 1959), the first evidence of a "take" has been 48 hours to 7 days later in the parenchyma cells of the liver, where young schizonts in active nuclear division have been observed. The schizonts grow remarkably in size with increase in the number of their nuclei and corresponding division of the cytoplasm of the parasite, to produce thousands of merozoites by the seventh or eighth day after inoculation (Shortt, 1951) (Fig. 47).

Following sporozoite-induced infection the minimum period of incubation (prepatency) for *P. vivax* is 8 days, for *P. falciparum* 6 days, and for *P. ovale*, 9 days (Garnham, 1954). In *P. malariæ*, 27 to 37 days elapse between inoculation of sporozoites and the first detection of the parasites in the blood.

Period of Asexual Development in the Red Blood Cells.—When merozoites which have developed in pre-erythrocytic foci enter the red cells they transform into trophozoites, which grow and develop into schizonts, each producing the number of merozoites characteristic of the species of plasmodium. When fully matured, the mërozoites break out of the parasitized red cell and soon actively enter undamaged red cells to repeat the asexual cycle. Merozoites of *P. vivax* have an affinity for young erythrocytes (reticulocytes), *P. falciparum* invades both immature and mature cells and *P. malariæ* prefers older red cells.

The time required to complete one asexual multiplication after erythrocytic infection has become well established varies with the different species: for *P. vivax* and *P. ovale* it is 48 hours, for *P. malariæ*, 72 hours, and for *P. falciparum*, 36 to 48 hours, but with much less regular rhythm or synchronization than in the other species. Moreover, in *P. falciparum* only the young trophozoites are typically seen in circulating erythrocytes, while the more mature trophozoites and schizonts tend to develop only in visceral blood.

Early Gametogony in the Human Host.—In individuals who have acquired malaria through the "bites" of infected *Anopheles* mosquitoes, immature sexual cells of the plasmodia typically begin to appear in circulating erythrocytes after a few to several asexual erythrocytic multiplications have occurred. These cells do not multiply in the human body, remain viable for a relatively short time, possibly a week or less, and are phagocytosed soon thereafter.

Mosquito Phase of the Life Cycle.—Once ripe gametocytes of human malaria parasites are ingested by a female *Anopheles* in a blood meal and reach the "stomach" (midgut), they transform into mature sex cells. One *macrogametocyte* develops a single *macrogamete* (*oöcyte* or unfertilized egg) and one *microgametocyte* produces a few flagellated male cells (*microgametes*). A microgamete then enters a macrogamete, resulting in a fertilized egg (*zygote*), which becomes motile (*oökinete*), migrates through the cells of the stomach wall and becomes encysted (*oöcyst*) just under the hemocelic membrane of the stomach.

The oöcyst grows rapidly and develops a considerable number of internal nuclear centers. Each center than produces a large number of delicate spindle-shaped bodies (*sporozoites*). By the time the sporozoites become mature the wall of the greatly enlarged oöcyst bursts, releasing the ripened sporozoites into the "body cavity" (hemocele) of the mosquito. Many of these sporozoites eventually migrate to the salivary glands which they enter, then pass down through the salivary ducts into the median tube (hypopharyngeal tube) of the mosquito's proboscis. When the mosquito next punctures human skin to take a blood meal, sporozoites are injected into the cutaneous blood vessels and initiate a new human infection.

The optimal temperature and corresponding time for complete development of the sexual phases in the mosquito vary considerably in the three common species of human malaria parasites: for *Plasmodium vivax*, 25° C. (77° F.) and about 11 days; for *P. falciparum*, 30° C. (86° F.) and 10 to 11 days, and for *P. malariæ*, 22° C. (71.6° F.) and 18 to 21 days respectively.

Geographical Distribution of Human Malaria.—Malaria occurs where *Anopheles* mosquitoes are abundant and human gametocyte carriers are present. The natural distribution of the disease includes all tropical areas and adjacent temperature regions. Exceptions to this general statement consist of certain desert areas and altitudes above 9,000 feet, where *Anopheles* mosquitoes can not breed. Islands in the Central and South Pacific are presently free of *Anopheles*, hence of malaria.

The known world distribution of malaria is shown in the accompanying map (Fig. 48).

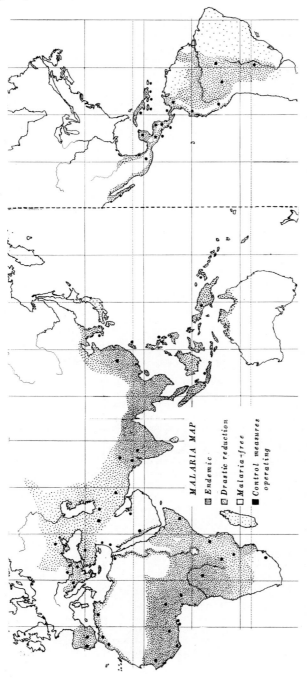

Fig. 48.—Present-day malaria distribution in the world, based on published information through 1959.   (Original, Faust.)

1. Normal-sized red cell with marginal ring-form trophozoite.
2. Young signet ring-form trophozoite in a macrocyte.
3. Slightly older ring-form trophozoite in red cell showing basophilic stippling.
4. Polychromatophilic red cell containing young tertian parasite with pseudopodia.
5. Ring-form trophozoite showing pigment in cytoplasm, in an enlarged cell containing Schüffner's stippling.°
6, 7. Very tenuous medium trophozoite forms.
8. Three ameboid trophozoites with fused cytoplasm.
9, 11, 12, 13. Older ameboid trophozoites in process of development.
10. Two ameboid trophozoites in one cell.
14. Mature trophozoite.
15. Mature trophozoite with chromatin apparently in process of division.
16, 17, 18, 19. Schizonts showing progressive steps in division (" presegmenting schizonts").
20. Mature schizont.
21, 22. Developing gametocytes.
23. Mature microgametocyte.
24. Mature macrogametocyte.

°Schüffner's stippling does not appear in all cells containing the growing and older stages of *P. vivax* as would be indicated by these pictures, but it can be found with any stage from the fairly young ring-form onward.

Reproduced with permission from the Manual for the Microscopical Diagnosis of Malaria in Man, National Institutes of Health Bulletin No. 180. (By Aimee Wilcox.)

PLATE IV

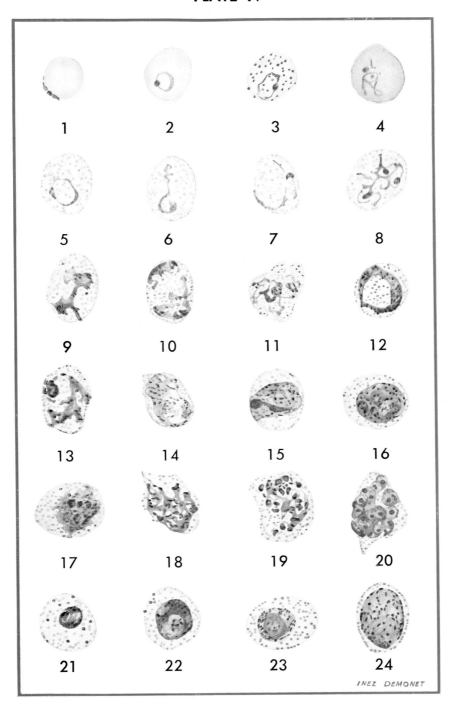

1 2 3 4

5 6 7 8

9 10 11 12

13 14 15 16

17 18 19 20

21 22 23 24

INEZ DEMONET

PLATE V

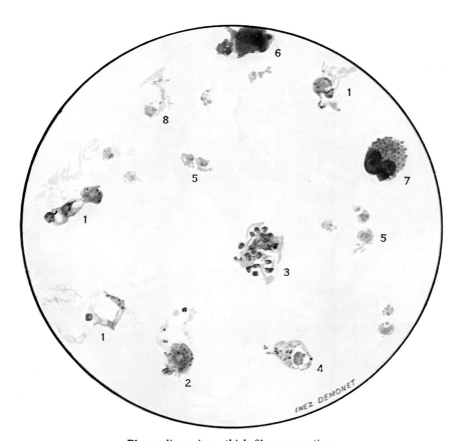

Plasmodium vivax, thick-film preparation.

The film contains three developing trophozoites, an immature and a mature schizont, a microgametocyte, clumps of blood platelets, an eosinophil and a neutrophil.

1. Ameboid trophozoites. 2. Schizont—2 divisions of chromatin. 3. Mature schizont. 4. Microgametocyte. 5. Blood platelets. 6. Nucleus of neutrophil. 7. Eosinophil. 8. Blood platelet associated with cellular remains of young erythrocytes. (From Wilcox's Manual for the Microscopical Diagnosis of Malaria in Man, courtesy National Institutes of Health.)

LEGEND FOR PLATE VI

Stages of *Plasmodium falciparum* in human erythrocytes from thin-blood preparation.

1. Very young ring-form trophozoite.

2. Double infection of single cell with young trophozoites, one a "marginal form," the other, "signet ring" form.

3, 4. Young trophozoites showing double chromatin dots.

5, 6, 7. Developing trophozoite forms.

8. Three medium trophozoites in one cell.

9. Trophozoite showing pigment, in a cell containing Maurer's spots.

10, 11. Two trophozoites in each of two cells, showing variation of forms which parasites may assume.

12. Almost mature trophozoite showing haze of pigment throughout cytoplasm. Maurer's spots in the cell.

13. Estivo-autumnal "slender forms."

14. Mature trophozoite, showing clumped pigment.

15. Parasite in the process of initial chromatin division.

16, 17, 18, 19. Various phases of the development of the schizont ("presegmenting schizonts").

20. Mature schizont.

21, 22, 23, 24. Successive forms in the development of the gametocyte—usually not found in the peripheral circulation.

25. Immature macrogametocyte.

26. Mature macrogametocyte.

27. Immature microgametocyte.

28. Mature microgametocyte.

Reproduced with permission from the Manual for the Microscopical Diagnosis of Malaria in Man, National Institutes of Health Bulletin No. 180. (By Aimee Wilcox.)

PLATE VI

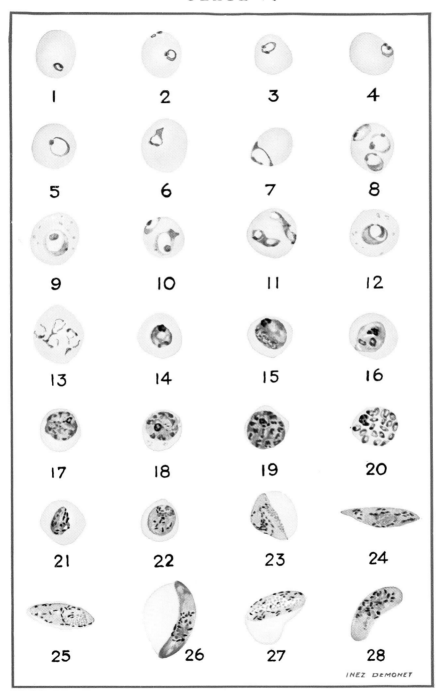

INEZ DEMONET

PLATE VII

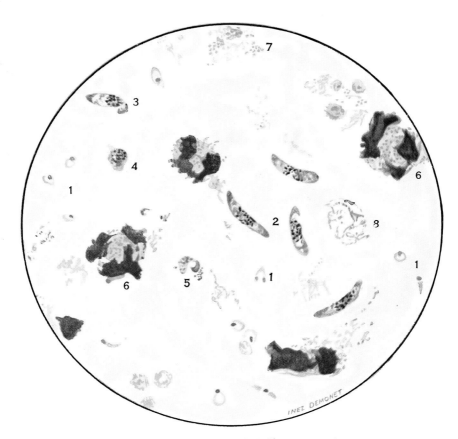

Plasmodium falciparum, thick-film preparation.

The film contains numerous ring-stage trophozoites, 5 normal gametocytes, one rounded-up and one degenerate gametocyte, leukocytes, blood platelets and remains of red cell stroma.

1. Small trophozoites. 2. Gametocytes—normal. 3. Slightly distorted gametocyte. 4. "Rounded-up" gametocyte. 5. Disintegrated gametocyte. 6. Nucleus of leukocyte. 7. Blood platelets. 8. Cellular remains of young erythrocyte. (From Wilcox's Manual of Microscopical Diagnosis of Malaria in Man, courtesy National Institutes of Health.)

LEGEND FOR PLATE VIII—*P. malariæ*

1. Young ring-form trophozoite of quartan malaria.
2, 3, 4. Young trophozoite forms of the parasite showing gradual increase of chromatin and cytoplasm.
5. Developing ring-form trophozoite showing pigment granule.
6. Early band-form trophozoite—elongated chromatin, some pigment apparent.
7, 8, 9, 10, 11, 12. Some forms which the developing trophozoite of quartan may take.
13, 14. Mature trophozoites—one a band-form.
15, 16, 17, 18, 19. Phases in the development of the schizont ("presegmenting schizonts").
20. Mature schizont.
21. Immature microgametocyte.
22. Immature macrogametocyte.
23. Mature microgametocyte.
24. Mature macrogametocyte.

Reproduced with permission from the Manual for the Microscopical Diagnosis of malaria in Man, National Institutes of Health Bulletin No. 180. (By Aimee Wilcox.)

PLATE VIII

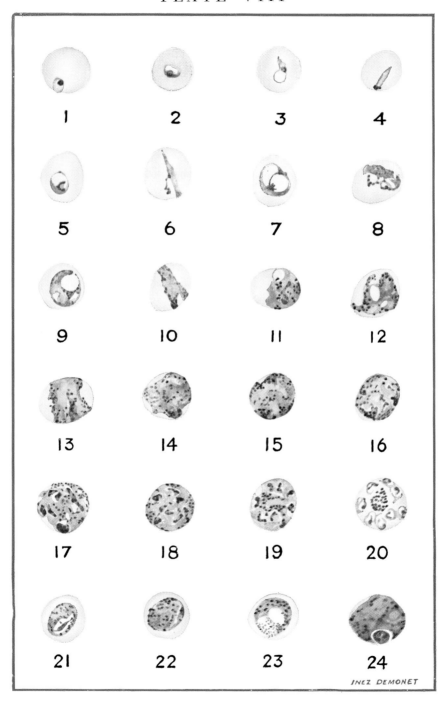

INEZ DEMONET

PLATE IX

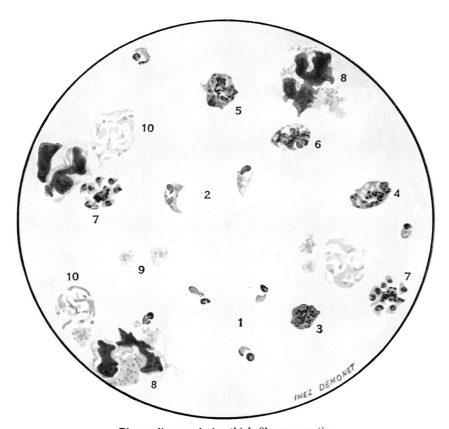

Plasmodium malariæ, thick-film preparation.

The film contains young and developing trophozoites, mature trophozoites, young and mature schizonts, neutrophilic leukocytes, blood platelets and remains of red cell stroma.
1. Small trophozoites. 2. Growing trophozoites. 3. Mature trophozoites. 4, 5, 6. Schizonts (presegmenting) with varying numbers of divisions of the chromatin. 7, Mature schizonts. 8. Nucleus of leukocyte. 9. Blood platelets. 10. Cellular remains of young erythrocytes. (From Wilcox's Manual of Microscopical Diagnosis of Malaria in Man, courtesy, National Institutes of Health.)

THE SPECIES OF PLASMODIA PRODUCING HUMAN MALARIA

Plasmodium vivax (Grassi and Feletti, 1890) Labbé, 1899

Plasmodium vivax is the most widely distributed of all the malaria parasites of man and in cooler climates is the only indigenous species.

Stages of P. vivax in the Human Host.—These consist of (1) the sporozoite introduced into the skin by the "bite" of the infected mosquito, (2) preerythrocytic schizogony, (3) asexual forms in the red blood cells and (4) gametocytes in the red corpuscles.

The Sporozoite.—This stage is a minute, motile, spindle-shaped object with rather blunt ends, measuring approximately 15 microns long by 1 micron in mid-diameter, which is injected by the mosquito into the cutaneous blood vessels and remains in the circulation not longer than 30 minutes.

Pre-erythrocytic Development.—The sporozoite enters a parenchyma cell of the liver, where it transforms into a trophozoite. By the eighth day it has grown to 42 microns in diameter and has produced more than 10,000 merozoites (Fig. 47). On rupture of the parasitized host cell some of the freed merozoites gain access to the blood stream and enter red blood cells, to initiate erythrocytic infection. In *vivax* malaria, likewise *malariæ* and *ovale* infections, some of the first brood of preërythrocytic merozoites enter other hepatic cells, to continue the exoërythrocytic focus.

Asexual Infection in the Red Blood Cells (Plate IV).—Once a merozoite has entered a red blood cell it transforms into the young trophozoite, containing a large vacuole and a distinct nuclear mass on one margin, the so-called "signet ring" stage. The ring rapidly enlarges, its cytoplasm develops ameboid movement and increases as it grows in size at the expense of the red cell. The iron component of the hemoglobin is deposited within the cytoplasm of the parasite as hematin ("malaria pigment"), in the form of delicate granules having a yellowish sheen. Meanwhile the red cell swells and becomes paler and in Giemsa- or Wright-stained thin blood films minute dots, the Schüffner's granules, are detected within the uninfected stroma of the red cells. Soon the ameboid outline of the growing parasite becomes its most conspicuous feature.

By the 36th hour practically all of the swollen host cell is occupied by the parasite, which becomes irregularly rounded and as a maturing schizont proceeds to segment into 12 to 24 merozoites arranged rather irregularly in rosetted pattern around a central mass of hematin.

Shortly before the 48th hour the merozoites break out of the host cell and are temporarily free in the plasma. Soon they actively enter uninfected red blood cells and initiate a replication of the asexual process. Repeated asexual production of the parasites builds up the parasitemia, with corresponding reduction of circulating red blood cells. Typically, however, there is host response to parasite activity consisting of phagocytosis of the free merozoites and even some of the parasitized red cells, so that decreased destruction of erythrocytes now results, and after several asexual cycles the primary parasitemia is temporarily terminated. After a period of weeks in tropical-strain infections or months in temperate-zone strains, parasitemia again develops, due to a new supply of merozoites released from exoërythrocytic foci.

Gametocyte Production (Plate IV).—The gametocytes are believed to develop from merozoites produced in exo-erythrocytic fixed-tissue cells. They first appear in the circulation as solid rounded parasites within swollen, pale red cells. Schüffner's granules are already present in the unparasitized stroma of the red cell. As the gametocytes grow they retain a rounded contour and do not exhibit ameboid activity. When fully developed, the male (microgrametocyte) has a diffuse cytoplasm and a rather loose skein of nuclear chromatin typically lying within a hyaline vacuole; and the hematin pigment is scattered throughout the cytoplasm. The mature female (macrogametocyte) has denser cytoplasm, a solid nucleus and little if any hyaline area around it. The hematin pigment is arranged in small agglomerations or in a wreath-like configuration near the margin of the cytoplasm. These mature gametocytes constitute the stage of transfer to the mosquito host.

Thick Blood Films.—In well-stained, thick films prepared by Giemsa's or Field's technic (see TECHNICAL AIDS, pages 432–433), malaria parasites are condensed or shrunken. Likewise, the films have been dehemoglobinized so that red-cell boundaries are not apparent (Plate V). Special training is therefore required for thick-blood film diagnosis (Field and LeFleming, 1939–1941).

Young trophozoites (ring forms) of *Plasmodium vivax* may appear as "normal" unbroken rings, considerably smaller than in thin films. More usually they look like interrupted partial rings, with a distinct chromatin dot but with the cytoplasm broken into several fragments; or with the cytoplasm as a solid mass, with the chromatin in the center and the cytoplasm on either side. More mature trophozoites have a larger chromatin body, more substantial cytoplasm and the characteristic hematin pigment of *P. vivax*. The *schizonts* likewise in their early segmentation have substantial cytoplasm and hematin pigment and two to several deeply red chromatin masses. Ripe schizonts have 12 to 24 merozoites arranged around the mass of hematin granules.

The young *gametocytes* are usually as large as late trophozoites, have a more continuous cytoplasm and more hematin pigment. Older gametocytes may be very irregular in outline, with dispersed cytoplasm, but have a wealth of characteristic hematin pigment.

Since the hemoglobin of the red blood cells has been dissolved, there will be no Schüffner's granules to help confirm the diagnosis and no opportunity to compare the size or color index of parasitized and uninfected cells.

Plasmodium falciparum (Welch, 1897) Schaudinn, 1902

(Causing falciparum, tropical, malignant tertian, estivo-autumnal malaria)

Plasmodium falciparum is essentially limited to warm climates.

The stages of *P. falciparum* in the human host are: (1) the entering sporozoite, (2) the preërythrocytic schizont, (3) asexual forms in the red blood cells, and (4) gametocytes developing in the red blood cells.

The Sporozoite.—This stage of *P. falciparum* resembles the sporozoite of *P. vivax*, although it is more slender, more pointed at the ends and more swollen in the center around the nuclear mass.

Pre-erythrocytic Development.—In approximately 30 minutes after inoculation the sporozoites disappear from circulating blood. The first fixed-tissue infection discovered in human volunteers submitted to sporozoite inoculations has been on the third day (Jeffery *et al.*, 1952), in the parenchyma cells of the liver. By the sixth day the trophozoite has grown to 60 microns in diameter and has produced about 40,000 merozoites. Except for the somewhat shorter time required for development and ripening of the trophozoite into a mature schizont, pre-erythrocytic development in *falciparum* infection closely parallels that of *P. vivax*. However, probably only one brood of merozoites is discharged by exoërythrocytic schizonts, after which residual infection is maintained by erythrocytic parasites.

Asexual Infection in Red Blood Cells (Plate VI).—The first appearance of *P. falciparum* in circulating blood is on the seventh day following sporozoite inoculation, (Jeffery *et al.*, 1952). The earliest stage of the red-cell parasite is a very minute oval or circular ring with a distinct nuclear dot on one side and a very delicate rim of cytoplasm surrounding the vacuole. Frequently the young *falciparum* parasite is found as a blister (appliqué form) on the margin of the red cell just under the cell membrane, with the nuclear dot producing a minute median bulge on the external aspect. Various stages of binary nuclear division in the ring stage of the trophozoite can often be observed, followed by binary fission of the cytoplasm to form two ring-stage parasites. As the rings enlarge they develop a small cytoplasmic bib. There is typically no ameboid movement of the cytoplasm in the falciparum ring.

Later stages of the *falciparum* trophozoite and the stages of schizogony typically develop only in visceral blood. The trophozoite continues to grow as an oval or rounded body, with relative decrease in size of the vacuole, never occupying a major portion of the area of the red cell, nor does it cause a swelling or appreciable reduction in the color value of the residual stroma. Moreover, there is no granular staining reaction of the uninfected portion of the parasitized red cell such as Schüffner's granules of *vivax* and *ovale* infections.

Schizogony usually begins about 24 hours after infection of the red cell and continues during the next 12 to 24 hours, with a total production of 8 to 36 (average 18 to 24) minute merozoites arranged in a rosetted pattern around a hematin pigment center.

Escape of the merozoites from a ruptured cell, their short existence free in the blood plasma and their entry into uninfected red cells typically occur in visceral blood. One asexual erythrocytic development commonly requires 36 to 48 hours.

Gametocyte Production (Plate VI).—The immature gametocytes are seldom seen in peripheral blood. They are rounded or oval, with distinct cell membranes. Somewhat later when they appear in the circulation they are jelly-bean-shaped, then as they mature they become crescentic, tending to occupy one side of a considerably distended red cell. Finally the red cell membrane becomes only a thin, almost transparent veil which can be observed clearly on the concave side of the parasite, and when fully ripe the gametocyte may slip out of this envelope.

Immature gametocytes of *P. falciparum* are sexually indistinguishable, but the mature cells are readily differentiated. The microgametocytes have delicate diffuse nuclear chromatin and diffuse hematin, and the macrogametocytes a more condensed nucleus and compact mass of hematin. The female is typically longer, with more narrowly rounded ends, and the male, shorter, more reniform.

Thick Blood Films.—Although the asexual stages of *Plasmodium falciparum* are the smallest of the three common species of malaria parasites, they are the most readily recognized and diagnosed in thick films. (Plate VII.) The young trophozoite is a completed or partial azure-stained ring and the chromatin dot takes an intensely deep-red stain. In placental blood the mature trophozoites tend to become an irregular solid mass with obliteration of the vacuole, and a moderately large deep-red dot of chromatin which is eccentric in position. The schizonts consist of dense masses of purplish-red chromatin surrounded by one common or individual cytoplasmic envelopes. The hematin pigment is readily recognized as a few grains or one small mass of dark metallic material. The mature gametocytes ("crescents") are frequently as characteristic as in thin films. All have a wealth of hematin pigment, which is either dispersed (male) or clumped together (female).

Plasmodium malariæ (Laveran, 1881) Grassi and Feletti, 1890
(causing quartan malaria)

Plasmodium malariæ is probably the species which Laveran first observed and studied. It is much less frequently seen than *P. vivax* and *P. falciparum* and is rarely dominant in a malarious region.

The stages of *P. maloriæ* in the human host are: (1) the entering sporozoite, (2) the preërythrocytic schizont, (3) successive exoërythrocytic and erythrocytic schizonts, and (4) gametocyte development in red blood cells.

The Sporozoite.—This resembles the sporozoite of *P. vivax* and *P. falciparum* but is somewhat coarser in appearance.

Pre-erythrocytic Development.—This has been demonstrated by Bray (1959) in Liberia, employing a human strain of *P. malariæ* passed through *Anopheles gambiæ*, followed by sporozoite inoculation of chimpanzees. Development of trophozoites into mature schizonts in parenchyma cells of the liver requires about 11 days, with production of about 2000 primary merozoites. As in *vivax* infection, that with *malariæ* indicates continued exoërythrocytic schizogony in the hepatic foci.

Asexual Infection in Red Blood Cells (Plate VIII).—The erythrocytic asexual development of *P. malariæ* is exactly synchronized, with replication every 72 hours. The earliest trophozoite is small, ovoidal or ring-like, with very little ameboid activity. It is smaller, more compact and utilizes less hemoglobin than *P. vivax*. As it enlarges, it ranges in morphology from broadly oval to delicate or broad band-form extending across the entire diameter of the parasitized red cell. The fully developed trophozoite never quite fills the unswollen red cell, which may manifest a slightly dusky hue.

The hematin pigment is dark, usually coarse and gradually accumulates in a dark greenish-black mass in the center of the trophozoite.

Schizogony results in 8 or 9 (6 to 12) nuclear centers, around each of which there is a small oval envelope of cytoplasm. These merzooites are arranged fairly symmetrically around a mass of hematin granules. On maturity the merozoites break out of the parasitized red cells and after a short, free interval in the blood plasma invade other red cells.

Gametocyte Production (Plate VIII).—The immature mother sex cells of *P. malariæ* bear a general resemblance to those of *P. vivax* but are smaller and are more compact. When they reach maturity their size is never as great as the normal red blood corpuscle and the parasitized cell is not enlarged. The ripe microgametocyte is rounded, has relatively pale cytoplasm, diffuse hematin granules, and an oval aggregation of nuclear chromatin dots. The ripe macrogametocyte has denser cytoplasm, frequently more concentrated coarse hematin granules, and a dense subspherical nucleus in the midst of a vacuole.

Thick Blood Films.—On the whole, thick films of *Plasmodium malariæ* are more readily diagnosed than are those of *P. vivax* because the plasmodia have more continuous cytoplasm and appear less shrunken. (Plate IX.) Early *trophozoites* usually have a relatively regular subspherical cytoplasm in which the chromatin mass lies to one side. More mature trophozoites are solid, rather regular masses, with a few distinct dots of hematin pigment and an identifiable eccentric chromatin mass. Young *schizonts* are difficult to identify as such because their chromatin masses are poorly defined. The ripe schizonts almost always consist of distinct merozoites massed around a hematin center. The *gametocytes* are characterized as small compact bodies, with undivided chromatin masses in the female, granular dispersed chromatin in the male, and always a wealth of characteristic hematin pigment.

Plasmodium ovale Stephens, 1922

Stephens (1922) gave this plasmodium species identity on the basis of the enlarged, irregularly oval distortion of many of the parasitized red cells.

All of the stages which develop in the human host in the exoërythrocytic foci and red blood cells in the case of *P. vivax* and *P. malariæ* are also found in *P. ovale*.

Sporozoite and Pre-erythrocytic Stages.—Garnham *et al.* (1954) demonstrated pre-erythrocytic schizonts in the parenchyma cells of the liver of a human volunteer 9 days after *P. ovale*-infected mosquitoes fed on the subject.

Asexual Infection in Red Blood Cells.—In certain respects this phase of the cycle of *P. ovale* resembles *P. vivax*; in other characters it is more like *P. malariæ*. The asexual erythrocytic cycle requires 48 hours. The unparasitized portion of the infected red blood corpuscle (Fig. 49) exhibits Schüffner's stippling to an even more marked degree than it does in *P. vivax*. The young trophozoite is ring-formed, with a condensed nuclear mass but cytoplasm which is more compact than that of *P. vivax*. The vacuole is

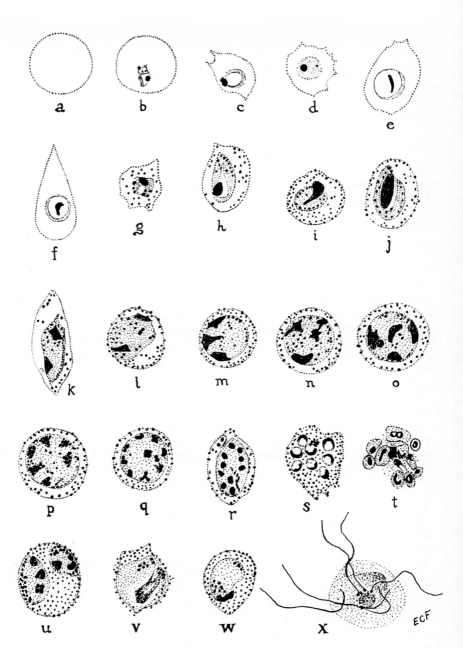

Fig. 49.—*Plasmodium ovale* in thin-blood films. *a*, uninfected red blood cell for comparison with *ovale*-infected cells; *b–j*, stages in development of the trophozoite, showing oval and irregular contours of many parasitized cells; *k–s*, developing schizont; *t*, merozoites which have escaped from exhausted red blood cell; *u*, 2 developing schizonts in one red cell; *v*, mature male gametocyte (microgametocyte); *w*, mature female gametocyte (macrogametocyte); *x*, exflagellation (maturation) of the microgametocyte, with production of about six microgametes. *g* through *w* show Schüffner's granules in the unparasitized stroma of the parasitized red cell. (Original adaptations; *b–r* and *t*, after Stephens and Owen, *s* and *u–x*, after James, Nicol and Shute.)

frequently less conspicuous and there is lack of ameboid movement. Occasionally two plasmodia develop in the same red cell.

As the trophozoite grows it continues to be relatively condensed like *P. malariæ*; it is frequently rounded, at times distinctly oval or elongated but not typically band-form. Meanwhile many of the parasitized red cells become oval in contour, or even tear-drop-shaped, and at times have one to several sharp projections. The red cell may be normal in size or somewhat swollen but is not appreciably paler than normal. The hematin pigment is relatively scant and of a light brown color. When schizogony is initiated the nucleus divides until a relatively small number of chromatin masses (6 to 12, usually 8) are produced, as in *P. malariæ*. The mature schizont is rounded or oval and nearly fills the infected red cell. The hematin granules are concentrated in a single central mass, around which the maturing and mature merozoites are irregularly arranged. The ripe merozoites are irregularly oval, relatively large, and their nuclei have a tendency to be lenticular or vacuolated.

Gametocyte Production.—The gametocytes in the red blood corpuscles (Fig. 49) are very much like those of *P. malariæ*, are rounded in outline, are compact, and have similar staining reaction; but they can readily be differentiated in thin blood films by the presence of Schüffner's granules in the host cell. Differentiation from the same stage of *P. vivax* has to be made on the smaller, more compact character of *P. ovale*.

Thick Blood Films.—Although these films effectively concentrate *P. ovale*, by employing thick films it is practically impossible to differentiate these organisms from *P. malariæ*, since the shape of the parasitized cell and Schüffner's granules are not available to orient the diagnostician.

PATHOGENESIS AND SYMPTOMATOLOGY

During development of malaria parasites in exo-erythrocytic foci, the relatively small amount of tissue destruction is apparently insufficient to provoke systemic reaction or to evoke symptoms (Russell, 1952).

Pathogenesis.—The plasmodia which invade the red blood cells grow and segment at the expense of these host cells. As the number of parasites increases, the number of erythrocytes is decreased with each successive schizogony, owing not only to rupture of the parasitized cells but to lysis of non-parasitized cells. When the débris of the ruptured cells, together with the merozoites and their metabolic by-products, are set free into the blood stream, they stimulate chemo-receptors of the temperature-regulating mechanism of the host in order to conserve heat. At first the amount of pyrogen released at one time is not enough to produce a marked reaction, although it may cause prodromal symptoms (*vide infra*). As the number of invaded red cells increases and the asexual cycle of the parasites becomes more synchronized, the quantity of pyrogen becomes sufficient to produce the characteristic chills and fever of a malaria attack. The rapidity with which this process develops depends on the species of plasmodium and on the host's immunologic reaction to the invader. *Vivax* infection builds up rapidly, *ovale* about one half as fast and *malariæ* only about one-third as rapidly as *vivax*.

Falciparum infection differs from the other types in a number of respects. The schizogonic cycle in the blood stream requires not more than 48 hours but is frequently less synchronized. Moreover, in *P. falciparum* there is a tendency for more than one parasite, frequently several, to develop in a single red cell. Thus, in two or three asexual cycles the number of infected red cells frequently reaches a dangerous threshold, often without the production of a typical chill followed by fever. Likewise, *falciparum* parasites tend to adhere to one another and to vessel walls, causing blockage of blood capillaries in the brain, lungs, kidneys, etc., and hemostasis in the sinuses of the spleen, liver and bone marrow (Clark and Tomlinson, 1949).

With each successive escape of merozoites from ruptured red cells and discharge of necrotic red-cell débris into the plasma, there is new stimulus to humoral and cellular systemic reaction.

Destruction of the red blood corpuscles by the plasmodia produces an anemia which may be normocytic and normochromic or, in chronic and relapsing cases, may resemble pernicious anemia. In severe infections the number of erythrocytes may be reduced to one-fifth of normal. Except at the time of the paroxysms there is typically a leukopenia but with relative monocytosis (Kitchen, 1949). Moreover, agglutination of the parasitized red cells in *falciparum* infection and loss of plasma within the blood vessels in all types of malaria are responsible for so-called "sludging" of the corpuscular elements in the vessels. Thus, there is (1) a progressive decrease in the number and quality of circulating erythrocytes, with corresponding reducing in oxygen conveyance, hence oxygen starvation of the tissues, (2) multiple thrombosis in the smaller blood vessels, and (3) progressive decrease in circulating blood volume (Maegraith, Jones and Andrews, 1951). Additionally, hypersensitization on cyclic discharge of merozoites and necrotic remains of destroyed red cells at times causes serum anaphylaxis.

The infected red cells and metabolic débris are phagocytized by cells of the reticuloendothelial system, and accumulate in the sinuses of the spleen, liver and bone marrow. The *spleen* is typically enlarged, congested, soft and hemorrhagic in the acute primary stage, hard in the chronic stage. Its color darkens as the amount of hematin increases. In chronic *vivax infection* the organ may weigh as much as a kilogram, and in chronic *falciparum* infection between 300 and 700 grams (Ash and Spitz, 1945). The *liver* is hypertrophic and congested in acute malaria and its color index is greater than normal. As the infection becomes chronic the organ becomes firmer in consistency but not cirrhotic. The *bone marrow* undergoes the same changes as the spleen but to a lesser degree. The *kidneys* are congested, the glomerular capillaries become thrombotic with accumulation of parasitized red cells, free hematin and wandering macrophages, and may rupture to produce multiple extravasations. The *adrenals* may also be damaged by hemorrhage or affected by the general toxemia. The *pulmonary capillaries* partake of the same congestive process. All *mucous membranes* may exhibit petechial hemorrhage. The *heart* also suffers from the embolic blockage of the coronary vessels, and is embarrassed by oxygen want (Ash and Spitz, 1945). The *placenta* in *falciparum* malaria manifests a remarkable concentration of plasmodia in all stages of their development in the red cells of the relatively slow-moving blood in the maternal blood sinuses.

Symptomatology.—The *biological incubation period* for each of the four species of plasmodia which are natural parasites of man has been provided earlier in this Chapter (p. 101). (Consult p. 105 for *Plasmodium vivax*; p. 107 for *P. falciparum*; p. 108 for *P. malariæ*, and p. 109 for *P. ovale*.) As soon as the plasmodia can be detected in thick films of peripheral blood, patent infection (*viz.*, parasitemia) is initiated. For one to several days thereafter, during which one or more asexual erythrocytic multiplications have taken place and synchronization of schizogony is being accomplished, there are no distinctive manifestations of the disease, although during the latter part of this *prodromal period* there is usually a slight elevation of temperature and the patient may experience malaise. When a sufficient number of parasitized erythrocytes are simultaneously ruptured a definite febrile episode ensues.

The Malaria Paroxysm.—Primary overt *vivax, ovale* or *quartan* malaria characteristically develops suddenly with a shaking chill (and rigor in vivax infection), followed by a fever of 40° to 40.6° C. (104° to 105° F.), accompanied by evidences of an acute febrile disease, such as headache, muscular pains, malaise, nausea and vomiting, abdominal pain, and increased pulse and respiration rates. After continuing for several hours the fever terminates by crisis and there is a drenching sweat. Thereafter the patient is exhausted but feels marked relief. In *falciparum* infection the initial chill is usually less pronounced and the fever more prolonged. Much more frequently than in the other types, *falciparum* malaria is accompanied by pernicious manifestations, which may consist of coma, convulsions or cardiac failure, and there may be no remarkable rise in temperature.

Following an essentially symptomless remission which varies with the species, there is a second paroxysm of essentially equal intensity, followed by several additional ones of somewhat lesser magnitude extending over a period up to 3 weeks or more before the symptoms are terminated. *This series of paroxysms constitutes the primary attack.*

Relapse.—Following the termination of the primary attack, parasites may completely disappear from the blood. In *falciparum* malaria this constitutes cure, since in *falciparum* infection exoërythrocytic development does not persist. In the other three types of malaria one to several more attacks, *i.e., relapses*, characteristically occur. Relapses of vivax malaria usually continue over a period of 2 to 3 years before the infection is terminated; those of *quartan* malaria may develop many years after the primary attack.

Complications in Malaria.—*Vivax* and *quartan* malaria do not usually cause complications. *Falciparum* malaria, on the other hand, is prone to produce serious complications, particularly in infants. The signs and symptoms vary depending on the organs most affected by tissue anoxia, *i.e.,* cerebral, gastrointestinal, hyperpyretic, and algid. In cerebral malaria due to falciparum infection there may be a sudden primary onset with hyperpyrexia, convulsions, deepening coma, and often death resulting from shock and anoxia. Gastro-intestinal malaria is responsible principally for

8

vomiting and diarrhea. Hyperpyrexia in falciparum infection mimics that of heat stroke. Algid malaria is characterized by vascular collapse and shock.

Malaria in Hyperendemic Areas.—In populations living in highly malarious areas and subject to periodic reëxposure throughout life, typical overt manifestations are observed only in the young; they are the subjects from whom the true malaria index of the community should be obtained on the basis of parasitemia and the degree of splenic enlargement. Older children and adults who have survived earlier attacks have developed considerable tolerance to the disease. They are the ones with the hardened, enlarged spleen.

Blackwater Fever (Hemoglobinuric Fever).—This is an acute clinical episode complicating *falciparum* malaria. Although it frequently occurs only after repeated exposure to this parasite, it may be precipitated within a few weeks following a primary paroxysm (Ash and Spitz, 1945). Typically within a few days of onset there are severe chills, with rigor, high fever, jaundice, vomiting, rapidly progressive anemia, and the passage of dark-red or black urine. Hemoglobinuria occurs only in persons who have lived in areas where *falciparum* infection abounds; likewise this disease is most common during the *falciparum* season. It tends to develop in malaria patients who have been subject to unusual amounts of fatigue, privation, exposure, exhaustion, shock or injury, intercurrent infection, childbirth or alcoholic excess (Salisbury, 1949), and who have received inadequate treatment with quinine.

The most conspicuous feature of this disease is the massive hemolysis and the release of hemoglobin by the glomeruli into the urine. The most tenable explanation of blackwater fever is an immune reaction with uncontrolled production of hemolysin.

DIAGNOSIS AND TREATMENT

Diagnosis.—Malaria is frequently confused with other diseases which simulate malaria in the production of chills and fever. On the other hand, the typical paroxysm may be lacking in malaria.

Clinical Diagnosis.—After a typical primary or relapsed attack has gotten under way and two or three regularly spaced paroxysms have been experienced by the patient there is some justification for making a presumptive diagnosis of malaria. In *bona fide* malaria, blood-film examination at the time of the first paroxysm will confirm the diagnosis by demonstration of parasites, will save the patient several days of suffering and in the case of pernicious *falciparum* infection may prevent fatal outcome. However, a history of "chills and fever" is likely to lead to a clinical misdiagnosis of malaria and to antimalarial therapy, whereas many other diseases produce a similar picture. Only if laboratory diagnosis is not available is there a reasonable excuse for undertaking a therapeutic test.

Laboratory Diagnosis.—Since the malaria paroxysms are due to the release of plasmodial merozoites at the end of each period of schizogony, blood films taken just before, or at the height of the malarial paroxysm will contain a detectable number of the parasites. If the films are made during afebrile intervals there will be fewer or no parasites in the red cells. However, once the infection becomes chronic, both trophozoites and gametocytes may at times be found in the blood of persons presenting no particular symptoms. Parasites are not likely to be circulating in the blood during suppressive therapy, immediately following curative treatment, or soon after self-medication with anti-malarial drugs.

While thin-blood films are valuable for studying the morphologic characters of different asexual and gametocyte stages of the different species of plasmodia, thick-blood films are almost invariably employed for diagnosis. In a smaller area on the microscopic slide the thick film allows rapid examination of a much larger volume of blood, thus saving valuable time.

Staining of thick-blood films is carried out according to the Giemsa or Field technic. (See TECHNICAL AIDS, pages 432–433). Description of the three common malaria parasites and illustrations indicating their appearance in thick-blood films have been included in a preceding section of this chapter (for *Plasmodium vivax*, page 106, Plate V; for *P. falciparum*, page 106, Plate VII, and for *P. malariæ*, page 109, Plate IX). Thick films of *P. ovale* provide comparable concentration of the parasites, but without Schüffner's granules and the bizarre outlines of infected red cells it is difficult to distinguish this species from *P. malariæ*.

Comparative information on the differential diagnostic characters of the four malaria parasites of man is found in the accompanying table (Table 3).

Treatment.—Antimalarial drugs may be used for the following purposes: (1) treatment of the malarious attack, (2) suppression, (3) prophylaxis, (4) interference with transmission to other persons. Drugs which are capable of destroying some stages of one species of *Plasmodium* are ineffective against other stages or other species. The efficacy of a drug in accomplishing the above objectives depends on its spectrum of activity.

Treatment of the Malarious Attack.—In treating the patient who is suffering from an attack of malaria it is desired to provide as rapid and certain relief as possible from the miseries and perils that accompany the erythrocytic infection. At present chloroquine and amodiaquin are the most effective drugs available for this purpose. These drugs are usually given orally, but parenteral preparations are available for use in comatose or vomiting patients. Pyrimethamine and chlorguanide eradicate the parasites, but since they act primarily against the schizont, their action may be delayed. Chloroquine and amodiaquin have no effect against the exoërythrocytic parasites.

Suppression.—Malaria suppression is the administration of a drug to clinically well persons for the purpose of preventing or postponing attacks of malaria, although infection is not prevented. Drugs which destroy the erythrocytic parasites are used, including chloroquine, amodiaquin, pyrimethamine and chlorguanide. After a variable period following the termination of suppression of vivax, quartan or ovale malaria a delayed primary attack may occur, since the exoërythrocytic forms are not affected by the drugs. Delayed primary attacks do not occur in falciparum malaria because the exoërythrocytic forms do not persist. Furthermore pyrimethamine and probably chlorguanide are capable of destroying falciparum exoërythrocytic parasites (see Table 7, page 418).

Table 3.—The Differential Characters of the Malaria Parasites of Man (Giemsa-Stained Thin Films)

(Adapted from Faust and Russell's *Clinical Parasitology*, 1957.)

	Plasmodium vivax	Plasmodium malariæ	Plasmodium falciparum	Plasmodium ovale
Duration of schizogony	48 hours	72 hours	36 to 48 hours	48 hours
Motility	Active ameboid until about half-grown	Slightly ameboid during trophozoite stage	Seldom ameboid during trophozoite stage	Slightly ameboid during trophozoite stage
Pigment (Hematin)	Yellowish-brown, in fine grains and minute rodlets, irregularly scattered	Dark brown or almost black in coarse grains, rods, or irregular small clumps	Very dark brown or black in coarse granules or small masses	Dark brown in coarse granules or irregular masses
Stages of development seen in peripheral blood	Trophozoites, schizonts and gametocytes	Trophozoites, schizonts and gametocytes	Usually only trophozoites and gametocytes. In pernicious infections rarely schizonts may be seen	Trophozoites, schizonts and gametocytes
Multiple infection of red blood corpuscle	Quite common	Very rare	Very common	Rare
Character of infected red blood cell occupied by fully developed schizont	Entire red blood cell enlarged and pale; Schüffner's dots usually present	Red blood cell not enlarged, often has dusky hue	Red blood cell not enlarged	Red blood cell enlarged, pale; Schüffner's dots characteristic
Trophozoites (ring-forms)	Small and large rings with vacuole and usually one chromatin dot. Ameboid	Small and large rings with vacuole and usually one chromatin dot; or early "band" forms; compact	Very small and larger rings with vacuole and frequently with 2 chromatin dots. Peripheral forms common. (Forms appliqué.)	Small and large rings with vacuole; compact

Segmenting schizonts	Irregular, bizarre forms. Vacuole present in early stage. Chromatin in fine grains or small irregular clumps	Oval or round, with vacuole in early stage. Chromatin in coarse granules or irregular clumps. Band forms often seen	Not usually seen in peripheral blood. Oval or round with chromatin in large granules and in small clumps	Round and oval with vacuole in early stage. Chromatin in irregular clumps or filamentous masses
Segmented schizonts	Fill greatly enlarged red blood corpuscle. 12 to 24 merozoites (usually 18 to 20) irregularly arranged about a mass of pigment	Almost fill a normal sized red blood corpuscle. 6 to 12 merozoites (usually 8 to 10) arranged like the petals of a flower surrounding a central pigment mass	Not usually seen in peripheral blood. Fill two-thirds to three-quarters of red blood corpuscle. 8 to 36 merozoites (usually 18 to 24) arranged about a central pigment mass	Fill about three-quarters of red blood corpuscle. 6 to 12 merozoites arranged about a central or eccentric pigment mass
Gametocytes	Round and fill the enlarged red blood corpuscle. Chromatin undistributed in cytoplasm. Cytoplasm in microgametocyte light blue, in macrogametocyte dark blue	Round and fill the normal sized red blood corpuscle. Chromatin undistributed in cytoplasm	Crescentic or kidney-bean in shape. Usually appear free in blood. Chromatin undistributed in cytoplasm of microgametocyte, more compact in macrogametocyte	Round and fill about three-quarters of the enlarged red blood corpuscle. Chromatin undistributed in cytoplasm

Prophylaxis.—True causal prophylaxis of malaria would imply the destruction of sporozoites as they enter the body. No drug yet available is capable of this objective. On the other hand, since the exoërythrocytic development of the parasites produces no detectable disease, for practical purposes a drug which destroys the exoërythrocytic forms may be considered prophylactic. Thus pyrimethamine may be used for prophylaxis of falciparum malaria. Primaquine destroys the exoërythrocytic forms of vivax, ovale and quartan infections, and so may be used for prophylaxis, but is not useful in the treatment of the attack.

Interference with Transmission.—When pyrimethamine is administered to a patient who has gametocytes of *P. falciparum* in his blood, these parasites may be eradicated, or if not destroyed, they fail to produce normally developing oöcysts in the stomach of the *Anopheles* mosquito. Primaquine eliminates *falciparum* gametocytes from the blood. Thus, either of these drugs may be given to a patient carrying *falciparum* gametocytes to cause interference with the transmission of his infection to other persons.

Strains of malaria may develop resistance to chloroquine, amodiaquin, pyrimethamine or chlorguanide, especially the latter two drugs. Primaquine has the disadvantage of causing hemolysis, especially in Negroes, when given in excessive amounts. If administered in suboptimal amounts, vivax parasites develop resistance to primaquine, so that tolerated doses fail to control the parasitemia or fever (Arnold *et al.*, 1961).

For *clinical attacks of malaria* (all species of *Plasmodium* which parasitize man), the recommendations for treatment are as follows: (*a*) *chloroquine phosphate*, orally, 1 Gm. immediately, then 500 mgm. in 6 hours, and 500 mg. on the 2nd and 3rd days; or (*b*) *amodiaquin hydrochloride*, orally, 780 mgm. (600 mg. base) immediately, followed by 520 mgm. (400 mgm. base) on the 2nd and 3rd days.

For *suppressive treatment*, (*a*) *chloroquine phosphate*, orally, 500 mgm. weekly during period of exposure; or (*b*) *amodiaquin hydrochloride*, orally, 520 mgm. (400 mgm. base) every 2 weeks during period of exposure; or *pyrimethamine*, orally, 25 mgm. (base) weekly during period of exposure.

For *prophylaxis and interference with transmission:* (*a*) for *Plasmodium falciparum*, *pyrimethamine*, in suppressive doses; (*b*) for the other 3 species of plasmodia of man, *primaquine phosphate*, orally, 26.3 mgm. (15 mgm. base) daily, for 14 days, to be administered following clinical treatment or beginning 1 to 2 weeks before completion of suppressive treatment.

In holoëndemic areas of malaria smaller amounts of chloroquine may be adequate for treating clinical attacks and for suppressive purposes (Clyde, 1961). On the other hand, recommended doses of chloroquine may occasionally fail to eradicate *falciparum* infection (Moore and Lanier, 1961).

Epidemiology.—The epidemiology of human malaria comprehends basic information on the etiologic agents in man and *Anopheles* mosquitoes. Occasionally malaria is transmitted by transfusion of whole blood from an infected donor, or from one drug addict to another through use of a common hypodermic needle.

The Etiologic Agents.—Different strains of the same species differ in virulence and in their relationship to relapse. Tropical strains of *Plas-*

modium vivax are likely to relapse much earlier than those originating in temperate regions; they also have a tendency to produce more relapses. *P. malariæ* is much slower in development but is more difficult to eradicate, In contrast, *P. falciparum*, the most dangerous of all the malaria parasites of man, has only a moderate tendency to relapse and is eradicable by use of modern drugs which destroy only the erythrocytic parasites of *P. vivax*, *P. malariæ* and *P. ovale*.

All species of human malaria parasites are capable of producing infection in all species of *Anopheles* mosquitoes which are satisfactory hosts of any of these plasmodia.

Factors Relating to the Human Host.—No race of mankind is naturally immune to infection with any of the four species of malaria parasites but races develop considerable tolerance to the parasite to which they have been exposed. Infants and other young children in endemic areas are highly susceptible. There is no difference in susceptibility with respect to sex. Persons whose occupation brings them in contact with infected mosquitoes are more liable to infection than others.

Malaria is more commonly hyperendemic in tropical than in temperate climates, yet within each area there may be zones of hyperendemicity and nonmalariousness, even near one another.

There is no demonstrated proof of natural immunity. Whatever immunity exists results from previous exposure.

Other Factors in the Human Host.—These include the stages of the parasite in the patient's circulating blood and the number of infected individuals in a community. Transmission requires gametocytes of both sexes in the proper stage of ripeness in the circulating blood, and in sufficient numbers. The vitality of the gametocytes is also critical and this will vary from individual to individual patient, at different times during the infection and probably also with the virulence of the strain of plasmodium.

Persons in whom gametocytes are commonly circulating in peripheral blood over a considerable period of time are *carriers* who constitute a continuing danger to the community. Malaria is frequently introduced into a non-malarious community by one or more gametocyte carriers who have acquired the infection in an endemic area. *Anopheles* mosquitoes acquire the infection from the carrier and pass it on to susceptible human beings.

Factors Relating to the Mosquito Host.—The breeding habits of different species of *Anopheles* mosquitoes differ widely: Some select quiet pools, some slowly moving irrigation ditches, others backwaters or seepage channels of mountain streams, still others brackish water along coastal plains and a few species breed in bromeliads in tropical jungles. The site chosen by an *Anopheles* for oviposition may be densely shaded or sunny, and it may be related to particular types of aquatic vegetation or plankton.

It is not uncommon for several species of *Anopheles* to occur in the same area. Only one is usually the dangerous transmitter, the others are of secondary importance. A few species are avid for human blood (*i.e.*, they are *anthropophilous*) while most species are less selective (*i.e.*, they are *zoöphilous*). The former are characteristically the human malaria transmitters and usually breed near human habitations. The most notorious malaria transmitter is *Anopheles gambiæ*, a native of tropical Africa. Other examples of anthopophilous species are *A. darlingi* of tropical America and *A. culicifacies* of India.

CONTROL

Control of malaria has as its main objective reduction of *Anopheles* below the transmission level (Boyd, 1949). The most dangerous species are those whichprefer human blood, since they are most apt to transmit the infection to man. The complementary line of attack is to prevent transmission of the plasmodia from man to mosquito by treatment of human infections, prophylactic chemotherapy, and protection of infected and uninfected populations from anopheline "bites."

Treatment of Human Infections.—Gametocytes are the stage for continuation of the cycle when ingested by the *Anopheles*. Thus, the dangerous patients are the gametocyte carriers.

Chloroquine, amodiaquin chlorguanide and pyrimethamine, even in suppressive doses, prevent the development of all erythrocytic stages of the *falciparum parasites* and effect their eradication, thus eliminating the source from which falciparum gametocytes are derived. In *vivax, quartan* and *ovale malaria,* none of the drugs valuable in terminating erythrocytic schizogony are particularly satisfactory against the exoërythrocytic foci, hence against their gametocyte production. In contrast, the 8-aminoquinoline, primaquine, is very effective in terminating exoërythrocytic infection and hence gametocyte production. Although pyrimethamine when administered in the amount of 50 mgm. weekly to a malaria-exposed population over a period of months is only suppressive, this method does prevent transmission during the period of administration (Gabaldon and Guerrero, 1959). Addition of chloroquine or pyrimethamine to salt consumed by persons in a malarious area has a similar effect (Coatney *et al.,* 1958). However, pyrimethamine tends to produce resistant strains of plasmodia (Young and Burgess, 1959; Burgess and Young, 1959.)

Protecting Gametocyte Carriers from Mosquitoes.—This includes the use of repellents on the uncovered areas of the skin, adequate screening of dwellings, bed nets, face nets and mosquito boots, all of which serve to keep the mosquito from direct contact with the skin.

Measures Directed against Adult Anopheles.—Adequate screening of homes and bed nets will greatly reduce exposure, and repellents will temporarily prevent these mosquitoes from alighting on the skin. Spraying of pyrethrum-DDT emulsion on the inside walls and in and around doors and windows of homes and adjacent buildings has many advantages over screening and repellent measures alone. Pyrethrum produces rapid "knockdown" of mosquitoes with which it comes in contact; DDT and other chlorinated hydrocarbons, acting more slowly, are lethal to the mosquito. However, *Anopheles* mosquitoes are developing resistance to these insecticides, or at least an avoidance reaction to residual particles of these toxicants on walls.

Measures Directed against Anopheles Breeding.—Malaria mosquitoes breed in quiet streams, pools, impounded bodies of water, irrigation canals, borrow pits, seepage channels, residual water from temporarily flooded plains, and swampy areas. Drainage, naturalistic technics (Williamson, 1949) and larvicidal measures have been employed to prevent such breeding.

Larvicidal control is the most universally applicable technic to reduce mosquito breeding. DDT or other chlorinated hydrocarbon, made up as a 5% concentrate in solvents with a detergent which serves as an emulsifier, acts as a contact and a stomach poison and is sprayed periodically on breeding sites by hand-compressor sprayer, by power sprayer or by airplane application over extensive areas such as swamps and tidal flats which can not be reached on foot or by land conveyance.

Conrol of malaria can not be effectively carried out without accurate epidemtologic information concerning the amount and kind of malaria in the comimunity, use of approved methods to determine the prevalence of the infection in the community and in the *Anopheles* vectors, the bionomics of their larval stages and of the adults. Coöperation of the native population should be developed by educational propaganda demonstrating the value of malaria control (Russell 1952).

THE SARCOSPORIDEA

Sarcocystis lindemanni Rivolta, 1878

The members of this group (Class Sarcosporidea) belong to a single genus, *Sarcocystis*, many described species of which parasitize the muscles of mammals, birds and reptiles. Wenyon (1926, p. 760) placed them under "Parasites of Undetermined Position." Nevertheless Kudo (1954) classifies

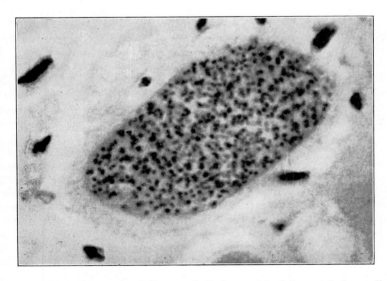

Fig. 50.—Photomicrograph of *Sarcocystis lindemanni* in left ventricular wall of a Panamanian child. The cyst contained about 170 spores. Except for enlargement and slight hyaline degeneration of the muscle fibers there were no myocardial lesions. × 1500. (After Gilmore, Kean and Posey, Am. J. Trop. Med., courtesy Williams & Wilkins, Baltimore.)

them as Sporozoa having a spore membrane and a single sporozoite for each spore.   On a few occasions a species of the Sarcosporidea, *Sarcocystis lindemanni,* has been recorded as a parasite of man.

The organisms (Fig. 50) are cylindrical, elongated or fusiform objects ("Miescher's tubes"), ranging in length from microscopic to 5 cm., lying in the parasitized muscle fibers, most commonly those of the tongue, larynx, esophagus, diaphragm, chest, abdomen and myocardium.   They are hyaline and are surrounded by an outer envelope which may be somewhat radially striated.   Within this outer layer the cyst is divided into compartments, the inner ones of which contain rounded, ovoidal, elongated or sickle-shaped spores ("Rainey's corpuscles"), measuring 12 to 16 microns in length by 4 to 9 microns in breadth.   Each spore contains a nucleus near its rounded end.   Thousands of these spores are developed in one cyst.   When such a cyst containing ripe spores is ingested, the cyst membrane is dissolved in the small intestine and the spores each digest a path into the intestinal mucosa.   Here they multiply, migrate to striated muscle and develop into new cysts.

Although *Sarcocystis* is pathogenic and frequently fatal to sheep and other animals, it has not produced detectable symptoms in man (Gilmore, Kean and Posey, 1942.)

SUMMARY

1. Two species of the coccidia, *Isospora belli* and *I. hominis,* produce infection in man.   Like other Sporozoa, the coccidia require an alternation of asexual and sexual generations but utilize a single host.   They are widely distributed in the Southwest Pacific region, and both are endemic in southern Brazil, Natal (Africa), western Colombia and Chile.   Elsewhere they occur sporadically.   Only the oöcyst stage passed in the stool has been described.   Symptomatic cases suffer from moderate to severe diarrhea.   No specific treatment is known.   Epidemiology and control of these infections have not been studied.

2. The malaria parasites have become adapted to life in the fixed tissues of the body and the circulating red blood cells of their vertebrate hosts.   Unlike the coccidia they require two hosts, one for asexual multiplication (schizogony) and early gametogony, and the other for completion of gametogony and sexual multiplication (sporogony).

3. The four species of malaria parasites which parasitize man (*Plasmodium vivax, P. falciparum, P. malariæ* and *P. ovale*) have no other common natural hosts for the asexual phase of their life cycle and are adapted exclusively to *Anopheles* mosquitoes for the sexual phase.   When the infected mosquito injects the sporozoites of these plasmodia into man, they disappear from the circulation in 30 minutes and invade the parenchyma cells of the liver, in which they produce large broods of preërythrocytic merozoites.   On escape into the blood stream these merozoites enter red blood cells, initiating parasitemia.   Meanwhile exoërythrocytic infection of *P. vivax, P. malariæ* and *P. ovale* is continued, providing a source for relapse.

4. In man erythrocytic schizogony occurs typically every 48 hours in *Plasmodium vivax* and *P. ovale,* every 72 hours in *P. malariæ,* and about every 36 to 48 hours in *P. falciparum.*

5. The development of plasmodia in exoërythrocytic foci, both preceding and subsequent to the infection of red blood cells, produces only incidental tissue pathology. The *essential pathogenesis* of the disease is associated with increased invasion and destruction of red blood corpuscles.

6. *Pathologic changes* due to malaria involve not only the blood cells but the spleen and other visceral organs, and in *falciparum* malaria hemostasis in the blood sinuses and capillaries, particularly in the brain, lungs, coronary vessels and kidneys.

7. The notable *symptoms* produced in malaria first develop with the synchronized release of considerable numbers of parasites and necrotic red cell detritus into the blood plasma, resulting in the malarial paroxysms, which consist of a shaking chill, then burning fever followed by sweating. Several of these paroxysms constitute an attack. After one attack there is a remission from a few weeks to several months, then a relapse.

8. In *falciparum* malaria the manifestations may be atypical, the paroxysms are frequently less marked, and the fever less intense but extending over a longer period. Yet acute development of cerebral symptoms may suddenly supervene.

9. Except in emergencies or when laboratory facilities are unavailable, *diagnosis* of malaria should always be checked by microscopic examination of the patient's blood.

10. *Treatment* of malaria has been remarkably advanced in recent years. Chloroquine and amodiaquin are excellent suppressants, are rapidly effective in curative doses in eradicating erythrocytic asexual parasites, and terminate *falciparum* malaria. Primaquine has proved very satisfactory in eradicating the exoërythrocytic foci of the other 3 types of infection.

11. Malaria may be endemic, hyperendemic, epidemic or sporadic. In order to be maintained in a community there must be persons in whom gametocytes are present in the circulating red cells, the source of infection for the mosquito. The extrinsic cycle requires adequate breeding of *Anopheles* mosquitoes close to human habitations.

12. *Falciparum* malaria is indigenous in tropical and subtropical regions wherever *Anopheles* mosquitoes breed. *Vivax* infection prevails not only in warm climates but in temperate regions where there is a warm period of the year. *Quartan* malaria (*P. malariæ* infection) is confined to tropical areas having consistently high atmospheric humidity. *Ovale* malaria is commonly endemic only in certain regions of tropical Africa.

13. *Control* of malaria involves both the gametocyte carrier and the *Anopheles* mosquito. Reduction in malaria may be temporarily obtained by treating patients with antimalarial drugs and screening human carriers from the *Anopheles* vectors. A more effective procedure is to kill adult *Anopheles* mosquitoes by use of residual insecticidal sprays on the inside and outside of habitations. A more lasting attack on the mosquito consists in a continued program to reduce *Anopheles* breeding.

14. *Sarcocystis lindemanni* is a relatively rare sporozoan parasite of man, but is common in sheep and other mammals. It develops as an elongated microscopic or macroscopic cyst within striated muscle. It is probably acquired from contaminated food or drink. In man the infection is essentially asymptomatic.

REFERENCES

The Coccidia

DOBELL, C.   1919.   A Revision of the Coccidia Parasitic in Man. Parasitol., *11*, 147–197.
ELSDON-DEW, R., and FREEDMAN, L.   1953.   Coccidiosis in Man: Experiences in Natal. Trans. R. Soc. Trop. Med. & Hyg., *47*, 209–214.
FAUST, E. C., GIRALDO, L. E., CAICEDO, G., and BONFANTE, R.   1961.   Human Isosporosis in the Western Hemisphere. Am. J. Trop. Med. & Hyg., *10*, 343–349.
HITCHCOCK, D. J.   1955.   The Life Cycle of *Isospora felis* in the Kitten. J. Parasitol., *41*, 383–387.
JARPA, A., MONTERO, E., NAVARRO, C., MAYERHOLZ, M., VASQUEZ, A., and ZULOAGA, M.   1960.   Isosporosis humana. Bol. Chileno Parasitol., *15*, 50–54.
JEFFERY, G. M.   1958.   Epidemiologic Considerations of Isosporiasis in a School for Mental Defectives. Am. J. Hyg., *67*, 251–255.
MATSUBAYASHI, H., and NOZAWA, T.:   1948.   Experimental Infection of *Isospora hominis* in Man. Am. J. Trop. Med., *28*, 633–637.
ORREGO, F., FAIGUENBAUM, J., and APABLAZA, A.   1959.   Hallazgo de *Isospora belli* en jugo duodenal. Bol. Chileno de Parasitol., *14*, 55–56.
PIEKARSKI, G.   1954.   *Lehrbuch der Parasitologie*. 759 pp., Berlin.
ROUTH, C. F., McCROAN, J. E., JR., and HAMES, C. G.   1955.   Three Cases of Human Infection with *Isospora*. Am. J. Trop. Med. & Hyg., *4*, 1–8.
THOMSON, J. G., and ROBERTSON, A.   1926.   Coccidia of Fish Which May Pass through the Human Intestine. Trans. R. Soc. Trop. Med. & Hyg., *20*, 132–133.
WENYON, C. M.   1923.   Coccidiosis in Cats and Dogs and the Status of the *Isospora* of Man. Ann. Trop. Med. & Parasitol., *17*, 231–276.

The Malaria Parasites

ARNOLD, J., ALVING, A. S., CLAYMAN, C. B., and HOCHWALD, R. S.   1961.   Induced Primaquine Resistance in Vivax Malaria. Trans. R. Soc. Trop. Med. & Hyg., *55*, 345–350.
ASH, J. E., and SPITZ, S.   1945.   *Pathology of Tropical Diseases. An Atlas*, 350 pp., W. B. Saunders Co., Philadelphia and London.
BOYD, M. F. (Editor).   1949.   *Malariology*, 2 vols., 1643 pp., W. B. Saunders Co., Philadelphia.
BRAY, R. S.   1959.   Pre-erythrocytic Stages of Human Malaria Parasites: *Plasmodium malariæ*. Brit. Med. J., *ii*, 679–680.
BURGESS, R. W., and YOUNG, M. D.   1959.   The Development of Pyrimethamine Resistance by *Plasmodium falciparum*. Bull. World Health Org., *20*, 37–46.
CLARK, H. C., and TOMLINSON, W. J.   1949.   The Pathologic Anatomy of Malaria, in Boyd's *Malariology*, pp. 874–903, W. B. Saunders Co., Philadelphia.
CLYDE, D. F.   1961.   Chloroquine Treatment for Malaria in Semi-immunes. Am. J. Trop. Med. & Hyg., *10*, 1–4.
COATNEY, G. R., MICKELSEN, O., *et al.*   1958.   Chloroquine or Pyrimethamine in Salt as a Suppressive against Sporozoite-induced Vivax Malaria (Chesson Strain). Bull. World Health Org., *19*, 53–67.
FAIRLEY, N. H.   1945.   Chemotherapeutic Suppression and Prophylaxis in Malaria. Trans. R. Soc. Trop. Med. & Hyg., *38*, 311–365.
FIELD, J. W. and LeFLEMING, H.   1939–1941.   The Morphology of Malarial Parasites in Thick Blood Films. Trans. R. Soc. Trop. Med. & Hyg., *32*, 467–480; *33*, 507–520; *34*, 297–304.
GABALDON, A., and GUERRERO, L.   1959.   An Attempt to Eradicate Malaria by the

Weekly Administration of Pyrimethamine in Areas of Out-of-doors Transmission in Venezuela. Am. J. Trop. Med. & Hyg., *8, 8,* 433–439.

GARNHAM, P. C. C. 1954. Life History of Malaria Parasites. Ann. Rev. Microbiol., *8,* 153–166.

GARNHAM, P. C. C., BRAY, R. S., COOPER, W., *et al.* 1954. Pre-erythrocytic Stages of Human Malaria: *Plasmodium ovale.* A. Preliminary Note. Brit. Med. J., *i,* 257.

JEFFERY, G. M., WOLCOTT, G. B., YOUNG, M. C., and WILLIAMS, D., JR. 1952. Exoërythrocytic Stages of *Plasmodium falciparum.* Am. J. Trop. Med. & Hyg., *1,* 917–926.

KITCHEN, S. F. 1949. Symptomatology: General Considerations: Falciparum Malaria; Quartan Malaria; Vivax Malaria; Ovale Malaria, in Boyd's *Malariology,* pp. 966–1052, W. B. Saunders Co., Philadelphia.

MAEGRAITH, B., JONES, E. S., and ANDREWS, W. H. H. 1951. Pathological Processes in Malaria. Trans. R. Soc. Trop. Med. & Hyg., *45,* 15–42.

MANSON, P. 1900. Experimental Proof of the Mosquito-Malaria Theory. Brit. Med. J., *ii,* 949–951.

MOORE, D. V., and LANIER, J. E. 1961. Observations on Two *Plasmodium falciparum* Infections with an Abnormal Response to Chloroquine. Am. J. Trop. Med. & Hyg., *10,* 5–9.

RUSSELL, P. F. 1952. *Malaria-Basic Principles Briefly Stated,* 210 pp., Blackwell Sci. Publ., Oxford.

——————. 1955. *Man's Mastery of Malaria,* 285 pp., Oxford Univ. Press.

SALISBURY, E. I. 1949. In Boyd's *Malariology,* pp. 1053–1070.

SHORTT, H. E. 1951. History of Recent Researches on Tissue Phases of the Malaria Parasite at the London School of Hygiene and Tropical Medicine. Trans. R. Soc. Trop. Med. & Hyg., *45,* 175–188.

SHORTT, H. E. and GARNHAM, P. C. C. C. 1948. The Pre-erythrocytic Development of *Plasmodium cynomolgi* and *Plasmodium vivax.* Trans. R. Soc. Trop. Med. & Hyg., *41,* 785–795.

WILLIAMSON, K. B. 1949. Naturalistic Methods of Anopheline Control, in Boyd's *Malariology,* pp. 1360–1384, W. B. Saunders Co., Philadelphia.

YOUNG, M. D., and BURGESS, R. W. 1959. Pyrimethamine Resistance in *Plasmodium vivax.* Bull. World Health Org., *20,* 27–36.

The Sarcosporidea

GILMORE, H. R., KEAN, B. H. and POSEY, F. M. 1942. Sarcosporidiosis with Parasites Found in the Heart. Am. J. Trop. Med., *22,* 121–125.

KUDO, R. R. 1954. *Protozoölogy,* 4th. ed., 966 pp., Charles C Thomas, Publisher, Springfield.

WENYON, C. M. 1926. *Protozoölogy. A Manual for Medical Men, Veterinarians and Zoologists,* 2 vols., 1563 pp., Baillière, Tindall & Cox, London.

Chapter 7

Protozoa of Undetermined Relationship

Toxoplasma gondii Nicolle and Manceaux, 1908
(Causing toxoplasmosis)

THIS organism was discovered by Nicolle and Manceaux, in 1908, in a small North African rodent, *Ctenodactylus gundi*, and since that time has been found frequently in a large number of birds and mammals, including man. Human infection is cosmopolitan both in lower animals and in man, but is more prevalent in moist warm climates than in those that are cold or dry.

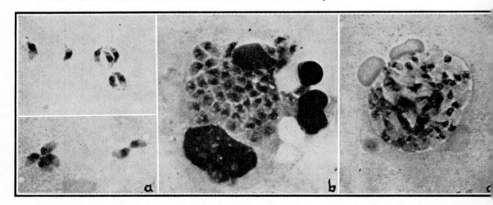

FIG. 51.—Photomicrographs of microscopic smear of *Toxoplasma gondii*, stained by Wright's technic. *a*, crescent-shaped organisms from peritoneal fluid; *b*, mass of toxoplasmas (pseudocyst) completely filling a macrophage; *c*, cyst, developed extracellularly in chronic infection. × 1000. (After Sabin, Brennemann's *Practice of Pediatrics*, courtesy W. F. Prior Co., in Faust and Russell's *Clinical Parasitology*, Lea & Febiger, Philadelphia.)

Morphology.—*Toxoplasma gondii* is a delicate, ovoidal, pyriform or crescentic body measuring 4 to 6 microns long by 2 to 3 microns in breadth. One extremity is more pointed than the other. Employing Giemsa stain, one sees a delicate azure coloration of the cytoplasm and a reddish ovoidal nucleus, which lies somewhat towards the blunter end of the body. *Toxoplasma* lacks the characteristic kinetoplast of the leishmaniæ and has no flagellar stage. Multiplication is by longitudinal binary fission. Electron microscope photographs reveal a conoid at the more pointed end of the cytoplasm, similar to that found in *Atoxoplasma* (Garnham, personal communication).

Pathogenesis.—*Toxoplasma gondii* is primarily if not exclusively a parasite in fixed cells of the reticulo-endothelial system (Fig. 51) but frequently it has been found within wandering macrophages in peritoneal, pleural or cerebral exudates and occasionally in circulating blood. It does not grow free of host cells; to obtain the organism for diagnostic tests it must be inoculated into suitable laboratory animals (Frenkel, 1953).

Once *Toxoplasma* becomes implanted it develops within wandering or fixed macrophages comparable to *Leishmania donovani* (page 48). It tends to produce clear serous fluids in body cavities, necrosis of invaded tissues and centers of granulomas, frequently becoming calcified in cerebral foci. Pseudocysts have been described in active infections, and cysts in chronic ones (Lainson, 1958). The degree of injury to organs varies remarkably from essentially insignificant, microscopic changes to profound, extensive, irreversible damage. The organs commonly attacked are the lymph nodes, brain, eyes and lungs (Beattie, 1957).

Symptomatology.—The most seriously affected human cases are those of the newborn, with infection acquired *in utero* during the second or third trimester of fetal development, usually from a symptomless mother (Sabin, 1950). These infants at birth or during the first week or two *post-partum* commonly have evidences of cerebral calcification and chorioretinitis, at times with hydrocephalus or microcephaly and psychomotor disturbances. The most common type of the disease acquired post-natally is lymphangitis, with glandular fever (Roth and Piekarski, 1959), which requires differentiation from mononucleosis. In other cases, there may be rather indefinite symptoms produced by microscopic granulomas and necrotic areas in which the parasites occur. In the pulmonary type, the lungs are congested and the bronchioles infiltrated with macrophages packed with toxoplasmas. At times the myocardium is invaded by the parasitized macrophages. Still another variety is one with maculo-papular eruption, high fever, mental stupor and atypical pneumonia.

Infection may be acquired *in utero*, with the probability of fatal termination soon after birth or irreversible changes leaving the child a helpless invalid; or it may be acquired at any period after birth. The prognosis depends on the amount and virulence of the inoculum and the threshold of resistance of the host (Kaufman *et al.*, 1959).

Diagnosis may be made clinically on the basis of cerebral calcification, as demonstrated by the ventriculogram, and chorioretinitis, especially in the region of the macula, but this should be confirmed by demonstration of *Toxoplasma* in smear preparations, inoculation of laboratory mice with blood or suspected tissues, by immunologic tests, and *post-mortem* by demonstration of the parasites in the tissues (Cathie, 1957). The complement fixation test and the neutralization test have been largely supplanted by the microchemical dye test (Sabin and Feldman, 1949) and intraperitoneal inoculation of mice with suspension of suspected minced tissue cells or blood (Jones, Eyles, Coleman and Gibson, 1958). (See "TECHNICAL AIDS," pp. 449–450).

Treatment.—There is no effective treatment in toxoplasmosis. Pyrimethamine with sulfasuxidine is helpful but will not kill all of the toxoplasmas.

Epidemiology.—There is no conclusive evidence as to how this infection is propagated in nature. It has caused epizoötics in flocks of chickens and abortion in ewes (Garnham, 1959). Human infection has at times been associated with infected domestic animals, including those of the house and farmyard (Gibson and Eyles, 1957). Experimentally in animals it may be induced by inoculating material containing the parasites by the oral, intranasal, intravenous, intracutaneous, subcutaneous, intraperitoneal or intracerebral route. Both in human cases and experimental mammals the disease is transmitted from mother to offspring, and in lactating mice it has been acquired from mother's milk. Moreover, the large number of persons with toxoplasmin-positive tests but without symptoms suggests that there may be many inapparent cases for each symptomatic one.

Control.—Until the epidemiology of toxoplasmosis is better understood it is impossible to plan effective control.

Pneumocystis carinii Delanoë and Delanoë, 1912

This protoplast which is described from dogs, guinea pigs, rats, mice, rabbits, goats, sheep, foxes, and from new-born and premature children, much less commonly from human adults, is considered by many competent persons to be a protozoan parasite. In human cases it appears in epidemics of interstitial plasma-cell pneumonia. In tissue sections the organism is identified with difficulty but in Giemsa-stained impression smears from lungs exhibiting the typical lesions with frothy alveolar exudates, rarely in macrophages and interstitial cells, three arrangements of the organism have been observed: isolated uninucleate forms, those with more

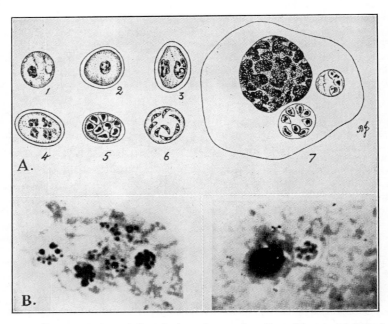

Fig. 52.—*Pneumocystis carinii.* A, from impression film of lung of infected dog. × 2000. (After Carini and Maciel, 1914, in Wenyon's Protozoölogy, courtesy of Baillière, Tindall & Cox, London); B, Gram-stained impression films of *P. carinii* from lung. × 1500. (After Westphal, courtesy Zeitschr. f. Tropen med. u. Parasitol. Hamburg.)

than one nucleus, and rosettes of eight units within a common membrane (Westphal, 1953; Pizzi and Diaz, 1956). The organisms are rounded, ovoidal, slightly irregular or occasionally crescentic, measure one to 3 microns in longer diameter, and have extremities equally pointed; they possess a central nucleus and lack a parabasal body. The characteristic rosette averages 7 microns in diameter (Fig. 52).

Infection with *Pneumocystis* is associated with interstitial plasma-cell pneumonia, which is contagious, frequently develops epidemically in children's wards in a hospital, usually in prematures or in full-term infants with retarded development. The lesion commonly develops in the smooth muscle of the alveolar walls, and is characterized by extensive plasma-cell infiltration in and around the alveoli, with a frothy, honeycombed exudate (Lunseth *et al.*, 1955). The usual duration of the illness is less than two months and is frequently terminated by sudden death.

Recovered cases have no residual respiratory manifestations. No satisfactory chemotherapy has been found.

Human infections with confirmed diagnosis of the parasite have been reported from Germany, Scandinavia, Belgium, Czechoslovakia, Hungary, Turkey, Chile, Canada and the United States. Probably domestic animals serve as the source for human infection but this has not been confirmed. Infants with symptoms of the disease should be placed in strict isolation to prevent exposure of other children.

SUMMARY

1. *Toxoplasma gondii*, which has a cosmopolitan distribution in man, mammals and birds, is an intra-cytoplasmic parasite, principally in reticuloendothelial cells, in which it divides by longitudinal binary fission. In man this infection (toxoplasmosis) appears in all age groups; in most infected persons it is essentially symptomless; symptomatic disease is most common in infants, who may acquire the disease from a symptomless mother during fetal development. The pathologic process in the newborn frequently causes cerebral calcification, chorioretinitis, pneumonitis and myocarditis. Diagnosis consists in demonstrating the organism in the tissues, in inoculating experimental mice, or by immunologic technics. There is no satisfactory therapy. The method by which infection is acquired has not been elucidated. No effective control program has been developed.

2. *Pneumocystis carinii* is believed to be the etiological agent in epidemics of interstitial plasma-cell pneumonia in new-born children. It is considered to be a protozoön, which develops in interstitial cells of the lungs in the form of rosettes containing 8 units measuring one to 3 microns in length. This infection, reported from several European countries, Turkey, Canada, the United States and Chile, usually has a fatal termination. There is no specific treatment. Since the disease is highly contagious, strict isolation of human cases is indicated.

REFERENCES

Toxoplasma gondii

BEATTIE, C. P. 1957. Clinical and Epidemiological Aspects of Toxoplasmosis. Trans. R. Soc. Trop. Med. & Hyg., *51*, 96–103.

CATHIE, I. A. B. 1957. An Appraisal of the Diagnostic Value of the Serological Tests for Toxoplasmosis. Trans. R. Soc. Trop. Med. & Hyg., *51*, 104–110.

FRENKEL, J. K. 1953. Host, Strain and Treatment Variation as Factors in the Pathogenesis of Toxoplasmosis. Am. J. Trop. Med. & Hyg., *2*, 390–411.

GARNHAM, P. C. C. 1959. Personal Communication to E. C. Faust.

GIBSON, C. L., and EYLES, D. E. 1957. *Toxoplasma* Infections in Animals Associated with a Case of Human Congenital Toxoplasmosis. Am. J. Trop. Med. & Hyg., *6*, 990–1000.

JONES, F. E., EYLES, D. E., COLEMAN, N., and GIBSON, C. L. 1958. A Comparison of Methods for the Isolation of *Toxoplasma* from Suspected Hosts. Am. J. Trop. Med. & Hyg., *7*, 531–535.

KAUFMAN, H. E., MELTON, M. L., REMINGTON, J. S., and JACOBS, L. 1959. Strain Differences of *Toxoplasma gondii*. J. Parasitol., *45*, 189–190.

LAINSON, R. 1958. Observations on the Development and Nature of Pseudocysts and Cysts of *Toxoplasma gondii*. Trans. R. Soc. Med. & Hyg., *52*, 396–407.

9

ROTH, F., and PIEKARSKI, G. 1959. Ueber die Lymphknoten-Toxoplasmose der Erwachsenen. Virchows Arch. path. Anat., *332*, 181–203.
SABIN, A. B. 1950. Toxoplasmosis. Am. J. Ophth., *33*, 1255–1268.
SABIN, A. B., and FELDMAN, H. A. 1949. Dyes as Microchemical Indicators of a New Immunity Phenomenon Affecting a Protozoön Parasite (Toxoplasma). Science, *108*, 660–663.

Pneumocystis carinii

LUNSETH, J. H., KIRMSE, T. W., PREZYNA, A. P. and GERTH, R. E. 1955. Interstitial Plasma Cell Pneumonia. J. Pediatr., *46*, 137–145.
PIZZI, T., and DÍAZ, M. 1956. Neumonia intersticial plasmocelular. II. Investigación parasitológica del *Pneumocystis carinii*. Rev. Chilena de Pediatría, *27*, 281–299.
WESTPHAL, A. 1953. Zur Diagnose der *Pneumocystis carinii*-Infektion des Menschen. Zeitschr. f. Tropenmed. u. Parasit., *4*, 549–554.

SECTION III

Helminths as Agents of Human Disease

Chapter 8

Introduction to the Helminths

THE designation "helminth" (from the Greek ἕλμινς) means "worm." Broadly interpreted, it refers to any worm or worm-like animal; in a more restricted sense, it refers to a parasitic worm. It does not connote a single group or phylum of the Animal Kingdom but comprehends two large phyla, the Platyhelminthes (flatworms) and the Nematoda (true round-worms), as well as two smaller phyla, the Nematomorpha ("hair snakes") and Acanthocephala (thorny-headed worms) and one class group of the Annelida, *viz.*, the Hirudinea (leeches).

The two Classes of the Platyhelminthes which will be considered in this text, the Trematoda (flukes) and Cestoidea (tapeworms) are exclusively parasitic during all or a predominant part of their life. Many species of the Phylum Nematoda are free-living; possibly an equal number are parasitic, either throughout their entire life or during an essential part of the cycle. The Nematomorpha are parasitic in the hemocele of certain insects from the larva hatched from the egg until they are almost mature, at which time they escape into freshwater to oviposit. The Acanthocephala are exclusively endoparasitic. The Hirudinea are free-living worms which can be considered as parasites only during the period when they attach themselves to engorge on the blood of their victim.

Each of these groups will be considered separately in the chapters which follow.

References

BELDING, D. L. 1952. *Textbook of Clinical Parasitology*, 2nd. ed., pages 327–739. Appleton-Century-Crofts, Inc., New York.
BRAND, T. VON. 1952. Chemical Physiology of Endoparasitic Animals. 339 pp., Academic Press, New York.
BUEDING, E., and MOST, H. 1953. Helminths: Metabolism, Nutrition and Chemo-therapy. Ann. Rev. Microbiol., 7, 295–326.
CHANDLER, A. C. 1955. *Introduction to Parasitology with Special Reference to the Parasites of Man*, 9th. ed., pages 239–499, John Wiley & Sons, Inc., New York.
FAUST, E. C. 1949. *Human Helminthology*, 3rd. ed., 744 pp. Lea & Febiger, Philadelphia.
FOSTER, A. O. 1960. Parasitological Speculations and Patterns. J. Parasitol., 46, 1–9.
STOLL, N. R. 1947. This Wormy World. J. Parasitol., 33, 1–18.

Chapter 9

Intestinal, Hepatic and Pulmonary Flukes (Trematodes)

TREMATODES AS A GROUP

Introduction

FLUKES, or trematodes (Class Trematoda), constitute a major subdivision of the flatworms (Phylum Platyhelminthes). Members of this phylum are many-celled animals which are bilaterally symmetrical along a longitudinal axis, are usually flattened dorsoventrally, have three body layers but lack a true body cavity. Their most conspicuous common feature is the bilateral excretory system ending internally in so-called "flame cells" (*solenocytes*). There is no blood system.

Of the three major subdivisions of the Platyhelminthes, The Class Turbellaria are almost exclusively free-living and the Class Trematoda and Class Cestoidea are exclusively parasitic. Of the three recognized subclasses of the Trematoda, *viz.*, Monogenea, Aspidogastrea and Digenea, only the Digenea (digenetic trematodes) produce infection in man and higher animals.

Life Cycle.—Digenetic trematodes have a complicated life cycle in 2 or more hosts, consisting of three (or more) consecutive generations. The definitive stage is usually hermaphroditic but in some species of schistosomes (blood flukes) it is diecious. In most Digenea the fertilized egg (Fig. 53), after its discharge from the definitive host, hatches in water, with the escape of a ciliated larva (*miracidium*), which swims about for a relatively short time, but in order to proceed with its development must penetrate the soft tissues of an appropriate mollusc, usually a snail. This is accomplished by the secretion of digestive enzymes elaborated in penetration glands.

Within the lymph spaces of the moluscan host, the miracidium sheds its ciliated epithelium and transforms into a simple elongated sac, a *first-generation sporocyst*, or in some species a slightly more elaborate form called a *redia*. Germ cells developed from the inner wall of the sporocyst (or redia) give rise to a number of *second-generation sporocysts* or *rediæ*. The investigations of Cort and his students (Cort, 1944, etc.) provide convincing proof that the characteristic mechanism is one of polyembryony, *e.g.*, germ cell lineage. The second-generation organisms escape from their mothers, grow and produce internally third-generation larvæ, which, when mature, break out of the mollusc and temporarily become free-living organisms in the water. This stage is the *cercaria*, or tailed larva.

The cercaria possesses certain uniquely larval organs, namely, cystogenous and penetration glands. Secretion of cystogenous material provides a temporary protective wall around the organism. Secretion of digestive enzymes elaborated in the penetration glands aids the larva to penetrate the tissues of its next host. Some groups of cercariæ develop the one type of mechanism, some the other, and some have both types.

Depending on the particular group of digenetic trematodes, the cercaria (1) becomes attached to the skin of a definitive vertebrate host, discards its tail, penetrates into the tissues, and after a period of migration and growth matures in this host (schistosomes or blood flukes); (2) crawls upon an aquatic plant (*Fasciolopsis buski, Fasciola hepatica*), drops its tail, rounds up and encysts; or (3) shedding its tail, penetrates into the tissues of an aquatic animal (*Clonorchis sinensis, Opisthorchis felineus, Paragonimus westermani*), or a terrestrial animal (*Dicrocœlium dendriticum*), in which it becomes encysted. In the latter two types of development the definitive host becomes infected when it ingests the plant or animal tissues on which or in which the encysted stage occurs.

As soon as the cercaria becomes separated from its tail it is referred to as a *metacercaria*. In its definitive host the metacercaria develops into the adult worm. Cercaria, metacercaria and adult worm constitute the third generation in the life cycle.

The Mature Worm in its Definitive Host.—While a majority of digenetic trematodes are located in the digestive tract of their definitive hosts, several reside in the bile passages, a few in the parenchyma of the lungs, and the schistosomes in portal-caval venous blood. These worms vary in size and shape: Some (*Fasciola, Fasciolopsis*) are large and fleshy; others are as small as a mustard or turnip seed (heterophyid species); still others are thin and flabby (*Clonorchis, Opisthorchis, Dicrocœlium*), and the blood-inhabiting schistosomes are more or less delicately cylindrical (Fig. 53).

The adult trematode is covered with a cuticle secreted by the hypodermis. This may be smooth or may have spines or plaque-like denticles. In addition to a sucker which surrounds the mouth, in most families there is a median ventral, blind acetabulum. Under the hypodermis there are successively a transverse and a longitudinal muscle layer, oblique muscles and a loose parenchymatous matrix surrounding the internal organs.

The Digestive System.—This consists of a mouth (buccal cavity), then an esophagus which is provided with a spherical or pyriform, usually muscular pharynx, and finally a pair of ceca which in most species are simple and end blindly in the subdistal portion of the worm.

Typically the nutriment in which the trematode lies is taken into its digestive tract, where the digestible part is absorbed through the cecal wall, after which the wastes are expelled by regurgitation.

The Nervous System.—Relatively large saddle-like nerve commissures are located in the anterior portion of the worm dorsal to the pharynx. Connected with this central nerve mass are three pairs of nerve trunks, one pair each in the lateral, dorsolateral and ventrolateral positions, extending both anteriorwards and posteriorwards. Numerous transverse commissures are found in the region of the ventral acetabulum and the genital organs.

The Excretory System.—This system consists of a median posterior bladder emptying dorsally through a posterior pore; primary and secondary collecting tubules which are bilaterally symmetrical, and capillaries with terminal "flame cells" (*solenocytes*). Similar groups of digenetic trematodes usually have the same fundamental type of excretory pattern in the miracidium, cercaria, metacercaria and mature worm.

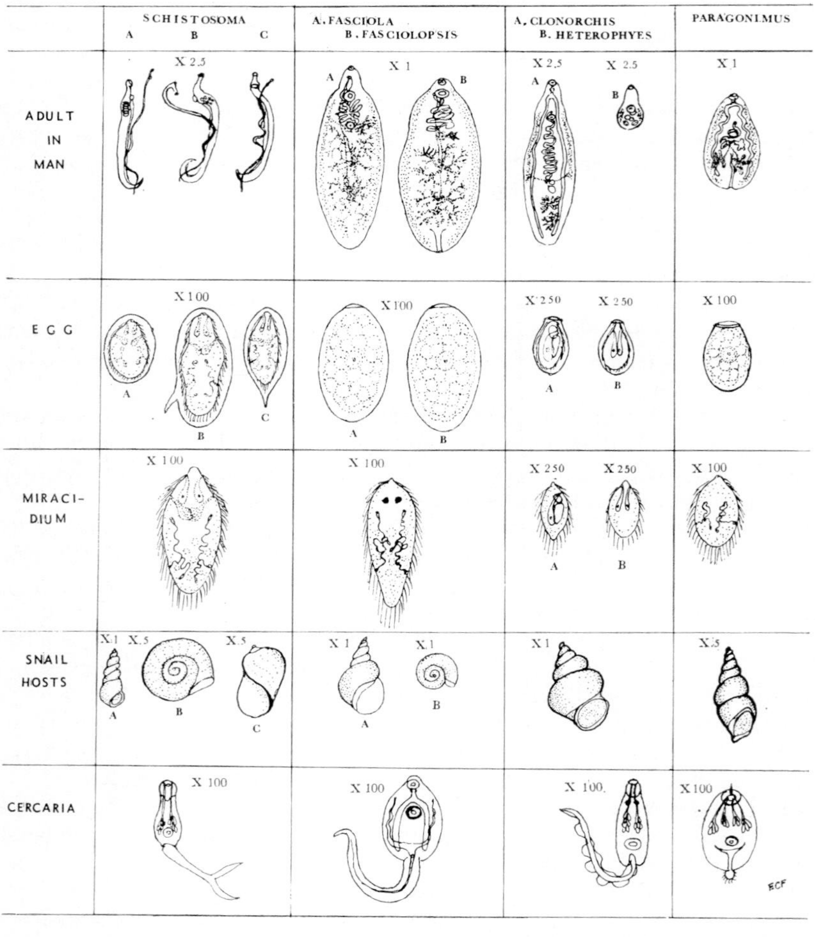

FIG. 53.—Important stages and differential characteristics of the common digenetic trematodes which parasitize man. Under Schistosoma, A represents *Schistosoma japonicum*, B, *S. mansoni* and C, *S. hæmatobium*. (Original, Faust.)

Lymph-Vascular System.—Two or four main longitudinal lymphatic trunks with numerous collateral branches have been observed in several groups of trematodes, particularly those which have an encysted metacercarial stage.

The Genital System.—All digenetic trematodes except the blood flukes are hermaphroditic. Each organism is typically self-fertilizing, so that an isolated worm is able to reproduce its kind.

The usual *male reproductive organs* (Fig. 54) are the *testes*, commonly two; for each testis a *vas efferens*, a common *vas deferens*, a swollen *seminal vesicle*, *prostate glands*, and a muscular *cirrus* or penial organ. A sacculate *cirrus sac* surrounds these terminal male genitalia. The male system opens into the common *genital atrium* (*ga*), which is provided with a *genital pore*.

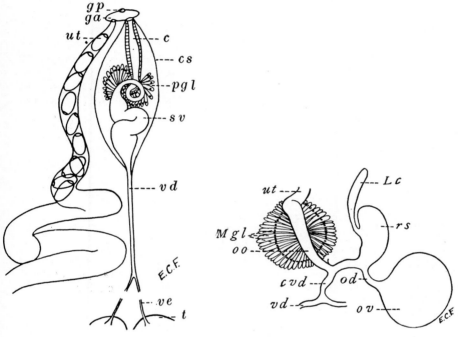

FIG. 54   Digenetic Trematodes   FIG. 55

FIG. 54.—Male and female reproductive organs leading to the genital pore. *c*, cirrus organ; *cs*, cirrus sac; *ga*, genital atrium; *gp*, genital pore; *pgl*, prostate gland; *sv*, seminal vesicle; *t*, testis; *ut*, uterus; *vd*, vas deferens; *ve*, vas efferens. (Original, from Faust's *Human Helminthology*, Lea & Febiger, Philadelphia.)

FIG. 55.—Female reproductive organs in the vicinity of the oötype. *cvd*, common vitelline duct; *Lc*, Laurer's canal; *Mgl*, Mehlis' gland; *od*, oviduct; *oo*, oötype; *ov*, ovary; *rs*, seminal receptacle; *ut*, proximal end of uterus; *vd*, vitelline duct. (Original, from Faust's *Human Helminthology*, Lea & Febiger, Philadelphia.)

The *female genitalia* (Fig. 54, left; Fig. 55) consist of a single *ovary*, an *oviduct*, a *seminal receptacle*, *Laurer's canal*, the so-called "*vitellaria*" probably containing in part shell-gland material, paired and common collecting ducts, the *oötype*, surrounded by *Mehlis' gland*, and the coiled *uterus*, which originates on the anterior face of the oötype and proceeds in tortuous coils to the genital atrium.

Spermatozoa which reach the genital atrium from the male system proceed up the uterus and reach the seminal receptacle, where they are stored. The naked egg (the *ovum*), the spermatozoa and the vitelline-shell gland material pass into the oötype and then into the proximal segment of the uterus. Here the naked ovum is first surrounded by vitelline cells rich in glycogen, fertilization occurs and fused basophilic granules, containing orthodihydrophenol and protein, form the enveloping shell. As each egg is completed it is carried forward in the uterus to make way for other eggs about to be produced.

Eggs of *Fasciola, Fasciolopsis, Paragonimus*, echinostomes, amphistomes and monostomes are unembryonated when oviposition occurs, and require a period of development in the water before they hatch. Eggs of schistosomes are partially embryonated when oviposited but are usually mature when they are discharged in the excreta and soon hatch when they reach fresh water. Although eggs of *Clonorchis, Opisthorchis* and heterophyid species are mature when they are evacuated in the host's stool, they do not hatch in water but must be ingested by the appropriate snail before the miracidia are released.

The eggs of most digenetic trematodes are operculate; a few, particularly in the schistosomes, are non-operculate.

INTESTINAL FLUKES

Fasciolopsis buski (Lankester, 1857) Odhner, 1902
(The giant intestinal fluke, causing fasciolopsiasis)

Historical and Geographical Notes

Fasciolopsis buski was first observed by Busk in the duodenum of a Laskar sailor who was autopsied in London. Its natural geographical distribution is limited to Oriental countries. The life cycle for man was elucidated by Barlow (1925).

Morphology, Biology and Life Cycle

The Adult Worm.—The mature *F. buski* lives attached to the wall of the duodenum or jejunum. It is a large, fleshy worm, at times broadly ovate but more often elongate ovoidal (Fig. 56), measuring 20 to 75 mm. in length, 8 to 20 mm. in breadth and 0.5 to 3.0 mm. in thickness. The integument is spinose. The oral sucker (*os*) is much smaller than the nearby ventral acetabulum (*vs*). Conspicuous features of the genitalia are the extensive, highly branched testes (*t*) which occupy much of the posterior three-fifths of the body, the small branched ovary (*ov*), and the relatively short, convoluted uterus (*ut*).

The eggs are large, hen's-egg-shaped, measure 130 to 140 microns by 80 to 85 microns, have a thin, transparent shell with a small, slightly convex operculum at one end, and are unembryonated when evacuated in the host's feces. They are very difficult to differentiate from eggs of *Fasciola hepatica*.

To proceed with their development the eggs of *F. buski* must reach quiet fresh water. Here they embryonate in 3 to 7 weeks at a temperature of 80°

to 90° F. (26.7° to 32° C.), following which a miracidium with a pair of conspicuous eye spots breaks out of the shell through the opened operculum, then escapes from its embryonic membrane and swims about vigorously in the water. On contact with an appropriate small planorbid snail (species of *Segmentina*, *Hippeutis*, *Gyraulus*, etc.) the miracidium penetrates the soft tissues and transforms into a sporocyst. In this mother spore sac a

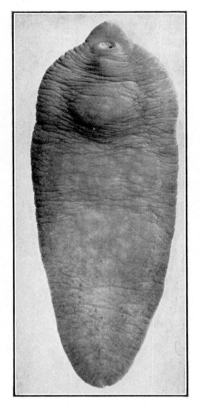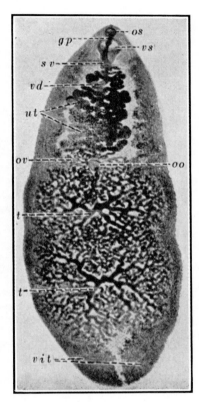

Fig. 56.—Adult *Fasciolopsis buski*. *Left*, photograph of living worm, ventral view. × 4. (Courtesy of Professor Doctor José G. Basneuvo, Habana); *right*, stained specimen, ventral view. × 4. *gp*, genital pore; *oo*, oötype; *os*, oral sucker; *ov*, ovary; *sv*, seminal vesicle; *t*, testis; *ut*, uterus; *vd*, vas deferens; *vit*, vitellaria; *vs*, ventral acetabulum. (Adapted by Faust from Roudabush, from Faust and Russell's *Clinical Parasitology*, Lea & Febiger, Philadelphia.)

generation of rediæ is produced, then within each redia a second brood of rediæ. Usually the second redial generation produces a number of vigorous cercariæ, which erupt from the snail and, after swimming about, crawl onto aquatic vegetation and become encysted. Man commonly becomes infected while peeling off the hull of the seed pods of the water buffalo nut or the skin of the "water chestnut" between his teeth and lips, so that some of the encysted metacercariæ are set free and are swallowed. After excystation in the duodenum, the larvæ become attached to nearby mucosa and in about three months develop into mature worms (Barlow, 1925).

Pathogenicity and Symptomatology

The damage produced by these large fleshy worms is traumatic, obstructive and toxic. At each site of attachment to the wall of the duodenum or jejunum, a mucosal ulcer is produced. A few worms cause no serious inintestinal symptoms but frequently there are dozens to hundreds of worms in an infection. These embarrass digestion and at times cause acute obstruction. The toxic metabolites of the parasite are absorbed systemically and produce edema of the face, especially around the eyes, of the abdomen and lower extremities. There is characteristically a high-grade eosinophilia.

The early symptoms are diarrhea and hunger pains; those in heavy infections mimic peptic ulcer. Ascites and asthenia are notable characteristics, as well as generalized abdominal pain and the passage of unformed foul-smelling stools containing much undigested food. The appetite is at times capricious, but anorexia, nausea and vomiting typically occur. In heavy infections death results from anasarca.

Diagnosis

This is based on recovery of the characteristic eggs of *F. buski* in the stools (Fig. 53).

Treatment

This consists in the oral administration of *hexylresorcinol crystoids* in a single dose, in the amount of 0.4 Gm. for children under 7 years of age and increasing to one Gm. for those 13 years or older. Treatment may be repeated at weekly intervals if required. This drug is both safe and relatively efficient. Conservative measures are indicated in cases of profound toxemia or intestinal obstruction due to the worms.

Epidemiology

The natural definitive hosts of *Fasciolopsis buski* are man and the hog. Endemicity is associated with the cultivation of buffalo nuts (*Trapa natans* in China, *T. bicornis* in Thailand and Bengal), the "water chestnut" (*Eliocharis tuberosa*), the lotus, water bamboo and other aquatic plants, portions of which are consumed raw by native populations (Sadun and Maiphoom, 1953). Use of human excreta containing the eggs of *F. buski* to fertilize fields of aquatic plants provides a major source of inoculum for the molluscan stages of the life cycle. Children are particularly apt to have heavy infections.

Control

While individual patients may be freed of their infection by appropriate anthelmintic medication, persons in endemic areas, especially children, are periodically reëxposed by consuming raw plant products from the infested sites. To be effective, control requires that human excreta be sterilized before use as fertilizer and that hogs not be allowed to forage in the fields where these plants are grown so that these animals will not pollute the ground with their feces.

AMPHISTOMATE FLUKES

Two amphistomes have been reported as human parasites. These medium-sized fleshy worms have the following common characteristics: a large ventral sucker situated at the posterior end of the worm; large, operculate eggs which are unembryonated when evacuated in the stool, and metacercariæ which encyst like those of *Fasciolopsis buski* on vegetation, so that exposure of the definitive host results from consumption of infested grass or other plant vectors. Herbivorous and omnivorous mammals are the usual definitive hosts.

Watsonius watsoni (Conyngham, 1904) Stiles and Goldberger, 1910 has been obtained only once from man, a West African Negro who died of a severe diarrhea. At necropsy many worms were found attached to the duodenal and jejunal mucosa and free in the large bowel. Monkeys are considered to be the natural reservoirs.

Gastrodiscoides hominis (Lewis and McConnell, 1876) Leiper, 1913 is a relatively common human parasite in Assam and has been reported as endemic in Indo-China. Pigs in India and deer (*Tragulus napu*) in Malaya are known reservoirs. The parasite, which is attached to the human cecum and ascending colon, produces a mucous diarrhea. The eggs (Plate II, *W*, p. 25) are elongate spindle-shaped, with bluntly rounded ends, and measure 150 to 152 microns by 60 to 72 microns.

ECHINOSTOMATE FLUKES

Members of this group are characterized by a collarette of distinctive spinose processes mounted on a circumoral disc. The spines are interrupted on the ventral side and in the genus *Echinochasmus* also mid-dorsally. Frequently there is a distinct constriction at the posterior level of the collarette. A few echinostomes are natural human parasites in Oriental countries, while several others have been incidentally reported from man.

Echinostoma ilocanum (Garrison, 1908) Odhner, 1911.—This infection is relatively common among the Ilocano population of Luzon, and occurs on other Philippine islands, in Java and in Canton, China, where the dog is commonly infected. Exposure results from raw consumption of fleshy snails containing the encysted metacercarial stage.

The living worms (Fig. 57) are reddish-gray in color, measure 2.5 to 6.5 mm. in length by 1 to 1.35 mm. in breadth, are attenuate at both ends and are attached to the wall of the host's small intestine. The small circumoral disc is provided with 49 to 51 spines. The large, straw-colored, hen's-egg-shaped eggs measure 83 to 116 microns by 58 to 69 microns, have a small operculum at one end and are unembryonated when discharged in the feces. They mature in 6 to 15 days in fresh water, following which hatching occurs. The molluscan hosts are species of planorbid and lymneid snails, in which the miracidia transform into rediæ, which produce a second generation of rediæ, and these, in turn, cercariæ which have the same number and characteristics of collarette spines as the adult worms. After the cercariæ escape from the snail they enter the soft tissues of large edible snails such as *Pila conica* (Philippines) and *Viviparus javanicus* (Java) in which they encyst.

The worms produce inflammatory reaction and ulceration at the sites of their attachment to the intestinal wall. In some patients there are likewise toxic manifestations. The usual symptoms are intestinal colic and diarrhea. Diagnosis is based on recovery of the eggs and their differentiation from those of other echinostomes, *Fasciolopsis buski* and *Fasciola hepatica*. Treatment consists in administration of hexylresorcinol crystoids, as in *Fasciolopsis* infection, or tetrachloroethylene as in hookworm infection. (See Table 7, p 418.) Control requires that all edible snails be thoroughly cooked before they are eaten.

Fig. 57.—Adult *Echinostoma ilocanum*, ventral view. × 20. (After Odhner, from Faust's *Human Helminthology*, Lea & Febiger, Philadelphia.)

Other species of echinostomes which have been reported occasionally as human parasites include: *Echinostoma lindoensis* from Celebes, *E. malayanum* from Malaya, Sumatra and India, *E. melis* from Roumania and China, *E. revolutum* from Formosa and Indonesia, *E. cinetorchis* from Japan, Formosa and Java, *Paryphostomum sufrartefex* from Assam, *Himasthla muehlensi* once from New York City, *Echinoparyphium paraulum* from U.S.S.R., and *Echinochasmus perfoliatus* from Japan.

PLAGIORCHID FLUKES

Species of this family group utilize grubs of certain insects as second intermediate hosts. The cercaria, after emerging from its molluscan host, invades these larval insects and encysts within them. Birds and mammals which eat the infected grubs acquire the definitive stage of the worm, which matures in the small intestine. Rodents, cats, dogs and on rare occasions man have been found to harbor species of *Plagiorchis*. *P. philippinensis* has been obtained once at necropsy in Manila, *P. javanensis* (Fig. 58) from a native Javanese at post-mortem, and *P. muris* has been developed as an experimental human infection.

Fig. 58.—Adult *Plagiorchis javanensis* from human host. × 40. (After Sandground, from Faust's *Human Helminthology*, Lea & Febiger, Philadelphia.)

Troglotrema salmincola (Chapin, 1926) Witenberg, 1932

This minute fluke, a distant relative of the lung flukes (*Paragonimus*), is a common parasite of the small intestine of the dog, coyote, fox, raccoon, mink and lynx on the Pacific Coast of North America and has been reported from the aborigines of Eastern Siberia. Infection in North America is acquired from eating raw salmon and trout caught in coastal streams. The flukes are small (0.8 to 2.5 mm. by 0.3 to 0.5 mm.), pyriform, are dorso-ventrally flattened and produce at one time only a few broadly ovoidal, yellowish, thick-shelled, operculate, unembryonated eggs, measuring 87 to 97 microns by 38 to 55 microns. After maturing in cool fresh water the eggs hatch and the miracidia penetrate snails of the genus *Oxytrema* (Bennington, 1960). The cercarial progeny which emerge from the molluscan host have an oral stylet and a knob-like tail. They enter the fish and become encysted in the muscles. Fish constitute the source of infection for the mammalian hosts.

The flukes themselves produce no appreciable damage in the intestine of the definitive host. However, an associated rickettsia, *Neorickettsia helmintheca*, is responsible for a severe, frequently fatal disease in dogs, coyotes and foxes, referred to as "salmon poisoning." In this instance the helminth replaces an arthropod as vector of the rickettsia (Philip, 1958). This infection has not been reported for man.

HETEROPHYID FLUKES

Members of this family group are very small, compact, ovoidal, pyriform or occasionally tongue-shaped organisms which live attached to the mucosa at the upper levels of the small intestine of birds and mammals. They are found at the base of the mucosal crypts and may be partially buried in the glands. In routine autopsies they are frequently overlooked, but if present are readily obtained by examining superficial scrapings of the mucosa after these have been shaken for 10 to 15 minutes in a 0.5% solution of sodium sulfate.

The small, ovoidal, operculate eggs each contain a fully mature miracidium at the time they are evacuated in the feces of the definitive host, but hatching occurs only after ingestion by an appropriate snail. Within the soft extra-intestinal tissues of the mollusc the miracidium transforms into a sporocyst. In *Stellantchasmus falcatus* a second generation of sporocysts is produced (Noda, 1959). There are two generations of rediæ which produce cercariæ with a pair of pigmented "eye-spots" and a long tail which has a dorsal and a ventral fluted fin (*e.g.*, is lophocercous). The cercaria, after escape from the snail, becomes attached to the underside of the scales of fishes or penetrates into superficial tissues, where it discards its tail, rounds up and becomes encysted. Fish-eating birds and mammals which consume the infected fish in an uncooked condition become the hosts for the definitive stage.

Heterophyes heterophyes (von Siebold, 1852) Stiles and Hassall, 1900

Historical and Geographical Notes. — This minute fluke was first found by Bilharz, in 1851, at the autopsy of a native of Cairo, Egypt (Bilharz, 1852). It is a common parasite in the lower Nile valley and occurs in the Orient.

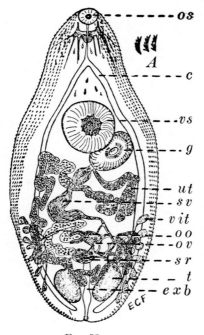

FIG. 59   FIG. 60

FIG. 59.—Adult *Heterophyes heterophyes*, ventral view. × 50. *c*, cecum; *exb*, excretory bladder; *g*, genital sucker (gonotyl); *oo*, oötype; *os*, oral sucker; *ov*, ovary; *sr*, seminal receptacle; *sv*, seminal vesicle; *t*, testis; *ut*, uterus; *vit*, vitellaria; *vs*, ventral acetabulum. (Adapted from Looss, in Faust's *Human Helminthology*, Lea & Febiger, Philadelphia.)

FIG. 60.—Egg of *Heterophyes heterophyes*. × 1120. (Original, from Faust's *Human Helminthology*, Lea & Febiger, Philadelphia.)

Morphology, Biology and Life Cycle.—The mature *Heterophyes heterophyes* (Fig. 59) is a minute pyriform worm, broadly rounded posteriorly and somewhat narrower anteriorly. It measures 1 to 1.7 mm. in length by 0.3 to 0.4 mm. in breadth. It is covered with minute spines set close together. The oral sucker is very small (90 microns in diameter) and the ventral acetabulum considerably larger (230 microns in diameter). A conspicuous feature of this species is the genital sucker which lies on the lateral posterior border of the ventral acetabulum. The seminal vesicle lacks an enveloping cirrus sac and there is no cirrus organ.

The eggs (Fig. 60) are small (28 to 30 microns by 15 to 17 microns), have a conspicuous conical operculum, and contain a mature miracidium. When these eggs are ingested by *Pironella conica* (Egypt) or *Cerithidia cingula alata* (Japan), they hatch and proceed with their intra-molluscan stages of development. The cercariæ which escape from the mollusc encyst superficially in fresh- or brackish-water fishes, which constitute the source of infection for man and other mammals.

Pathogenicity and Symptomatology.—The presence of *Heterophyes* and related species in the mucosal crypts of the duodenum and jejunum produces superficial irritation of the glands, with excess secretion of mucus and superficial necrosis of the mucosa. In heavy infections this may be accompanied by colicky pains and a mucous diarrhea. More serious is the occasional deep penetration of the worms into the mucous coat of the intestine, so that their minute eggs get into mesenteric venules or lymphatics and are carried to the heart, brain or spinal cord, where they may stimulate granulomatous reaction with symptoms related to these lesions (Deschiens, 1958).

Diagnosis.—Eggs of *H. heterophyes* (Fig. 60) and other heterophyid flukes following their recovery in the stool must be differentiated from eggs of *Clonorchis sinensis* and species of *Opisthorchis* which are about the same size and general shape.

Treatment.—This consists in the administration of hexylresorcinol crystoids by mouth as recommended in *F. buski* infection (page 138), or tetrachloroethylene by mouth as recommended in hookworm infection (page 255) (See Table 7, page 418).

Epidemiology.—Infection is acquired from eating fresh- or brackish-water fish (frequently the mullet) in a raw, salted or dried condition. Fresh-water snails become infected when they ingest the eggs of the fluke discharged in the definitive host's excreta which reach the water.

Control.—Control can be effected by the thorough cooking of all fish intended for human consumption.

Metagonimus yokogawai Katsurada, 1912

Historical and Geographical Notes—*Metagonimus yokogawai* was first described by Katsurada, in 1912. This is probably the most common heterophyid fluke in the Orient, Maritime Provinces of U.S.S.R., northern Siberia and the Balkans. It has also been reported from human cases in Spain.

Morphology, Biology and Life Cycle.—*Metagonimus yokogawai* (Fig. 61) resembles *H. heterophyes* in its habitat in the definitive host, its shape, size (1 to 2.5 mm. by 0.4 to 0.75 mm.) and its life cycle. The distinctive features concern the ventral acetabulum, which is deflected to one side of the midline, and the genital opening, which lacks an independent sucker but has its muscular rim fused with that of the ventral acetabulum.

The eggs of *M. yokogawai*, measuring 26.5 to 28 microns by 15.5 to 17 microns, closely resemble those of *H. heterophyes* (Fig. 60) and are also readily mistaken for those of *Clonorchis sinensis*. The snail hosts are species of *Melania*, *Semisulcospira*, etc., which ingest the eggs and in which the miracidia transform into sporocysts, with two successive generations of rediæ and finally the development of cercariæ having a pair of pigmented "eye-spots" and a dorsal and a ventral fluted tail fin.

The cercariæ which escape from the snails become attached to fresh-water fishes and encyst under the skin.   Consumption of the uncooked infected fish provides the opportunity for infection of the definitive hosts.

Pathogenicity and Symptomatology.—These minute worms are attached to the cells in the mucosal crypts, usually at the duodenal and jejunal levels of the small intestine, causing excess secretion of mucus, superficial erosion of the mucosa and granulomatous infiltration around eggs deposited in the stromal tissues.   The worms have also been demonstrated deep in the mucosal layer, where they remain until they die (Africa, 1937) but without host-tissue encapsulation.   The symptoms consist of mild to moderate mucous diarrhea of a persistent type.

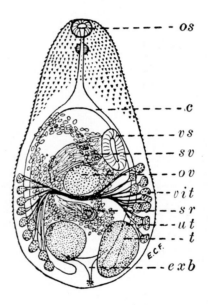

Fig. 61.—Adult *Metagonimus yokogawai*, ventral view.   × 36.   *c*, cecum; *exb*, excretory bladder; *os*, oral sucker; *ov*, ovary; *sr*, seminal receptacle; *sv*, seminal vesicle; *t*, testis; *ut*, uterus; *vit*, vitellaria; *vs*, ventral acetabulum.   (Original, from Faust's *Human Helminthology*, Lea & Febiger, Philadelphia.)

Diagnosis.—This is based on recovery of the eggs in the stool and their differentiation from those of other heterophyid flukes, *Clonorchis sinensis* and species of *Opisthorchis*.

Treatment.—This consists in the administration of hexylresorcinol crystoids by mouth as recommended in *F. buski* infection (page 138), or tetrachloroethylene by mouth as in hookworm infection (page 255) (See Table 7, page 418).

Epidemiology.—Man, other fish-eating mammals and the pelican are the natural hosts, which become infected from consuming the fresh-water trout (*Plectoglossus altivelis*), *Odontobutis obscurus* and *Salmo perryi*.   Pollution of water with the egg-laden excreta of the definitive hosts provides the source of infection for the molluscan and fish hosts.

Control.—Thorough cooking of fresh-water fish will safeguard the human population.

OTHER HETEROPHYID INFECTIONS OF MAN

Other heterophyid flukes have been reported from the human host. Most of these species occur in the China Sea area but two species have also been diagnosed in Hawaiians and Tokelau islanders who have eaten locally caught mullet. All have the capacity to produce ectopic lesions in case their eggs get into the lymphatics or blood stream from the intestinal wall.

HEPATIC FLUKES

Fasciola hepatica Linnaeus, 1758
(The sheep liver fluke, causing fascioliasis hepatica)

Historical and Geographical Notes

Fasciola hepatica was the first trematode to be described (de Brie, 1379) and was likewise the one first on which the complete life cycle was elucidated, in Germany (Leuckart, 1882) and in Australia (Thomas, 1883). It is particularly prevalent in sheep-raising areas, following the importation of sheep from Europe. In many regions fascioliasis is economically an important disease. In several countries human infection is an increasing clinical and public health problem.

Morphology, Biology and Life Cycle

The Adult Fluke.—The mature *Fasciola hepatica* (Fig. 62) is a relatively large worm, measuring up to 30 mm. in length by 13 mm. in breadth. It is more or less flattened and leaf-like along the margins, fleshy throughout the middle. At the anterior end there is a distinct, conical projection, while the posterior end is broadly rounded. The most conspicuous morphologic features of species of *Fasciola* are the extensive branching of the intestinal ceca, of the two testes and the vitelline follicles, and the relatively short, convoluted uterus.

F. hepatica adults reside typically in the proximal bile passages and the gall bladder. Occasionally they fail to reach this location and are found ectopically in the peritoneal cavity or other anatomical sites.

The Life Cycle.—The eggs are unembryonated when expelled from the genital pore. They pass from the common bile duct into the duodenum and intestinal tract of the host, to be evacuated in the stools. These eggs are large (130 to 150 microns by 63 to 90 microns), regularly hen's-egg-shaped, grayish hyaline, relatively thin-shelled, and have a small flat operculum at one end. They require 9 to 15 days to mature in fresh water at an optimum temperature of 22° to 25° C. (72° to 77° F.). Upon hatching the miracidium invades a lymneid snail, shedding its ciliated epithelium as it enters (Dawes, 1960), and transforms into a sporocyst. Within 30 days, second and third generation rediæ and cercariæ have been produced. Then the cercariæ swarm out of the snail, and after crawling upon moist vegetation shed their tail, round up and encyst as minute white spherules. These cysts survive for a considerable time in a moist atmosphere but soon succumb to drying.

10

When the viable cysts ingested by mammals reach the duodenal level, they excyst and the metacercariæ actively burrow through the intestinal wall, migrate across the peritoneal cavity to the liver, then burrow through Glisson's capsule and the hepatic parenchyma to the bile ducts, where they develop into adults in 3 to 4 months after exposure.

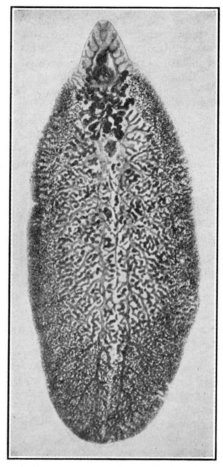

FIG. 62.—Adult *Fasciola hepatica*, ventral view. × 4. (Photograph by Professor H. J. Van Cleave, adapted from Faust in Brennemann's *Practice of Pediatrics*, W. F. Prior Co.)

Pathogenicity and Symptomatology

The migrating young *Fasciola hepatica en route* through the hepatic parenchyma to the bile ducts cause both traumatic damage and toxic irritation, with necrosis of tissues along the pathway. In the larger bile passages they cause hyperplasia of the biliary epithelium, with leukocytic infiltration and development of a fibrous capsule around the ducts.

Early symptoms in human infections consists of right upper quadrant abdominal pain, fever and hepatomegaly; biliary colic with coughing and vomiting; marked jaundice; generalized abdominal rigidity; diarrhea; irregular fever; profuse sweating; urticaria; significant eosinophilia; and Loeffler's syndrome may appear (Derom *et al.*, 1959). Later there may be profound systemic toxemia, and occasionally macrocytic anemia; empyema of the gall bladder (Westermeyer *et al.*, 1958), cholecystitis or cholelithiasis.

The mature or adolescent worms have been found in abscess pockets in bloodvessels, lungs, subcutaneous tissues, ventricles of the brain and the orbit, often associated with mature worms in the bile passages.

False fascioliasis refers to the recovery of the eggs of *Fasciola* in the stool following ingestion of infected livers of sheep, goats or cattle, raw or cooked.

Diagnosis

Most cases of true fascioliasis hepatica are first apprehended by recovery of the eggs in the patient's stool. These require differentiation from eggs of *Fasciolopsis buski*, which are almost identical in size and appearance. This difficulty may be avoided by obtaining samples of uncontaminated bile B for microscopic examination. In cases of false fascioliasis, eggs of *Fasciola* will no longer appear in the feces after the patient has been placed on a liver-free diet.

Treatment

The usual treatment for fascioliasis consists in the subcutaneous administration of *emetine hydrochloride*, which provides symptomatic relief and permanent disappearance of the eggs in both feces and bile (See Table 7, page 418).

Epidemiology

Sheep liver fluke infection is contracted by ingesting vegetation on which the metacercariæ of *F. hepatica* have encysted. In the case of sheep and many other herbivorous and omnivorous mammals, exposure results from eating grass which has grown in marshy meadows or around ponds or streams where the infected snail hosts abound. Human infection is usually due to eating fresh water-cress (*Nasturtium officinale*) to which the metacercarial cysts are attached. Up to 1957 300 published autochthonous human cases have originated in Latin America, Mediterranean countries, Poland, U.S.S.R., China, Hawaii, East and South Africa (Faiguenbaum, 1958). In Cuba, Chile and other Latin-American countries, southern France and Algeria, human infection is relatively frequent and clinically important. Epidemics have been reported from Cuba, Mexico (Hernández Chiñas, 1959) and France. Only one case of human fascioliasis has been demonstrated for continental United States, although the disease is prevalent in sheep and cattle in the South and West, and has become established in the Middle West. (Personal communication of Dr. Lee Monroe, La Jolla, Calif., to Dr. Faust, 1960; Norton, R. A., and Monroe, L., 1961, Gastroenterol., *41*, 46–48.)

Control

Fundamental control requires the institution of measures to eradicate the natural infection in sheep and other herbivorous mammals. Since most human infections result from use of water-cress as salad greens, control of human fascioliasis hepatica will usually be obtained if this delicacy is omitted from the diet in enzoötic areas.

Fasciola gigantica Cobbold, 1856

(The giant liver fluke, causing fascioliasis gigantica)

This fluke differs from *Fasciola hepatica* in its greater length, more attenuate shape, shorter anterior cone, slightly larger ventral acetabulum, the more anterior position of the testes and the larger size of the eggs (160 to 190 microns by 70 to 90 microns). The natural hosts are the camel, cattle, water buffalo and other herbivorous mammals. The life cycle parallels that of *F. hepatica*, including lymneid snails as first intermediate hosts. Human infections have been reported from Senegambia, Indochina, Tashkent and Hawaii (Alicata, 1953; Stemmermann, 1953). The clinical aspects of this infection are essentially the same as in fascioliasis hepatica. Control has not been studied.

Dicrocœlium dendriticum (Rudolphi, 1818) Looss, 1899

(The lancet fluke, causing dicrocœliasis)

This delicate fluke is a common parasite of the bile passages of sheep and other herbivorous mammals in Europe, North Africa, northern Asia, parts of the Orient and to a lesser extent in North and South America. Numerous diagnoses of human infection have been reported from the U.S.S.R. and elsewhere; most of these are cases of false parasitosis resulting from consumption of infected livers, with the evacuation of eggs of *D. dentriticum* in the consumer's feces, but genuine human cases have been diagnosed from Europe, Asia and Africa.

Morphologic and Biologic Aspects.—The adult worm (Fig. 63) resides in the smaller bile ducts. It is lancet-shaped, flat, thin and transparent. It is relatively small, measuring 5 to 15 mm. in length by 1.5 to 2.5 mm. in breadth, and has a smooth cuticle. The most conspicuous features of its internal anatomy are the position of the two testes anterior to the ovary in the anterior half of the body and the distribution of the major portion of the long uterine coils in the median field of the posterior half of the body. The eggs are asymmetrically ovoidal, thick-shelled, dark brown in color, have a broad convex operculum, measure 38 to 45 microns by 22 to 30 microns and typically contain a mature miracidium when evacuated in the feces of the definitive host.

In order to proceed with their development the eggs must be ingested by a land snail, in which the hatched miracidium transforms into a first generation sporocyst which produces a brood of second-generation sporocysts. Each of these, in turn, produces cercariæ which are elongated-oval organisms having a delicate oral stylet and a long attenuated tail. The cercariæ emerge from their molluscan host only when rains succeed a long dry period, and become massed in slime balls. Krull and Mapes (1952), demonstrated the need for a second intermediate host, a foraging ant (*Formica fusca*), which eats the slime balls and in which the metacercariæ become encysted. Infection is acquired accidentally by ingesting the infected ants.

Clinical Data—The presence of *D. dendriticum* in the bile passages provokes hyperplasia of the biliary epithelium, fibrosis around the ducts and in heavy infections, pressure portal cirrhosis. In human cases the common symptoms consist of biliary colic, hepatitis, abdominal distress, flatulent dyspepsia, diarrhea, vomiting, chronic constipation and systemic intoxication. Diagnosis is based on the continued recovery of the characteristic eggs in the stool or from biliary drainage. (See Plate II *Q*, p. 25) No dependable chemotherapy has been discovered. Control measures have not been developed.

Fɪɢ. 63.—Adult *Dicrocœlium dendriticum*, ventral view. × 10. (Adapted from M. Braun, in Faust's *Human Helminthology*, Lea & Febiger, Philadelphia.)

Clonorchis sinensis (Cobbold, 1875) Looss, 1907
(The Chinese liver fluke, causing clonorchiasis)

Historical and Geographical Notes

This fluke was first reported by McConnell (1875) from the bile passages of a Chinese carpenter who came to autopsy in Calcutta. It was first reported from Japan in 1883 and from South China in 1908.

The endemic-enzoötic area of *C. sinensis* extends from Japan to Indochina.

Morphology, Biology and Life Cycle

The Adult Worm.—The mature *C. sinensis* lives typically in the bile passages, most frequently in the more distal tributaries under the surface of the liver. The worms (Fig. 64) are elongated, lanceolate, flat and flabby, transparent, golden brown to pinkish in the living condition and measure 10 to 25 mm. in length by 3 to 5 mm. in breadth. The cuticle is smooth and shiny. All of the important internal structures are visible in the unstained living worm. At the anterior tip there are a globose oral sucker and at about one-fifth the body length posteriorly, a smaller ventral acetabulum.

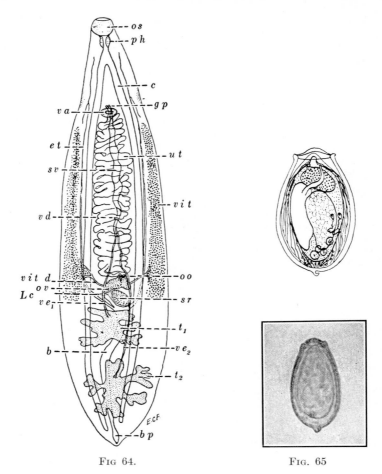

FIG. 64.   FIG. 65

FIG. 64.—Adult *Clonorchis sinensis,* ventral view. × 8. *b,* excretory bladder;
bp, excretory pore; *c,* cecum; *et,* excretory tubule; *gp,* genital pore; *Lc,* Laurer's canal;
oo, oötype; *ov,* ovary; *ph,* pharynx; *sr,* seminal receptacle; *sv,* seminal vesicle; t_1, t_2,
testes. *ut,* uterus; *va,* ventral acetabulum; *vd,* vas deferens; ve_1, ve_2, vasa efferentia;
vit, vitellaria; *vit d,* vitelline duct. (Original, from Faust's *Human Helminthology,*
Lea & Febiger, Philadelphia.)

FIG. 65.—Eggs of *Clonorchis sinensis. Upper,* showing asymmetrical internal structure
of miracidium. × 1200 (after Faust and Khaw); *lower,* × 830 (after Faust in Brennemann's *Practice of Pediatrics*).

The eggs (Fig. 65) are broadly ovoidal, have a moderately thick, light
yellowish-brown shell with a distinct convex operculum which fits into a
circular rim of the shell, and usually a small knob at the opposite end.
They measure 27 to 35 microns in length by 12 to 20 microns in greatest
diameter and are fully embryonated when discharged into the bile ducts
and later evacuated in the host's feces. They hatch only when they
are ingested by appropriate species of operculate snails (*Parafossarulus,*

Bulimus, Semisulcospira, Alocinma, Melanoides tuberculatus, etc.) and reach the snail's mid-gut; the miracidia penetrate into the soft tissues surrounding the intestine, where they transform into first-generation sporocysts, in which second-generation rediæ are produced. The third-generation larvæ, the cercariæ (Fig. 66), escape from the snail and swim about for a short time in the water. In contact with fresh-water fishes the cercariæ

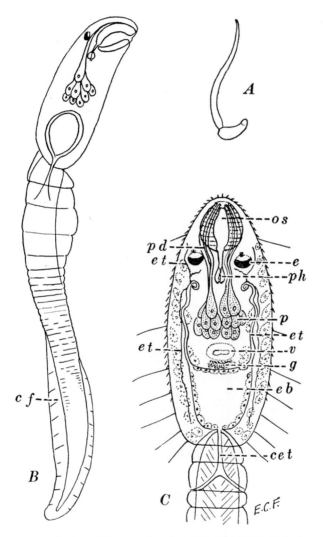

Fig. 66.—Cercaria of *Clonorchis sinensis*. *A*, × 75; *B*, × 300; *C*, body and adjacent portion of tail, × 616. *cet*, caudal excretory tubule; *cf*, tail fin; *e*, "eye-spot;" *eb*, excretory bladder; *et*, excretory tubule; *g*, genital primordium; *os*, oral sucker; *p*, penetration gland; *pd*, penetration gland duct; *ph*, pharynx; *v*, ventral acetabulum. (Adapted from Yamaguti, in Faust's *Human Helminthology*, Lea & Febiger, Philadelphia.)

penetrate into the flesh and become encysted. On consumption of the uncooked fish the metacercariæ are digested out of the flesh and excyst in the duodenum, whereupon the larvæ migrate through the ampulla of Vater to the smaller bile radicles, become attached and develop into adult worms.

Clonorchis infection in man is long-lived, surviving for at least 20 to 25 years. In endemic areas it develops in childhood and increases quantitatively at least past middle life as a result of repeated consumption of the raw infected fish (Faust and Khaw, 1927).

Essential stages in the life cycle are shown in Figure 53 (p. 134).

Pathogenicity and Symptomatology

Mature *Clonorchis sinensis* in the bile passages provoke marked hyperplasia of the biliary epithelium with subsequent dense fibrous encapsulation of the duct. As the number of worms gradually increases over a period of years, practically all of the terminal bile ducts come to have reduced lumens, fibrous thickening of the walls and pressure necrosis of adjacent hepatic parenchyma.

In human cases of light infection symptoms suggestive of very mild liver disturbances can be discovered. With involvement of more extensive areas, there is capricious appetite, a sense of fullness in the abdomen, hepatomegaly with nodular thickenings on the surface of the liver evident on palpation, diarrhea and toxic edema.

In an extensive epidemic of clonorchiasis described by Koenigstein in Shanghai (1949) prodromal symptoms were observed less than a month after exposure and before eggs were detected in the stools. The clinical onset was gradual or sudden, with chills and fever up to 40° C. The liver was large and tender and the scleræ were yellowish tinged. In some cases there was congestive splenomegaly. Eosinophil counts ranged from 10 to 40%. Some weeks later the picture was one of cholecystitis and hepatitis.

Diagnosis

This is based on recovery of the characteristic eggs (Fig. 65) by direct fecal films, sedimentation of the stools, acid-ether technic (see "TECHNICAL AIDS," page 426), or by duodenal or biliary drainage.

Treatment

No satisfactory chemotherapy has been developed for chronic *Clonorchis* infections.

Epidemiology

Infection is contracted by eating fresh-water fish containing the encysted metacercarial stage of *C. sinensis,* in a raw condition, pickled in brine or rice wine, smoked or dried (Faust and Khaw, 1927). In heavily endemic areas the use of human night soil as food for fishes greatly increases the opportunity for maintaining heavy infection in the mollusc and later the fish hosts.

Control

Sterilization of human excreta in highly endemic areas will materially reduce opportunity for heavy exposure, although the excreta of infected dogs and cats will probably provide enough inoculum to maintain the infection in the snails and fishes. The thorough heating of all fish intended for consumption will safeguard the human population.

Opisthorchis felineus (Rivolta, 1884) Blanchard, 1895
(The cat liver fluke, causing opisthorchiasis felinea)

This worm was originally described from the cat in Italy, and a few years later from man in Siberia (Winogradoff, 1892). It has a wide distribution in eastern and southeastern Europe and Asiatic U.S.S.R. It is reportedly common in Indochina and has been recovered from man in Japan and India, although it is probably not indigenous in these latter two countries.

The adult worm (Fig. 67) closely resembles *Clonorchis sinensis* (Fig. 64) in size and general appearance. One notable difference is the smaller size and lesser notching of the testes. The eggs of *O. felineus* are narrower (30 by 11 microns) than those of *Clonorchis* but otherwise bear a close resemblance. The demonstrated common molluscan host is the snail *Bulimus tentaculatus* (Vogel, 1934). Several

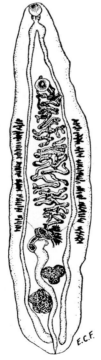

Fig. 67.—Adult *Opisthorchis felineus*, dorsal view, × 10. (After Stiles and Hassall, from Faust's *Human Helminthology*, Lea & Febiger, Philadelphia.)

fresh-water fishes serve as secondary intermediate hosts. In addition to man, the dog, cat, fox, wolverine and seal have been found naturally infected.

The clinical aspects of *O. felineus* infection are similar to those due to clonorchiasis. Therapy is not particularly promising. Control measures have not been developed but thorough heating of fish consumed by man is indicated.

Opisthorchis viverrini (Poirier, 1886) Stiles and Hassall, 1896

This worm, which is closely akin to *O. felineus*, is endemic in Northern Thailand, where 25% of the population is infected (Sadun, 1955). The eggs are smaller than those of *O. felineus* (26 by 13 microns). In addition to man, the civet cat and other fish-eating mammals are infected in the endemic area. The life cycle has not been elucidated but undoubtedly parallels that of *Clonorchis* and *O. felineus*. Clinical aspects of the infection have received little consideration.

PULMONARY FLUKES

Paragonimus westermani (Kerbert, 1878) Braun, 1899
(The Oriental lung fluke, causing Oriental paragonimiasis, pulmonary distomiasis, or endemic hemoptysis)

Historical and Geographical Notes

This fluke was first discovered in the lungs of two Bengal tigers which died in Hamburg and Amsterdam (Kerbert, 1878). The next year a Portuguese resident of Formosa was found by Ringer to have a pulmonary worm. In 1880 Manson found eggs of this fluke in rusty-brown sputum of a Chinese patient. Baelz found similar eggs in bloody sputum of a native Japanese and three years later discovered the flukes in lungs of Japanese subjects. The life cycle has been elucidated by Kobayashi (1918–1921) in Korea, and Yokogawa (1919) in Formosa.

The heavily endemic region of Oriental paragonimiasis is confined to Japan, Korea, Formosa and the Philippines. Additional infections have been reported from other Oriental countries, India, Indonesia, Africa, and northern South America, possibly due to other species of *Paragonimus*.

Morphology, Biology and Life Cycle

The Adult Worm.—The Oriental lung fluke resides normally in fibrous capsules in the lungs but it may also develop in other soft tissues of the body. This worm (Fig. 68) is a plump, ovoidal object, reddish-brown in the living state, gray or grayish-brown after preservation. It measures 7.5 to 12 mm. in length, 4 to 6 mm. in breadth and 3.5 to 5 mm. in thickness. The cuticle is provided with scale-like spines. The oral sucker (*os*) and the ventral acetabulum (*vs*) are subequal (0.75 to 0.8 mm.) in diameter.

The eggs of *P. westermani* (Fig. 69 *A*) are broadly ovoidal, relatively thick-shelled, golden-brown in color, with a somewhat flattened operculum, and measure 80 to 118 microns by 48 to 60 microns. They are unembryonated when laid by the parent worm.

Life Cycle.—When deposited in the pulmonary capsules the eggs usually accumulate around the worm but some eggs reach the respiratory passages

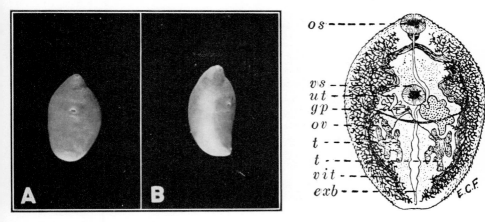

FIG. 68.—Adult *Paragonimus westermani*. *A*, ventral view and *B*, ventrolateral view of worm obtained from brain, × 2 (courtesy Lt.-Colonel L. E. Zimmerman, Armed Forces Institute of Pathology, Washington, D. C.); *right*, compressed, stained specimen, ventral view, × 5. *exb*, excretory bladder; *gp*, genital pore; *os*, oral sucker; *ov*, ovary; *t, t*, testis; *ut*, uterus; *vit*, vitellaria; *vs*, ventral acetabulum. (Original adaptation from Leuckart, in Faust's *Human Helminthology*, Lea & Febiger, Philadelphia.)

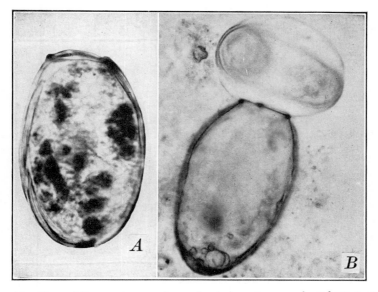

FIG. 69.—Eggs of *Paragonimus westermani*. *A*, immature egg from human sputum; *B*, miracidium hatching from egg, still within embryonic membrane. (*A*, after Faust in Brennemann's *Practice of Pediatrics; B*, photomicrograph by Dr. O. K. Khaw, from Faust's *Human Helminthology*, Lea & Febiger, Philadelphia.)

and are coughed up, imparting a rusty tinge to the sputum. Many are swallowed, pass down the digestive tract and are evacuated in the feces. If the eggs reach clear, usually cool, running water, they embryonate in 16 or more days, then hatch (Fig. 69 *B*). The free-swimming miracidia then enter suitable operculate snails, including several species of *Semisulcospira*, one of *Tarebia* and one of *Assimenia*. Within these snails the miracidium transforms into a first-generation sporocyst, in which rediæ are developed. Each redia, in turn, produces a brood of cercariæ, which escape from the snail and are temporarily free in the water.

The cercaria of *P. westermani* is a flattened oval object with a relatively large oral sucker beset with a dorsal stylet, a smaller ventral acetabulum somewhat posterior to the equatorial plane, two conspicuous groups of penetration glands, a triangular excretory bladder and a delicate knob-like tail. These cercariæ invade the viscera and muscles of fresh-water crabs or, in Korea, species of crayfishes, in the soft tissues of which they become encysted.

When the viable cysts are ingested by the definitive host, excystation occurs in the duodenum and the young worms migrate through the intestinal wall to the peritoneal cavity, burrow through the diaphragm, enter the lungs, and finally settle down near a bronchiole where they develop into adult worms within a fibrous capsule laid down by the host. Sexual maturity occurs when two or more worms are present, permitting cross fertilization (Yokogawa *et al.*, 1960). The circuitous migration from the duodenum to the peribronchial tissues provides opportunity for the worms to wander into organs and tissues far removed from the typical residence of the adult worms (Yokogawa, Cort and Yokogawa, 1960).

Pathogenicity and Symptomatology

If the lung fluke reaches the pulmonary parenchyma, the host-tissue reaction consists of an eosinophilic and neutrophilic infiltration around the growing worm, followed by the development of a thick fibrous envelope 6 to 10 mm. in diameter in the deeper lung tissue. Almost invariably small blood vessels in the capsule provide leakage from the cystic cavity into a bronchiole, so that with the irritation caused by discharge of the eggs and the fluke's metabolites into a bronchiole, paroxysmal coughing occurs, frequently resulting in hemorrhage, with the expulsion of blood in the sputum.

Worms have also been discovered in many ectopic locations, including the liver, intestinal wall, mesenteric lymph nodes, peritoneum, visceral and somatic muscles, testes, pleura and the brain. In these abnormal sites there is a tendency for development of abscesses and pseudo-tubercles, or the lesion may be suppurative or frankly ulcerative (Musgrave, 1907).

Paragonimiasis of the lungs is usually insidious in its onset and mildly chronic in its course. There may be no symptoms other than the occasional coughing up of rusty sputum, but there may be a history of periodic hemoptysis or at least of occasional discharge of blood-tinged sputum. However, dyspnea, fever, malaise, easy fatiguability and anorexia have been observed in cases of extensive pulmonary involvement (Roque, Ludwick and Bell, 1953). Secondary anemia rarely occurs as a result of the hemoptysis.

Paragonimiasis in ectopic locations usually causes significant symptoms. In the pleura there may be a thick purulent effusion and aspirated material may contain an abundance of the fluke's eggs. Glandular involvement characteristically provokes a notable leukocytosis with fever. In the brain the worms reside in granulomatous tissues characteristically producing a Jacksonian type of epilepsy. Numerous cases of cerebral paragonimiasis are reported in the medical literature from Japan and Korea (Mitsuno, Takeya-Sikô, Inanaga and Zimmerman, 1952; Sadun and Buck, 1960.)

Diagnosis

Specific diagnosis can readily be made by recovery of the eggs of *P. westermani* (Fig. 69*A*) in rusty or blood-tinged sputum, or from the feces, pleural aspirate or peritoneal abscesses. Intradermal tests and complement fixation, using antigen prepared from adult worms, provide better evidence of infection than fecal examination (Suzuki, 1958; Sadun and Buck, 1960). Clinically the roentgenogram may be helpful in making a tentative diagnosis of pulmonary paragonimiasis (Lü *et al.*, 1957), although the chest shadows strongly parallel those of pulmonary tuberculosis. Roque, Ludwick and Bell (1953) suggest that paragonimiasis should be considered seriously in endemic areas *only* in those cases in which the sputum is negative for tubercle bacilli. Cerebral paragonimiasis can be determined only after exploratory operation and recovery of the worm or its eggs.

Treatment

No chemotherapeutic agent has heretofore been developed which is specifically lethal for *P. westermani*. Recently Yokogawa *et al.* (1961) have shown both experimentally and clinically that Bithionol (2.2′-thiobis [4.6-dichlorophenol]) has definite helminthicidal effect on this worm within host's tolerance.

Epidemiology

The definitive host commonly acquires the infection from eating the tissues of fresh-water crabs or, in Korea, also of the crayfishes *Astacus japonicus* and *A. similis*, raw or pickled in brine, vinegar or rice wine. These crustaceans live typically in clear, fresh water, usually mountain streams, which are contaminated with the egg-laden excreta of human and reservoir hosts, which provide the inoculum for the molluscan hosts and subsequently the crustaceans.

In addition to man many crab-eating mammals have been found to be naturally infected.

Control

For the individual in endemic areas, the disease may be prevented by meticulous care not to eat the soft tissues of crabs or crayfishes unless they have been thoroughly heated, and care not to contaminate fingers during preparation of the raw crustaceans for the table. No public health program has been developed to control the infection.

Paragonimus kellicotti Ward, 1908

This lung fluke is a natural parasite of a number of mammals in the Mississippi River drainage of the United States and of southern Canada. It was reported once from man. The life cycle parallels that of *P. westermani* in Korea.

SUMMARY

1. The digenetic trematodes have three basic generations in their life cycle *viz.*, (1) egg→ciliated larva (miracidium)→sporocyst (or redia); (2) 2nd generation sporocyst (or redia), and (3) cercaria→metacercaria→adult. Multiplication of progeny occurs in each generation. Molluscs, usually snails, are required as hosts for the miracidium-to-cercaria stages. Depending on the life cycle, the metacercaria will directly invade the definitive host (man or reservoir), encyst on vegetation or within a second intermediate host. In the latter types the definitive host acquires infection from eating the infected vegetation or animal tissue in an uncooked condition.

2. The large intestinal fluke, *Fasciolopsis buski*, is a common parasite of man and hogs throughout the Orient. Infection is acquired from consumption of raw aquatic vegetation to which the encysted metacercariæ have adhered. These larvæ excyst in the duodenum and jejunum, where they become attached and develop into adults, producing ulceration and causing dyspepsia, diarrhea and systemic intoxication. Diagnosis is based on demonstration of the typical eggs of the fluke in the feces. Hexylresorcinol crystoids, administered by mouth, provides satisfactory therapy. Prevention requires cooking of all aquatic vegetation consumed by man in endemic areas.

3. Many species of heterophyid flukes, of minute size, are acquired from consumption of raw fresh-water fish. Several species of echinostomes also develop in man following his ingestion of second intermediate hosts. The adult worms lodge in the crypts of the small intestine, producing erosion and causing diarrhea. Diagnosis is based on identification of the eggs of the particular species in the feces, confirmed by recovery of the adult worms following chemotherapy. Hexylresorcinol crystoids and tetrachloroethylene are relatively satisfactory anthelmintic agents. Prevention consists in cooking the flesh of fresh-water fish and other suspected sources of these parasites.

4. *Fasciola hepatica*, the cosmopolitan liver fluke of sheep, parasitizes man in several parts of the world, usually as a result of eating raw watercress on which encysted metacercariæ have lodged. After excystation in the duodenum the larvæ migrate through the intestinal wall, invade the liver through Glisson's capsule, burrow through the parenchyma and become established in the larger bile ducts. Migration through the liver produces trauma and necrosis; the presence of the worms in the bile

ducts provokes hyperplasia and fibrosis of their walls. The symptoms include acute hepatitis and gall-bladder disease. The infection is detected by demonstration of the fluke's eggs in the feces or from biliary drainage. Emetine hydrochloride administered subcutaneously provides cure in most cases. Avoidance of consumption of watercress in raw salads in endemic areas constitutes a sound preventive measure.

5. Three related liver flukes, *Clonorchis sinensis* in the Orient, *Opisthorchis felineus* in eastern Europe, U.S.S.R. and Indochina, and *O. viverrini* in northern Thailand, are acquired by man and reservoir hosts from eating uncooked fresh-water fish containing the encysted metacercariæ. On arrival in the duodenum the larvæ excyst and migrate through the ampulla of Vater to the distal bile ducts, where they mature. Here they produce hyperplasia of the biliary epithelium and fibrosis of the wall, in heavy infections causing symptoms of gall-bladder disease and peptic ulcer. Typical eggs are diagnosed from the feces. There is no satisfactory treatment. Prevention consists in cooking all fresh-water fish.

6. The lung fluke *Paragonimus westermani* has extensive distribution in the Orient and Southwest Pacific islands, and is endemic in small foci of Africa and northern South America. Infection of man and reservoir mammals results from eating uncooked soft tissues of fresh-water crabs (also crayfish in Korea), containing the encysted metacercariæ. On arrival in the duodenum the larvæ excyst and undergo migration through the intestinal wall to the lungs, where they settle down in peribronchial sites and mature. Their presence provokes partial encapsulation, typically with a fistulous opening into a bronchiole, allowing discharge of the eggs in blood-tinged sputum, or in the feces after the eggs have been swallowed. The worms may get into ectopic sites, such as the pleural or peritoneal cavity and the brain, evoking symptoms resulting from abscesses or granulomas in these locations. Diagnosis depends on domonstration of the eggs. There is no established treatment. Prevention consists in cooking all crabs and crayfish intended for human consumption and avoiding contamination of the fingers when handling the uncooked tissues.

REFERENCES

AFRICA, C. M. 1937. Ova in the Spinal Cord of Man. Philippine J. Sci., *62*, 393–399.

ALICATA, J. E. 1953. Human Fascioliasis in the Hawaiian Islands. Hawaiian Med. J., *12*, 196–201.

BARLOW, C. H. 1925. The Life Cycle of the Human Intestinal Fluke *Fasciolopsis buski* (Lankester). Am. J. Hyg , Monogr. Ser. No. 4, 98 pp.

BENNINGTON, E. 1960. The Life History of the Salmon-poisoning Fluke, *Nanophyetus salmincola* (Chapin). J. Parasitol., *46*, 91–100.

CORT, W. W. 1944. The Germ Cell Cycle in the Digenetic Trematodes. Quart. Rev. Biol., *19*, 275–284.

DEROM, E., REGNIERS, P., MARLIER, R., and DEROM, F. 1959. Distomatose hepatique humaine par *Fasciola hepatica:* observation d'un nouveau cas, queri par emetine et choledocotomie, Bull. l'Acad. R. Med. Belg., *24*, 683–703.

DESCHIENS, R. 1958. Distomatose cerebrale à *Heterophyes heterophyes.* Abstr. 6th Int'l Congr. Trop. Med. & Malaria, p. 265.

FAIGUENBAUM, J. 1958. Distomatosis hepatica humana con especial referencia a complicaciones quirúrgicas. Bol. Chileno Parasitol., *13*, 29–31.

FAUST, E. C., and KHAW, O. -K. 1927. Studies on *Clonorchis sinensis* (Cobbold). Am. J. Hyg., Monogr. Ser., No. 8, 284 pp.

HERNÁNDEZ-CHIÑAS, J. C., TAY, J. and BIAGI, F. F. 1959. Epidemia familiar de fascioliasis en la ciudad de México. Medicina, Rev. Méx., *39*, 529–531.

KOBAYASHI, H. 1918–1921. Studies on the Lung Fluke in Korea. I. On the Life History and Morphology of the Lung Fluke. II. Structure of the Adult Worm. III. Development in the First Intermediate Host. Mitt. Med. Hochsch. Keijo, pp. 1–21, 5–16, 97–115.

KOENIGSTEIN, R. P. 1949. Observations on the Epidemiology of Infections with *Clonorchis sinensis*. Trans. R. Soc. Trop. Med. & Hyg., *42*, 503–506.

KRULL, W. H., and MAPES, C. R. 1952. Studies on the Biology of *Dicrocœlium dendriticum* (Rudolphi, 1819) Looss, 1899 (Trematoda: Dicrocœliidæ), Including Its Relationship to the Intermediate Host *Cionella lubrica* (Müller). VII. The Second Intermediate Host of *Dicrocœlium dendriticum*. Cornell Veterinarian, *42*, 603–604.

LEUCKART, R. 1882. Zur Entwichlungsgeschichte des Leberegels. Arch. f. Naturgesch. *1*, 80–119.

Lü, C.-H., SHANG, E. T., JU, T.-C., and HSÜ, Y.-C. 1957. Clinical Observations on 195 Cases of Paragonimus in Children. Chinese J. Pediatr., *8*, 143–146.

MARTIN, W. E., and KUNTZ, R. E. 1955. Some Egyptian Heterophyid Trematodes. J. Parasitol., *41*, 374–382.

MITSUNO, T., TAKEYA-SIKÔ, INANAGA, K., and ZIMMERMAN, L. E. 1952. Cerebral Paragonimiasis. A Neurosurgical Problem in the Far East. J. Nerv. & Mental Dis., *116*, 685–714.

MUSGRAVE, W. E. 1907. Paragonimiasis in the Philippine Islands. Phillippine J. Sci., B, *2*, 15–63.

NODA, K. 1959. The Larval Development of *Stellantchasmus falcatus*. J. Parasitol., *45*, 635–642.

PHILIP, C. B. 1958. A Helminth Replaces the Usual Arthropod as Vector of a Rickettsialike Disease. Proc. 10th Int'l Congr. Entomol., *3*, 651–653.

ROQUE, F. T., LUDWICK, R. W., and BELL, J. C. 1953. Pulmonary Paragonimiasis. Ann. Int. Med., *38*, 1206–1221.

SADUN, E. H. 1955. Studies on *Opisthorchis viverrini* in Thailand. Am. J. Hyg., *62*, 81–115.

SADUN, E. H., and BUCK, A. A. 1960. Paragonimiasis in South Korea. Immunodiagnostic, Epidemiologic, Clinical, Roentgenographic and Therapeutic Studies. Am. J. Trop. Med. & Hyg., *9*, 562–599.

SADUN, E. H., and MAIPHOOM, C. 1953. Studies on the Epidemiology of the Human Intestinal Fluke, *Fasciolopsis buski* (Lankester) in Central Thailand. Am. J. Trop. Med. & Hyg., *2*, 1070–1084.

STEMMERMANN, G. M. 1953. Human Infestation with *Fasciola gigantica*. Am. J. Path., *29*, 731–759.

THOMAS, A. P. W. 1883. The Life History of the Liver Fluke (*Fasciola hepatica*). Quar. J. Micr. Sci., *23*, 99–133.

VOGEL, H. 1934. Die Entwicklungszyklus von *Opisthorchis felineus* (Riv.), nebst Bemerkungen über Systematik und Epidemiologie. Zoologica, *33*, 1–103.

WESTERMEYER, J., FAIGUENBAUM, J., and ROMERO, G. 1958. Un caso de distomatosis hepática complicado con empiema vesicular. Bol. Chileno Parasitol., *13*, 11–13.

YOKOGAWA, S. 1919. A Study of the Lung Distoma. Third Rept., Formosan Endoparasitic Dis. Research, 289 pp. (Japanese text.)

YOKOGAWA, S., CORT, W. W., and YOKOGAWA, M. 1960. Paragonimus and Paragonimiasis. Exp. Parasitol., *10*, 81–137, 139–205.

YOKOGAWA, M., SUGURO, T., YOSHIMURA, H., and TSUJI, M. 1960. Studies on the Experimental Infection of Dogs with Three Metacercariæ of *Paragonimus westermani* (Kerbert, 1878) Braun, 1899. J. Parasitol., *46*, (Sec.2), 35.

YOKOGAWA, M., YOSHIMURA, H., OKURA, T., SANO, M., TSUJI, M., IWASAKI, M., and HIROSE, H. 1961. Chemotherapy of Paragonimiasis with Bithionol. Jap. J. Parasitol., *10*, 162–173, 177–187.

Chapter 10

The Blood-Flukes or Schistosomes

Introduction

THE group of digenetic trematodes which inhabit the blood stream of vertebrate hosts are commonly referred to as blood flukes or schistosomes (so-called because of the "split body" on the ventral side of the male, in which the female is held during insemination and egg laying. All blood flukes are diecious).

The Adult Blood Flukes.—These worms live typically in pairs in portal venous bloodvessels or in the vesical venules of the caval system. At times, however, they become dislodged and are carried into the intra-hepatic portal vessels, pelvic veins, pulmonary arterioles, or to distant ectopic sites. The adults probably never migrate through blood capillaries except in the rich anastomoses between the portal and caval systems.

The mature schistosomes are delicate cylindroidal objects accommodated to the smaller blood vessels, and usually lie with their anterior extremities directed towards the capillaries. The somewhat larger, more muscular male is attached by its suckers to the wall of the vessel, holding the thread-like female in its sex canal, thus enabling the female to extend its anterior extremity into the smaller-calibered venules in which it deposits eggs (Fig. 70).

The blood flukes which parasitize man secure nutriment from glucose (Bueding, 1950), and from other soluble substances in the plasma. The worms may live for 20 to 30 years or more in the human host.

The Life Cycle.—The eggs of schistosomes are relatively thin-shelled, non-operculate, and each contains a partially developed miracidium at the time they are laid in the smaller venules, in which they obstruct the normal flow of blood. Mechanical obstruction of the venules produced by the eggs, lytic enzymes secreted by the maturing miracidia and hypermotility of the parasitized organ cause weakening and rupture of the wall of the blood-vessel and discharge of the eggs into the surrounding tissues. Where eggs are deposited in previously undamaged mucosa they are extruded into the lumen of the organ and are evacuated in the stool (intestinal types) or the urine (vesical type).

When egg-laden stools or urines are discharged into fresh water, hatching occurs through a rent in the shell, and the miracidia become free-swimming organisms (Fig. 71). If appropriate species of snails are in the immediate vicinity, the miracidia attack the snail's soft tissues, penetrate a short distance and transform into first-generation sporocysts. Within each sporocyst several second-generation sporocysts are developed and on escape from the parent sporocyst migrate further into the snail's tissues (Fig. 72).

11

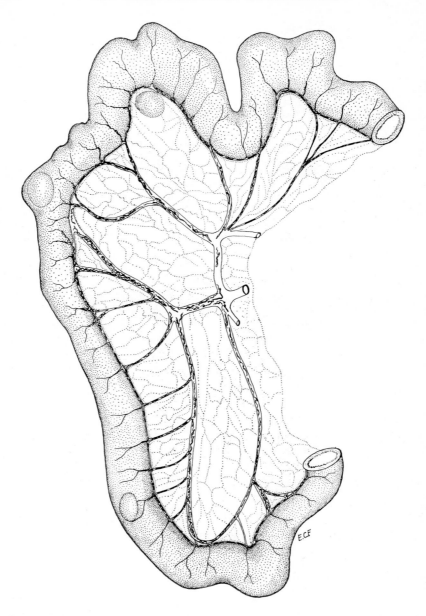

FIG. 70.—Loop of small intestine with terminal branches of mesenteric vein, showing pairs of blood flukes (*Schistosoma japonicum*) in the venules. A majority of the eggs deposited by the female worms are still within the blood vessels, blocking the flow of venous blood, but some have escaped through rupture of the vessels into the submucosa and mucosa and are filtering through to the intestinal canal. Diagrammatic representation based on sections from experimental infection of dogs by Faust and Meleney (1924). (Original from Faust's *Human Helminthology*, Lea & Febiger, Philadelphia.)

Here a brood of many fork-tailed cercariæ is produced over a period of several weeks. When mature these larvæ escape from the second-generation sporocysts, break out of the snail and swim about in the water (Fig. 73).

On contact with the skin of man or other susceptible mammals, the cercariæ burrow and digest their way into the skin, meanwhile discarding their tails. After penetration into cutaneous blood capillaries or venules, the larvæ are

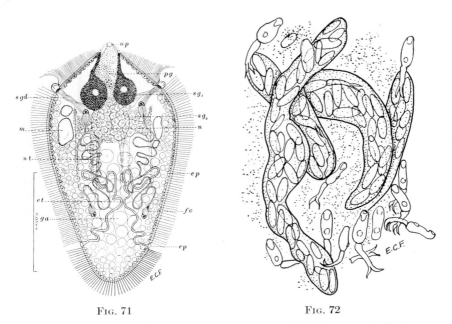

FIG. 71   FIG. 72

FIG. 71.—Miracidium of *Schistosoma japonicum*, hatched from egg in fresh water. *ep*, excretory pore; *et*, excretory tubule; *fc*, flame cell (solenocyte); *ga*, germ cell of second-generation sporocyst; *m*, metabolic secretions; *n*, nerve center; *nt*, posterior nerve trunk; *op*, opening of primitive gut; *pg*, primitive gut; *sg₁*, anterior secretory (penetration) gland; *sg₂*, lateral group of secretory glands; *sgd*, lateral secretory gland duct. × 550 (After Faust and Meleney, from Faust's *Human Helminthology*, Lea & Febiger, Philadelphia.)

FIG. 72.—Second-generation sporocysts of *Schistosoma japonicum* with escaping cercariæ, dissected out of *Oncomelania quadrasi*, the intermediate host in the Philippines. × ca, 100. (Original, from Faust's *Human Helminthology*, Lea & Febiger, Philadelphia.)

carried in the blood stream through the right chambers of the heart into the pulmonary arteries. They reach and slowly squeeze through the pulmonary capillaries, following which they are carried through the left chambers of the heart into the aorta and large arterial vessels. A majority are usually carried into the mesenteric artery and pass through the capillaries into intra-hepatic portal blood. Here the little larvæ feed and grow. About 16 days later they begin migrating against incoming portal blood to the locations where they are destined to reside.

Serological studies conducted with the three species of human schistosomes in experimental animals and man indicate that three separate stages of the parasite stimulate antibody reaction, *viz.*, cercaria, adult worm and egg. Cercarial precipitins and agglutinins have high titer in early infections. Adult precipitins appear later and have low titer. Circumoval precipitins develop with oviposition and become more pronounced in later infections. These antibodies are stage-specific (Oliver-Gonzáles, Bauman and Benenson, 1955).

Pathogenesis.—Pathologic changes resulting from blood-fluke infection in a susceptible host are divided into three consecutive periods, *viz.*, (1) *biologic incubation,* from skin penetration until the worms have arrived and matured in the venules of the intestine or urinary bladder and the females are ready to oviposit; (2) the *acute stage,* which is one of active egg deposition and extrusion, and (3) the *chronic stage,* that of tissue proliferation and repair.

(1) *Biologic Incubation.*—Minute hemorrhages are produced at the sites of penetration from the surface of the skin into the cutaneous venules. After arrival of the larvæ in the pulmonary capillaries, there is considerable infiltration around the delicate blood-vessels through which the worms are passing, with a predominance of eosinophils and at times of giant cells. Larvæ which break out of the capillaries or which are carried to sites unfavorable for development are destroyed by phagocytes. On arrival in intra-hepatic portal blood the worms' metabolites provoke an acute hepatitis and systemic intoxication and sensitization. These reactions continue as the adolescent worms migrate to the sites where they mature, mate and oviposit.

(2) *The Acute Stage.*—With the production and extrusion of eggs from the venules into the lumen of the intestine or bladder, there is traumatic damage and hemorrhage. Meanwhile, some of the eggs become trapped in perivascular tissues by the development of a pseudo-abscess around each egg (Fig. 74). Gradually

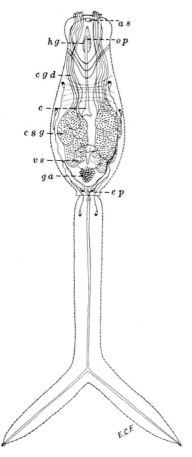

Fig. 73.—Cercaria of *Schistosoma japonicum. as,* opening of anterior sucker; *c,* primitive gut; *cgd,* penetration gland duct; *csg,* penetration gland; *ep,* excretory pore; *ga,* genital primordium; *hg,* head gland; *op,* opening of primitive gut; *vs,* ventral sucker. × 340. (Original, from Faust's *Human Helminthology,* Lea & Febiger, Phila.)

many of the eggs of *S. japonicum* and *S. mansoni* are swept into the intra-hepatic portal vessels, are trapped and filter into periportal tissues, provoling pseudo-tubercle formation. In *S. hæmatobium* infection eggs and at times the worms themselves are carried out of the vesical plexus into adjacent pelvic veins, or to the pulmonary arterioles, where they produce similar lesions. Moreover, *S. mansoni* and *S. japonicum* adults and eggs may pass from portal to caval blood and *S. hæmatobium* from caval to portal blood. Occasionally worms and eggs of all three species may be recovered at distant sites.

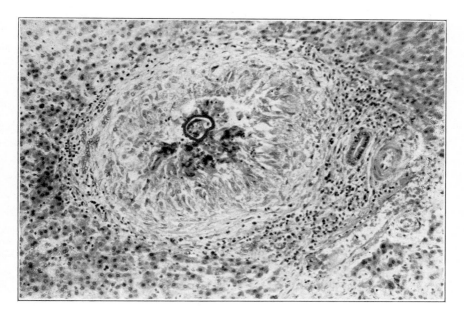

Fig. 74.—Organizing pseudo-tubercle around egg of *Schistosoma mansoni* in intestinal wall. (After Ash and Spitz.)

(3) *The Chronic Stage.*—Continued host-cell proliferation and fibrous repair of damage produced by eggs in infection with *S. japonicum* and *S. mansoni* cause fibrosis of the intestine and cirrhosis of the liver. In the chronic stage of the vesical type of schistosomiasis, the wall of the urinary bladder becomes gradually thickened and fibrosed, and the urethra becomes thickened and its lumen reduced by strictures. These same chronic processes extend at times into adjacent pelvic organs and into the external genitalia.

To a somewhat lesser degree, eggs of *S. hæmatobium*, *S. mansoni* and *S. japonicum*, in the order named, infiltrate perivascularly in the lungs, where they stimulate pseudo-tubercle formation and cirrhotic changes. Nests of schistosome eggs may reach the brain and spinal cord, provoking granulomas. Carcinomas of the rectum, liver and urinary bladder are not infrequently found in chronic blood-fluke disease.

Symptomatology, Diagnosis and Treatment.—These topics will be considered separately under each of the etiologic agents presented below (*Schistosoma japonicum*, page 169; *S. mansoni*, page 174, and *S. hæmatobium* page 177).

Epidemiology.—The free-living cercariæ of these flukes become attached to the skin of their definitive host, which they actively enter, and in which after a period of migration through the bloodvessels they develop to maturity in this host. The usual methods of human exposure consist in wading, swimming, bathing or washing clothes in shallow water near the infected snail hosts.

The excreta of man and reservoir hosts containing viable schistosome eggs provide the inoculum which initiates the extrinsic phase of the life cycle of the parasite . The eggs hatch in fresh water, the escaping miracidia enter snails in the vicinity, undergo two sporocyst generations of development and multiplication within the snails, and the fork-tailed cercariæ are then discharged into the water. For *Schistosoma japonicum* there are many mammalian reservoirs, yet the use of human feces as fertilizer for crops in endemic areas probably constitutes the most important source of eggs. In contrast, *S. mansoni* and *S. hæmatobium* have less common natural reservoirs; infection with these parasites is perpetuated almost exclusively by the promiscuous discharge of human wastes into nearby water (feces in the case of *S. mansoni*, urine and feces in the case of *S. hæmatobium*).

The geographical distribution of these three blood-flukes is shown in Figure 75.

Control.—See separate discussion under *S. japonicum* (page 171), *S. mansoni* (page 175) and *S. hæmatobium* (page 178); also Wright, Dobrovolny and Berry (1958) for molluscicidal control.

Olivier (1955) has concluded that, except for limited areas, eradication of the molluscan transmitters of schistosomiasis "is probably not attainable in the near future." Thompson (1959) has voiced the considered opinion that "the greatest challenge in medical parasitology today is provided by the schistosomiases," and Gear (1961) considers it to be "a major problem."

Schistosoma japonicum Katsurada, 1904

(The Oriental blood fluke, causing intestinal and hepatic schistosomiasis, Oriental schistosomiasis or schistosomiasis japonica)

Historical and Geographical Notes

Katsurada first described the worm, which he named and incriminated as the causative agent of the disease. Fujinami and Nakamura (1909) demonstrated that the skin was the portal of entry into the definitive host; Miyairi and Suzuki (1913–1914) elucidated the extrinsic stages of the life cycle.

Schistosomiasis japonica is confined to the Far East, coëxtensive with the distribution of snails of the genus *Oncomelania* (Fig. 75, p. 167). In Formosa *S. japonicum* is enzoötic and rarely produces patent infection in

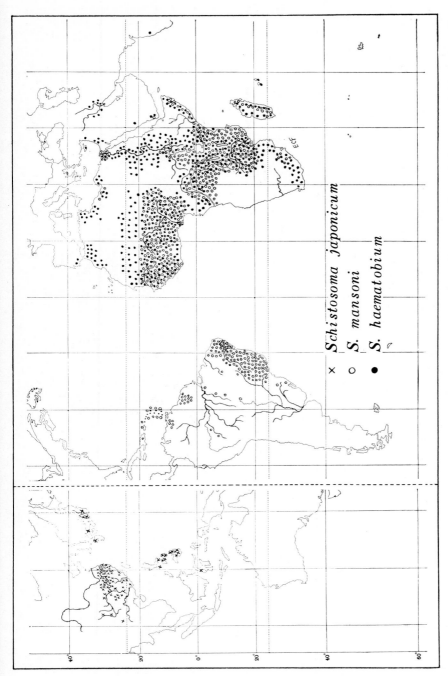

Fig. 75.—Map showing the distribution of the three species of schistosomes which commonly parasitize man. (Original, Faust.)

man. This infection has been discovered in southern Thailand, among natives in an area occupied by Japanese troops during World War II.

Stoll (1947) has estimated that the total incidence of infection with *S. japonicum* is 46 million persons, all of whom acquired the disease in the Far East.

Morphology, Biology and Life Cycle

The Adult Worms.—The adult males of *S. japonicum* (Fig. 76) measure 12 to 20 mm. in length by about 0.50 mm. in greatest breadth. Their

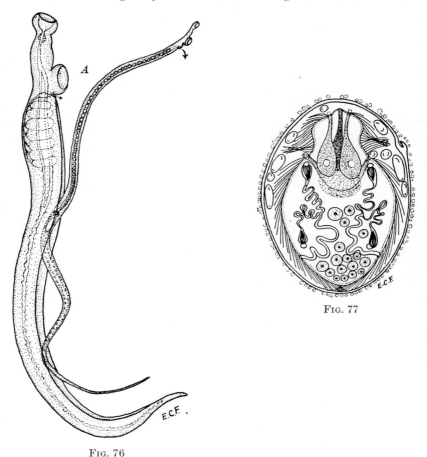

Fig. 76

Fig. 77

Fig. 76.—Adult male and female *Schistosoma japonicum*. *A*, female in sex canal of male, in position for egg laying; testes of male are compactly piled on one another just behind ventral acetabulum; arrows indicate genital pores of male and female worms. (After Faust, from *Human Helminthology*, Lea & Febiger, Philadelphia.)

Fig. 77.—Fully embryonated egg of *Schistosoma japonicum*, with enclosed miracidium and host cells adherent to the sticky surface of the shell. × 60. (Original, from Faust's *Human Helminthology*, Lea & Febiger, Philadelphia.)

cuticle lacks tuberculations. Conspicuous features of the body are the subequal oral and ventral suckers, the long ventral sex canal and the relatively large, compressed, ovoidal testes (usually 7) piled on top of one another behind the ventral sucker.

The females are much more delicate than the males, with a length of about 15 to 30 mm. and a breadth of 0.1 to 0.3 mm. Eggs discharged in the stool are usually rotund, measure 70 to 100 microns by 50 to 65 microns, and each contains a ciliated miracidium.

The earliest habitat of the young adult *S. japonicum* is the tributaries of the superior mesenteric vein adjacent to the small intestine. Later some worms migrate into the inferior mesenteric vein, or even into the caval system. In all of these locations, the females continue to lay a considerable number of eggs daily over a period of years.

The Life Cycle.—Fully embryonated viable eggs of *S. japonicum* (Fig. 77) soon hatch in fresh water and the miracidia attack and enter the soft tissues of species of small operculate snails of the genus *Oncomelania*. After approximately four weeks of development the intra-molluscan phase is completed and cercariæ begin to emerge into the water; but during dry weather they remain within the snail. On contact with the skin of man or other mammals the cercariæ become attached to and enter the skin, penetrate into cutaneous capillaries and begin their blood migration. Approximately 4 to 5 weeks later they have matured in the smaller branches of the superior mesenteric vein and egg-laying is initiated (See Faust and Meleney, 1924).

Pathogenesis and Symptomatology

Pathogenesis.—The tissue and humoral changes produced by *S. japonicum* in the human body conform to the general picture described earlier in this chapter (page 164), but the following points require special emphasis in schistosomiasis japonica: The biologic incubation period is relatively short, *e.g.*, 4 to 5 weeks; the number of eggs produced by each female *S. japonicum* is larger than in infection with the other two species commonly parasitizing man, and the brunt of the damage is borne by the small intestine and the liver.

Traumatic damage is produced as each egg escapes from a venule, filters through the tissues and is extruded into the lumen of the intestine, with accompanying hemorrhage. The eggs pass down the intestinal canal and are evacuated in the stool in a menstruum of bloody mucus (Fig. 78). Meanwhile the worms' metabolites continue to produce toxic hepatitis and systemic sensitization, the latter demonstrated by the eosinophilic leukocytosis which occasionally reaches 90% of the total leukocyte count. Over a period of 5 years the picture may assume grave proportions, with the development of fibrosis, papillomas and stenosis of the intestinal tract, hepatic cirrhosis with ascites, splenomegaly, and at times moderate pulmonary cirrhosis.

Symptoms.—Towards the end of the biologic incubation period the patient begins to have late afternoon fever, night sweats, and prodromal diarrhea. He usually has an enlarged, tender liver, complains of epigastric distress and pain in the back, groin or legs. Some cases develop giant urticaria about this time or somewhat later.

The acute stage is characteristically ushered in with dysentery and the appearance of eggs in the stools. There are daily fever, excruciating epigastric pain and continued increase in the size of the liver. The patient loses appetite and weight and takes to his bed, but after a few weeks may feel better and return to work, only to have a recurrence of symptoms on physical exertion. The blood picture indicates a microcytic hypochromic type of anemia and an increase in serum globulin, with continued high eosinophilia (Faust *et al.*, 1946).

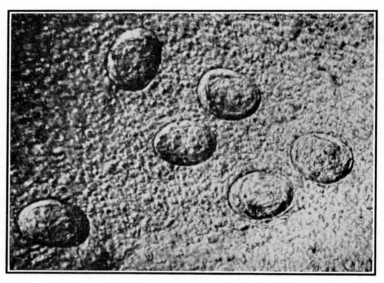

Fig. 78.—Eggs of *Schistosoma japonicum* in dysenteric stool during acute stage of infection.   × 200. (After Faust and Meleney, from *Human Helminthology*, Lea & Febiger, Philadelphia.)

As the chronic stage develops, palpation of the liver reveals an increasingly cirrhotic organ with multiple minute granules (*e.g.*, pseudo-tubercles) on the surface. The mesentery and omentum may be thickened so as to bind down the colon and separate the abdomen into an upper and a lower portion. Somewhat later there is increasing evidence of ascites, severe emaciation, hepatic facies, dyspnea on slight exertion, dilatation of the superficial abdominal veins, and in some patients a hypertensive myocarditis due to infiltration of eggs in the cardiac wall. The patient gradually goes into a decline and may die of exhaustion or a supervening infection.

Among natives in endemic areas reëxposure is common, so that new infections are superimposed on older ones, complicating the clinical picture. Dwarfism and sexual immaturity, loss of physical endurance and marked reduction in life expectancy are notable features of this group (Huang *et al.*, 1957).

Diagnosis

During the biologic incubation period specific diagnosis is not possible. With the development of the acute stage eggs of *S. japonicum* can usually be recovered in bloody mucus in the stool, although sedimentation or acid-ether concentration technics may be required to recover the eggs. (See "Technical Aids," pages 426 and 427.) Intradermal and other serological tests with schistosome antigen (see "Technical Aids," pages 451 and 452) will provide additional evidence of the causative agent of the disease (Expert Committee on Bilharziasis, 1953). In chronic cases rectal biopsy will often supply demonstration of eggs when they are not found in the stools.

Treatment

The only satisfactory drugs for treating schistosomiasis japonica are *potassium antimony tartrate* (tartar emetic) and *sodium antimony tartrate*, administered slowly by vein in a filtered 0.5% solution, in increasing amounts on alternate days for one month, amounting to a total of 320 ml. These trivalent organic antimonials act by interfering with the carbohydrate metabolism of the worms. One full course of treatment provides about 84% cures (See Table 7, page 419.)

Epidemiology

All mammals naturally exposed to the cercarial stage of the parasite are susceptible hosts, including cats, dogs, cattle, water buffaloes, pigs, several species of rodents and man. Exposure occurs when the cercariæ in infested water come in contact with unprotected skin, most frequently during wading, bathing or washing clothes in infested canals. The principal source of inoculum consists of eggs of *S. japonicum* in human feces. Additional eggs are provided in the feces of reservoir mammals, particularly the beasts of burden used to prepare the rice fields for cultivation.

In the Philippines, discovery of the susceptible snail host, *Oncomelania quadrasi*, in streams in virgin forests in alluvial plains suggests potential opportunity for extension of old areas of endemicity or the development of new ones (McMullen *et al.*, 1953).

Control

Schistosomiasis japonica is most difficult to control because of the numerous reservoir hosts. Moreover, it is impractical for natives in endemic enzoötic areas to avoid contact with infested water.

A method of control which may become practical in the extensive endemic territories in the Far East is the application of chemicals to kill the snail hosts. The most effective molluscicides (sodium pentachlorophenate and dinitro-o-cyclohexylphenol), when applied to the irrigation ditches of rice fields in the spring before the fields are planted and again in the fall after harvest, will kill most of the *Oncomelania* snails (90% or more) at each application. The former has been tested in Japan and in the Philippines and appears to have sufficient promise to justify extensive application (McMullen, 1952; Hunter *et al.*, 1952).   Where the terrain is not suitable for the application of molluscicides naturalistic methods may be valuable (Pesigan *et al.*, 1958).

Schistosoma mansoni Sambon, 1907
(Manson's blood fluke, causing schistosomiasis mansoni)

Historical and Geographical Notes

Bilharz (1852), studying human blood fluke infection in Egypt, found that some of the female worms which he recovered contained lateral-spined eggs.   In 1907 Sambon proposed the name *mansoni* for this type of schistosome.   Leiper (1918) found a series of morphologic and life-cycle differences between *Schistosoma mansoni* and the previously described *S. hæmatobium*.

Manson's blood fluke is fundamentally a parasite of the Continent of Africa (Fig. 75, p. 167) in which man is the important host.   It is heavily endemic in the Nile delta but is elsewhere much less prevalent in Egypt. It is common throughout practically all of tropical Africa, where it is frequently coëxistent with *S. hæmatobium*.   It is present in several foci of the Arabian peninsula.   Importation of infected African slaves to tropical America provided opportunity for establishment of the disease in Brazil, Surinam and Venezuela, and in several of the West Indies.   Stoll (1947) has estimated that 39.2 million persons are infected with this blood fluke.

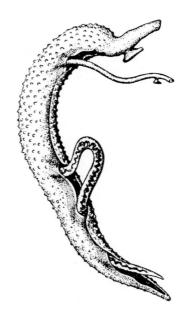

Fig. 79.—Adult male and female *Schistosoma mansoni* in copula. Note the cuticular tuberculations on the male. × 10. (After Gonnërt, from Faust and Russell's *Clinical Parasitology*, Lea & Febiger, Philadelphia.)

Morphology, Biology and Life Cycle

The Adult Worms.—The adults of *S. mansoni* (Fig. 79) are considerably shorter than those of *S. japonicum*. The males have a length of 6.4 to 9.9 mm., and the females, 7.2 to 14 mm. The cuticle of the male is provided with numerous warty excrescences. The testes, numbering 6 to 9, are minute bodies lying in a grape-like cluster a short distance behind the ventral acetabulum. The most striking internal feature of the female is the short uterus, providing storage space for very few lateral-spined eggs. The worms usually reside in the tributaries of the inferior mesenteric vein

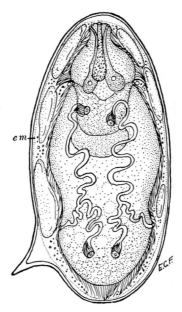

FIG. 80.—Fully embryonated egg of *Schistosoma mansoni*, with enclosed miracidium, lateral view. *em*, embryonic membrane. × 500. (Original, from Faust's *Human Helminthology*, Lea & Febiger, Philadelphia.)

adjacent to the lower colon, although they may be found at higher levels of the intestine, in intra-hepatic portal blood, in the vesical venules, in the pulmonary arterioles and rarely in ectopic foci (Faust, 1948).

The fully developed eggs of *S. mansoni* as recovered in the stool (Fig. 80) are large, elongated-ovoidal objects, rounded at both ends and provided with a conspicuous, lateral spine near one pole, extending at an obtuse angle from the shell's long axis. They measure 114 to 175 microns by 45 to 68 microns.

The Life Cycle.—On dilution of the host's excreta with fresh water the fully embryonated eggs hatch within a few hours and the miracidia are soon found attached to the soft parts of planorbid snails in the immediate vicinity. The cercariæ which later emerge from the snail enter human skin and migrate *via* blood vessels to the mesenteric-portal blood. The time required for migration of the adolescent worms from the intra-hepatic portal vessel to the branches of the inferior mesenteric vein, their maturity and initiation of egg laying is 3 to 4 weeks in the human host. The total incubation period is 6 to 7 weeks.

Pathogenesis and Symptomatology

Pathogenesis.—The humoral and tissue changes caused by *S. mansoni* closely resemble those due to infection with *S. japonicum* (page 169) but (1) The biologic incubation period is about two weeks longer; (2) the early intestinal lesions develop typically in the colon rather than the small intestine, and (3) the number of eggs produced by each *S. mansoni* worm is about $\frac{1}{10}$, hence there are fewer eggs extruded from the intestinal wall and fewer which later become trapped in the perivascular tissues of the intestine and liver; therefore intestinal fibrosis and hepatic cirrhosis develop more slowly in Manson's schistosomiasis.

Symptomatology.—There is no notable difference in the prepatent symptoms between infection with *S. mansoni* and *S. japonicum*. Hepatic cirrhosis develops much more gradually than in schistosomiasis japonica, frank ascites is less frequent and fibrosis of the mesentery-omentum is rarely demonstrated. Nevertheless, very heavy infections with *S. mansoni* produce severe toxic symptoms and rapidly developing dysfunction of the intestinal wall and periportal tissues. Pulmonary lesions and symptoms are relatively common in Manson's schistosomiasis (Meira, 1951).

Diagnosis

This is usually made on demonstration of the characteristic eggs of *S. mansoni* with their distinct lateral spine (Fig. 80), evacuated in the stool. More frequently than in infection with *S. japonicum* concentration methods (see "TECHNICAL AIDS," pages 427 and 428) are required because of the scanty number of eggs. Likewise, rectal biopsy is a particularly fruitful procedure (Ottolina and Atencio, 1943; Hernández-Morales and Maldonado 1946). Intradermal and complement-fixation reactions with schistosome antigen are at times valuable. Pellegrino *et al.*, (1959) found a 95.5% coincidence between stool examination and intradermal tests among school children in an endemic area in Brazil.

Treatment

The most satisfactory chemotherapeutic in Manson's schistosomiasis is potassium antimony tartrate (tartar emetic), administered intravenously as a 0.5% solution, in the dosage schedule recommended for schistosomiasis japonica (page 171).

Epidemiology

Although several species of mammals have been found infected in nature with *S. mansoni*, both in Africa and Brazil, the only important definitive host is man. The molluscan intermediate hosts are planorbid snails, including several species of *Biomphalaria* throughout Africa and *Australorbis glabratus* in the Americas.

Human exposure to Manson's schistosomiasis results from wading, bathing, swimming, washing clothes, and by a variety of agricultural pursuits in which hands or legs are immersed in cercaria-infested water. Kuntz (1952) has reported that in the Yemen the Moslem ablution pools are infested with *S. mansoni* and *S. hæmatobium*.

Control

Although there are no important reservoir hosts for Manson's schistosomiasis, the insanitary disposal of human excreta constitutes a very great obstacle. Rice fields and sugar cane plantations under irrigation, truck gardens using human nightsoil as fertilizer and other cultivated areas provide a challenge to the sanitary engineer. The most practical known molluscicidal agent is sodium pentachlorophenate, (Wright and Dobrovolny, 1953; Dobrovolny, 1958), since it destroys the eggs as well as the young adults of these snails in flowing water. Biological control using predators of the molluscan host may provide assistance in reducing the essential snail population (Ferguson *et al.*, 1958).

Schistosoma hæmatobium (Bilharz, 1852) Weinland, 1858

(The vesical blood fluke, causing vesical schistosomiasis or vesical bilharziasis, endemic hematuria)

Historical and Geographical Notes

Vesical blood fluke disease was prevalent in Lower Egypt in ancient times, as demonstrated by pathologic studies on mummies dating many centuries B.C. The adult worms were first recovered by Theodor Bilharz, in 1851, from the mesenteric veins of a native of Cairo. In 1918 Leiper provided conclusive experimental evidence that *S. hæmatobium* and *S. mansoni* were separate species.

The ancient home of *S. hæmatobium* was the lower Nile Valley, where infection with this worm is still hyperendemic. The present-day distribution (Fig. 75, p. 167) includes practically the entire African Continent; the island of Madagascar; areas in the Arabian peninsula; a focus in southern Palestine; one in Lebanon; several centers in Syria near the Turkish border; the lower Tigris-Euphrates valley; the coast of Iran; an endemic focus on the west coast of India south of Bombay, and two endemic centers on the south coast of Portugal.

Morphology, Biology and Life Cycle

The Adult Worms.—The male is considerably stouter than its mate (Fig. 81), measuring 10 to 15 mm. in length by about 1 mm. in greatest girth. Four or at times 5 small subglobose testes can be demonstrated close to one another immediately behind the ventral acetabulum.

The female is delicately cylindrical, with a length measurement of about 20 mm. and a diameter of 0.25 mm. The genital organs, exclusive of the vitellaria, occupy the median longitudinal field. On oviposition the eggs of *S. hæmatobium* are immature but when excreted they have usually become fully embryonated.

Life Cycle.—The fully mature egg of *S. hæmatobium* (Fig. 82) is elongated ovidal, rounded at the anterior pole and is provided posteriorly

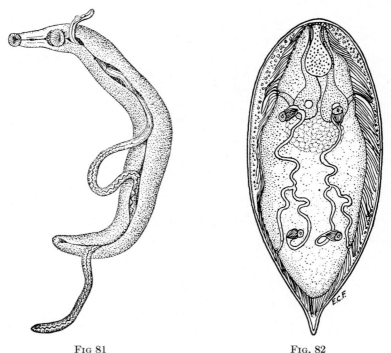

Fig 81   Fig. 82

Fig. 81.—Adult male and female *Schistosoma hæmatobium*. Note fine cuticular spinosities on male. × 12. (After Looss, in Faust's *Human Helminthology*, Lea & Febiger, Philadelphia.)

Fig. 82.—Fully embryonated egg of *Schistosoma hæmatobium*, with enclosed miracidium × 640. (Original, in Faust's *Human Helminthology*, Lea & Febiger, Philadelphia.)

with a terminal spine. It measures 112 to 170 microns in length by 40 to 70 microns in breadth, is straw-colored and relatively transparent. When these eggs reach fresh water they soon hatch and the escaping miracidia, after a short free-swimming period, are attracted to, and penetrate the soft tissues of appropriate snails, in which they undergo development and multiplication, with the emergence of fork-tailed cercariæ 4 to 8 weeks after exposure of the snails.

On contact with human skin the cercariæ penetrate and migrate in blood vessels into portal blood, where they feed and grow, then about 3 weeks after skin exposure begin to migrate against the venous current into the inferior mesenteric vein, and into the rectal vessels. In this location some of the adolescent worms mature and oviposit (Barlow and Meleney, 1949). Possibly a majority migrate through the hemorrhoidal anastomoses and pudendal vein to the vesical plexus, the optimum location for this species. Usually 7 to 9 weeks after exodus of the adolescent worms from the intra-hepatic portal blood eggs first appear in the urine, *e.g.*, 10 to 12 weeks following skin penetration.

S. hæmatobium, like *S. japonicum* and *S. mansoni*, may live for 20 to 30 years provided the host survives that long.

Pathogenesis and Symptomatology

Pathogenesis.—The prepatent incubation period in schistosomiasis hæmatobia parallels that of the two intestinal types of the disease, but there is usually less evidence of acute hepatitis and systemic intoxication.

Egg deposition and extrusion cause local traumatic damage and hemor-rhage, either in the wall of the rectum or the urinary bladder. Vesical lesions include hyperplasia of the wall, then gritty phosphatic deposits on the surface and dense fibrosis of the muscular and submucous coats, through which it is increasingly difficult for the eggs to filter. Meanwhile the urethral lumen becomes greatly constricted, at times completely closed. Similarly the ureters and the pelves of the kidneys, the penis or scrotum may develop obstruction, and fistulas may break through the skin. In women the vulvæ are frequently hyperplastic and indurated. Advanced cases of vesical schistosomiasis usually have septic involvement.

In Egypt there is a high correlation between chronic schistosomiasis of the bladder and malignancies of this organ.

Symptomatology.—During the biologic incubation period, the patient may be essentially symptomless or he may have an increasing malaise with late afternoon fever, moderate hepatic pain or epigastric distress, and an elevated eosinophil count. If the worms mature in the rectal veins there may be severe tenesmus with dysentery. More often the first evidence of the infection is the painless passage of blood at the end of the period of micturition, but more and more there is also discharge of pus cells and necrotic tissue débris, decrease in the interval between periods of urination, and eventual incontinence, or anuria due to urethral stricture. Bladder colic is a cardinal symptom.

Schistosomiasis hæmatobia may be responsible for symptoms referable to the kidneys, testes or prostate, lungs, heart, central nervous system and eye, appendix or liver.

Diagnosis

This is most easily accomplished in a majority of cases by recovery of the characteristic eggs (Fig. 82) in the sediment which settles out of urine in an inverted conical glass container. Immunological tests may be valuable, especially in epidemiological surveys. At times a small bladder biopsy specimen will provide positive evidence not present in the urine. Due to the common involvement of the rectum in this infection (Gelfand and Ross,

12

1953; Azar, Schraibman and Pitchford, 1958), stool examination, (see TECHNICAL AIDS," pages 427 and 428), or at times rectal biopsies, should be employed.

Treatment

As in the other types of human schistosomiasis, the most effective drugs in vesical schistosomiasis are potassium antimony tartrate (tartar emetic) and sodium antimony tartrate, administered as in schistosomiasis japonica (p. 171). Miracil D (Nilodon) apparently has considerable usefulness in *S. hæmatobium* infection; it is administered orally and a complete course requires only 3 to 5 days. It lends itself to treatment of small children whose veins are difficult to enter by needle and to use in dispensary practice in rural areas.

Epidemiology

Man is the only important definitive host of *S. hæmatobium*. Eggs of this worm are commonly extruded from the wall of the urinary bladder and excreted in the urine. Promiscuous urination into bodies of fresh water including ponds and irrigation canals, primitive latrines situated over small rivers or ponds and the emptying of excreta from night pails into small village streams all provide infection for the snail hosts. Moreover, the studies of Gelfand and Ross (1953) and Azar *et al.* (1958) show that *S. hæmatobium* eggs are as commonly deposited in the wall of the colon and rectum as in the urinary bladder, indicating that the stools of infected individuals are a potential medium for the evacuation of eggs into fresh water.

The incidence of schistosomiasis hæmatobia varies from small percentages to near saturation of a native population. The infection is particularly prevalent among young boys who wade or swim in polluted water. The snails which serve as intermediate hosts with few exceptions belong to the genera *Bulinus* and *Physopsis,* but in Morocco and southern Portugal *Biomphalaria dufourii* is the susceptible mollusc.

Extension of irrigation projects throughout Africa and in the Tigris-Euphrates valley is responsible for the spread of vesical schistosomiasis into previously uninfected contiguous areas due to carriage of the snail hosts into the new canals.

Control

Theoretically vesical schistosomiasis is amenable to practical control, since there are essentially no reservoir mammalian hosts. The most effective method for controlling the disease is the eradication of the snail intermediate hosts (WHO Expert Committee on Bilharziasis, 1961). The molluscicidal drug sodium pentachlorophenate is satisfactory in attacking the non-operculate snail hosts of this schistosome which live in flowing as well as still water (McMullen, 1953). Nevertheless there is little evidence of snail control by use of this agent under field conditions. Correction of the insanitary habits and customs of native peoples with respect to the discharge of their excreta will require long-time health education.

Other Blood Flukes Reported as Human Parasites

Several additional species of *Schistosoma* have been reported as human parasites.

Schistosoma bovis (Sonsino 1876) Blanchard, 1895

This is a common parasite in the mesenteric-portal system of cattle and sheep in southern Europe, Iraq and Africa. The eggs (Fig. 83, *4*) are much narrower, more spindle-shaped and considerably longer (230 to 380 microns by 70 to 90 microns) than those of *S. hæmatobium* (Fig. 83, *2*), and in the reservoir hosts can not be easily misdiagnosed. Eggs believed to be those of *S. bovis* have been found in human urine in South Africa but the worms have not been recovered from man (Pitchford, 1959).

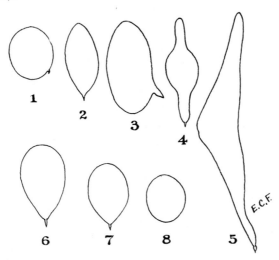

Fig. 83.—Eggs of representative blood flukes parasitizing man and other mammalian hosts. 1. *Schistosoma japonicum; 2, S. hæmatobium; 3, S. mansoni; 4, S. bovis; 5. S. spindale; 6, Ornithobilharzia bomfordi; 7, S. indicum; 8, Schistosomatium douthitti* (syn. *pathlocopticum*). Drawn to scale, much enlarged. (Original, from Faust's *Human Helminthology,* Lea & Febiger, Philadelphia.)

Schistosoma spindale Montgomery, 1906

This is a relatively common parasite in the caval blood of cattle, water buffaloes, sheep and goats in India, Sumatra and South Africa. The elongated fusiform eggs (Fig. 83, *5*) are very large (400 microns by 72 microns). Eggs considered to be those of *S. spindale* have been reported from human urine in South Africa but not in India where the infection is much more heavily enzoötic.

Schistosoma intercalatum Fisher, 1934

This species was created for cases of human infection in tropical Africa in which terminal-spined *Schistosoma* eggs were found exclusively in the stools and the symptoms were referable only to the organs drained by mesenteric-portal blood. Chesterman (Fisher, 1934) observed several hundred cases in the former Belgian Congo and studied at autopsy the distribution of the worms, their eggs and the tissues parasitized. No involvement of the bladder was discovered. The eggs (140 to 240 microns by 50 to 85 microns) are intermediate in size and shape between those of *S. hæmatobium* and *S. bovis*. Experimentally *Physopsis africana* has been found to be a satisfactory molluscan host. This appears to be a *bona fide* species, or a subspecies of *S. hæmatobium*.

Schistosoma matthei Veglia and Le Roux, 1929

This schistosome has been reported as a natural parasite in the mesenteric-portal blood of sheep and monkeys in southern Rhodesia, where Blackie (1932) has diagnosed the worm in human infections on the basis of terminal-spined eggs (210 to 240 microns by 40 to 70 microns) recovered in the urine, and adult worms in association with *S. hæmatobium* at two human autopsies.

Schistosoma incognitum Chandler, 1926

Chandler (1926) created this species on the basis of eggs measuring 95 to 100 microns by 41 to 50 microns, somewhat resembling those of *S. indicum* (Fig. 83, 7), with a small terminal spine, diagnosed twice from human stools in India. Pigs and dogs are reservoir hosts, and the snail host is a species of *Lymnæa* (Sinha and Srivastava, 1960).

Schistosoma faradjei Walkiers, 1928

This species, the validity of which is very doubtful, was proposed for eggs of a schistosome recovered from stools of natives in the former Belgian Congo. The eggs were somewhat smaller than those of *S. mansoni* and lacked a spine.

SCHISTOSOME DERMATITIS

(Swimmer's itch, clam digger's itch, Gulf Coast itch, cercarial dermatitis)

Historical, Geographical and Biological Notes

In 1928 Cort demonstrated that the cercariæ of certain non-human blood flukes were the causal agents of an aggravating form of dermatitis. Intensive investigations in many geographical regions have demonstrated that this skin infection usually occurs during the warm months and is due to skin penetration of the schistosome cercariæ; that non-operculate snails in bodies of fresh water serve as intermediate hosts for these blood flukes, the adults of which are usually parasitic in migratory birds; that transient birds pollute the water with their excreta containing the eggs of the parasite, and that miracidia hatched from the eggs initiate infection in the snails.

Schistosome dermatitis resulting from contact with cercaria-infested fresh water has been reported from many regions of the United States, Europe, Latin America, India, Australia and New Zealand. Species of *Lymnæa, Stagnicola, Physa, Physella, Planorbis, Polyplis, Chilina*, etc. serve as intermediate hosts and the definitive hosts are commonly ducks and geese but passerine birds are naturally infected with some of these avian schistosomes. The adult worms which develop from cercariæ producing the dermatitis belong to the genera *Trichobilharzia* (McMullen and Beaver, 1945; Stauber, 1958; Ulmer, 1958) and *Ornithobilharzia* (Szidat, 1951).

Other areas of schistosome dermatitis are found along salt water beaches in Hawaii (Chu, 1958), southern California, Florida, Rhode Island, and Connecticut. In these areas marine snails are the molluscan hosts of the blood flukes (Fig. 84) and terns, as well as other water and migratory birds, are the natural definitive hosts. Stunkard and Hinchliffe, (1952) identified the adult worm of their cercaria as a species of *Microbilharzia*.

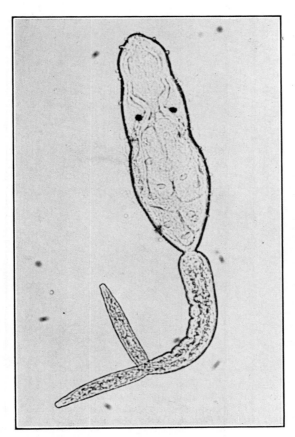

FIG. 84.—Oculate cercaria of avian blood-fluke producing schistosome dermatitis in Hawaii. Penetration glands and ducts are clearly shown. × *ca.* 210. (Photomicrograph courtesy of Dr. George Chu.)

A third epidemiologic type of schistosome dermatitis is due to invasion of the human skin with non-human mammalian schistosomes, including the cattle blood flukes *Schistosoma spindale* and *S. bovis* (Buckley, 1938; Biocca, 1960).

Olivier (1949) regards schistosome dermatitis as a sensitization reaction which is intensified by repeated exposure. Furthermore, the dermatitis is much more likely to develop from skin penetration of blood flukes not adapted to development in man than to those which mature in the human host.

Clinical Aspects of Schistosome Dermatitis

The lesions produced in schistosome dermatitis (Fig. 85) consist of an initial prickling or nettling sensation, which may be accompanied by erythema of the invaded area and, in individuals who have been previously exposed, by local or generalized urticaria. Soon the initial irritation subsides, leaving only a macule at each site of penetration, but in a few hours there is intense itching of the involved area and the macules transform into papules. The reaction reaches its maximum between the second and third day, then gradually decreases.

Treatment consists in the topical application of palliatives such as calamine lotion, to relieve the itching, and, if required, sedation to reduce nervousness.

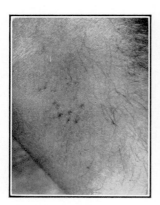 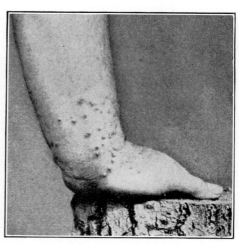

Fig. 85.—Experimental lesions of schistosome dermatitis. *Left,* a few sites of skin invasion on the forearm, with developing papules (photograph courtesy of Dr. George Chu, Hawaii); *right,* multiple pustules on the wrist, with some local edema (after Cort, from Faust's *Human Helminthology,* Lea & Febiger, Philadelphia.)

Control

If the schistosome cercariæ responsible for the dermatitis utilize freshwater snails as intermediate hosts, a molluscicidal chemical such as copper sulfate or copper carbonate may be dissolved in the water along the shore of lakes or in canals and ditches where the snails are found. McMullen and Beaver (1945) urge that beaches in endemic areas be protected from migratory birds, to reduce the opportunity for infection of the snails and thus provide considerable reduction in the dermatitis the following summer.

The control of schistosome dermatitis along salt-water beaches poses a more difficult problem, the solution to which has not been explored.

SUMMARY

1. The blood flukes or schistosomes are typically diecious; the mated pairs normally live in the smaller vessels of the mesenteric-portal and caval blood systems, where they lay non-operculate, partially embryonated eggs. These escape into the lumen of the intestine or urinary bladder and are evacuated in the excreta, meanwhile completing embryonation. They hatch in fresh water and the active ciliated larvæ (miracidia) enter appropriate species of snails, in which they metamorphose into sporocysts, with production internally of a brood of second-generation sporocysts, which, in turn, produce tailed larvæ (cercariæ). These larvæ swarm out of the snails and, on contact with the skin of man or mammalian reservoirs, enter the cutaneous bloodvessels and initiate infection in the definitive host.

2. Three species of blood flukes, *Schistosoma japonicum*, *S. mansoni* and *S. hæmatobium*, are important parasites of man. *S. japonicum* is distributed in Japan, China and the Philippines; *S. mansoni* in Africa, adjacent Arabia and in several countries of tropical America, and *S. hæmatobium* throughout Africa and the Middle East.

3. The metacercariæ of these blood flukes are carried in bloodvessels from the skin, through the lungs, into the mesenteric arteries, thence into intra-hepatic portal blood. Here they feed and grow and, in about 3 weeks after entering the body, migrate against incoming blood into the mesenteric veins. *S. japonicum* lodges in the superior mesenteric veins, where the mated pairs mature in one or two weeks and egg production begins; *S. mansoni* selects the inferior mesenteric veins, in which the worms mature and begin egg deposition in 3 to 4 weeks; *S. hæmatobium* typically proceeds through the rectal veins, hemorrhoidal plexus and pudendal vein to the vesical venules, in which the worms mature 7 to 9 weeks after leaving the portal system.

4. The pathological changes in the human host resulting from schistosome infection consist of (1) intoxication and sensitization, which develop during the incubation period and continue throughout the infection, (2) damage due to egg extrusion through the tissues, and (3) tissue reaction around trapped eggs.

5. In infection with *S. japonicum* and *S. mansoni*, toxic and allergic symptoms, fever and acute hepatitis develop early, followed by epigastric distress, dysentery, enlargement of liver and spleen, later with profound intestinal and hepatic dysfunction. In infection with *S. hæmatobium*, the characteristic early sign is hematuria, followed by increasing dysfunction of the urinary bladder and urethra, and dysentery in case of rectal involvement.

6. Diagnosis of blood fluke infection is made by recovery of the eggs of the three species in the feces or urine, or by rectal or bladder biopsy. Antimony tartrates, administered by vein, are the most effective schistosomicidal chemotherapeutics.

7. Pollution of fresh water by excreta of man or reservoir hosts containing the viable eggs of the blood flukes initiates the extrinsic phases of the life cycle, allowing the eggs to hatch, the emerging miracidia to infect the susceptible snails, and, after two generations of multiplication in

the snails, the emergence of swarms of cercariæ which leave the snail and on contact with human skin initiate infection in man or reservoirs. Eggs of *S. japonicum* and *S. mansoni* are evacuated almost always in the feces, those of *S. hæmatobium* usually in the urine but at times in the feces. Only *S. japonicum* has important reservoir hosts. Human exposure results from wading, bathing, swimming, washing clothes and carrying on agricultural pursuits which expose the skin to cercariæ infesting the water.

8. Prevention of blood fluke infection is a difficult problem. Sterilization of human excreta and avoidance of contact with infested water are not practical. Destruction of the snail hosts provides some promise of control.

9. Schistosome dermatitis results from human skin exposure in fresh or brackish water to cercariæ almost exclusively of avian schistosomes. This type of dermatitis is cosmopolitan and has been discovered in all areas where careful study has been conducted. Infection by these non-human blood flukes produces a severe prickling as the metacercariæ enter the skin from infested water, with development of a macule at each site of penetration, local edema and at times generalized urticaria; later an intense nettling sensation as the macules change into pustules. No overall effective control has been demonstrated.

REFERENCES

AZAR, J. E., SCHRAIBMAN, I. G., and PITCHFORD, R. J. 1958. Some Observations on *Schistosoma hæmatobium* in the Human Rectum and Sigmoid. Trans. R. Soc. Trop. Med. & Hyg., *52*, 562–564.

BARLOW, C. H., and MELENEY, H. E. 1949. A Voluntary Infection with *Schistosoma hæmatobium*. Am. J. Trop. Med., *29*, 79–87.

BIOCCA, E. 1960. Osservazioni sulla morfologia e biologia del ceppo sardo di *Schistosoma bovis* e sulla dermatitis umana da esso provocada. Parassitol., *2*, 47–54.

BUCKLEY, J. J. C. 1938. On a Dermatitis in Malaya Caused by the Cercariæ of *Schistosoma spindale* Montgomery, 1906. J. Helminthol., *16*, 117–120.

BUEDING, E. 1950. Carbohydrate Metabolism of *Schistosoma mansoni*. J. Gen'l Physiol., *33*, 475–495.

CHU, G. W. T. C. 1958. Pacific Area Distribution of Fresh-water and Marine Cercarial Dermatitis. Pacific Science, *12*, 299–312.

CORT, W. W. 1950. Studies on Schistosome Dermatitis. Am. J. Hyg., *52*, 251–307.

DOBROVOLNY, C. G. 1958. Some Observations on Schistosomiais Control in Brazil. Abstracts, 6th. Int'l Congr. Trop. Med. & Malaria, p. 29.

Expert Committee on Bilharziasis. 1953. First Report. World Health Org. Techn. Ser. No. 65, Geneva. 45 pp.

FAUST, E. C., and MELENEY, H. E. 1924. Schistosomiasis Japonica. Am. J. Hyg., Monogr. Ser., No. 3, 339 pp.

FAUST, E. C., WRIGHT, W. H., McMULLEN, D. B., and HUNTER, G. W., III. 1946. The Diagnosis of Schistosomiasis Japonica. I. The Symptoms, Signs and Physical Findings Characteristic of Schistosomiasis Japonica at Different Stages in the Development of the Disease. Am. J. Trop. Med., *26*, 87–112.

FERGUSON, F. F., OLIVER-GONZÁLEZ, J., and PALMER, J. R. 1958. Potential for Biological Control of *Australorbis glabratus*, the Intermediate Host of Puerto Rican Schistosomiasis. Am. J. Trop. Med. & Hyg., *7*, 491–493.

FISHER, A. C. 1934. A Study of the Schistosomiasis of the Stanleyville District of the Belgian Congo. Trans. R. Soc. Trop. Med. & Hyg., *28*, 277–306.

GEAR, J. H. S. 1961. Schistosomiasis—a Major Problem. Industry & Tropical Health, IV, Harvard Sch. Pub. Hlth., 16 pp.

GELFAND, M., and ROSS, W. F. 1953. The Distribution of Schistosome Ova in the

Alimentary Tract in Subjects of Bilharziasis. Trans. R. Soc. Trop. Med. & Hyg., *47*, 215–217.

HERNÁNDEZ-MORALES, F., and MALDONADO, J. F. 1946. Diagnosis of Schistosomiasis Mansoni by Rectal Biopsy Technique. Am. J. Trop. Med., *26*, 811–820.

HUANG, M. H., *et al.* 1957. Schistosomiasis Dwarfism. Chinese Med. J., *75*, 448–461.

HUNTER, G. W., III., *et al.* 1952. Studies on Schistosomiasis. VI. Control of the Snail Host of Schistosomiasis in Japan with Sodium Pentachlorophenate (Santobrite). Am. J. Trop. Med. & Hyg., *1*, 831–847.

KUNTZ, R. 1952. *Schistosoma mansoni* and *S. hæmatobium* in the Yemen, Southwest Arabia: with a Report of an Unusual Factor in the Epidemiology of Schistosomiasis Mansoni. J. Parasitol., *38*, 24–28.

McMULLEN, D. B., and BEAVER, P. C. 1945. Studies on Schistosome Dermatitis. IX. The Life Cycles of Three Dermatitis-Producing Schistosomes from Birds and Discussion of the Subfamily Bilharziellinæ (Trematoda: Schistosomatidæ). Am. J. Hyg., *42*, 128–154.

McMULLEN, D. B., HUBENDICK, B., PESIGAN, T. P., and BIERSTEIN, P. 1953. Observations Made by the World Health Organization Schistosomiasis Team in the Philippines. J. Parasitol., *39* (No. 4, Sec. 2), 17.

MEIRA, J. A. 1951. Esquistosomiase Mansoni Hépato-Esplênica. Tese, Fac. de Med., Univ. S. Paulo (Brasil). 607 pp.

OLIVER-GONZÁLEZ, J., BAUMAN, P. M., and BENENSON, A. S. 1955. Immunological Aspects of Infections with *Schistosoma mansoni*. Am. J. Trop. Med. & Hyg., *4*, 443–452.

OLIVIER, L. 1955. The Natural History and Control of the Snails That Transmit the Schistosomes of Man. Am. J. Trop. Med. & Hyg., *4*, 415–423.

————: 1949. Schistosome Dermatitis, a Sensitization Reaction. Am. J. Hyg., *49*, 290–301.

OTTOLINA, C. 1951. Valor absoluto de la biopsia rectoscópica por transparencia. Estudio en 138 rectos humanos enteros preparados con una téchnica adecuata. Rev. Policl. Caracas, *19*, 79–151.

PELLEGRINO, J., BRENER, Z., and POMPEU-MEMORIA, J. M. 1959. A Comparative Study of Intradermal Tests and Stool Examination in Epidemiological Surveys of Schistosomiasis Mansoni. Am. J. Trop. Med. & Hyg., *8*, 307–311.

PESIGAN, T. P., GARCIA, E. G., SANTOS, B. C., BESA, A. A., and JAUREGUI, J. J. 1958. Ecological Control of Schistosomiasis in Leyte, Philippines: Progress Report. Abstracts, 6th Int'l Congr. Trop. Med. & Malaria, pp. 21–22.

PITCHFORD, R. J. 1959. Cattle Schistosomiasis in Man in the Eastern Transvaal. Trans. R. Soc. Trop. Med. & Hyg., *53*, 285–290.

SINHA, P. K., and SRIVASTANA, H. D. 1960. Studies on *Schistosoma incognitum* Chandler, 1926. II. On the Life History of the Blood Fluke. J. Parasitol., *46*, 629–641.

STAUBER, L. A. 1958. Swimmer's Itch in New Jersey. J. Parasitol., *44*, 108.

STOLL, N. R. 1947. This Wormy World. J. Parasitol., *33*, 1–18.

STUNKARD, H. W., and HINCHLIFFE, M. C. 1952. The Morphology and Life History of *Microbilharzia variglandis* (Miller and Northrup, 1926) Stunkard and Hinchliffe, 1951, Avian Blood-flukes Whose Larvæ Cause "Swimmer's Itch" of Ocean Beaches. J. Parasitol., *38*, 248–265.

SZIDAT, L. 1942. Was ist *Cercaria ocellata* La Valette? Morphologische und Entwichlungsgeschichte Untersuchungen ueber der Erreger der Europäischen Cercarien-Dermatitis des Menschen. Deutsh. Trop. Zeitschr., *46*, 481–597; 509–524.

THOMPSON, P. E. 1959. Recent Developments in the Chemotherapy of Parasitic Infections. Bull. Calcutta School Trop. Med., *7*, 186–190.

ULMER, M. J. 1958. Schistosome Dermatitis at Lake Okoboji, Iowa. J. Parasitol., *44*, (Sec. 2), 13.

WRIGHT, W. H., and DOBROVOLNY, C. G. 1953. Experiments in the Control of Schistosomiasis in Brazil. Pub. Health Repts., *68*, 1156–1160.

WRIGHT, W. H., DOBROVOLNY, C. G., and BERRY, E. G. 1958. Field Trials of Various Molluscicides (Chiefly Sodium Penthachlorophenate) for the Control of Aquatic Intermediate Hosts of Human Bilharziasis. Bull. World Health Org., *18*, nos. 5–6.

W H O EXPERT COMMITTEE ON BILHARZIASIS. 1961. Wld. Hlth. Org. Tech. Rept., Ser. 1961, p. 214.

Chapter 11

The Cestodes (Tapeworms)

INTRODUCTION

THE cestodes or tapeworms constitute the Class Cestoidea (Phylum Platyhelminthes), of which all members are parasitic during all or a major part of their life cycle. Typically the adults are intestinal parasites of vertebrates.

Adult Tapeworms as a Group

The Adult Worm.—The sexually mature tapeworm is securely anchored by its "head" to the mucosa of the small intestine of its host. A few species of primitive tapeworms (Cestodaria) have only a single reproductive unit containing both male and female genitalia, but all of the others (Cestoda) consist of a chain of units made up of the following parts: (1) a *scolex*, or attachment organ, the "head;" (2) a delicate "neck" immediately behind the scolex, the region of growth from which all of the more distal portion of the worm is derived, and (3) a series of *proglottids*, commonly called "segments," beginning with *immature* units, arising directly from the "neck," then *mature* units which contain the fully developed sex organs, and distalmost the *gravid* units which are reservoirs for the eggs. The entire series of "segments" is a *strobila*. All of the species of tapeworms which parasitize man and higher animals belong to the Cestoda. The number of their proglottids varies from three or four in the hydatid worms (*Echinococcus granulosus* and *E. multilocularis*) to a thousand or more in the beef tapeworm (*Tænia saginata*) and three or four thousand in the fish tapeworm (*Diphyllobothrium latum*).

The worm is typically dorso-ventrally flattened, creamy to chalky white in color, and is covered with a glistening, smooth cuticle, which is derived from the underlying layer, the hypodermis. Internal to the hypodermis are the longitudinal muscles and within this layer the transverse muscle fibers. Cuticle, hypodermis and muscular tissue engirdle the loose meshwork of undifferentiated parenchyma cells, within which are the nervous, excretory and genital systems. A digestive tract is lacking.

The *scolex* or attachment organ in most species of human tapeworms (Fig. 86) is more or less knob-like and is provided with four cupped suckers which lie in the same transverse plane equidistant from one another, two being situated ventrolaterally and two dorsolaterally. In species of *Diphyllobothrium*, the scolex is spatulate and is provided with a long median ventral and a similar medium dorsal sucking groove.

The *nervous system* of tapeworms serves to coördinate the rather sluggish movements of the entire worm. Its center is situated in the scolex, and from this there arise three pairs of nerve trunks in the lateral positions, which extend through the distalmost proglottid. At the posterior end of each proglottid there is a transverse commissure which connects all six of the longitudinal trunks with one another.

The *excretory system* consists of two ventrolateral and two dorsolateral longitudinal canals joined to one another by anastomoses in the scolex and by a transverse anastomosis near the posterior margin of each proglottid. Opening into the longitudinal canals at frequent intervals there are numerous capillaries, each of which originates internally from a cell (the *solenocyte*) which has a number of delicate vibrating cilia extending

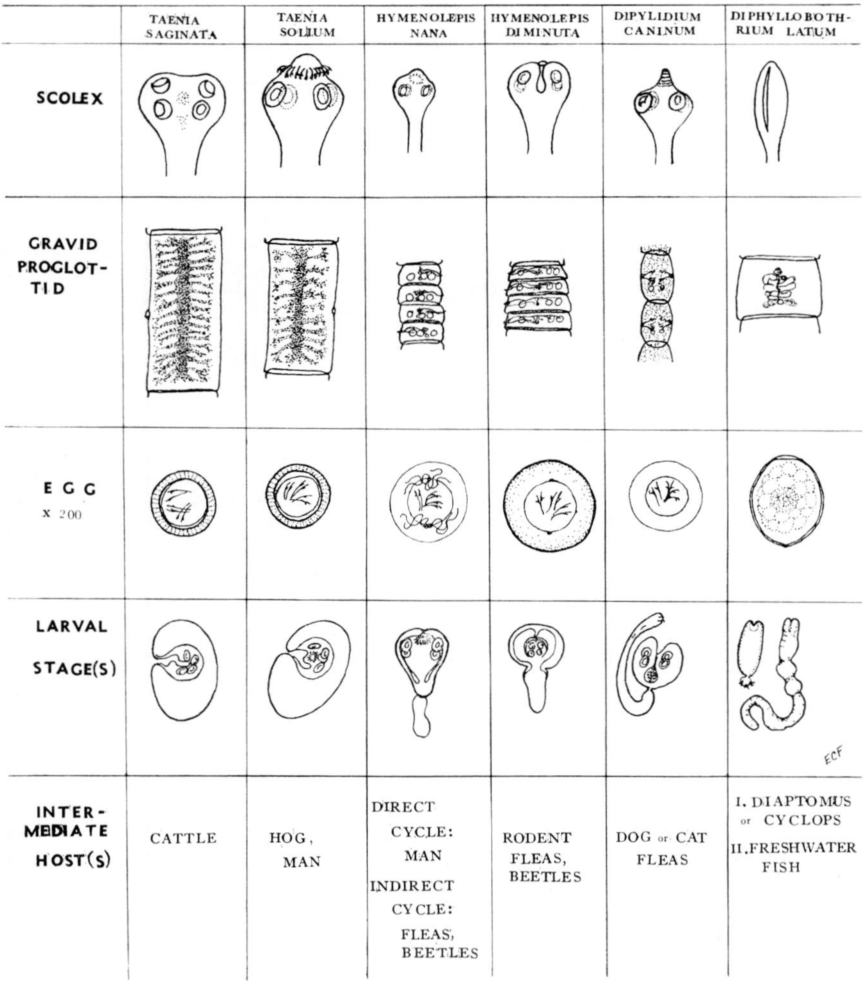

	TAENIA SAGINATA	TAENIA SOLIUM	HYMENOLEPIS NANA	HYMENOLEPIS DIMINUTA	DIPYLIDIUM CANINUM	DIPHYLLOBOTHRIUM LATUM
SCOLEX						
GRAVID PROGLOTTID						
EGG x 200						
LARVAL STAGE(S)						
INTERMEDIATE HOST(S)	CATTLE	HOG, MAN	DIRECT CYCLE: MAN INDIRECT CYCLE: FLEAS, BEETLES	RODENT FLEAS, BEETLES	DOG or CAT FLEAS	I. DIAPTOMUS or CYCLOPS II. FRESHWATER FISH

Fig. 86.—Important stages and diagnostic characteristics of the tapeworms which commonly parasitize man. (Original, Faust.)

into the lumen of the capillary and gives the impression of a flickering candle flame, hence the popular designation "flame cell."

The *genital organs* begin to develop in the more distal immature proglottids and reach full growth and function in the mature proglottids. In most species, there is one complete set of male and female organs for each proglottid. In *Tænia saginata* and other cyclophyllidean forms the genital openings are mid-lateral in position; however, in the Pseudophyllidea, the group to which species of *Diphyllobothrium* belong, these openings are midventral near the anterior end of the proglottid. For *Tænia saginata* the general arrangement of the genitalia is illustrated in Figure 87.

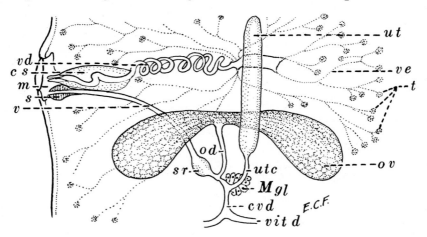

Fig. 87.—Diagram of the genital organs of *Tænia saginata. cs*, cirrus sac; *cvd*, common "vitelline" (*i.e.*, shell gland) duct; *m*, common genital atrium, or metraterm; *Mgl*, Mehlis' gland; *od*, oviduct; *ov*, ovary; *s*, sphincter at outer end of vagina; *sr*, seminal receptacle; *t*, testes; *ut*, uterus; *utc*, uterine canal; *v*, vagina; *vd*, vas deferens; *ve*, vas efferens; *vit d*, vitelline duct. (From Faust's *Human Helminthology*, Lea & Febiger, Philadelphia.)

During the period of egg production the naked ovum is passed through the oviduct, is fertilized on its way into the *oötype* or soon thereafter, is provided with yolk material, then a thick shell is secreted. Another thin membrane (the embryonal envelope) is added and the fully formed shell is shuttled into the uterus, where the egg matures. The club-shaped uterine pouch soon begins to expand by the production of a considerable number of main lateral branches, which, in turn, develop secondary and tertiary branches. Meanwhile all of the egg-producing organs characteristic of the mature proglottid atrophy. In this way the proglottid is transformed into a reservoir for the storage of ripening eggs, *i.e.*, it becomes gravid (Fig. 86).

The essential difference between the genital system of *Tænia saginata* and species of *Diphyllobothrium* lies in the fact that the uterus of the latter group is provided with a pore, through which eggs are discharged before they have an opportunity to embryonate.

Although attached by its scolex to the intestinal mucosa, the worm is a lumen parasite. During periods of hypermotility of the small bowel, the main portion frequently breaks away from the scolex, and is evacuated in the stool. However, as long as the scolex remains attached, a completely new strobila will usually be formed from the neck.

Lacking a digestive system, the worms absorb nutriment selectively through the integument (Daugherty and Foster, 1958). Tapeworms have a high ratio of glycogen, lipids and phospholipids to protein, stored in the parenchyma cells (Hedrick, 1958). It has been suggested that they obtain their oxygen supply from stored glycogen (Smyth, 1947). There is a large reserve of calcium carbonate throughout the parenchyma, in the form of numerous rounded granules. Vitamins, particularly vitamin G, are essential for the normal development of tapeworms (Read, 1951; Chandler, 1955).

Developmental Stages of Tapeworms.—In the group to which *Diphyllobothrium* belongs, the eggs are discharged from the uterus and are evacuated in the stool in an unembryonated stage. In order to proceed with their development, they must reach cool, fresh water. All other tapeworms parasitizing man retain their eggs *in utero* until they are mature. In species of *Hymenolepis* the fully developed eggs are recovered in the feces; but in species of *Tænia* and in *Dipylidium caninum* the gravid proglottids become detached from the strobila and pass out of the bowel, usually without liberating their eggs. The mature egg contains the *hexacanth embryo* provided with three pairs of hooklets. The eggs of tapeworms commonly parasitizing man are illustrated in Plate II, *J–O* (page 25).

The mature embryos of species of *Diphyllobothrium* and their relatives have a ciliated epithelium. All other species of human tapeworms produce eggs in which the hexacanth embryo lacks a ciliated epithelium.

There are several morphological types of larvæ characteristic of different species of tapeworms (Fig. 86). Species of *Diphyllobothrium* have two distinct stages in their larval development, the *procercoid* and the *plerocercoid*, both of which are solid structures lacking a bladder. In *Hymenolepis nana, H. diminuta* and *Dipylidium caninum* the single larval stage, *cysticercoid*, contains only a residual bladder in the caudal portion. In species of *Tænia* it is a *cysticercus*, which has a conspicuous bladder surrounding the invaginated head. In *Multiceps* there is a somewhat larger bladder, the *cenurus*, into which a number of heads (scolices) protrude. In *Echinococcus* the larval stage is a *hydatid*, a large bladder into which multiple scolices project and later may become freed from the germinal membrane to develop as daughter hydatids within the parent cyst.

When the mature larva surrounded by its host tissues is ingested by the definitive host and reaches the small intestine, the larva is digested out of the tissues, the head then evaginates, becomes attached to the intestinal mucosa and in the course of a few weeks or months develops into a complete strobilate worm.

Tænia saginata Goeze, 1782 (subgenus Tæniarhynchus)
(The beef tapeworm, causing beef tapeworm infection, or teniasis)

This tapeworm was widely known in ancient Egypt and Greece and was highly prevalent in Europe during the Middle Ages. The larva was apparently first reported from the muscles of cattle by Wepfer in 1675. Leuckart (1862) first demonstrated that human infection resulted from consumption of infected raw beef.

Beef tapeworm infection has a cosmopolitan distribution among beef-eating peoples, particularly in Ethiopia and Mohammedan countries. It is widely distributed in Australia, New Zealand, France, Switzerland, Denmark, Italy, Latin America and the United States.

Morphology, Biology and Life Cycle

The Adult Worm.—The adult worm develops typically in the middle third of the small intestine, attached by its scolex to the mucosa. The average length of the relaxed worm is approximately 5 meters, although there are records of specimens of 25-meters length or more. There are 1000 to 2000 proglottids, of which from one-third to one-half are gravid. Usually only a single specimen occurs in an infection, but there may be two or more (Fig. 88), in which case the size of each worm is correspondingly reduced. New proglottids produced from the neck serve to compensate for the daily loss of the distalmost gravid ones, which become separated from the strobila and pass out of the bowel.

The fully developed worm is delicate anteriorly and more robust posteriorly. The rhomboidal scolex (Fig. 86) is provided with 4 hemispherical suckers. Instead of hooklets on a rostellar prominence as in *T. solium* (see Fig. 92, page 194) there is a slight apical depression. Rather commonly there is melanotic pigmentation anterior to, and between each two suckers. Immediately behind the delicate unsegmented neck there is a region of immature proglottids in which the genital organs are not yet developed. Gradually the more distal of these proglottids increase in breadth and width until they reach a maximum width of 12 mm. These are the mature ones, each of which contains a full set of functioning male and female reproductive organs (Fig. 89). Still more distally the mature units have transformed into more elongated, narrower, gravid ones, due to the development of the large number of branched lateral arms of the uterus (15 to 20) characteristic of *T. saginata* (Fig. 86). The terminal proglottids become separated from the strobila and actively migrate out of the bowel or are evacuated in the stool, usually in an intact condition without rupture of the uterus or liberation of the eggs.

The eggs of *T. saginata* are essentially spherical, measure 31 to 43 microns in diameter, have a thin, transparent outer embryonal envelope and a thick, sienna-brown shell composed of many truncated pyramids cemented together. Within this shell there is a hexacanth embryo which has delicate lancet-shaped hooklets (Fig. 90).

Developmental Stages.—Once the evacuated gravid segments disintegrate on moist earth or in sewage, the eggs are set free and are ready for development in the intermediate host. Cattle grazing on infested ground pick up the eggs, which hatch in their duodenum. The emerging embryos penetrate into the mesenteric venules or lymphatics and reach skeletal muscles or the heart, where they transform in 60 to 75 days into the typical cysticercus stage (*Cysticercus bovis*), which has a miniature head like that

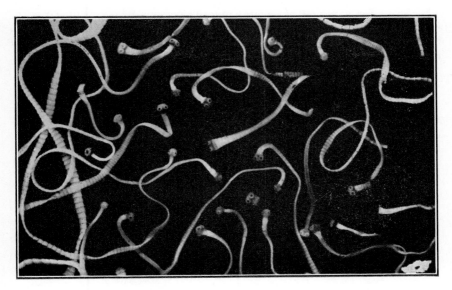

Fig. 88.—Multiple *Tænia saginata* infection, showing characteristic scolex, neck and adjacent immature proglottids. Twenty-eight worms (scolices) were recovered from this patient in Beirut, Lebanon. Note the melanotic pigmentation of several of the scolices. Natural size. (Courtesy, Dr. D. A. Berberian.)

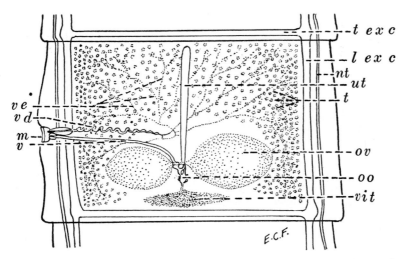

Fig. 89.—Mature proglottid of *Tænia saginata*, showing important organs. *l ex c*, lateral excretory trunk; *m*, genital atrium, or metraterm; *nt*, lateral nerve trunk; *oo*, oötype; *ov*, ovary; *t*, testes; *t ex c*, transverse excretory canal; *ut*, uterus; *v*, vagina; *vd*, vas deferens; *ve*, vasa efferentia; *vit*, so-called "vitellaria" (*i.e.*, shell gland follicles). × 10. (From Faust's *Human Helminthology*, Lea & Febiger, Philadelphia.)

of the adult worm, invaginated into the fluid-filled bladder (Fig. 91). Thereafter for a period of several months persons who consume raw or inadequately processed infected beef are subject to infection. In three to six months after human exposure the complete worm has been developed and gravid proglottids are being shed.

Pathogenicity and Symptomatology

Infection with *T. saginata* may be symptomless except for the inconvenience resulting from gravid proglottids crawling out of the anus. However, towards the end of the prepatent period there are typically a diarrhea, false hunger pains and moderate loss of weight. The blood picture at this time shows an eosinophilic leukocytosis but later there may be a slight

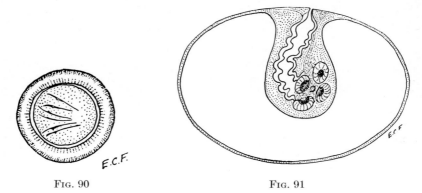

Fig. 90   Fig. 91

Fig. 90.—Fully embryonated egg of *Tænia saginata*, showing the thick outer shell and three pairs of hooklets within the embryo. × 666. (From Faust's *Human Helminthology*, Lea & Febiger, Philadelphia.)

Fig. 91.—Optical view of the cysticercus stage of *Tænia saginata* (*Cysticercus bovis*) from striated muscle of beef. Note that the head is invaginated within the fluid-filled bladder. × 6. (From Faust's *Human Helminthology*, Lea & Febiger, Philadelphia.)

neutropenia. At times liver damage may develop as a result of absorption of toxic metabolites discharged by the worm. Occasionally chronic diarrhea may produce complete exhaustion with fatal termination unless specific therapy is instituted in time. Gravid proglottids may become lodged in the appendiceal lumen and cause appendicitis (Altenkamp, 1935; Upton, 1950). Rarely a mass of tangled worms may cause acute intestinal obstruction (Minning, 1952).

Diagnosis and Treatment

Eggs of *T. saginata* are often found in small numbers in the feces. They are indistinguishable from those of *T. solium*. In all mature infections gravid proglottids (Fig. 86), are being evacuated. When the unpreserved proglottids are gently compressed between two slides and held in front of a bright light it is easy to count the number of main lateral arms of the uterus

(15 to 20, usually 18) on each side of the main uterine stem. This constitutes specific diagnosis.

Many anthelmintics have been employed in the treatment of *T. saginata* infection. Careful clinical studies have indicated that *quinacrine hydrochloride* (Atabrine) is probably more dependable and at the same time less toxic than older preparations (Sodeman and Jung, 1952). A satisfactory method of administration is as follows: Following a milk diet and evening castor-oil purgation, the drug is given the following morning on an empty stomach, as a single dose in the amount of 0.5 to 1.2 Gm. (depending on the weight of the patient), preceded 30 minutes earlier by administration of an anti-emetic. One hour later castor-oil purgation is employed to evacuate the worm, which is characteristically passed intact, living but considerably contracted and stained a deep safranin yellow. Food may be taken as soon as the post-treatment purge has been effective. Failure to remove the worm results from inadequate preparation for treatment or failure of the patient to retain the drug (See Table 7, page 419).

Epidemiology

Cattle acquire the larval stage of *T. saginata* by grazing on moist pasture land polluted by sewage containing the fully embryonated eggs of this tapeworm. Under suitable conditions of moisture and temperature the eggs may remain viable for 8 weeks or more (Penfold *et al.*, 1937; Newton *et al.*, 1949). Approximately 2 to 3 months after the cattle are exposed the larvæ have matured and the meat is infective. Within a year, however, they often become calcified. Infection of young calves provides relatively solid immunity to subsequent exposure (Urquhart, 1961). In some human populations infection results from eating frankly raw beef. In most endemic areas, it is due to consumption of steaks or hamburgers which are browned on the surface but are still red in the center. While a majority of infections in the United States are contracted from heavily infected country-killed cattle, about 0.3 per cent of inspected beef in the large slaughter houses has a minimal infection.

With rare exceptions man is the only definitive host of *T. saginata*

Control

Basically the control of teniasis consists in the sanitary disposal of human feces, so that eggs of *T. saginata* in the excreta or community sewage do not reach swampy pastures where cattle graze. The mature eggs withstand temperatures of 24° F. (−4.5° C.) for 2 weeks or more (Lucker, 1960). Beef which has been kept 24 hours or longer in a deep freezer is sterilized. Likewise, heating the meat to 65° C. is a safeguard since the critical thermal death point (LD 100) for the cysticerci embedded in beef muscle is 56° C. (Allen, 1947).

Tænia solium Linnaeus, 1758

(The pork tapeworm, causing pork tapeworm infection, or teniasis)

The larval stage of this worm (*Cysticercus cellulosæ*) was described from swine by Greek naturalists. Gessner (1558) and Rumler (1588) first re-

13

ported human infection with the cysticercus. Goeze (1782) first differentiated the adult *T. solium* from *T. saginata*, and Küchenmeister (1855) and Leuckart (1856) first conducted life cycle studies.

Pork tapeworm infection is cosmopolitan wherever raw or inadequately processed pork is consumed. It is relatively common in the Balkan states and Slavic countries, in North China and Manchuria and in the outcasts of India. It is widespread in continental Latin America, from Mexico to Chile, but is not found in Mohammedan populations or among orthodox Jews. Autochthonous cases of *T. solium* in the United States apparently have ceased to exist.

Morphology, Biology and Life Cycle

The Adult Worm.—In most respects *Taenia solium* resembles *T. saginata.* Grossly *T. solium* is shorter, usually having a length of less than 3 meters, due to a smaller number of proglottids (fewer than 1000) and shorter gravid proglottids. The neck region is also stouter and anterior to the four cup-shaped suckers on the scolex there is a double circle of alternating large and small hooklets, numbering from 22 to 32 and measuring 160 to 180 microns and 110 to 140 microns respectively (Fig. 92).

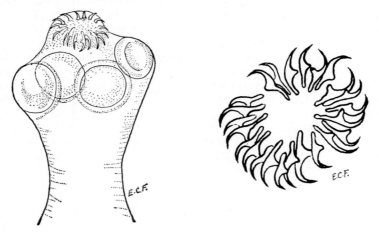

FIG. 92.—*Left,* scolex of *Tænia solium,* showing four suckers and rostellar crown of hooklets. × 40. (Adaptation of photomicrograph by Dr. L. Szidat, from Faust and Russell's *Clinical Parasitology,* Lea & Febiger, Philadelphia); *right,* head-on view of the rostellar hooklets of *T. solium,* showing two alternating rows of larger and smaller hooklets. × 120. (Original, Faust.)

The mature proglottid of *T. solium* closely resembles that of *T. saginata,* but is readily differentiated because it contains approximately one-half the number (7 to 13, usually 9) of main lateral uterine arms on each side of the longitudinal uterine stem (see Fig. 86). The eggs of *T. solium* are indistinguishable from those of *T. saginata.*

Developmental States.—Gravid proglottids passed in the stool or actively migrating out of the anus of the host disintegrate when they are deposited on the ground. To develop, the eggs must be ingested by hogs or by man himself. The hexacanth embryos hatch in the hog's duodenum and migrate from the intestinal wall through blood and lymphatic channels until they reach striated muscles, including skeletal muscle and myocardium. Here the embryos transform in 2 to 3 months into the cysticercus-type of larva (*Cysticercus cellulosæ*), glistening pearly white objects (Fig. 93). These cysticerci measure about 5 mm. in length by 8 to 10 mm. in breadth. The head is deeply invaginated into the fluid-filled bladder and is

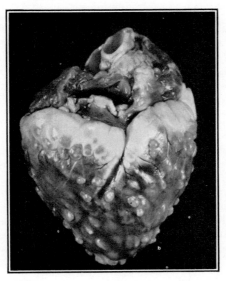

Fig. 93.—Numerous cysticerci of *Tænia solium* (*C. cellulosæ*) in wall of "measly" heart of a hog. × ⅔. (Photograph courtesy of Dr. D. A. Berberian.)

provided with four suckers and an apical crown of hooklets. When human beings eat pork containing the viable cysticerci, the larvæ are digested out of the meat, the heads evaginate from the bladder, become attached to the wall of the proximal portion of the ileum and in approximately three months each develops into a complete worm.

Pathogenicity and Symptomatology

The adult *T. solium* in the human small intestine produces the same train of pathologic processes and clinical manifestations as *T. saginata* (see page 192). However, because of the shorter length of the worm there is less likelihood that intestinal obstruction will develop. The extra-intestinal development of cysticerci of *T. solium* in the human host and the serious clinical consequences of human cysticercosis are considered on page 205.

Diagnosis and Treatment

Although eggs of *T. solium* are occasionally found in the host's stools or in anal swabs, specific diagnosis is based on demonstration of the relatively small number of main lateral arms of the uterus (7 to 13, usually about 9) in gravid proglottids compressed between two glass slides (Fig. 86).

Specific treatment of intestinal *T. solium* infection is important not only to remove the adult worm but also to prevent autoinfection with the eggs, which are responsible for extra-intestinal cysticercosis. *Quinacrine hydrochloride* (Atabrine) as administered for the removal of *T. saginata* (page 193) is the drug of choice in *T. solium* infection.

Epidemiology

Human infection with the adult *Tænia solium* results from the consumption of essentially raw pork containing viable *Cysticercus cellulosæ*. It may be fresh or smoked loin, shoulder, ham or sausage. The hog is the only known source from which man obtains the larval stage, and man is the only natural host of the adult worm. However, man is also a suitable host for the cysticercus (page 205).

Control

The serious, frequently disabling, and at times fatal consequences of human cysticercosis resulting from larval *T. solium* infection indicate the peculiar need for adequate control of this infection. In endemic areas human feces should not be deposited in locations where hogs have access to them. Pork should be adequately processed before it is eaten, by thorough cooking, one-half hour for each pound of meat at 350°F., or by freezing in deep-freezers for at least 24 hours. Persons harboring this worm should be freed of their infection by adequate anthelmintic treatment.

Hymenolepis nana (von Siebold, 1852) Blanchard, 1891
(The dwarf tapeworm, causing dwarf tapeworm infection,
or hymenolepiasis nana)

Hymenolepis nana was discovered by Bilharz, in 1851, in the small intestine of a native boy in Cairo, Egypt, and its life cycle was first elucidated by Grassi (1887) and Grassi and Rovelli (1892), who demonstrated that no intermediate host is required.

Dwarf tapeworm infection in human beings is primarily limited to children in warm climates. It is prevalent throughout India, the U.S.S.R., the countries bordering on the Mediterranean, all of the countries of Latin America, Hawaii, and most of the islands of the South and Southwest Pacific. It is the common tapeworm in the southeastern United States.

Morphology, Biology and Life Cycle

The Adult Worm. — *H. nana* is the smallest of the tapeworms which parasitize the human intestine (Fig. 94). The entire worm has a length of only 25 to 40 mm. and a maximum breadth not usually exceeding 1 mm. The small head is provided with 4 cup-shaped suckers and a rostellar crown of 20 to 30 minute hooklets. The neck is long and slender, all of the approximately 200 proglottids are broader than long and the terminal gravid proglottids usually disintegrate before separation from the strobila, so that the eggs are thoroughly mixed with the feces. The average infection consists of a few to several worms, but thousands have been reported from some patients. The eggs of *H. nana* (Fig. 94 *C*) are grayish hyaline, nearly spherical objects which measure 30 to 47 microns in diameter. There are two thin membranous shells, the inner one of which has two polar thickenings, each provided with 4 to 8 long thread-like filaments extending into the space between the two shells. Each worm produces only about one egg per 80 mgm. of formed stool (Beaver and Sodeman, 1952).

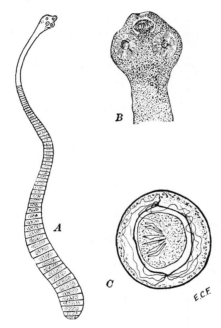

FIG. 94.—*Hymenolepis nana.* *A*, complete worm, × 10; *B*, scolex, greatly enlarged, with rostellar hooklets invaginated into crown of the scolex; *C*, egg, × 466. (*A*, original; *B*, after Blanchard; *C*, after Brumpt; from Faust's *Human Helminthology*, Lea & Febiger, Philadelphia.)

Developmental States.—When eggs get into the mouth and are swallowed, they hatch in the duodenum and the liberated embryos penetrate into the stroma of nearby villi, where they rapidly transform into cysticercoid larvæ (Fig. 86, page 187). These then migrate out to the duodenal or jejunal canal, become attached to the mucosa, and in about 2 weeks develop into complete worms. Thus, both the larval and mature stages are developed in the same individual. Moreover, in heavy infections it seems entirely probable that reinfection may occur by internal autoinfection, due to hatching of eggs in the upper levels of the small bowel.

Heyneman *et al.*, (1958) and others have demonstrated that certain strains of the murine variety of *H. nana* can utilize fleas and beetles for development of the cysticercoid larval stage.

Pathogenicity and Symptomatology

Infection with a few *Hymenolepis nana* may produce no detectable symptoms or it may be responsible for diarrhea, anorexia, vomiting, insomnia, loss of appetite and weight, irritability and peevishness, pruritus of the nose and anus, urticaria, and rarely choreiform symptoms (Donckaster and Habibe, 1958). Heavy infection invariably is pathogenic, causing moderate to profuse bloody-mucous diarrheic stools, abdominal pain, anorexia and exaggerated nervous disorders, or extreme apathy.

Diagnosis and Treatment

This is based on recovery of the species-characteristic eggs (Fig. 94*C*) in the stools.

Quinacrine hydrochloride (Atabrine) is the drug of choice (Beaver and Sodeman, 1952). It is administered as for *Tænia saginata* infection (page 193). Most cases can be cured by two or three administrations at fortnightly intervals, provided reëxposure is prevented.

Epidemiology

H. nana (human strain) requires no extrinsic development and has only a single host; infection is essentially one of anus-to-mouth transmission. For this reason younger children are particularly favorable subjects. Moreover, although young children can be infected with *H. nana* eggs from rodent sources, this type of infection is probably uncommon. Lack of personal cleanliness and particularly the soiling of clothing with egg-laden feces provide opportunity for repeated exposure of the small child and his playmates.

Control

Control of dwarf tapeworm infection will result only after cleanly personal habits have been developed in children, a goal which is difficult to achieve.

Hymenolepis diminuta (Rudolphi, 1819) Blanchard, 1891

(The rat tapeworm, causing rat tapeworm infection, or hymenolepiasis diminuta)

This is a cosmopolitan tapeworm of rats, mice and other rodents; it has been reported from human hosts, usually children, from India, Indonesia, the U.S.S.R., Japan, the Philippine Islands, southern Europe, Latin America from Argentina to Mexico and Cuba, and from several parts of the United States. The strain of *H. diminuta* recovered from man is identical to that found in rodents.

H. diminuta is small compared with *T. saginata* and *T. solium* but is not dwarf like *H. nana*. It measures 20 to 60 cm. in length by 3.5 to 4.0 mm. in maximum width at its distal end and may consist of a thousand or more proglottids. The knob-like scolex (Fig. 86, page 187) is provided with four relatively small suckers and a deep apical suctorial pocket. Rostral hooklets are lacking. The neck is short and stout. The terminal gravid proglottids disintegrate while still attached to the strobila, liberating fully embryonated eggs (Fig. 95), which are broadly ovoidal to subspherical, hyaline with a straw-colored hue and measure 72 to 86 microns by 60 to 79 microns in greater and lesser diameters. There is considerable space between the outer and inner egg membranes. The latter is provided with a pair of polar thickenings but lacks the polar filaments characteristic of *H. nana* eggs.

In order to proceed with their development, the eggs voided in the feces of the definitive host must be ingested by an arthropod, usually the larval stage of rodent fleas which breed in rat nests, but many species of beetles, also meal moths, earwigs and diplopods have been found naturally or experimentally to be suitable intermediate hosts. When the infected arthropod is ingested by the definitive host and reaches the duodenum, the cysticercoid is digested out of its vector-host, the head becomes evaginated and attached to the duodenal or jejunal mucosa, and develops into the adult worm in a few weeks. There is characteristically only a single worm in human infections, although as many as 19 have been recovered from one individual (Minning, 1952).

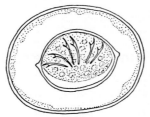

Fig. 95.—Egg of *Hymenolepis diminuta.* × 500. (From Faust's *Human Helminthology,* Lea & Febiger, Philadelphia.)

The symptoms resulting from *H. diminuta* infection usually consist of mild digestive upsets, pain in the pit of the stomach and loss of appetite, at times with associated nervous disorders due to absorption of the worm's metabolites. Diagnosis is made on the recovery of the typical eggs (Fig. 95) in the stool and their differentiation from those of *H. nana* (Fig. 94 *C*). Treatment is similar to that employed in *H. nana* infection. Control consists fundamentally in measures to eradicate rats and mice around the home and in residual spraying of their nests and burrows with DDT to kill their ectoparasites.

Dipylidium caninum (Linnæus, 1758) Railliet, 1892

(The dog tapeworm, causing dog tapeworm infection, or dipylidiasis)

This cosmopolitan tapeworm of dogs and cats has been found in children who fondle infected dogs or cats. Human cases have been diagnosed from Europe, the Orient, Africa, Latin America, and the southern United States.

The adult worms are medium-sized, measuring from 10 to 50 cm. in length, and consist of several hundred proglottids. The mature proglottids contain twinned genitalia and a genital pore at each lateral margin. The distalmost gravid proglottids are more or less pumpkin-seed-shaped. The scolex is roughly rhomboidal in shape, measures about 0.3 to 0.4 mm. in diameter, has 4 conspicuous, deeply excavated suckers and an introversible apical club-shaped proboscis provided with 6 rows of minute hooklets. The neck is distinctly constricted. In dogs and cats the infection typically consists of several to many worms; in children it is almost always solitary. The intact gravid proglottids, containing polygonal-shaped masses of mother egg capsules, separate from the strobila, at times singly but more often in chains, and pass down the intestinal canal and out of the anus.

Once the proglottids reach the soil they begin to disintegrate, setting free the mother capsules, each of which contains several fully embryonated eggs. (See Plate II, Fig. *O*, page 25). When the larva of the dog flea or the cat flea, the dog louse, and possibly other arthropods, ingests the egg capsules or individual eggs, hatching occurs in the midgut and the liberated embryo migrates into the arthropod's hemocele, where it transforms into a cysticercoid larva (Fig. 86). The definitive host becomes infected when the infected adult flea is accidently taken into the mouth and swallowed.

This infection in the child may produce profuse diarrhea and unrest. Occasionally there may be severe sensitization reactions, such as urticaria, fever, significant eosinophilia and rarely convulsions (Schaeppi, 1949). Diagnosis is made on recovery of the characteristic gravid proglottids evacuated in the stool or migrating out of the anus, and observing the polygonal pattern of the mother embryonic membranes within the uterus. Treatment is similar to that recommended for *Tænia saginata* (page 193) and *Hymenolepis nana* (page 198).

Control of dog tapeworm infection consists in periodic administration of teniafuges to dogs and cats to remove their tapeworms and disinfestation to get rid of their ectoparasites.

OTHER (LESS COMMON) CYCLOPHYLLIDEAN TAPEWORMS

Bertiella studeri of simian hosts, has been reported on a few occasions from man A related species, **B. mucronata,** also a simian parasite, has been found once in Cuba in an immigrant from the Canary Islands. The adult worms of *B. studeri* are medium-sized (20 to 30 cm. long), and have a subspherical scolex with four suckers and a rudimentary apical proboscis lacking hooklets. The eggs have an irregular ovoidal outer shell measuring 49 to 50 microns by 45 to 46 microns and an inner shell which has a distinct bicornuate protrusion. Certain species of oribatid mites (*Scheloribates lævigatus* and *Galumna* spp.) serve as suitable intermediate hosts, in which a cysticercoid-type of larva develops (Stunkard, 1940).

Inermicapsifer cubensis has been found as a relatively common human parasite, mostly in children, on the island of Cuba and primarily in the vicinity of Havana. The worm has a length of 27 to 42 cm., contains 310 to 368 proglottids and has a scolex with four prominent suckers and a very inconspicuous apical region lacking hooklets. Gravid proglottids are crowded with many mother egg capsules, each containing 6 to 11 spherical eggs measuring 49 to 55 microns in diameter. **I. arvicanthidis,** a rodent parasite of Africa, has been identified once from a 2-year-old white male in Kenya and once from a 6-year-old native of Ruanda-Urundi, Central Africa.

Mesocestoides variabilis, a fairly common parasite of carnivorous mammals, has been reported once from a 13-months-old white child in Texas (Chandler, 1942) and once from Denmark in a native of Greenland (Chandler, 1955).

Raillietina madagascariensis, R. celebensis and **R. demerariensis** have been described from man in different parts of the world (Chandler and Anond, 1957). Rodents are the known reservoirs of the first two species.

Drepanidotænia lanceolata, a cosmopolitan parasite of geese, has been recovered once from a German boy 12 years of age, who spontaneously passed two complete worms. The intermediate host is a species of *Cyclops* (Ruszkowski, 1932).

Diphyllobothrium latum (Linnæus, 1758) Lühe, 1910
(Synonym: *Dibothriocephalus latus*)

(The fish tapeworm, producing diphyllobothriasis lata)

Diphyllobothrium latum was undoubtedly prevalent in the Baltic Sea area at an early period and became widely disseminated as the Germanic peoples overran Europe during the decline of the Roman Empire.

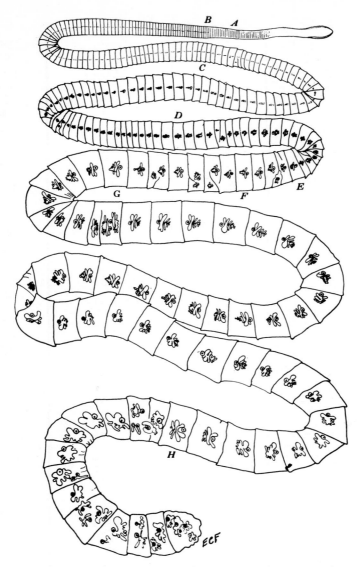

Fig. 96.—Complete strobila of *Diphyllobothrium latum*, with the original terminal proglottid still attached; obtained 24 days after experimental feeding of a dog with *Salmo irideus* containing sparganum larvæ. *A*, immature proglottids of post-cervical region in which genital primordia have not yet developed; *B*, proglottids with earliest evidence of genital primordia; *C*, proglottids with developing but undifferentiated genitalia; *D*, proglottids with early differentiation of genital sucker and external vaginal pore; *E*, proglottids with male genital sucker, uterine coil with external pore, vagina and vaginal pore, oötype and vitelline follicles (in lateral fields), but no evidence of ovaries, testes or vasa efferentia; *F*, proglottids containing uterine coils and imperfectly formed egg shells *in utero*; *G*, proglottids with uterus differentiated into inner and outer coils, vitelline material consolidating into follicles, vitelline ducts distinguishable, testes and ovaries forming, but only infertile eggs *in utero*; *H*, proglottids with all genital organs fully developed. Note the formation of accessory proglottids at different levels of the strobila. × 8⅓. (After Faust, An. Inst. Med. Trop., Lisbôa.)

Today *D. latum* is indigenous throughout many parts of the U.S.S.R., in the Baltic Sea countries, Central and Southeastern Europe, Lake N'gami, Africa, northern Manchuria and Japan.   In the Americas it is found in northern Minnesota, extensive areas of Canada, and Alaska, and in the lakes of southern Chile and Argentina.   It has likewise become established in New South Wales, Australia.

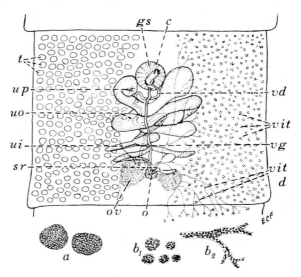

Fig. 97.—Mature proglottid of *Diphyllobothrium latum*, ventral view. *a*, two testes greatly enlarged to show internal structure; *b₁*, vitelline follicle and *b₂*, portion of vitelline duct, both greatly enlarged; *c*, cirrus organ; *gs*, male genital sucker; *o*, oötype; *ov*, ovary; *sr*, seminal receptacle; *t*, testes, shown only in left field but symmetrically present also in right field; *ui*, inner uterine coils; *uo*, outer uterine coils; *up*, uterine pore; *vd*, vas deferens; *vg*, vagina; *vit*, vitelline follicles, shown only in right field but symmetrically present in left field; *vit d*, vitelline ducts.   × 16⅔. (After Faust, An. Inst. Med. Trop., Lisbôa.)

Morphology, Biology and Life Cycle

The Adult Worm.—The fully developed worm of *D. latum* (Fig. 96) is ivory colored and has a length up to 10 meters or more, and has up to 4000 proglottids.   The scolex is elliptical, or spatulate, measures about 2.5 mm. in length by one mm. in breadth, and is provided with a median ventral and a median dorsal grooved sucker in place of the four cup-shaped suckers of cyclophyllidean tapeworms.   The adjacent portion of the neck is unusually delicate.   Proglottid formation in *D. latum* occurs at the distal end of the neck as it does in other strobilate tapeworms, but accessory proglottids are produced at all levels of the worm (Fig. 96).   The genitalia in a mature proglottid are shown in Figure 97.

The eggs within the fully developed uterus are continuously discharged through the uterine pore.   The terminal proglottids gradually become non-productive and disintegrate.   The egg of *D. latum* (Fig. 98) differs in several respects from that of the cyclophyllidean tapeworms.   In addition to being unembryonated at the time it is evacuated in the host's stool, it is broadly ovoidal, has an operculum at one end and a small but distinct thickening of the shell at the opposite end. The size of the egg varies considerably (56 to 76 by 40 to 51 microns), with an average range of 59 to 71 by 42 to 49 microns (Faust, 1952).

Developmental Stages.—Embryonation of the eggs which reach cool fresh water (15 to 25° C.) requires 11 to 15 days. Then the embryo escapes through the opened operculum, casts off its embryonal envelope and by means of its ciliated covering swims about in the water. In order to proceed with its development it must be eaten within 12 hours by an appropriate species of water "flea" (*Diaptomus*, rarely *Cyclops* in Europe,

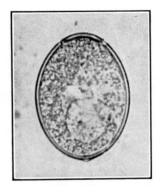

Fig. 98.—Egg of *Diphyllobothrium latum*. *Left*, camera lucida drawing, × 500 (after Faust); *right*, photomicrograph, × 550 (after Fülleborn, in Vogel and Minning's Wurmkrankheiten, courtesy, Springer-Verlag, Berlin, Göttingen and Heidelberg).

Diaptomus in North America). Once ingested by this copepod, the embryo burrows into the hemocele and transforms into the procercoid larva (Fig. 86, p. 187). If the infected copepod is then consumed by a fish, the larva migrates into the flesh or connective tissue of this host and transforms into a sparganum larva (Fig. 86). The larger, edible fishes acquire the infection from eating infected smaller species or infected young of their own kind.

Consumption of infected fish flesh by man or other suitable definitive host completes the epidemiologic cycle. In approximately 3 to 5 weeks the worm develops to maturity and egg production is initiated.

Pathogenicity and Symptomatology

D. latum may produce no symptoms, but in approximately 50% of the infections there are digestive disturbances, including diarrhea, heartburn, a sense of fullness in the epigastrium, hunger pains, or loss of appetite, anorexia, nausea and vomiting (Minning, 1952). Von Bonsdorff (1947) states that sudden vomiting of portions of the worm is characteristic, and is accompanied by symptoms suggesting peptic ulcer, cholelithiasis, ileus or appendicitis. The infection may be multiple.

In certain instances, particularly noted in Finland, there is a macrocytic, hyperchromic anemia, the so-called "bothriocephalus anemia," although in these patients, unless there is an underlying aplastic anemia, the reticulo-cyte count is normal or only slightly elevated. Von Bonsdorff (1956) found that severe symptoms are associated with jejunal attachment, which this investigator believes to be responsible for an impairment of the interaction of the extrinsic and intrinsic factors of Castle (*i.e.*, failure to assimilate vitamin B_{12}). In the average case the only change in the blood picture is a moderate eosinophilia and slight leukocytosis.

Diagnosis and Treatment

Diagnosis depends on finding the characteristic eggs (Fig. 98) in the stool or the occasionally vomited proglottids. A single worm at the height of productivity may produce up to 15,000 eggs per gram of formed stool, amounting to approximately 15 eggs per average fecal smear.

Treatment is similar to that recommended for *Tænia saginata* infection (p. 193).

Epidemiology

A number of epidemiologic conditions must exist before the life cycle of *Diphyllobothrium latum* can be completed: (1) Eggs of the worm must be discharged into cool fresh water, where they embryonate and hatch; (2) the emerging ciliated embryos must be eaten by certain species of water "fleas" (*Diaptomus* or *Cyclops*), in which the embryos transform into procercoid larvæ; (3) the infected water "fleas" must then be eaten by plankton-feeding fishes, in the flesh of which the procercoids transform into the sparganum larval stage, and (4) the infected fish must be consumed raw by the definitive host, in the intestine of which the spargana develop into adult worms.

Although dogs, and in some areas probably bears, are reservoirs of *D. latum*, man is primarily responsible for establishing and maintaining the life cycle in which he is involved. Moreover, fish caught in some endemic areas are shipped on ice to distant cities, where persons consuming the raw fish become infected.

Control

Control of fish tapeworm infection in endemic areas requires (1) sanitary disposal of human excreta so that viable eggs of *D. latum* do not reach bodies of fresh water in which the intermediate hosts breed, and (2) thorough cooking of all fish obtained from the area. Deep-freezing of the fish is not a safeguard, since the spargana in the fish survive prolonged low temperatures, although they are killed by a temperature of $-10°$ C. sustained for 48 hours.

INFECTIONS IN MAN PRODUCED BY OTHER SPECIES OF PSEUDOPHYLLIDEA

Diphyllobothrium cordatum, a common intestinal parasite of the seal, the walrus and the dog in Greenland and Iceland, of the dog in Japan, and of the bear in Yellowstone National Park, Wyoming (U.S.A.), has incidentally been reported as a human parasite in Greenland (1860) and Japan (1929). The distinguishing external character of this species is the inverted heart-shaped scolex. The eggs are indistinguishable from those of *D. latum*.

Diphyllobothrium houghtoni, an intestinal parasite of the dog and cat in China, has been recovered twice from the human intestine in that country.

Diplogonoporus grandis, a common intestinal parasite of whales, has been reported 6 times in Japanese subjects. The proglottids are very broad compared with their length, and are provided with twinned genital organs.

Digramma brauni has been recovered twice from the intestine of Roumanian patients. The worm, about 12 cm. long, has externally inconspicuous proglottid formation, slit-like dorsal and ventral suctorial grooves on the scolex, a very inconspicuous neck and twinned genitalia. Birds are believed to be the normal hosts of this worm.

Ligula intestinalis has been obtained twice from man in Roumania and once from a French patient. The worm is ribbon-like, 18 to 20 cm. long by 8 to 12 mm. wide, has a triangular scolex, lacks a distinct neck region and has a middorsal and a midventral sucking groove extending the entire length of the worm. The normal hosts are fish-eating birds.

LARVAL TAPEWORMS IN EXTRA-INTESTINAL FOCI

Introduction

While a majority of tapeworms parasitize man in their adult stage in the small intestine, a few produce human infection in their larval stage, always in extra-intestinal foci, *viz.*, the cysticercus of *Tænia solium*, the cenurus of *Multiceps* species, the hydatid cyst of *Echinococcus granulosus* and *E. multilocularis* and the sparganum (plerocercoid) of several species of *Diphyllobothrium*. Except for the cenurus of *Multiceps* all of the these larval forms are relatively common in the human host in certain geographical areas.

Cysticercus of Tænia solium

Biological Notes.—The larval stage of *Tænia solium*, the pork tapeworm, is referred to as *Cysticercus cellulosæ* and infection with this larva as cysticercosis cellulosæ. Except for two incidental findings of the cysticercus of the beef tapeworm (*C. bovis*) in human skeletal muscles and one from a lymph node of the meso-appendix, all known cases of human cysticercosis have resulted from infection with *C. cellulosæ*.

Man is the only proven host of the definitive stage of *T. solium* and the hog is the usual intermediate host in which the hexacanth embryo hatched from the egg develops into the cysticercus, or bladder worm (see Fig. 86, page 187). However, man is also a satisfactory host for development of this larva.

Pathogenicity and Symptomatology.—The lesions produced and the symptoms evoked by cysticercosis depend primarily on the tissues in which the embryos become established but also on the number of cysticerci which develop. Infection is more frequently multiple than solitary. If there are many visible or palpable cysticerci in the subcutaneous tissues or superficial muscles, one or more will usually have matured in the brain or other internal organs (MacArthur, 1934).

The cysticerci may remain viable in the human host up to 4 or 5 years. Except in the cysticercus *racemosus type*, or when present in the vitreous, pia mater or ventricles of the brain, these little bladder worms in human tissues are surrounded by a tough adventitious capsule (Fig. 99). The racemosus type is an unencapsulated larva which develops in the subarachnoid spaces at the base of the brain and occasionally in the choroid plexus. It may reach an over-all length of 15 cm., and produces numerous branches, hence the designation "racemosus."

Cysticerci which develop in the subcutaneous and muscle tissues cause essentially no pain unless they encroach on nerve endings, but when they become calcified they may occasion considerable inconvenience. Likewise, during the life of the larvæ in the meninges little if any evidence of their presence is usually provided, but if they develop as emboli in blood or lymphatic vessels acute symptoms will result.

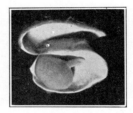

Fig. 99.—*Cysticercus cellulosæ* within outer adventitious capsule, removed from the biceps muscle of a patient with multiple cysticercosis without a history of intestinal *Tænia solium* infection. Natural size. (Photo by the senior author, from Faust's *Human Helminthology*, Lea & Febiger, Philadelphia.)

Except for superficial tissues the most common location of *C. cellulosæ* is the eye (Andrade, 1940), where the living unencapsulated cysticerci are constantly changing shape. Usually the subjective symptoms are minimal except for discomfort caused by the shadows cast in front of the retina. However, the parasite may cause damage to any tissue of the eyeball resulting in uveitis, iritis, dislocation of the retina or atrophy of the choroid membrane. The larva may also invade the palpebral conjunctiva, the subconjunctiva or become encapsulated in the muscular funnel of the orbit.

Epilepsy is the most frequent symptom of cysticercosis of the meninges (Dixon and Hargreaves, 1944; Obrador, 1948; Asenjo and Bustamente, 1950). Infection of the fourth ventricle is responsible for hydrocephalus, headache commonly at the base of the brain, diplopia and other ocular manifestations, dizziness, nausea and vomiting (Minning, 1952; Bickerstaff, 1955).

Significant symptomatic cysticercosis results from death of the larva in visceral locations and its discharge of foreign proteins. This stage may appear as early as 6 months after earliest possible infection (1 case studied by the senior author in China) or as late as 20 years afterward (Dixon and Hargreaves, 1944).

Diagnosis.—This may be made from biopsy of one or more of the little bladder-worm nodules appearing as slight elevations of the subcutaneous tissue, superficial muscles on any part of the body, or mucous membranes, compressed between two glass slides and examined under low power of the microscope. The presence of a single scolex having four suckers and a crown of rostellar hooklets (Fig. 86) is specifically diagnostic. Yet the first suggestion of cysticercosis may consist of defective vision or a series of epileptiform seizures without a history of epilepsy in early childhood. The ophthalmoscope will frequently visualize the motile organism in the eye with sufficient fidelity to provide the diagnosis. If the symptoms are due to a brain lesion, only a tentative diagnosis can be made of a space-occupying object which at times may be fairly accurately located topographically by encephalography and, in infection of the fourth ventricle or at the base of the brain, by determining the exact pattern of visual impairment. Specific diagnosis of the causative agent can be made only after exploratory removal or at necropsy (Dent, 1957).

Treatment.—Surgery is the sole therapeutic procedure in cysticercosis. Removal of superficial nodules is a simple procedure but is not usually necessary except for diagnostic purposes, since the organisms provoke little tissue reaction and are not capable of migrating to vital centers. In cases involving the eye, Lech Junior (1949) recommends removal of the parasite as early as possible while it is still alive, to prevent total loss of sight in the affected organ. Asenjo and Bustamente (1950) state that extirpation of a solitary cysticercus of the brain results in complete or partial recovery but with generalized cerebral infection operative technics are inadequate. Prognosis is excellent with respect to superficial lesions but evidence of cysticerci in the eye, brain or other foci modifies the prognosis.

Epidemiology.—Human exposure to cysticercosis results when the ripe eggs of *T. solium* reach the duodenum. There are three possible ways in which this may occur, *viz.*, (1) Eggs which have been liberated from disintegrating gravid proglottids passed by one individual, get into the mouth of another and are swallowed (hetero-infection); (2) eggs may be transferred from anus to mouth on unclean finger tips of an individual who has an intestinal infection with *T. solium* (external auto-infection), and (3) gravid proglottids in an individual harboring the adult *T. solium* may become detached from the main strobila, be regurgitated into the stomach and then return to the duodenal canal, where they disintegrate and liberate ripened eggs (internal auto-infection). Dixon and Hargreaves (1944) found that 26% of 284 cases of cerebral cysticercosis in British service troops who had been stationed in India were due to auto-infection, and Lech (1949), in Brazil, found that 23% of ophthalmic cases also harbored the adult *T. solium*. But Minning (1952) regards hetero-infection as the common method. Some of these cases are due to the custom of fertilizing gardens of green vegetables with human night soil.

Control.—The prevention of cysticercosis requires a twofold attack, namely, on the hog, which is the source of human intestinal infection with *Tænia solium*, and on the human carrier of the adult worm. Yet fundamentally control is a problem of personal and community hygiene, particularly in rural areas.

Cenurus of Multiceps Species

General Considerations.—A cenurus is the larval stage of tapeworms belonging to the genus *Multiceps*, the adults of which develop in the small intestine of dogs, cats and their wild relatives. Identification of the particular species of *Multiceps* is difficult and at times practically impossible (Nagaty and Ezzat, 1946). The mature eggs of *Multiceps* are indistinguishable from those of *Tænia*; they hatch in the duodenum of herbivorous or omnivorous mammals and the liberated hexacanth embryos migrate to extra-intestinal sites in which they grow and transform into the cenurus-type of larva, which is characterized by having multiple scolices developing from the germinative membrane lining the cavity of the bladder-like larva. Infection with a cenurus larva is called cenurosis.

Multiceps multiceps.—This is the commonest species and is cosmopolitan in sheep-raising areas. Dogs are the usual hosts of the adult worm. The larval hosts are principally sheep and goats, but other herbivores on grasslands polluted with the excreta of the infected dog hosts are also subject to infection. The embryos that hatch from the egg may lodge in any soft tissue of the body but typically develop in the brain or spinal cord (*Cœnurus cerebralis*), producing lesions which cause "blind staggers" or giddiness.

Human infections have been reported twice from France, once from South Africa, twice from England and once from U.S.A. The infected persons have ranged in age from early childhood to late middle life. This series of 5 cases probably represents only a small percentage of the actual number.

Depending on the location in which the growing cenurus is located, it may be rotund or produce finger-like ramifications between relatively dense nerve tissues. The patient may develop aphasia, epileptiform seizures, or other manifestations of neurologic lesions. In most cases only a single larva with multiple scolices has been recovered, but in at least one instance (Johnstone and Jones, 1950) 20 cenuri were obtained at exploratory operation and many others at necropsy.

Diagnosis made tentatively on the basis of a space-occupying lesion must be confirmed after recovery of the larva and study of its morphologic characters. Infection is invariably serious. No therapeutic procedure has been found to be effective. Control consists in meticulous care not to contaminate food, drink or finger tips with excreta of dogs in enzoötic areas.

Multiceps serialis.—The adult worm of this species is found in the small intestine of dogs and their wild relatives, and the cenurus larva in the muscles of rabbits and other rodents, rarely monkeys. Two human infections have been reported from France and one from rural California (Johnstone, personal communication, 1943).

Multiceps glomeratus.—The adult worm has not been discovered, so that the species description is limited to the cenurus stage, first diagnosed from human musculature in northern Nigeria, with one additional case each from the former Belgian Congo and northern Nigeria.

Hydatid Cysts of Echinococcus Species

General Considerations.—A hydatid (or hydatid cyst) is the larval stage of species of *Echinococcus*, the adults of which are parasites attached to the intestinal mucosa of dogs, wolves, foxes and related carnivorous mammals. Usually there are a few to several adult worms in an infection and at times there may be hundreds or thousands. The complete worm (Fig. 100) is very small, rarely over a centimeter in length and consists of scolex, neck, one immature, one mature and one or two gravid proglottids. In addition to 4 minute suckers the scolex is provided with a double row of alternating

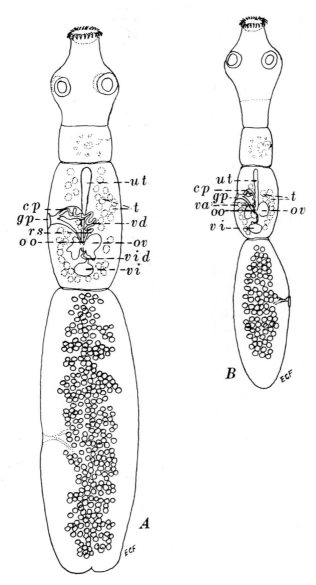

Fig. 100.—Adult *Echinococcus*, the larvæ of which produce hydatid cysts in man. *A, Echinococcus granulosus* from small intestine of dog, Jugoslavia; *B, E. multilocularis*, from fox, South Germany. *cp*, cirrus pouch; *gp*, common genital pore; *oo*, oötype; *ov*, ovary; *rs*, seminal receptacle; *t*, testes; *ut*, uterus; *va*, vagina; *vd*, vas deferens; *vi*, vitellaria; *vit*, vitelline duct. × 50. (Original, Faust, from specimens generously furnished by Professor H. Vogel, Hamburg.)

14

rostellar hooklets. The gravid proglottids disintegrate in the small intestine of the definitive host, so that the eggs are evacuated in the feces. These eggs can not be distinguished from those of *Tænia* or *Multiceps* which are natural parasites of dogs, or from those of *T. saginata* (Fig. 90, page 192) and *T. solium* of the human host.

Almost any mammal which picks up and swallows *Echinococcus* eggs is a suitable intermediate host for the hydatid stage. The eggs hatch in the duodenal canal and the embryos work their way into the wall of the intestine, reach a mesenteric venule (or lymphatic vessel) and become lodged in capillary filter beds (hepatic, pulmonary, etc.). The embryo then transforms slowly into a hydatid larva, having a mother cyst wall and many scolices, which are derived from the germinative membrane. The hydatids of two species, *Echinococcus granulosus* and *E. multilocularis*, develop in the human host.

Echinococcus granulosus (Batsch, 1786) Rudolphi, 1805
(The tapeworm causing unilocular hydatid disease)

Although hydatid cyst was known to ancient physicians and historians, it was frequently confused with other cystic tumors. Goeze (1782) demonstrated that the organism was a tapeworm. The adult worm in the dog's intestine was discovered by Hartmann (1695), and von Siebold (1852) first fed cysts from cattle to dogs and in three weeks recovered the minute adult worms from the intestine.

E. granulosus is widely distributed throughout temperate and subtropical regions of the world, as well as in other areas where sheep, cattle or hogs are extensively raised. Autochthonous infection in man is limited to the enzoötic regions (see map, Fig. 101). Today human infection is common and in some areas on the increase in southern South America, South Africa, eastern and southern Europe, Palestine, Lebanon, Syria, and Algeria. It is also prevalent in southern Australia, New Zealand, in extensive areas of central Asia and in North China. A few autochthonous cases are diagnosed each year from the United States and southern Canada. Studies among the Eskimos in northern Canada (Miller, 1953) and Alaska (Rausch and Schiller, 1951; Rausch and Williamson, 1959) indicate the disease to be highly enzoötic and in some localities endemic in parts of these subarctic areas.

Morphology, Biology and Life Cycle.—The adult *E. granulosus* lives in the small intestine of the canine host, with its "head" embedded between the villi. The worm (Fig. 100*A*) measures 3 to 6 mm. long. It has a pyriform scolex provided with four suckers and a rostellar crown of 28 to 50 hooklets, a delicate neck, one immature, one mature and one or two gravid proglottids. Disintegration of the terminal proglottid causes discharge of the Tænia-like eggs. When the ripe eggs get into the mouth of sheep, cattle, hogs, other herbivores, or man, they hatch in the duodenum and the freed hexacanth embryos migrate through blood and lymphatic channels to the liver and less frequently to other viscera. Here they are trapped and develop rather slowly into vacuolated larvæ, the *unilocular hydatids,* which are characterized by having an external, milky white laminated membrane and an internal germinative layer typically producing scolices, each capable of developing into daughter hydatids within the parent cyst. Usually the cyst has a host-tissue capsule.

Pathogenesis and Symptomatology.—A majority of human hydatids develop in the liver, near the first capillary filter after the hexacanth embryos have burrowed into the intestinal wall and gotten into the mesenteric venules; infection of the lungs is next in prevalence, and if they pass the pulmonary filter the embryos may settle down in any organ or tissue

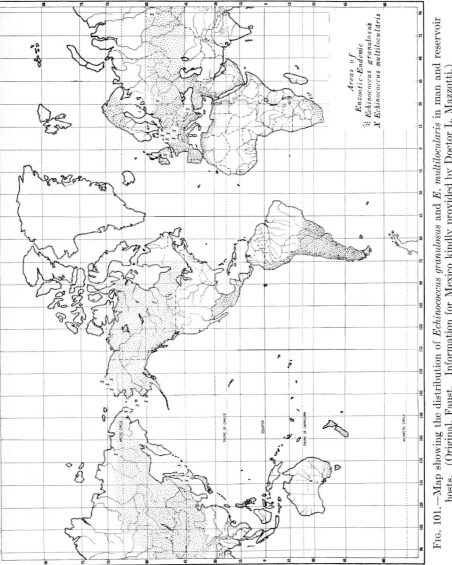

Fig. 101.—Map showing the distribution of *Echinococcus granulosus* and *E. multilocularis* in man and reservoir hosts. (Original, Faust. Information for Mexico kindly provided by Doctor L. Mazzotti.)

Areas of
Enzootic-Endemic
∷ *Echinococcus granulosus*
X *Echinococcus multilocularis*

of the body, including bone, and proceed to develop into hydatids. In heavily endemic areas in South America, the pulmonary location is more frequent than the hepatic one.

Primary hydatid cysts are usually single but they may be multiple. Moreover, Obrador *et al.* (1951) have reported on a Spanish case with multiple intradural hydatids associated with generalized cysticercosis of the somatic tissues.

Types of Hydatids Produced by E. granulosus.—There are two morphologic types in human tissues, *viz.*, unilocular and osseous. The *unilocular cyst* has a central, fluid-filled cavity lined with a germinative layer, surrounded by an intact but very friable laminated membrane covered with a host-tissue capsule (Fig. 102). A majority of human hydatids are

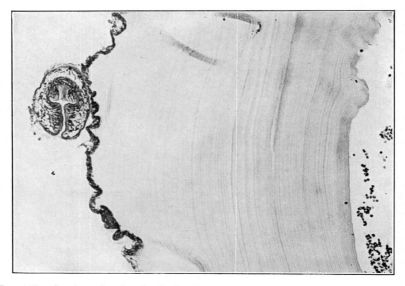

Fig. 102.—Section of unilocular hydatid cyst with scolex, showing broad laminated layer (*right*) and thin germinative layer with attached scolex (*left*). × 200. (Photomicrograph courtesy Doctor T. B. Magath, Meakin's *Practice of Medicine*, 6th ed., courtesy of C. V. Mosby Co., from Faust and Russell's *Clinical Parasitology*, Lea & Febiger, Philadelphia.)

unilocular, but if the hexacanth embryo is filtered out of blood vessels in bony tissues, no limiting membranes are produced and the organism proceeds to grow as a protoplasmic stream which erodes the cancellous structure, particularly of the long bones and pelvic arch. This is the *osseous hydatid.*

The size and contour of the unilocular hydatid are dependent on the site of implantation and on its age. If it is situated in non-resistant hepatic tissues, the cyst will enlarge under Glisson's capsule into the peritoneal cavity. After 12 to 20 years it may be as large as a football and hold several liters of clear, sterile hydatid fluid, typically with a large number of scolices and daughter hydatids. If the cyst becomes bacteriologically contaminated, the fluid will be purulent and have no viable scolices, or the cyst may be completely filled with caseous material. If the embryo becomes embedded near resistant tissues such as tendons and large blood vessels, the cyst may develop digitate processes around the tissues. In the lungs, the cyst is always encapsulated.

The amount of systemic intoxication or sensitization resulting from a unilocular hydatid depends on how well it is insulated from the surrounding host tissues. If a large abdominal cyst bursts, either spontaneously or following a severe blow on the abdomen, anaphylaxis may be precipitated by the sudden liberation of hydatid fluid into the peritoneal cavity. Moreover, scolices spilled out of the cystic cavity will become implanted on the peritoneum and produce multiple secondary growths. Rupture of a pulmonary cyst into a bronchus results in coughing up the contents and possibly the spontaneous clearance of the infection. Hydatid of the brain produces increasing symptomatic evidence of an intra-cranial tumor, with neurological manifestations corresponding to the location and size of the foreign body. Osseous hydatid is an insidious process which gradually erodes the bone to a stage where fracture or crumbling suddenly occurs.

Diagnosis and Treatment.—In endemic areas, experienced clinicians may obtain strong suspicion of hydatid disease from the patient's history, the presenting symptoms and the x-ray picture. More specific diagnosis can be obtained by the intradermal test, employing a known amount of hydatid antigen (see "TECHNICAL AIDS," page 452). A positive reaction of the immediate type, *i.e.*, within 15 minutes, indicates that the patient has, or has had hydatid disease. If this is confirmed by a positive precipitin or complement-fixation test, the evidence is much stronger that the infection is presently active and that the reaction is not merely a sensitization reaction from a previously active hydatid. Hemagglutination and the bentonite flocculation test are more sensitive than complement fixation, and may prove to be valuable diagnostic procedures in this infection (Faiguenbaum, 1961). Final diagnosis consists in the demonstration of free scolices or daughter cysts from aspirated hydatid fluid, or of the histologic structure of the cyst wall, with its laminated membrane, as seen in stained sections made from the excised cyst.

Chemotherapy is of no avail in hydatid disease. The standard procedure is surgical removal of the cyst.

Biological therapy has been employed in types of hydatid disease in which the parasites are in inoperable locations, as in the bone, or in which multiple cysts have developed in several anatomical locations. Without surgical intervention or biological therapy the eventual prognosis is poor.

Epidemiology.—Human infection with the hydatid cyst of *E. granulosus* is apt to occur where dogs harbor the adult worms and sheep or hogs serve as common reservoirs of the larval stage. Cattle do not often constitute a reservoir hazard since hydatid in these animals is characteristically sterile. Exposure most commonly takes place in childhood, particularly among boys who play with infected dogs. Herders of infected sheep and swine are likewise frequently exposed. Unless the embryos of the worm filter out in tissues where the developing hydatids will embarrass vital processes, the hydatid may grow for 5 to 20 years before it causes serious concern to the patient. Hence, exposure usually occurs several to many years before diagnosis is made. In England Barrett and Thomas (1952) found that human infection may be acquired from urban scavenger dogs or greyhound and whippet-racing animals.

Control.—Control must be directed against the dog, the carrier of the adult *Echinococcus granulosus*, and sheep and hogs, the common reservoirs of the viable hydatid. All infected carcasses should be deeply buried or incinerated. Stray dogs should be destroyed. Domestic dogs should be periodically de-wormed. Personal hygiene in endemic areas includes care that children do not contaminate their fingers with dog's excreta while playing with these animals.

Echinococcus multilocularis (Leuckart, 1863) Vogel, 1955
(The tapeworm causing alveolar hydatid disease)

As early as 1855 Virchow recognized a morphological form of human hydatid which differed from the usual unilocular type. Leuckart (1863) named it *multilocularis*. Yet until 1951 there was no accepted proof that there are two distinct species having hydatids which infect man and herbivorous mammals. In the Arctic region of Alaska Rausch and associates (1951–1958), and in South Germany Vogel (1957) demonstrated that foxes and other wild canines are the definitive hosts of *E. multilocularis*. Both investigators found that the natural hosts of the hydatid larvæ are native mice, respectively of the tundra (boreal) and of the field and forest (Central Europe).

Alveolar hydatid in man is endemic in Central Europe, the Balkans, Siberia, among Esquimos in Alaska (Rausch, 1960), and on Rebun Island, Japan. Sporadic cases have been reported from southern South America, Australia, New Zealand, and one indigenous human infection from England. The distribution of *E. multilocularis* is shown by the letter "X" in Figure 101.

Morphology, Biology and Life Cycle.—The adult *E. multilocularis* (Fig. 100B) is smaller than *E. granulosus*, viz., 1.2 to 3.7 mm. vs. 3.0 to 6.0 mm. long, and the disposition of the genital pore with respect to the reproductive organs as well as the number of testes are consistently different in the two species. The eggs are indistinguishable. In nature and in experimental tests, when eggs are ingested by native mice, tundra voles, ground squirrels and shrews (Alaska) and mice (South Germany), the hatched hexacanth embryos migrate from the intestine to the viscera, mostly the liver, where they lodge and proceed to grow by exogenous budding, in this way developing into the alveolar hydatids. When the infected viscera are consumed by canine hosts, the hydatids transform into adult *E. multilocularis*.

Pathogenesis and Symptomatology.—The site of the alveolar hydatid is commonly the liver, rarely the lungs. Here the hydatid develops minute irregular cavities, each within a hyaline membrane, frequently without fibrous encapsulation, so that the organism grows without capsular confinement, producing destruction of the surrounding host tissues like amebic liver abscess. Often the scolices in alveolar hydatidosis are few or wanting.

As the hydatid grows it causes central necrosis and cavitation of the lesion (Dew, 1953). Rarely the larva may metastasize to other viscera (Dew, *l.c.*).

The hepatic alveolar hydatid produces neither fever nor hepatomegaly, but jaundice, ascites and splenomegaly may appear in the later stages, resulting from intrahepatic portal hypertension (Rausch, 1958) (see Fig. 103). This infection is almost invariably fatal.

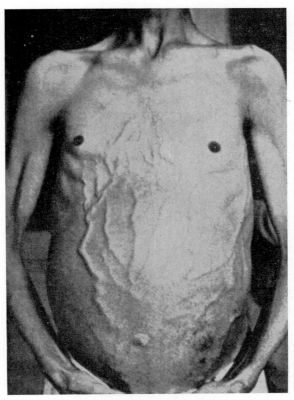

Fig. 103.—Advanced case of alveolar hydatid, showing remarkable dilatation of the cutaneous abdominal veins (caput medusæ) resulting from hepatic cirrhosis. (Photo by F. Paul, in Szidat and Wigand's *Wurmkrankheiten des Menschen*, 1934, courtesy Georg Thieme, Leipzig.)

Diagnosis and Treatment.—Specific diagnosis is likely to be missed in the living patient and may be missed at autopsy, due to unfamiliarity of most diagnosticians with this type of hydatid disease (Dew, *l.c.*).

Alveolar hydatid is not amenable to surgical removable. Biotherapy with hydatid antigen may be helpful but its use has not been reported.

Epidemiology.—In agricultural and woodland areas in Central Europe man probably acquires alveolar hydatid from eating raw fruits and vegetables picked off the ground and contamined with the feces of infected foxes and other Canidæ (Vogel, 1957); in boreal regions sledge dogs and foxes are the sources for eggs which may cause human infection (Rausch, 1958).

Control.—Because of the relatively slow growth of alveolar hydatid in man, it seems probably that exposure occurs in childhood. Hence young children in infected areas must be instructed not to suck their fingers or ingest objects possibly contaminated by foxes, dogs or wolves.

Sparganum of Diphyllobothrium Species

Historical, Biological and Geographical Notes.—In 1882, at Amoy, China, Patrick Manson discovered at autopsy a dozen glistening, ribbon-like worms, which Cobbold (1882) designated *"Ligula mansoni,"* and which were later found to be the sparganum (plerocercus stage) of *Spirometra mansoni*, a common parasite of dogs and cats in the Orient and in other parts of the world.

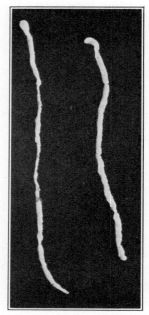

Fig. 104.—Mature spargana of *Spirometra mansoni* from muscle fascia of experimentally infected rabbits. × 2. (Original, from Faust's *Human Helminthology*, Lea & Febiger, Philadelphia.)

Several species related to *Diphyllobothrium*, all belonging to the genus *Spirometra*, are intestinal parasites of canine and feline hosts. These pseudophyllidean tapeworms utilize *Cyclops* as their first intermediate host. Various species of vertebrates other than fishes, *i.e.*, frogs, snakes, birds and mammals, are the hosts for the sparganum stage. Bonne (1942) and Gan (1949) elucidated the complete life cycle in Indonesia. More recently, in Korea, Weinstein, Krawzyk and Peers (1954) found that in that country snakes constitute an important second intermediate host for the sparganum stage of an undesignated species of *Spirometra*.

A large majority of human infections with unbranched spargana (Fig. 104) occur in the China Sea area (Japan and Korea, southern China and Indochina), and in Indonesia. Some cases have also been reported from Africa, Holland, Australia and the Western Hemisphere, including southern United States, Uruguay, Colombia and British Guiana. A branching type, *S. proliferum*, has been diagnosed 6 times in Japan and once in Florida (U.S.A.).

Pathogenesis and Symptomatology.—Infection with sparganum larvæ is called sparganosis. In the early stage there is apt to be relatively little host tissue reaction but more prolonged residence of the parasite provokes an infiltration of eosinophils, epithelioid cells and lymphocytes. As the infection becomes chronic there develops an extremely tender, puffy area around the parasite, filled with a chylous fluid, in the midst of which the larvæ are elongating and contracting. Later the parasite may die, causing an intense inflammatory reaction, with a preponderance of eosinophils and Charcot-Leyden crystals (Weinstein *et al.*, 1954).

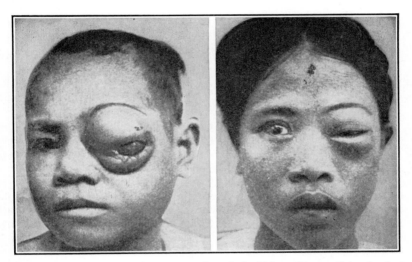

Fig. 105.—Ocular sparganosis, two cases from Indo-China. Note unilateral palpebral edema and in one case marked lagophthalmos. (After Keller, in Brumpt's *Précis de Parasitologie*, from Faust and Russell's *Clinical Parasitology*, Lea & Febiger, Philadelphia.)

Ocular sparganosis is usually a very serious disease. It is characterized by intense pain, irritation and palpebral edema (Fig. 105), with excessive lacrymation. If the worm lodges under the conjunctiva it is likely to provoke nodule formation; if its position is retrobulbar, lagophthalmos and corneal ulceration are characteristic. In the *proliferating* type of *sparganosis* the parasitized tissues become honeycombed, filled with chylous fluid, elephantoid if lymph channels are involved, and are responsible for intense itching of the skin if the subcutaneous tissues are invaded.

Diagnosis.—Unless physicians live in endemic areas and have had experience with cases of sparganosis, the living, contracting and elongating larva removed from a superficial furuncle or nodule will be a distinct novelty. It can be diagnosed only as a sparganum of some species of *Diphyllobothrium*, subgenus *Spirometra*, unless recovered intact in the living condition, fed to a kitten or puppy and grown to the adult stage.

Treatment.—A single sparganum in superficial tissues is easily removed after incision under procaine anesthesia and withdrawal of the worm by gentle traction.

Ocular sparganosis is a more serious matter and requires skill to remove the parasite without additional damage to the tissues of the eye. Miliary infection, particularly of the proliferating type, is not amenable to known medical or surgical treatment.

Epidemiology.—Human infection with the sparganum stage of these species of *Diphyllobothrium* results from (1) drinking unfiltered raw water containing procercoid-infected *Cyclops*; (2) eating infected tadpoles or snake flesh as a "tonic," or (3) applying plerocercus-infected flesh of frogs, snakes or possibly warm-blooded animals as a poultice on an inflamed eye or finger. Usually only a single sparganum is found in the human host but there may be several. Rarely the infection is miliary.

Control.—Effective control of sparganosis requires a radical change in the habits of persons living in highly enzoötic areas. Drinking water must be boiled or satisfactorily filtered. The flesh of animals apt to harbor the sparganum stage should be thoroughly cooked before it is eaten, and under no circumstance should it be used as a poultice for an inflamed part of the body.

SUMMARY

1. Adult tapeworms live in the intestinal tract of vertebrate hosts. Species which infect man have a scolex (organ of attachment), a "neck" or region of growth, and a series of a few to many proglottids arising from the "neck" and becoming more and more mature distally. In many species the most distal ones are gravid, *i.e.*, filled with eggs.

2. The mature egg contains a hexacanth embryo, which, after emergence from the egg shell and arrival in intermediate host tissue, transforms into a larva. The larva, in turn, develops into the adult worm on reaching the intestine of the definitive host.

3. Man is the sole definitive host of *Tænia saginata* and *T. solium*. The former species utilizes cattle as its only larval host; the latter species usually parasitizes hogs in its larval stage, but man is also an acceptable larval host. Both infections are cosmopolitan. Eggs of these tapeworms evacuated in human feces contaminate the soil and, on ingestion by cattle (*T. saginata*) or hogs (*T. solium*), migrate to muscle tissues where they transform in 2 to 3 months into small bladder worms (cysticerci). When man eats infected flesh inadequately processed he becomes infected and the worms mature in his intestine in about 3 months.

4. Both beef and pork tapeworms often produce digestive disturbances, occasionally intestinal obstruction. Eggs of these two species are indistinguishable but gravid proglottids evacuated in the feces can easily be differentiated, as can the scolices following successful treatment with quinacrine and their post-treatment recovery in the stools. Thorough cooking or freezing of beef and pork will prevent human infection, and sanitary disposal of human excreta will prevent infection of the intermediate hosts.

5. *Hymenolepis nana* (dwarf tapeworm), the smallest tapeworm which parasitizes the human intestine, is cosmopolitan and is the most common one in children. When ingested, the eggs evacuated in the stool are directly infective for the human host. After hatching the embryos temporarily invade the duodenal villi, in which they transform into larvæ, then emerge, become attached to the mucosa and in a few weeks develop into mature egg-laying worms. Infection with a few worms

may be essentially symptomless; hundreds of worms are responsible for severe digestive and nervous disorders. Diagnosis is based on recovery of the typical eggs of this species in the feces. Quinacrine is a moderately satisfactory therapeutic agent. Control is based on improvement in personal and group hygiene, especially among children.

6. *Hymenolepis diminuta* (rat tapeworm) and *Dipylidium caninum* (dog tapeworm) are occasional human parasites, due to accidental ingestion respectively of rat or dog and cat ectoparasites which are the required intermediate hosts of these worms. The infections may be symptomless or evoke mild digestive disorders. Diagnosis is made on discovery of the eggs of *H. diminuta* and the proglottids of *D. caninum* in the stools. Quinacrine therapy and improved personal and group hygiene are indicated.

7. *Dipyllobothrium latum* (fish tapeworm) is prevalent in the cooler fresh-water lakes and rivers of Europe, Asia, North America and in restricted areas in southern South America, Africa and Australia. Immature eggs of this large worm, evacuated in human feces, embryonate and hatch in cool water. When the emerging ciliated embryo is eaten by a copepod, it transforms into a first-stage (procercoid) larva. When fishes eat the copepod the parasite migrates to the flesh and transforms into a sparganum type of larva. When man consumes inadequately cooked fish he acquires the infection, which matures in a few months in his small intestine. Presence of one or more of these worms may provoke minor or major intestinal disturbances and may also cause a temporary macrocytic anemia. Diagnosis is based on discovery of the typical unembryonated eggs in the feces. Quinacrine treatment usually removes the worms and terminates the anemia. Man, less commonly the dog, initiates the extrinsic cycle in endemic areas by discharging *D. latum* eggs into nearby lakes. Later, after copepods and fishes successively accomplish their roles in the cycle, man is exposed by eating the infected fish. Sanitary disposal of human excreta and thorough cooking of fish from lakes and rivers in the endemic areas are indicated control measures.

8. The following types of larval tapeworms parasitize man: (*a*) cysticercus of *Tænia solium*; (*b*) cenurus of *Multiceps* spp.; (*c*) hydatid cyst of *Echinococcus granulosus* and *E. multilocularis*, and (*d*) sparganum (plerocercoid) of species of *Diphyllobothrium*, subgenus *Spirometra*. If eggs of *T. solium* (from human sources), of *Multiceps* spp. and *Echinococcus* spp. (from dogs) are accidently ingested by man, they hatch in the duodenum, permitting the hexacanth embryos to migrate to extra-intestinal foci and to develop into the respective larval stages. The location of the cysticercus may be in somatic tissues or in visceral sites, including the brain and eye; the cenurus of *Multiceps cerebralis* is invariably implanted in the brain or spinal cord; the unilocular hydatid cyst of *E. granulosus* develops in the liver, lungs, brain, body cavities and occasionally in osseous tissues; the alveolar cyst of *E. multilocularis* is almost always located in the liver. The sparganum stage of *Spirometra* is typically situated in superficial tissues.

The number of larvæ in an infection, their location, size and host reaction to the living and dying larvæ determine the pathological picture and the symptoms evoked. Infection with the cenurus of *M. cerebralis* and hydatid of *E. multilocularis* is always serious. When feasible, surgical removal of the other types of larvæ is the indicated therapeutic procedure.

Human infection with the cysticercus of *T. solium* and the hydatid of *E. granulosus* is relatively cosmopolitan but there are several areas of heavy endemicity. Cenurus infection is common in sheep, rare in man. The alveolar hydatid of *E. multilocularis* occurs principally in northern boreal regions and from Central Europe through the U.S.S.R. Sparganum in man is found most often in the Orient. Correction of habits of faulty hygiene is needed to prevent these infections.

REFERENCES

ALLEN, R. W. 1947. Thermal Death Point of Cysticerci of *Tænia Saginata*. J. Parasitol., *33*, 331–338.

ALTENKAMP, T. 1935. Akute Appendicitis bei Bandwurm. Münch. Med. Wochenschr., *82*, 418–419.

DE ANDRADE, C. 1940. Oftalmologia Tropical (Sul-America). Rio de Janeiro, pp. 111–115.

ASENJO, A., and BUSTAMENTE, E. 1950. Die Neurochirurgische Behandlung der Cysticerkose. Deutsche Med. Wochenschr., *75*, 1180–1183.

BARRETT, N. R., and THOMAS, D. 1952. Pulmonary Hydatid Disease. Brit. J. Surg., *40*, 222–244.

BEAVER, P. C., and SODEMAN, W. A. 1952. Treatment of *Hymenolepis nana* (Dwarf Tapeworm) Infection with Quinacrine Hydrochloride (Atebrin). J. Trop. Med. & Hyg., *55*, 97–99.

BICKERSTAFF, E. R. 1955. Cerebral Cysticercosis. Common but Unfamiliar Manifestations. Brit. Med. J., *i*, 1055–1058.

BONNE, C. 1942. Researches on Sparganosis in the Netherlands East Indies. Am. J. Trop. Med., *22*, 643–645.

VON BONSDORFF, B. 1947. *Diphyllobothrium latum* and Pernicious Anemia, IX, X. Acta Med. Scandinav., *129*, 142–155, 213–233.

————: 1956. *Diphyllobothrium latum* as a Cause of Pernicious Anemia. Exp Parasitol., *5*, 207–230.

CAMERON, T. W. M. 1960. The Development and Experimental Pathology of *Echinococcus multilocularis* and Alveolar Hydatid. Parasitol., *2*, 371–380.

CHANDLER, A. C. 1942. First Record of a Case of Human Infection with Tapeworms of the Genus *Mesocestoides*. Am. J. Trop. Med., *22*, 493–496.

————: 1955. *Introduction to Parasitology with Special Reference to the Parasites of Man*. 9th. ed., 799 pp. John Wiley & Sons, Inc., New York.

CHANDLER, A. C. and ANOND PRADATSUNDARASAR. 1957. Two Cases of *Raillietina* Infection in Infants in Thailand, with a Discussion of the Taxonomy of the Species of *Raillietina* (Cestoda) in Man, Rodents and Monkeys. J. Parasitol., *43*, 81–89.

DAUGHERTY, J. W., and FOSTER, W. B. 1958. Comparative Studies on Amino Acid Absorption by Cestodes. Exp. Parasitol., *7*, 99–107.

DENT, J. H. 1957. Cysticercus Cerebri—Cestode Infection of Human Brain. Report of a Case Occurring in Louisiana. J. Am. Med. Assn., *164*, 401–405.

DEW, H. R. 1953. Pleomorphism in Hydatid Disease. Arch. Intern. Hidatidosis, *XIII*, 284–295.

DIXON, H. B. F., and HARGREAVES, W. H. 1944. Cysticercosis (*Tænia solium*). Quart. J. Med., *13*, 107–121.

DONCKASTER, R., and HABIBE, O. 1958. Contribución al estudio de la infección por *Hymenolepis nana*. Bol. Chileno Parasitol., *13*, 9–11.

FAIGUENBAUM, J. 1961. Anotaciones de interés sobre la hidatidosis. Bol. Chileno Parasitol., *16*, 18–22.

FAUST, E. C. 1952. Some Morphologic Characters of *Diphyllobothrium latum*. An. Inst. Med. Trop. (Lisbôa), *9*, 1277–1300.

GAN, K. H. 1949. Research on the Life Cycle of *Diphyllobothrium ranarum*. Docum. Neerl. et Indones. Morbis Tropicis, *1*, 90–92.

HEDRICK, R. M. 1958. Comparative Histochemical Studies on Cestodes, II. The Distribution of Fat Substances in *Hymenolepis diminuta* and *Raillietina cesticellus*. J. Parasitol., *44*, 75–84.

HEYNEMAN, D. 1959. Experimental Autoinfection of *Hymenolepis nana* in Isolated Mice Restricted from Coprophagy. J. Parasitol., *45*, (Sec. 2), 25–26.

JOHNSTONE, H. G., and JONES, O. W., JR. 1950. Cerebral Cœnurosis in an Infant. Am. J. Trop. Med., *30*, 431–441.

LECH JUNIOR. 1949. Ocular Cysticercosis. Am. J. Ophthalm., *32*, 523–547.

LUCKER, J. T. 1960. A Test of the Resistance of *Tænia saginata* Eggs to Freezing. J. Parasitol., *46*, 304.

MACARTHUR, W. P. 1934. Cysticercosis as Seen in the British Army, with Special Reference to the Production of Epilepsy. Trans. R. Soc. Trop. Med. & Hyg., *27*, 343–363.

MILLER, M. J. 1953. Hydatid Infection in Canada. Canad. Med. Assn. J., *68*, 423–434.

MINNING, W. 1952. Cysticercose, in Vogel and Minning's *Wurmkrankheiten, Handbuch der Inneren Medizin*, pp. 947–952, Berlin-Göttingen-Heidelberg.

NAGATY, H. F., and EZZAT, M. A. E. 1946. On the Identity of *Multiceps multiceps* (Leske, 1780), *M. gaigeri* Holl, 1916, and *M. serialis* (Gervais, 1845), with a Review of These and Similar Forms in Man and Animals. Proc. Helm. Soc., Washington, *13*, 33–44.

NEWTON, W. L., BENNETT, H. J., and FIGGAT, W. B. 1959. Observations on the Effects of Various Sewage Treatment upon Eggs of *Tænia saginata*. Am. J. Hyg., *49*, 166–175.

OBRADOR, S. 1948. Clinical Aspects of Cerebral Cysticercosis. Arch. Neurol. & Psychiat., *59*, 457–468.

OBRADOR, S., RODRIGUEZ MIÑON, J. L., ALÉS REINLEIN, J. M., and SANCHEZ, J. J. 1951. Hidatidosis raquimedular asociada a cisticercosis generalizada. Rev. Clin. Españ., *40*, 323–326.

PENFOLD, W. J., PENFOLD, H. B., and PHILLIPS, M. 1937. *Tænia saginata:* Its Growth and Propagation. J. Helminthol., *15*, 41–48.

RAUSCH, R. 1958. *Echinococcus multilocularis* Infection. Abstracts, 7th Intern'l Congr. Trop. Med. & Malaria, Lisbon, p. 53.

————. 1960 Recent Studies on Hydatid Disease in Alaska. Parasitol., *2*, 391–398.

RAUSCH, R., and SCHILLER, E. L. 1951. Hydatid Disease (Echinococcosis) in Alaska and the Importance of Rodent Intermediate Hosts. Science, *113*, 57–58.

RAUSCH, R., and WILLIAMSON, S. L. 1959. Studies on the Helminth Fauna of Alaska. *XXXIV*. The Parasites of Wolves, *Canis lupus* L. J. Parassitol., *45*, 395–402.

READ, C. P. 1951. Studies on the Enzymes and Intermediate Products of Carbohydrate Degradation in the Cestode *Hymenolepis diminuta*. Exp. Parasitol., *1*, 1–18.

SCHAEPPI, TH. 1949. Hochgradige anaphylaktische Erscheinungen bei Infektion mit *Tænia cucumerina*. Praxis, Bern, *38*, 942.

SMYTH, J. D. 1947. The Physiology of Tapeworms. Biol. Rev., *22*, 214–238.

SODEMAN, W. A., and JUNG, R. C. 1952. Treatment of Teniasis with Quinacrine Hydrochloride. J. Am. Med. Assn., *148*, 285–286.

STUNKARD, H. W. 1940. The Morphology and Life History of the Cestode *Bertiella studeri*. Am. J. Trop. Med., *20*, 305–333.

UPTON, A. C. 1950. Tænial Proglottides in the Appendix: Possible Association with Appendicitis. Am. J. Clin. Path., *20*, 1117–1120.

URQUHART, G. M. 1961. Epizoötological and Experimental Studies on Bovine Cysticercosis in East Africa. J. Parasitol., *47*, 857–869.

VOGEL, H. 1957. Ueber den *Echinococcus multilocularis* Süddeutschlands. Zeitschr. f. Tropenmed. u. Parasitol., *8*, 404–456.

WEINSTEIN, P. O., KRAWZYK, H. J., and PEERS, J. H. 1954. Sparganosis in Korea. Am. J. Trop. Med. & Hyg., *3*, 112–129.

Chapter 12

The Nematodes of the Digestive Tract and Related Species

NEMATODES are non-segmented animals, typically elongate, cylindrical, with a fundamentally bilateral symmetry. They have a complete digestive tract and a body cavity which is not lined with mesothelium. With relatively few exceptions they are *diecious*. They range in size from species too small to be readily seen by the unaided eye to many centimeters in length and several millimeters in diameter (Fig. 106).

The *body wall* consists of an outer cuticle, an inner muscular layer, and an intermediate thin hypodermis which secretes the cuticle and binds the outer surface of the muscle fibers. Arising from the hypodermis, 4 cords project into the body cavity at the dorsal, ventral and 2 lateral lines, dividing the muscles into distinct quadrants. The muscle fibers, several in each quadrant, are oriented parallel to the long axis of the body; thus locomotion is accomplished by flexing the body, essentially as in eels and snakes (Fig. 107).

Specialized structures at the anterior extremity of the roundworm serve for attachment, penetration and for sensory purposes. The cuticle may also be provided with scales or spines, especially over the anterior portion, but the body surface of nematodes is generally finely ridged or smooth.

The *alimentary tract* (Fig. 108A) is divided into three main portions: (1) an anterior part consisting of oral cavity and esophagus (muscular except in the Trichinelloidea), both lined with an internal extension of the cuticle, (2) a midgut with a single layer of epithelial cells, without cuticle, and (3) a hindgut or rectum, which is lined with cuticle.

The *excretory system* (Fig. 108B) consists fundamentally of two longitudinal tubules embedded in the lateral cords. These tubules end blindly at their posterior ends; anteriorly they have a transverse ventral connection with a single mid-ventral opening close behind the mouth.

The *nervous system* is composed of a circum-esophageal nerve ring, six short anterior trunks and six long posterior trunks which unite near the caudal extremity.

Cuticular organs of peculiar importance in the nematodes are the amphids and the phasmids. The *amphids*, regarded as sensory receptors, consist of a pair of minute, lateral bodies at the anterior end of the worm, each with an external chamber which may be a simple pore, or a circular, spiral,

10 cm.

E.C.F.

Fig. 106.—Outline drawings of important nematode parasites of man, drawn to scale. *a, Trichuris trichiura,* female (*left*), male (*right*); *b, Necator americanus,* female (*left*), male (*right*); *c, Ancylostoma duodenale,* female (*left*), male (*right*); *d, Trichostrongylus orientalis,* female (*left*), male (*right*); *e,* parasitic female *Strongyloides stercoralis; f, Enterobius vermicularis,* female (*left*), male (*right*); *g, Trichinella spiralis,* female (*left*), male (*right*); *h, Ascaris lumbricoides,* female (*left*), male (*right*); *i, Loa loa,* female (*left*), male (*right*); *j, Acanthocheilonema* (vel *Dipetalonema*) *perstans,* female (*left*), male, (*right*); *k,* female *Mansonella ozzardi; l, Brugia malayi,* female (*left*), male (*right*); *m, Wuchereria bancrofti,* female (*left*), male (*right*); *n, Onchocerca volvulus,* female (*left*), male (*right*). (Original, Faust.)

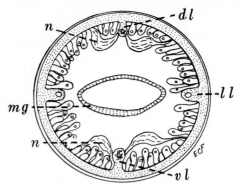

FIG. 107.—Cross section through the equatorial region of a generalized nematode. *dl*, dorsal longitudinal line; *ll*, lateral longitudinal line; *mg*, midgut; *n*, nerve; *vl*, ventral longitudinal line (sex organs not shown.) × 10. (Original, Faust.)

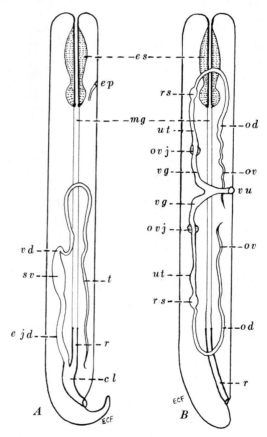

FIG. 108.—Diagrams showing important organs of a nematode: *A*, with male and *B*, with female reproductive systems. *cl*, cloaca; *ejd*, ejaculatory duct; *ep*, excretory pore; *es*, esophagus; *mg*, midgut; *od*, oviduct; *ov*, ovary; *ovj*, ovejector; *r*, rectum; *rs*, receptaculum seminis; *sv*, seminal vesicle; *t*, testis; *ut*, uterus; *vg*, vagina; *vu*, vulva. (Original, Faust.)

helical or elongate tubule. Most nematodes possess a pair of caudal organs called *phasmids*, which are post-anal in position.

The *reproductive organs* of nematodes usually are found in separate male and female individuals. However, in a few instances the male lives in the body of the female or the female may be *parthenogenetic*. Males are almost invariably somewhat smaller than females and may be very much smaller, as in *Dracunculus*.

The *male reproductive system* (Fig. 108*A*) consists typically of a single tubule, beginning at its inner end as a testis (*t*), then a vas deferens (*vd*), a seminal vesicle (*sv*), and an ejaculatory duct (*ejd*) lined with cement glands, opening into the cloaca. Accessory copulatory structures consist of one or two copulatory spicules, which may be of equal length and bristle-like or unequal and variously-shaped, and commonly a regulatory structure, the gubernaculum. In hookworms and their relatives the posterior end of the male is extended into an umbrella-like structure of cuticle supported by fleshy rays (*bursa copulatrix*), which is applied around the female at the vulva at the time of copulation.

The *female reproductive system* (Fig. 108*B*) may be composed of a single reproductive set (*viz.*, *Trichuris*) but in most nematodes it is bicornuate. It is tubular and is frequently coiled within the body cavity, so that its total length may be considerably longer than that of the worm. The following regions can usually be recognized: ovary (*ov*), oviduct (*od*), seminal receptacle (*rs*), uterus (*ut*), ovejector (*ovj*), vagina (*va*), and vulva (*vu*), which is ventral in position.

The *ovum* is characteristically provided with yolk material. After passing down the oviduct and being fertilized, it secretes around itself an inner, very resistant, thin vitelline membrane and a somewhat thicker chitinous layer. In some roundworms such as *Ascaris* an additional outer shell layer is laid on as a secretion from the uterine wall.

The daily production of eggs per female varies greatly in different species. The stage of development at the time of oviposition also varies. Eggs of *Ascaris* and *Trichuris* are completely unembryonated; those of hookworms are in the early stage of cleavage, and those of *Strongyloides* are frequently in the morula stage. In *Trichinella* and *Dracunculus* the eggs develop completely *in utero* and discharge the first larval stage, *i.e.*, they are *larviparous*. Filaria worms give birth to microfilariæ, prelarval snake-like embryos.

The fundamental stages in the nematode life cycle are the egg, 4 larval stages and the adult worm. At the end of each larval stage a new cuticle is secreted and the old one is shed (molted). The important stages in the life cycle of the common nematode parasites of man are shown in Plate X.

Several groups of parasitic nematodes require two hosts. In the case of *Trichinella spiralis* all stages in the life cycle are completed in one host but infection of a new host is dependent on consumption of the larvæ encapsulated in the striated muscles of the first host. *Dracunculus* infection in the definitive host results from ingesting water fleas (*Cyclops*) which harbor the larval stage. Blood-sucking arthropods are the required intermediate hosts of the filaria worms.

When intermediate hosts are not involved, as in the majority of intestinal

Plate X.—Stages in the Life Cycle of the Common Roundworms of Man—(Original, Faust)

Name	Enterobius vermicularis (pinworm)	Trichuris trichiura (whipworm)	Ascaris lumbricoides (large roundworm)	Trichinella spiralis (trichina worm)	Necator, Ancylostoma (hookworm)	Strongyloides stercoralis (threadworm)	Filariæ
Adults, size ♂	2–5 × 0.1–0.2 mm.	30–45 mm. long	15–31 × 0.2–0.4 cm.	1.4–1.6 mm. × 40–60 microns	7–11 × 0.3–0.5 mm.	lacking	19–45 mm. × 60–350 microns
♀	8–13 × 0.3–0.5 mm.	35–50 mm. long	20–35 × 0.3–0.6 cm.	3.0–3.5 mm. × 60–90 microns	9–13 × 0.4–0.6 mm.	2.2 mm. × 30–74 microns	33–100 mm. × 120–500 microns
Usual location	Free or superficially attached to mucosa of cecum, appendix of cecum, appendix and colon	Attached to mucosa of cecum, appendix, colon and rectum	Free in small intestine	Females in mucosa of small intestine	Attached to mucosa of small intestine	Females in mucosa of small and large intestines	Lymph channels and intercellular spaces of visceral and somatic tissues
Stage of progeny leaving human host	Almost fully embryonated egg 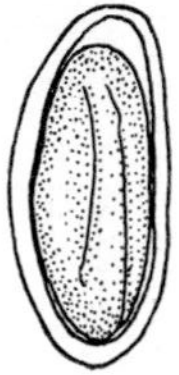	Unembryonated egg 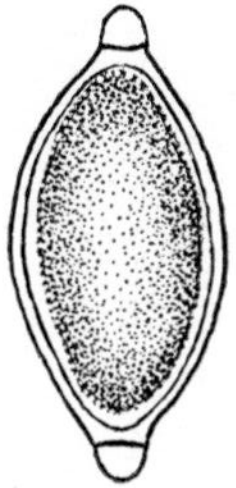	Unembryonated egg 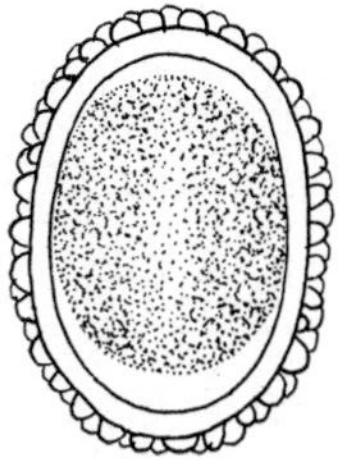	None; hatched larva migrates to muscles and encysts 	Egg in early stage of cleavage 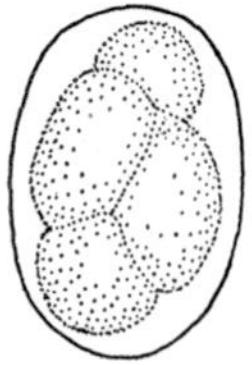	Rhabditoid larval stage 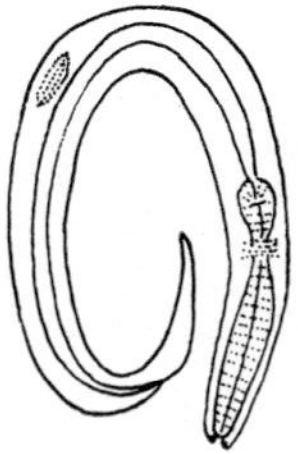	Microfilaria (prelarval embryo of Wuchereria bancrofti) 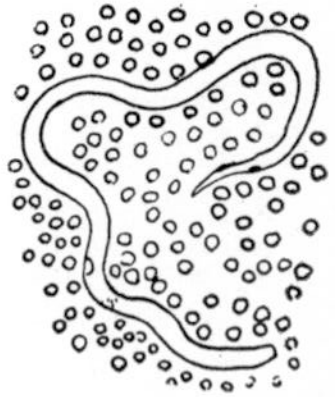

Required Extra-human development before becoming infective for man	Few hours before egg is infective	2–3 weeks minimum on soil before egg becomes infective	2–3 weeks in soil before 2nd larval stage in egg; 7 days or more in egg	None; but human exposure always results from consumption of flesh of reservoir host	One to several days for 2nd rhabditoid larva to change to filariform larva	Includes hatching, 2 rhabditoid larval stages, and change to filariform larva	Microfilaria, taken up by blood-sucking fly, transforms through 2 larval stages into filariform larva
Method of human exposure	Infective-stage egg taken into mouth and swallowed	Infective-stage egg taken into mouth and swallowed	Infective-stage egg taken into mouth and swallowed	Larvae encysted in hog's muscles; ingested in inadequately processed meat	Filariform larvae in soil invade exposed skin	Filariform larvae in soil invade exposed skin (or if developed in intestine may produce internal auto-infection)	Blood-sucking fly introduces infective larva into skin
Migration in human body and development to adult stage	Egg hatches in small intestine; larva migrates to cecum, and matures in 15–28 days	Egg hatches in small intestine; larva migrates to cecum, becomes attached to mucosa, and matures in 90 days	Egg hatches in small intestine; larva migrates via bloodstream to lungs, molts, returns to intestine via trachea, epiglottis, esophagus and stomach, and matures in 8 to 12 weeks	Excysted larvae freed in duodenum, invade mucosa, and mature in 5–7 days	Larvae in skin enter and are carried in afferent blood vessels to lungs; molt, then migrate to small intestine via trachea, epiglottis, esophagus and stomach, become attached and mature in 6 or more weeks	Larvae in skin enter lymphatic vessels to sites of adult predilection; females enter mucosa, mature in about 28 days or less	Larvae enter skin and migrate in lymphatic vessels to sites of adult predilection; mature in several months to one year.

roundworms of man, there is a necessary period of development outside the body, frequently in soil, after which the larva in the egg shell, or free, is infective. Eggs freshly passed in the feces are not infective. In general, the larva is second-stage (*i.e.*, has molted once) at the time it becomes infective while still in the egg shell, and is third-stage when it reaches the infective stage free in the soil or intermediate host.

Enterobius vermicularis (Linnæus, 1758) Leach, 1853

(The pinworm or seatworm, causing enterobiasis or oxyuriasis.)

This worm has been known since ancient times. It has a cosmopolitan distribution but is more common in persons living in cool or temperate zones than in strictly tropical areas. Although it is almost exclusively a parasite of man, on rare occasions it has been found in the chimpanzee.

Morphology, Biology and Life Cycle

The oral tip of the adult *E. vermicularis* is provided with three lips which are retractable into the minute oral vestibule. Likewise at the anterior end of the worm there are a dorsal and a ventral bladder-like inflation of the cuticle (Beaver, 1952).

The male worm (Fig. 109*A*) measures 2 to 5 mm. long and has a maximum width of 0.1 to 0.2 mm. With its strongly curved posterior end, the lateral view of the worm forms an inverted question mark. The female worm (Fig. 109*B*) is considerably larger than the male, having a length of 8 to 13 mm. and a maximum width of 0.3 to 0.5 mm. The sharply pointed postanal portion occupies nearly one-third of the total length.

The characteristic habitat of these worms is at the cecal level of the intestine, where they are free or insecurely attached to the mucosa. The worms are frequently found in the appendix. Gravid females migrate down the bowel and out of the anus onto the perinal and perianeal skin; in female subjects they may reach the vulva and wander up the genital tract, at times reaching the inner end of the tubules and the peritoneal cavity.

The eggs *in utero* are not fully embryonated until the female worms arrive at the lower levels of the colon. Hence the occasional batches of eggs which are laid within the bowel are relatively immature. Each female has been found to discharge an average of about 11,000 eggs (Reardon, 1938).

The eggs discharged on the skin (Fig. 109*C*, 110) are essentially mature and within a few hours contain a fully developed infective-stage larva. The eggs are flattened on one side, measure 50 to 60 by 20 to 30 microns, and are provided with a colorless double shell, an inner embryonic membrane and an outer albuminous layer which causes them to stick to each other and to clothing and other objects. Thus, some of the eggs almost invariably reach the mouth of persons in the contaminated environment. In the small intestine the eggs hatch and from each there emerges a stout rhabditoid larva which measures 140 to 150 by 10 microns. On reaching maturity in the cecal area the worms mate, and complete the life cycle in 15 to 28 days (Cram, 1943).

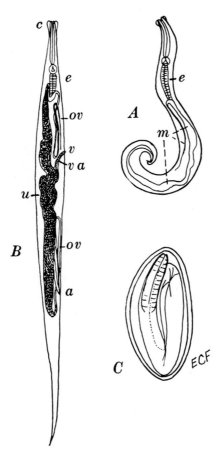

Fig. 109.—*Enterobius vermicularis* (pinworm or seatworm). *A*, male, *B*, female, showing digestive and reproductive organs; *C*, embryonated egg. *a*, anus; *e*, esophagus; *m*, midgut; *ov*, ovary; *u*, uterus; *v*, vulva; *va*, vagina. *A*, *B* × 16; *C*, × 600. (From Faust and Russell's *Clinical Parasitology*, Lea & Febiger, Philadelphia.)

Pathogenesis and Symptomatology

Commonly the first recognizable symptom is pruritus as the worms emerge from the rectum and crawl over the perianal and perineal skin. The itching is followed by scratching which adds to the irritation, with scarification or weeping eczema of the area, and allows bacteria to enter the lesion. As worms in various stages of development frequently are seen in the appendix, and occasionally are found deep in the inflamed mucosa, pinworms often are suspected of causing appendicitis. At times worms enter the female genital tract and become encapsulated within the uterus or Fallopian tubules, or wander into the peritoneal cavity and become encapsulated on the peritoneum.

The common symptoms in children, in addition to pruritus ani, consist of restless sleep, and tiredness during the daytime.

The blood picture in pinworm infection is not remarkably altered. There may be low-grade eosinophilia.

Diagnosis

Specific diagnosis may be made on recovery of the worms from the perianal area or following an enema, more frequently on demonstration of the eggs (Fig. 110). Only occasionally are eggs found in the feces.

The Scotch-tape technic for recovery of pinworm eggs has been demonstrated to be the most satisfactory (Beaver, 1949). (See "TECHNICAL AIDS," page 430.) These preparations are more likely to be positive when perianal impression smears are taken before the morning stool has been passed and before the bath.

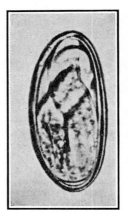

FIG. 110.—Photomicrograph of fully embryonated egg of *Enterobius vermicularis*, obtained on a perianal swab. × 800. (From Cram, *Introduction to Nematology*, in Faust and Russell's *Clinical Parasitology*, Lea & Febiger, Philadelphia.)

Treatment

Since oxyuriasis is a familial and environmental infection, longer lasting relief can be obtained if all infected individuals in the household are discovered and treated simultaneously.

Only two groups of drugs are useful in infections with *E. vermicularis*, viz., the piperazine compounds and cyanine dyes. *Piperazine hexahydrate* is highly effective and without important side effects (Brown and Chan, 1955) (see Table 7, page 419). Toxic manifestations including nausea, vomiting, asymmetrical flaccid paralysis and incoördination may occur either with overdose or faulty excretion, but are reversible. The therapeutic efficiency is very marked. Gentian violet medicinal was long the standard drug but has been superseded by other less toxic drugs. Of these, *dithiazanine* is effective but is more apt to cause side effects than is piperazine

(Swartzwelder *et al.*, 1957). The pamoate salt of pyrvinium, another cyanine dye, presumably eradicates pinworm infection in a single dose (Beck *et al.*, 1959).

The physician should warn the patient or parents of the probability of recurrent infection, which should not be regarded as treatment failure. Reinfection may be reduced by hygienic measures described below under "CONTROL." Individuals constantly exposed in the home, school or playground and highly susceptible to the annoyances of the infection may require re-treatment every 5 or 6 weeks. While oxyuriasis may be disturbing it is rarely the cause of serious damage. Occasionally, however, even light infections may result in grave injury, due to the presence of worms in the uterus or other ectopic sites and unnecessary resections under suspicion that the lesions are malignant.

Epidemiology

Pinworm infection is more prevalent in large family groups, in schools, asylums and mental institutions than it is in the population at large. Eggs containing almost mature larvæ are deposited by the female worms after they migrate out the anus onto the perianal and perineal skin. Within 6 hours or less these eggs are fully infective. Exposure may occur in any of four ways: (1) The person harboring the infection may scratch the contaminated skin and transfer the eggs on finger tips to the mouth; (2) individuals sleeping in the same bed or bedroom, or using the same toilet, may be exposed from contaminated fomites; (3) eggs which get into air currents from soiled undergarments may be breathed into the body by a large number of persons, who usually acquire light infection, and (4) eggs rarely may hatch in moist perianal folds and the emerging larvæ crawl into the rectum and up to the cecal area, where they develop into mature worms. The theory of internal autoinfection has been discarded (Madsen, 1945).

Cool, moist atmosphere is optimal for survival of the eggs on fomites, while dry heat and good ventilation produce rapid death of the enclosed larvæ (Jacobs, 1942; Heller, 1944).

Enterobius vermicularis infection is much commoner in children than in adults, and is particularly prevalent where several small children sleep together. High incidence is likewise invariably found in mental hospitals. In any population in which underclothing is worn day after day, where bathing is infrequent and where there are one or more carriers of the infection, a large percentage of the group will be found infected. The incidence of infection ranges from saturation to a relatively unimportant figure, depending on the environmental conditions and the level of personal and group hygiene. Under similar environmental conditions infection rates are lower in Negroes than in Caucasians.

Control

The infection can be controlled by a twofold method of attack, *viz.*, personal and group hygiene on the one hand and mass chemotherapy on the other.

Infection in a family group can be appreciably reduced by developing habits of personal hygiene in the children; by providing small children with closed sleeping garments and by keeping the finger nails short. Eggs of pinworm are not killed by chlorination of water in swimming and wading pools.

Syphacia obvelata (Rudolphi, 1802) Seurat, 1916

This pinworm of rats and mice is rarely reported in man. The adult worms somewhat resemble *Enterobius vermicularis* but are considerably smaller. Moreover, males as well as females have a long attenuated tail and the post-anal region of the male may coil ventrally up to 360 degrees. The worms live in the cecum of the mouse and rat. The eggs are shed in the perianal region in a fully embryonated state. They resemble those of *E. vermicularis* but are much larger (125 by 40 microns).

Trichuris trichiura (Linnæus) Stiles, 1901

(syn. Trichocephalus trichiurus)
(The human whipworm, causing trichuriasis)

The human whipworm was first specifically described and named by Linnæus in 1771. Its life cycle was studied by Grassi (1887) and later by Fülleborn (1923) and Hasegawa (1924).

T. trichiura is cosmopolitan in its distribution but is prevalent only in warm or temperate moist climates.

Morphology, Biology and Life Cycle

The adult whipworms (Fig. 111) have a capillary anterior three-fifths and a more fleshy posterior portion of the body. The anterior end is superficially but securely threaded into the intestinal mucosa, typically of the cecum and appendix, but if there are a large number of worms they are distributed posteriorwards through the colon and even the rectum. Typically the whipworm has a life expectation of several years.

The male (Fig. 111*A*) measures 30 to 45 mm. in length. Its more fleshy posterior end is curved ventrally into a watch-spring coil of 360 degrees or more. The female (Fig. 111*B*) measures 35 to 50 mm. in length. Its more fleshy posterior portion is club-shaped.

The daily egg output of the ovipositing female is not definitely known but the average probably lies between 3,000 and 6,000. Reduced production may be expected in infections where the worms are close together and the parasitized intestinal mucosa is badly damaged.

The barrel-shaped eggs (Fig. 111*C*) are laid in the one-celled stage. They possess a transparent inner shell, a golden-brownish outer shell and have a transparent blister-like prominence at each pole. When the fertilized eggs are evacuated in the stool on moist, shaded, sandy humus, they proceed normally with embryonation. The period of survival of these eggs on the soil is relatively short.

When viable infective-stage eggs are taken into the mouth and swallowed,

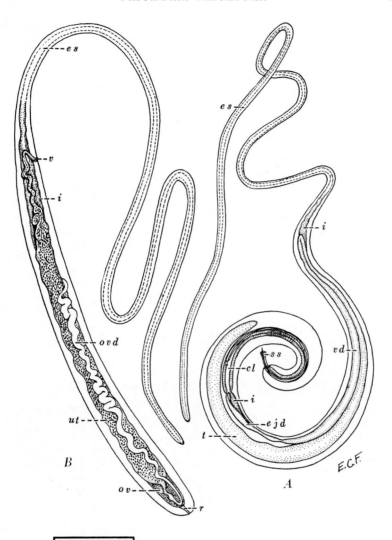

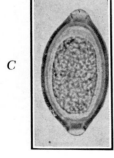

FIG. 111.—*Trichuris trichiura* (whipworm). *A*, male, *B*, female, showing digestive and reproductive systems; *C*, photomicrograph of unembryonated egg evacuated in the stool. *cl*, cloaca; *ejd*, ejaculatory duct; *es*, esophagus; *i*, midgut; *ov*, ovary; *ovd*, oviduct; *r*, rectum; *ss*, copulatory spicule and sheath; *t*, testis; *ut*, uterus; *v*, vulva; *vd*, vas deferens. *A*, *B*, × 12; *C*, × 666. (In Faust's *Human Helminthology*, Lea & Febiger, Philadelphia; *C*, after Faust, courtesy, W. F. Prior Co.)

hatching occurs in the duodenum. The delicately muscular larva temporarily enters the nearby intestinal crypts and secures harborage and nourishment by penetrating into the glands and stroma (Miller, 1941). For about 10 days, young worms are found in these locations at successively lower levels of the small intestine, and soon thereafter begin to appear in the cecum and appendix where they become attached. Approximately 90 days after the eggs are ingested the worms have matured, have copulated and a new cycle has begun.

Pathogenesis and Symptomatology

Light infections are relatively unimportant and produce no appreciable symptoms. As the number of attached worms increases there is a corresponding amount of intestinal damage. In heavy infections the mucosa of the entire large bowel is typically covered with the squirming wiry organisms, matted together in slimy, bloody feces. The mucosa itself is hyperemic, at times bleeding and superficially eroded, and may bear evidence of extensive inflammation. Irritation produced by these worms in the wall of the lower colon and rectum may eventually provoke prolapse of the rectum (Fig. 112).

Jung and Beaver (1952) studied whipworm infection in 352 children 1 to 11 years of age in the Charity Hospital of Louisiana in New Orleans; these patients constituted 18% of 2,000 hospitalized children whose stools were currently being examined for parasites. The heavily infected individuals, with more than 30 eggs per mgm. of stool and a calculated number of

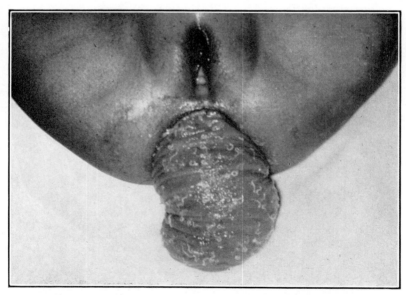

Fig. 112.—Prolapse of rectum in a Louisiana child, due to heavy infection with *Trichuris trichiura*. (Photo made by Drs. Paul C. Beaver and Ralph V. Platou; copy to senior author through courtesy of Dr. J. C. Swartzwelder.)

worms in excess of 200, suffered from chronic diarrhea or dysentery, and several had prolapse of the rectum.

Clinical trichuriasis is by no means rare in the warm humid coastal areas of the Southern United States, and at times is as severe as it is in tropical countries.

Diagnosis

Diagnosis of whipworm infection is made on demonstration of the characteristic eggs (Fig. 111*C*) recovered from the stool. In addition to eggs, diarrheic and dysenteric stools of whipworm patients contain many eosinophils and Charcot-Leyden crystals, which may be present several weeks before the worms mature and eggs appear in the stools. Adult worms may be seen attached to the prolapsed rectum (Fig. 112) or at sigmoidoscopy, and are occasionally present in the feces.

Treatment

Only two methods of treating whipworm infection are efficient. *Dithiazanine iodide*, a cyanine dye, is effective when administered orally over a period of several days (Frye *et al.*, 1957). Although this drug is the only one capable of completely eliminating whipworm infection, it produces side effects of nausea and vomiting (see Table 7, page 419).

For rapid results in hospital patients, particularly when it is especially desirable to avoid vomiting, the most useful treatment in heavy whipworm infection is *hexylresorcinol* in 0.2% enemas. A coating of petroleum jelly must be applied to the buttocks, thighs and perineum before instillation of the solution, to prevent burning of the skin from returned or spilled material. This treatment will not eradicate the infection but will produce clinical cure.

Light whipworm infections do not require treatment.

Prognosis

This is good for lightly infected persons but is poor for those with heavy infections, unless the worms are removed.

Epidemiology

Eggs of the whipworm are evacuated in the stool in an unembryonated condition and require a period of development on the ground to reach the infective stage. Conditions favorable for development of the egg consist of a moist, shaded, warm soil. A period of about 21 days is required until an active larva is coiled inside the egg shell. The egg is now infective when introduced into the mouth as a contamination of food, adhering to play objects dropped on the egg-infested ground and later taken into the mouth, or as a result of dirt eating.

In highly endemic foci small children develop heavy infection (Jung and Beaver, 1952), yet the greatest prevalence characteristically occurs in children of school age. In countries where trichuriasis is endemic adults with primitive personal hygiene also have high incidence of infection.

Human infection probably results exclusively from exposure to infective stage eggs derived from human sources, since there are no important reservoir hosts.

Control

Whipworm infection is controllable only by maintaining a high standard of environmental sanitation. At the present time mass treatment as a control measure is not feasible because drugs available, even though relatively effective, are toxic and expensive.

Capillaria hepatica (Bancroft, 1893) Travassos, 1915
(The capillary liver worm)

This relative of the whipworm is a tissue parasite in the liver of domestic and wild mammals, mostly rats and other rodents. The adult worms are considerably more delicate than *Trichuris*. The eggs, measuring 51 to 67 microns by 30 to 35 microns, resemble those of *T. trichiura* but have a velvety outer shell perforated by minute pores. They are deposited and retained in the hepatic parenchyma. When the infected liver is eaten by predator or scavenger animals, the eggs are liberated by tissue digestion, are passed in the feces, and embryonate in the same manner as those of *Trichuris*, *i.e.*, in damp shaded soil. Infection results from ingesting infective-stage eggs in contaminated soil. The larva hatched from the egg in the duodenum of the new host enters the intestinal wall and migrates *via* mesenteric-portal blood to the liver, penetrates into periportal tissues and matures in about 28 days.

From time to time eggs of this parasite have been found in human feces. Such spurious infection results from eating cooked livers of infected animals.

At least 9 human cases with liver involvement have been reported: 2 in adults and 7 in children (Ward and Dent, 1959; Calle, 1961). The clinical picture is that of visceral larva migrans. Diagnosis is made by liver biopsy. There is no known therapy. Prevention consists in avoiding ingestion of soil and prohibiting dirt-eating by children.

Ascaris lumbricoides Linnæus, 1758
(The large intestinal roundworm, causing ascariasis)

Ascaris lumbricoides has been known to physicians since the dawn of history. Davaine (1863) first discovered that fully mature *Ascaris* eggs hatch in the small intestine and Stewart (1916) showed that the hatched larvæ require a migration to the lungs before they complete their development in the intestine. Ransom and Foster (1917), Ransom and Cram (1921) and Koino (1922) demonstrated that the entire life cycle takes place in a single natural host.

With the possible exception of *Enterobius*, *Ascaris lumbricoides* is the most widely prevalent of all human roundworms and occurs endemically in all parts of the world except in cold, dry climates. Although the highest frequency of ascariasis is found in tropical areas, it is also common in many temperate regions of the world.

Morphology, Biology and Life Cycle

The adult *Ascaris* is the largest roundworm parasitizing the human intestinal tract (Fig. 113). It is elongated, cylindrical and tapers both anteriorly and posteriorly to relatively blunt conical ends. The head (Fig. 113*C*) is provided with three fleshy lips.

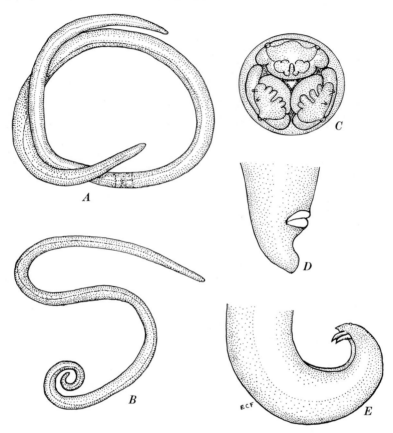

Fig. 113.—*Ascaris lumbricoides.* *A*, mature female, $\times$ ¾; *B*, mature male, $\times$ ¾; *C*, view of anterior extremity, showing the 3 fleshy lips with papillæ surrounding the triangular mouth, $\times$ 30; *D*, posterior extremity of female, with anal opening, $\times$ 9; *E*, posterior extremity of male, with 2 copulatory spicules, $\times$ 9. (Original, Faust.)

The sexually mature male worm measures 12 to 31 cm. in length by 2 to 4 mm. Its posterior end is curved somewhat ventrally. The female worm measures 20 to 35 cm. in length by 3 to 6 mm. in greatest diameter, but specimens up to 45 cm. are occasionally observed. The daily egg production per female averages about 200,000.

The fertilized egg of *A. lumbricoides* (Fig. 114,*b*) at the time of oviposition is broadly ovoidal, measures 65 to 75 microns by 35 to 50 microns, and consists of the following structures: (1) a coarsely granular, spherical egg cell which is separated from the shell at its two ends by a semi-lunar space; (2) a thin, innermost, lipoidal fertilization membrane, which is highly impermeable; (3) a relatively thick, colorless middle layer, which is smooth on both inner and outer surfaces, and (4) an outermost, coarsely mammillated, albuminoid layer, laid down *in utero*, serving as an auxiliary protective membrane.

Female worms without males produce infertile eggs (Fig. 114,*a*) which typically are narrower and more elliptical (88 to 93 microns by 38 to 44 microns) than fertilized eggs. Internally they contain a mass of disorganized granules and globules which completely fill the shell.

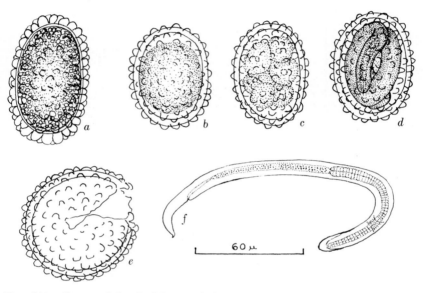

Fig. 114.—Eggs and hatched larva of *Ascaris lumbricoides*. *a*, unfertilized egg; *b*, fertilized egg as passed in the feces; *c*, partly embryonated egg; *d*, embryonated egg with motile larva; *e*, shell from which larva has escaped; *f*, hatched larva. (Original, Faust.)

Both fertile and infertile eggs are usually bile-stained by the time they are evacuated in the feces. The fertile eggs of *A. lumbricoides* are passed in the one-cell stage. They survive putrefaction and can withstand considerable desiccation and cold. At 22° C. to 33° C. complete development to the first-stage larva usually occurs in 9 to 13 days. Another week is required for the first molt, after which the eggs are infective and contain motile second-stage rhabditoid larvæ. These eggs may remain viable in the soil for months and even a year or longer.

When ingested, the fertile eggs hatch in the duodenum and the emerging robust larvæ penetrate into the nearby intestinal wall, enter mesenteric venules or lymphatics and *via* the liver and inferior vena cava or thoracic duct reach the chambers of the right heart and pass through the pulmonary vessels to capillaries, where they perforate into the alveoli. After about 10 days, during which growth and two additional molts take place, stout fourth-stage larvæ migrate to the bronchioles. From here they are carried by their own movement and by the mucus current to the pharynx, and are then swallowed. On reaching the small intestine a final molt occurs and the worms develop into adult males and females. The period from exposure to maturity requires 8 to 12 weeks (Vogel and Minning, 1942).

Pathogenesis and Symptomatology

Stage of Larval Migration.—Unless hundreds of larvæ are migrating simultaneously, the first passage from the intestine through the liver and lungs provokes no remarkable pathologic changes. Subsequent migrations cause intense tissue reactions in the liver and lungs, especially the latter, even when relatively few larvæ are involved. The liver pathology in man, not fully described, probably is much the same as that in animals, *viz.*, focal eosinophilic infiltration and granuloma formation around and in the paths of migrating larvæ, and general inflammation along the portal tracts where eosinophils are conspicuous in the acute phase. In later states there is more or less fibrosis of the periportal and interlobular spaces. More significant is the intense local cellular reaction around the larvæ in the air sacs, with infiltration of eosinophils, epithelioid cells and macrophages, and the production of a distinctive type of pulmonary pathology, *viz.*, *Ascaris* pneumonitis. Although the larvæ are seldom permanently trapped in the alveoli, their metabolites in intimate contact with the tissues initiate a generalized *Ascaris* sensitization.

The cardinal symptoms associated with larval *Ascaris* pneumonitis consist of dyspnea, often of the asthmatic type; a dry or productive cough; rales, frequently musical and wheezing, or coarse, rarely crepitant; fever, moderate to 40° C.; high but transient eosinophilia, and x-ray findings showing scattered, shifting mottling of the lungs, suggesting a possible diagnosis of pulmonary tuberculosis or viral pneumonia (Jung, 1953). This picture of pulmonary infiltration, which is often variable from day to day, and spontaneously clears after a few days to one or two weeks, along with high eosinophilia, which persists somewhat longer than the pulmonary changes, is called *Lœffler's syndrome*. During the period of productive cough the sputum characteristically contains many eosinophils and at times abundant Charcot-Leyden crystals. Migrating larvæ may also be seen in the sputum. Although Lœffler's syndrome is also caused by other agents, in areas where ascariasis is endemic, it and other nematode infections (hookworm, *Strongyloides*) are most frequently responsible. Pulmonary ascariasis is occasionally fatal, even in adults (Beaver and Danaraj, 1958).

The Adult Worms.—The maturing and adult worms live in the small intestine, deriving nourishment from semi-digested food. The detrimental effect on the host's nutrition is approximately proportional to the number of worms. In light infections there may be no apparent pathologic changes, although even a single worm may produce intestinal disturbances. In the average infection in children there are intermittent colic, loss of appetite, fretfulness, and at times nervous symptoms. The abdomen is character-istically protuberant.

From time to time there is spontaneous loss of worms unassociated with present or previous illness. These events are of no special significance. If attended with an acute febrile illness of any kind, however, the active movement of worms from the intestine is highly significant, and is to be interpreted as a direct consequence rather than the immediate cause of the illness. Disturbed by fever or other abnormal conditions, the worms migrate outwards in both directions, or congregate in closely packed masses which tend to occlude and often obstruct the intestine. In their forward excursions the worms occasionally enter and block the biliary and pan-creatic ducts or, more frequently, penetrate into the parenchyma of the liver and pancreas, where they perish. Liver abscesses in children probably are more frequently caused by *Ascaris lumbricoides* than by *Entamœba histolytica*. Worms leaving the intestine may enter the lungs *via* the trachea (in cases of deep coma), or move into the nasopharynx, where they emerge from the nares. On rare occasions immature worms have been seen coming from the lacrimal duct. Worms may also become lodged in the appendix or may perforate ulcerated and gangrenous areas of the intestinal wall. In the peritoneal cavity the worms die and are resorbed within a few days. The eggs remain, however, and generally become widely scattered before being trapped by granulomatous reaction. These complications of intes-tinal ascariasis give rise to a variety of symptoms depending on the organs and tissues involved.

The survival time of mature *A. lumbricoides* in the human intestine is relatively short, generally not exceeding a year. Yet in hyperendemic communities almost daily exposure is usual, so that new broods of larvæ are migrating through the lungs and reaching the intestine to replace the previous mature ones as soon as they are lost. Thus, there is one intestinal infection after another in these patients, while sensitization phenomena are maintained potentially at a high level.

Ascariasis is frequently associated with whipworm infection as well as diseases due to other causes. These complicate the clinical picture and often prevent accurate appraisal of the role played by the ascarids.

Diagnosis

During the prepatent period, unless immature worms are passed, specific diagnosis is not possible, although clinically the syndrome of larval *Ascaris* pneumonitis is relatively pathognomonic (Jung, 1953). Unfortunately this stage of the disease precedes the intestinal one by so many weeks that clinicians unaware of the relationship are apt to consider the pulmonary syndrome as an atypical pneumonia and treat it accordingly.

Once mature female worms are present in the intestine, the daily egg output of a single female, about 200,000, is sufficient to reveal several characteristic eggs (Fig. 113b) in an average direct fecal smear. Mature *Ascaris* in extra-intestinal sites are rarely suspected as causal agents ante-cedent to exploratory surgery, even though a diagnosis of intestinal ascariasis has previously been made.

Treatment

Chemotherapy.—There is no conclusive evidence that any anthelmintic presently employed in intestinal ascariasis is lethal to the larval worms migrating through the lungs.

The standard treatment for intestinal ascariasis consists in the administration of syrup of *piperazine citrate,* which is cheap, effective and has a large margin of safety (see Table 7, page 419). It may be given over a period of several days or in a single large dose which may be repeated after one or two days (Swartzwelder *et al.*, 1955). If ascariasis is complicated by infection with whipworm or *Strongyloides, dithiazanine* may be given to eliminate both helminths, but there is no indication for use of this drug in uncomplicated ascariasis.

Surgical Considerations.—The development of signs and symptoms of intestinal obstruction in a child who is passing *Ascaris* by mouth or anus indicates obstruction due to a bolus of worms. Such a condition warrants preparation of the patient for possible surgical intervention, including (1) search for the cause of the febrile illness which usually precipitates the complication before its treatment; (2) restoration of fluid and electrolyte balance; (3) antipyretic measures, and (4) decompression by intestinal catheter with constant suction. In the majority of instances the obstruction will be spontaneously resolved before surgical intervention is necessary. If the bolus persists in spite of adequate hydration and antipyretic therapy, laparotomy is indicated. The bowel is opened at the bolus and the worms removed with sponge forceps.

Obstructive jaundice in a child with intestinal ascariasis indicates the need for surgical intervention to remove the worm from the common bile duct. Liver abscess due to *Ascaris* must be treated by drainage and administration of antibiotics.

Syrup of piperazine may be given by intestinal catheter to patients suspected of intestinal or biliary obstruction due to ascariasis. The tube is clamped off for about 2 hours thereafter. No evidence has been reported that ill effects result from this procedure (Swartzwelder *et al.*, 1957).

Prognosis.—This is usually excellent following appropriate treatment, but at times it is grave when there is massive larval invasion of the lungs, in case of hypersensitization, or when surgical complications develop.

Epidemiology

Ascariasis is a disease due to fecal contamination of soil. In most hyperendemic areas infected small children in and around the home provide the major source for the infection by their promiscuous defecation. These excreta contain the eggs, which are relatively resistant to desiccation and putrefaction. Embryonation takes place in clay soil as well as in loam. Infective-stage eggs remain viable for weeks or months; only desiccation, freezing, heat and direct sunlight are detrimental to them. When viable, fully embryonated eggs are picked up on fingers, or as a result of dirt-eating, and get into the mouth, they hatch in the small intestine.

16

An important additional source of exposure exists in regions of the world where human nightsoil is used to fertilize garden and field crops. Persons who handle the excreta and others who consume unprocessed green vegetables and fruits such as strawberries are liable to infection.

Hogs infected with *Ascaris* probably constitute a negligible source for human infection.

Control

Anthelmintic medication constitutes only a temporary measure for the great majority of infected individuals, since with relatively few exceptions persons living in *Ascaris* environments are subject to repeated exposure. The problem of control is therefore concerned directly with home and community sanitation (Beaver, 1961). There is no practical method by which soil in and around the dooryard contaminated with *Ascaris* eggs can be rendered safe.

An additional control problem is presented in countries where human feces constitute the essential fertilizer for field crops or truck gardens. Winfield (1937) has demonstrated that storage of fresh excreta with straw in compost pits soon raises the temperature above 50° C., so that *Ascaris* eggs in all stages of development are killed, yet the nitrogen value of the compost is not reduced. This method of prophylaxis is equally effective in certain other widespread helminthic infections, including hookworm disease, trichuriasis and schistosomiasis.

Toxocara canis (Werner, 1782) Johnston, 1916 (dog ascarid), and
Toxocara cati (Schrank, 1788) Brumpt, 1927 (cat ascarid)

Toxocara canis, cosmopolitan ascarid of dogs, was reported once as a human intestinal worm in Egypt (Leiper, 1907) but the species diagnosis is questioned. The males have a length of 4 to 6 cm. and the females, 6.5 to 10 cm. There are a pair of lateral spear-like, cervical alæ or wings which are much longer than broad and extend distally an appreciable distance from the anterior end. The eggs are subglobose to ovoidal, densely granular internally, superficially pitted, and measure 85 by 75 microns. Infection results from ingesting eggs containing motile, second-stage rhabditoid larvæ. A migration route to the lungs is required before the worms mature in the lumen of the small intestine. Although adult dogs suffer little harm from this infection, the migrating larvæ in pregnant bitches are transmitted to their young, which frequently die of the infection. If young dogs survive this period, frequently the worms are spontaneously eliminated and a moderate level of immunity is established.

Toxocara cati, the common ascarid of the cat, has been reported 18 times as a human intestinal infection (Mendheim, Scheid and Schmidt, 1952). However, in the light of present knowledge of visceral larva migrans these records may be questioned. The mature males have a length of approximately 6 cm. and the females, 4 to 12 cm. There are a pair of lateral heart-shaped cervical alæ, which are not more than three times as long as broad. The eggs are subglobose, densely granular internally, thin-shelled, more delicately pitted than those of *T. canis*, and are somewhat smaller (75 by 65 microns). After embryonation on damp shaded soil to the motile second larval stage, the eggs are infective. Upon being swallowed they hatch in the duodenum and after a migration route to the lungs mature in the lumen of the small intestine. Congenital transmission does not occur.

Extra-intestinal infection with larval *Toxocara canis* and *T. cati* are considered under the heading "Larva Migrans," page 282.

Lagocheilascaris minor Leiper, 1909

This small ascarid is a normal parasite of the small intestine of the cloudy leopard (*Felis nebulosa*), but mature worms have been recovered 6 times from extra-intestinal tissues of man (Winckel and Treurniet, 1956). The male has a length of only 9 mm. and a maximum breadth of 0.4 mm.; the female, of 15 mm. and 0.5 mm. respectively. *L. minor* lacks cervical alæ but possesses a keel-like ledge which extends practically the entire length of each lateral line. There is a hare-lipped vertical cleft in the heavy cuticular covering of each of the three conspicuous lips (hence the generic name "hare-lipped ascaris"), while the entire labial structure is set off from the cervical region by a deep circumscribing furrow. The eggs are spherical, relatively transparent internally, thick-shelled with pittings resembling those of *Toxocara*, and measure about 65 microns in diameter. The life cycle of *L. minor* has not been elucidated.

Eustoma sp.—Larvæ of this ascaroid parasite of herrings have been held responsible for colic, fever and eosinophilic abscesses in the small intestine of eleven persons in Holland following consumption of the infected fish. Because of indication of acute obstruction, surgical intervention was instituted in a majority of the patients. However there were two deaths and one case of peritonitis (van Thiel, Kuipers and Roskam, 1960).

HOOKWORMS AND RELATED ROUNDWORMS

This group consists of many species which have in common the following morphologic characteristics: They lack distinct lips such as characterize ascarid nematodes; the posterior end of the male is extended into an umbrella-like copulatory bursa which is typically supported by 7 pairs of rays; the ovaries, oviducts and uteri of the female are twinned, and the thin-shelled, transparent eggs are in an early stage of embryonation when laid.

With few exceptions the adult worms live in the digestive tract of their host. Eggs discharged in the feces complete their development on the soil. Rhabditoid larvæ hatch from the egg, feed, grow and after two molts become infective third-stage larvæ. In some species the third-stage larva is infective for the host by the oral route; in other species infection is typically percutaneous. Many of these worms are economically important parasites of domestic animals, particularly herbivores, and only incidentally infect man, but two species of hookworms are among the most extensive disease-producing agents of mankind. Human hookworms belong to two genera, *viz.*, *Necator*, in which the buccal capsule is provided with semi-lunar cutting plates, and *Ancylostoma*, in which the capsule contains paired tooth-like processes.

Necator americanus (Stiles, 1902) Stiles, 1903
"New World hookworm," causing human hookworm infection
of warm climates)

The clinical manifestations of heavy hookworm infection were described from the West Indies as early as 1742 and from the southern United States

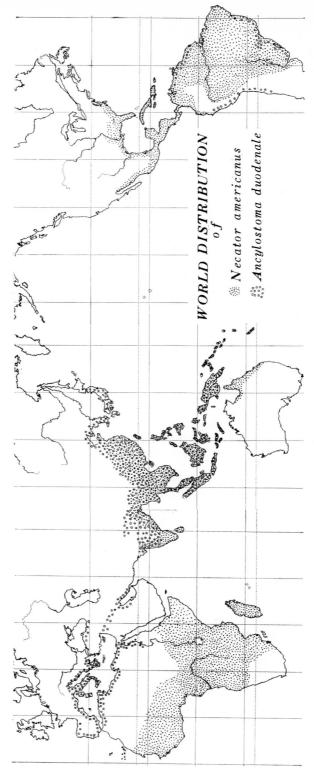

WORLD DISTRIBUTION
of
◌ *Necator americanus*
⦂ *Ancylostoma duodenale*

FIG. 115.—World distribution of human hookworm infection. (Original, Faust.)

by the middle of the 19th Century. The hookworms recovered from patients in the Americas were first regarded as *Ancylostoma duodenale*, which had been described by Dubini from Italy, in 1843, but Maréchal (1868) and Lutz (1888) considered them to be different. Stiles (1902) recognized that they belonged to a new species which he designated *Uncinaria americana*, and a year later placed in a new genus, *Necator* (the "killer" or "murderer"). Soon the "American hookworm" was found to be the prevailing species throughout the hookworm belt of the southern

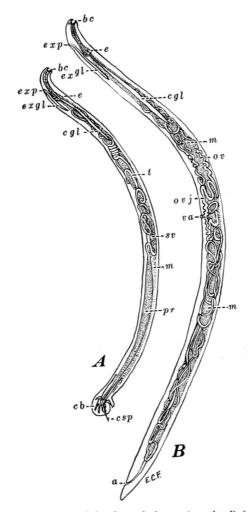

Fig. 116.—*Necator americanus* adults, lateral view. *A*, male; *B*, female. *a*, anal pore; *bc*, buccal capsule; *cb*, copulatory bursa; *c gl*, paired cephalic gland; *c sp*, copulatory spicules; *e*, esophagus; *ex gl*, excretory gland; *ex p*, excretory pore; *m*, midgut; *ov*, ovary; *ovj*, ovejector; *pr*, prostate gland; *sv*, seminal vesicle; *t*, testis; *va*, vulva. × 18. (Original adaptation from Lane.)

United States, Mexico, Central America, the West Indies and South America east of the Andes. Some years later *Necator americanus* was discovered to be the important autochthonous species in the Eastern Hemisphere south of 20° N. latitude (see map, Fig. 115). This hookworm was introduced into the Western Hemisphere with the importation of African slaves (Scott, 1943).

Morphology, Biology and Life Cycle

Necator americanus (Fig. 116) is strongly reflexed dorsally at the anterior end. The small buccal capsule (Fig. 117*A*) is provided with two upper (ventral) semilunar cutting plates, two poorly developed dorsal plates, a median dorsal tooth, and in the depth of the mouth cavity a pair of short triangular lancets. Opening from within into the depth of the buccal cap-

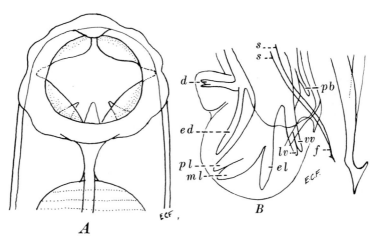

Fig. 117.—*Necator americanus.* *A*, view of head looking into the buccal cavity; *B*, posterior end of male, lateral view, showing bursal rays of one side, *ss*, 2 spicules, and, at right, enlarged fused distal end of the spicules; *d*, dorsal ray; *ed*, externo-dorsal ray; *f*, fused terminus of spicules; *lv*, latero-ventral ray; *ml*, medio-lateral ray; *pb*, pre-bursal ray; *pl*, postero-lateral ray; *vv*, ventro-ventral ray. *A*, × 266; *B*, × 64. (Original, Faust.)

sule are a pair of very long cephalic glands (Fig. 116 *cgl*) which secrete an anticoagulant for extravasated blood (Thorson, 1956*b*). Immediately internal to the buccal cavity there is a powerful, muscular esophagus. Within its wall there are a dorsal gland and paired ventrolateral glands which secrete proteolytic enzymes (Thorson, 1956*a*).

The male measures 7 to 9 mm. in length by 0.3 mm. in breadth. The copulatory bursa (Fig. 117*B*) is bilaterally symmetrical. The supporting rays for each half consist of a small distinctly separated dorsal, bifurcated at the tip; a slender, unbranched externo-dorsal; 3 laterals arising from a large fleshy trunk; 2 ventrals fused half-way or more to the tip; and an inconspicuous short pre-bursal. The two copulatory spicules (*ss*) are long delicate bristles which are fused at their outer ends, terminating in a barb. The female (Fig. 116*B*) measures 9 to 11 mm. in length by 0.4 mm. in breadth. The posterior tip is rather sharply conical. The vulvar opening is mid-ventral, somewhat anterior to the equatorial plane.

The eggs (Fig. 118*A*) are thin-shelled, transparent, broadly ovoidal, and measure 64 to 76 microns by 36 to 40 microns. They are in an early stage of cleavage when laid. In a freshly passed stool they range in development from 4-celled to a morula stage; in feces stored at room temperature for several hours they may reach the early larval stage (Fig. 118*B*).

Necator americanus is attached to the upper levels of the small intestine, from the mid-duodenum through the jejunum; but heavy infections may extend far down into the ileum and occasionally into the cecum.

A   B

Fig. 118.—Photomicrographs of eggs of human hookworm. *A*, 4-cell stage; *B*, egg with slightly immature rhabditoid larva. × 666. (From Faust's *Human Helminthology*, Lea & Febiger, Philadelphia.)

Larval Development.—When the host's feces are deposited on moist, sandy loam, in a warm, shaded location, or when diluted fresh human excreta are spread on the land as fertilizer, embryonation of viable hookworm eggs usually proceeds rapidly and hatching takes place in 24 to 48 hours. Optimal conditions include good aëration of the top soil, which must be moist but not saturated with water, protection from direct rays of the sun, and a temperature of 31° to 34.5° C. (Svensson, 1925). The larva emerging from the egg shell is typically *rhabditoid* (Fig. 119*B*) ,and measures 0.25 to 0.3 mm. in length by about 17 microns in maximum diameter. It feeds actively on bacteria and organic débris, grows, sheds its cuticle and continues to feed and increase in size up to 0.5–0.6 mm. in length, while retaining its rhabditoid form. Between the fifth and eighth day it stops feeding, becomes relatively inactive and transforms within the old cuticle into the more slender *filariform* larva (Fig. 120), which has a closed mouth, an elongated esophagus and a sharply pointed tail. Average survival of these larvæ probably does not exceed two weeks. On contact with exposed human skin they penetrate under epidermal scales or into hair follicles. The most common area of invasion is the tender skin between the toes, but other areas can be penetrated as well. While infection may be acquired by swallowing the filariform larvæ in soil or on leafy vegetables,

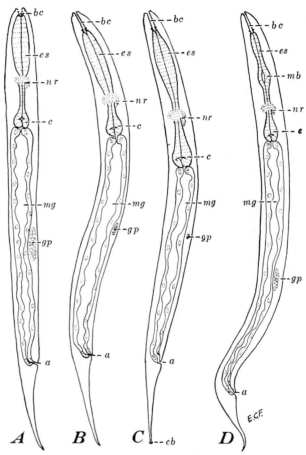

FIG. 119.—Diagrams of the rhabditoid larvæ of *A, Strongyloides, B,* hookworms, *C, Trichostrongylus* and *D, Rhabditis.* × ca. 400. *a,* anus; *bc,* buccal chamber; *c,* cardiac bulb of esophagus; *cb,* bead-like knob of caudal tip; *es,* esophagus; *gp,* germinal primordium; *mb,* mid-esophageal bulb; *mg,* midgut; *nr,* nerve ring. (From Faust and Russell's *Clinical Parasitology,* Lea & Febiger, Philadelphia.)

this route of entry into the body is less suitable for *Necator* than for *Ancylostoma.*

Migration in the Host and Development to the Adult Stage.—The filariform larvæ penetrate down through the epidermis, enter the cutaneous blood vessels and within 24 hours or less after skin contact are carried through the right heart to the lungs, where they break out of the pulmonary capillaries into the air sacs. After a period of about one week, during which there is considerable growth and development, they ascend the respiratory tree to the epiglottis, and descend to the upper levels of the small intestine; meanwhile they have undergone a third molt of cuticle and acquired a temporary buccal capsule. The young worms now become attached to the wall of the duodenum and jejunum, grow, shed the fourth cuticle including the temporary buccal capsule, and develop into adult worms. A minimum of 6 weeks is required from the time filariform larvæ enter the skin until the worms have matured in the intestine, have copulated and females begin to lay eggs. Under favorable conditions each female *Necator americanus* produces 5,000 to 10,000 eggs daily. Although these worms may remain in the human intestine up to 14 years (Palmer, 1955), a majority are evacuated in 5 years or less.

For pathologic and clinical aspects of infection with *Necator americanus*, see "Hookworm Infection and Hookworm Disease," pages 253–259, also "Larva Migrans," pages 279–282.

Ancylostoma duodenale (Dubini, 1843)
Creplin, 1845

(The "Old World hookworm," causing hookworm infection, or ancylostomiasis of temperate climates in the Eastern Hemisphere)

Although this species of hookworm was probably referred to in the Eber's papyrus (1600 B.C.), the first description was provided by Dubini (1843), based on autopsy study of a Milanese woman in 1838. Grassi and Parona (1878) demonstrated that the presence of hookworms in the bowel could be diagnosed from their eggs in the stool, and Perroncito (1880) hatched the eggs and studied the free-living stages in the soil. Looss (1896–1897) found that the infective-stage filariform larvæ enter the body by the skin route.

The original distribution of *A. duodenale* was probably limited to the subtropical and temperate regions of the Eastern Hemisphere north of the Equator. Extensive migrations of Asian peoples carried this infection to more tropical climates, so that today it is mixed with *Necator americanus* in southeastern Asia, the South Pacific and Southwest Pacific islands and Indonesia (see Fig. 115, p. 244). *A. duodenale* is the only important hookworm of man on the west coast of South America, where it was possibly introduced by the early

Fig. 120. — Filariform larva of *Necator americanus;* × 160. (From Faust's *Human Helminthology*, Lea & Febiger, Philadelphia.)

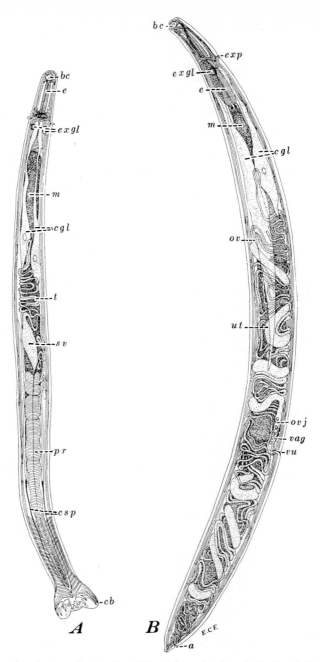

Fig. 121.—*Ancylostoma duodenale* adults. *A*, male, dorsal, *B*, female lateral view. *a*, anal pore; *bc*, buccal capsule; *cb*, copulatory bursa; *c gl*, paired cephalic gland; *c sp*, copulatory spicules; *e*, esophagus; *ex gl*, excretory gland; *ex p*, excretory pore; *m*, midgut; *ov*, ovary; *ovj*, ovejector; *pr*, prostate gland; *sv*, seminal vesicle; *t*, testis; *vag*, vagina; *vu*, vulva. × 20. (Adapted from Looss, in Faust's *Human Helminthology*, Lea & Febiger, Philadelphia.)

(250)

Spanish explorers and colonizers. Stoll (1947) has estimated that the total hookworm-infected population of the world is 456.8 millions, of which 359 millions live in Asia, 49 millions in Africa, 42 millions in tropical America and 1.8 millions in North America.

Morphology, Biology and Life Cycle

The adults of *A. duodenale* are cylindrical in shape, pinkish or ivory-gray in color, narrowed anteriorly and have the head curved somewhat dorsally (Fig. 121). The cup-shaped mouth capsule is heavily reinforced and is provided on the forward (ventral) side with 4 conspicuous, slightly curved, subequal teeth, one pair on either side of the median ventral line. In the depth of the capsule there is a pair of small teeth. Dorsally there is a plate with a median cleft (Fig. 122*A*).

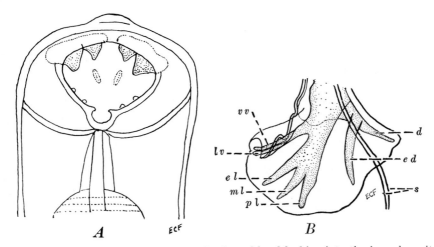

Fig. 122.—*Ancylostoma duodenale.* *A*, view of head looking into the buccal cavity with the characteristic 2 pairs of teeth; *B*, posterior end of male, lateral view, showing bursal rays of one side and the 2 unfused spicules. *d*, dorsal ray; *ed*, externo-dorsal ray; *el*, externo-lateral ray; *lv*, latero-ventral ray; *ml*, medio-lateral ray; *pl*, postero-lateral ray; *s*, spicules; *vv*, ventro-ventral ray. *A*, × 200; *B*, × 80. (*A*, original, Faust; *B*, from Faust and Russell's *Clinical Parasitology*, Lea & Febiger, Philadelphia.)

The male (Fig. 121*A*) measures 8 to 11 mm. in length by 0.4 to 0.5 mm. in breadth. It is provided with a bell-shaped copulatory bursa which is considerably broader than long and is supported by fleshy rays having the following pattern for each half of the bursa: dorsal, single at its root but bifurcated at the tip; externo-dorsal, arising from the root of the dorsal; three laterals, outwardly well separated from one another, and two ventrals, close to one another. The female (Fig. 121*B*) measures 10 to 13 mm. in length by 0.6 mm. in breadth and tapers rather bluntly at the posterior end. The anal pore lies ventrally near the caudal tip and the vulvar opening mid-ventrally at the beginning of the posterior third of the body. Each female lays 10,000 to 20,000 eggs daily.

Man is probably the only normal host of *A. duodenale*.

The broadly ovoidal eggs (Fig. 118*A*) average 60 by 40 microns, have a thin, transparent shell and are in the 2- to 8-cell stage of cleavage when evacuated. Embryonation to the first rhabditoid larval stage takes place in 24 to 48 hours on moist sandy loam in a shaded environment at an optimum temperature of about 25° C. (Svensson, 1925).

Hatching and free-living larval stages on the soil are similar to those of *Necator americanus* (see page 247).

Rhabditoid larvæ of hookworms (Fig. 119*B*) have a long buccal chamber and an inconspicuous genital primordium; those of *Strongyloides* have a short inconspicuous buccal chamber (Fig. 119*A*) and a distinct genital primordium. Filariform larvæ of hookworms have a sharply pointed tail; those of *Strongyloides* have a notched caudal termination (see page 262, Fig. 127*B, D*).

Except that the filariform larvæ are better adapted to entering the body by the oral route, infection with filariform larvæ of *A. duodenale*, their migration through the lungs and development to the mature male and female worms in the intestine parallel these phases of the life cycle of *Necator* (pages 248–249).

Ancylostoma braziliense Gomez de Faria, 1910

This species was first described from the intestine of cats and dogs in Brazil and subsequently from these hosts from many warm areas of the world. Human intestinal infection with *A. braziliense* does not occur or is relatively uncommon (Beaver, 1956).

A. braziliense is about 30% smaller than *A. duodenale* (males 7.7 to 8.5 mm. long females 9 to 10.5 mm. long). The most easily recognized morphologic difference between these two species is the buccal capsule: that of *A. braziliense* has a smaller aperture and the dental plate on each side of the mid-ventral line is provided with a very small inner tooth and a large outer one. Eggs of this species are indistinguishable from those of *A. duodenale*. The stages of larval development are also similar.

Clinical interest in *A. braziliense* is concerned primarily with human skin exposure to filariform larvæ of this species derived from canine and feline hosts, causing a dermatitis referred to as "cutaneous larva migrans" or "creeping eruption." This topic is considered under *"Larva Migrans."* (See pages 279–282).

Ancylostoma ceylanicum (Looss, 1911)

This species closely resembles *A. braziliense*, and apparently the 2 species have been frequently confused. According to Biocca (1951) *A. ceylanicum* is typically a parasite of cats in Southeast Asia and Brazil, but also occurs in dogs and man. The chief differences between the 2 species are in the buccal cavity and the bursa. On *A. braziliense* the inner denticles arising from the large ventral teeth are smaller and more internal, the lateral bursal rays are more curved, the medio-lateral and externo-lateral rays are more divergent, and the externo-dorsal rays arise much nearer the origin of the dorsal ray.

Ancylostoma caninum (Ercolani, 1859) Hall, 1913

This is the common hookworm of dogs and cats in temperate climates. It has been reported on four occasions as an incidental intestinal parasite of man (Deane,

1950). *A. caninum* is appreciably larger than *A. duodenale* (males 10 mm. long by 0.4 mm. broad, females 14 mm. long by 0.6 mm. broad). The buccal capsule is wide and has a large orifice. Each of the two upper (ventral) dental plates is provided with 3 teeth, of which the innermost is the smallest and the outermost the most fully developed. The eggs resemble those of *A. duodenale* but are slightly larger (64 by 40 microns). The life cycle is similar to that of *A. duodenale* but prenatal infection is common in the dog.

A. caninum has been employed experimentally for many years in the dog in studying the biological, immunologic and clinical aspects of hookworm infection and their application to hookworm disease in man. Occasionally creeping eruption of the human skin is caused by *A. caninum*. (See under *"Larva Migrans,"* page 280.)

Clinical Aspects of Hookworm Infection and Hookworm Disease

The Skin Lesion.—At each site on the feet, arms or other surface area where the filariform larva of *Necator americanus* or *Ancylostoma duodenale* enters the skin it produces a minute wound (Fig. 123). In 96% of 19,000 *N. americanus* patients Ashford and Gutiérrez Igaravidez (1911) obtained a history of penetration dermatitis, consisting typically of an initial intense itching and burning, followed by edema and erythema, then a papule which transformed into a vesicle. This is the uncomplicated "ground itch" of hookworm infection.

Occasionally *Necator* and *A. duodenale*, as well as *A. caninum* and *Bunostomum phlebotomum*, produce "creeping eruption" in the skin similar to *A. braziliense.*

Larval Migration through the Lungs.—Characteristically the migrating larvæ of *Necator americanus* and *A. duodenale* reach the pulmonary capillaries almost immediately after entry into the cutaneous venules. As they penetrate into the air sacs, they produce minute focal hemorrhages, but only in case of massive migration of larvæ simultaneously is a bronchial

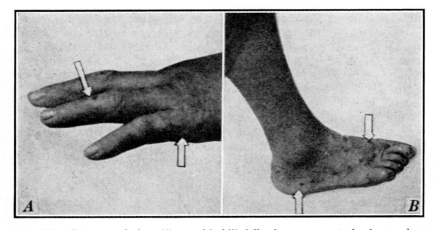

FIG. 123.—Cutaneous lesions ("ground itch") following exposure to hookworm larvæ in the soil. (After Chang *et al.*, courtesy of Johns Hopkins Press, in Faust and Russell's *Clinical Parasitology*, Lea & Febiger, Philadelphia.)

pneumonitis of clinical grade usually produced. Another item of clinical interest is that hookworm larvæ during transit through the lungs do not typically produce the high degree of sensitization characteristic of *Ascaris* (page 239) or *Strongyloides* (page 264).

Intestinal Infection.—Once the adolescent hookworms have migrated to the small intestine, they soon acquire a temporary mouth capsule and become attached to the mucosa (Fig. 124). Blood is sucked out of the tissues but greater amounts of blood are lost by hemorrhage at sites of attachment. Early in the intestinal infection blood loss from the intestine is especially great.

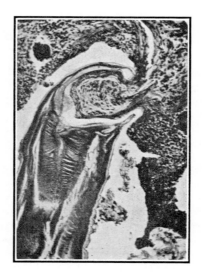

Fig. 124.—Photomicrograph showing method of attachment of *Necator americanus* to the human jejunum. (From collection, Armed Forces Institute of Pathology, in Faust and Russell's *Clinical Parasitology*, Lea & Febiger, Philadelphia.)

Etiology of Hookworm Disease.—The essential damage produced in hookworm infection is hemorrhage from the intestinal wall. In general, this is proportional to the number of attached worms. Thus, counts of less than 5000 eggs per cc. of feces are seldom of clinical grade, while those with counts of more than 10,000 eggs per cc. almost invariably have a significant hookworm anemia (Scott, 1945; Beaver, 1951).

The type of anemia produced by hookworms is typically microcytic and hypochromic (Foster and Landsberg, 1934; Rhoads, Castle, Payne and Lawson, 1934). In light infections, the blood loss can be completely compensated and in moderately heavy infections compensated by an adequate, well-balanced diet containing iron, other minerals, rich animal proteins and vitamin A. In severe hookworm disease, however, even with a highly fortified diet, the hematopoietic mechanism is unable to produce new supplies of normal red blood cells as rapidly as they are lost. Moreover, underlying protein deficiency in the diet, even with adequate absorbable iron intake, may contribute measurably to the anemia of hookworm patients, a majority of whom subsist essentially on carbohydrates.

In hookworm areas exposure begins fairly early in childhood and is repeated again and again throughout life.

Symptomatology.—In *acute cases* resulting from single heavy exposure there is characteristically a prodromal syndrome of nausea, headache, irritating cough (during lung migration of the larvæ) and a worn-out feeling. In the late prepatent and early patent periods there frequently are severe colicky pains in the pit of the stomach, flatulence, diarrhea, loss of weight and strength, dyspnea, dizziness and marked pallor. During this period there is an eosinophilic leukocytosis; later a significant anemia develops.

In *chronic* hookworm disease the signs and symptoms are essentially those of a profound iron-deficiency anemia. In varying degrees there are pallor, facial and pedal edema, dull expression, and listlessness. Hemoglobin levels may be reduced to 5 grams per cent or lower, and the heart is greatly enlarged. In children mental and physical development may be much retarded.

Diagnosis

Experienced clinicians state that they are unable by physical examination alone to distinguish between the anemia and edema of malnutrition and hookworm disease, and blood chemistry studies indicating a hypoproteinemia will fail to provide a differential diagnosis. On the other hand, by the direct fecal film egg-count technic (page 429) it is possible to obtain a rapid, relatively accurate diagnosis.

Treatment

Supportive Therapy.—In light to moderate hookworm infections in which the anemia is not severe, specific treatment can usually be undertaken without a preliminary period of supportive treatment. For individuals with low hemoglobin levels it is desirable to precede specific chemotherapy for a week to ten days with a diet rich in animal protein. Iron must also be administered to replace that lost through intestinal hemorrhage caused by the worms. Rarely whole blood transfusion may be needed. Administration of liver is not indicated in hookworm disease.

Specific Therapy.—There is no consistently successful treatment for hookworm infection. To date best results have been obtained with *tetrachloroethylene*. This is most effective when given on an empty stomach, without purgation (Carr *et al.*, 1954). Administration of this drug may cause gastric irritation and in overdosage produces central nervous system depression. Yet it is a relatively safe anthelmintic (See Table 7, page 419).

The hydroxynaphthoate and other salts of *bephenium* have recently been used with varying degrees of success in treating hookworm infection (Goodwin *et al.*, 1958). This drug has produced a high incidence of vomiting among white children in Southern Georgia (Jung and McCroan, 1960).

A week following specific therapy a follow-up stool examination should be made to determine the efficacy of the treatment. Re-treatment with tetrachloroethylene may be undertaken in a week to remove remaining hookworms.

Prognosis

Prognosis is good to excellent in uncomplicated hookworm infections following removal of the worms and relief of the anemia and hypoproteinemia. Nevertheless, if treatment of heavy infection is delayed, some degree of stunting may persist in spite of eventual cure. Untreated patients with severe hookworm disease may die from exsanguination, or, more commonly, intercurrent infection.

Epidemiology

Hookworm infection constitutes one of the most prevalent of all helminthic parasitoses of man in warm climates. For practical purposes only two causal agents of intestinal infection need to be considered, namely, *Necator americanus* and *Ancylostoma duodenale*. *N. americanus* is typically adapted to a warmer climate, although *A. duodenale* likewise thrives in the Tropics.

N. americanus and *A. duodenale* are parasites almost exclusively of man, so that wherever these infections are endemic they result from unsanitary methods of disposal of human feces containing the eggs of these two hookworms. Defecation on favorable soil or the spreading of the egg-laden feces in the form of nightsoil on the land provides opportunity for the eggs to complete embryonation, to hatch, and for the larvæ which emerge from the egg to feed, grow and transform into the infective filariform stage. These larvæ remain near the surface close to the sites where defecation occurs or where feces are spread on the ground.

An essential to the continued propagation of human hookworm infections is the custom of natives in warm climates to walk barefooted. When they step on polluted soil, the skin of their feet comes in contact with infective-stage larvæ, which enter the epidermis and initiate infection. Persons working in fields which have been recently fertilized with untreated human nightsoil are exposed wherever the hands or feet touch infested soil containing hookworm filariform larvæ, while miners in unsanitated underground tunnels may become infected on practically any area of the skin.

Data on the prevalence of hookworms in an area must be supplemented by a relatively accurate estimate of the intensity of the infection in each infected individual, *i.e.*, the worm burden. Darling (1922) employed mass treatment in heavily infected hookworm communities to obtain evacuation of the worms, which were collected from the stools and counted. Cort and his associates carried out a comprehensive study of hookworm epidemiology (1921–1925) and developed the Stoll technic (1923) for counting hookworm eggs passed in the stool. Beaver (1949, 1950) has devised a standardized direct fecal-film egg-count procedure. The hemoglobin and serum protein levels of each person surveyed are useful in evaluating the clinical importance of the infection at different intensities of infection. It is equally necessary to consider associated disease processes in assessing the role of the hookworms in the over-all clinical picture.

Another measure for studying hookworm epidemiology is related to the sites on the soil polluted with human excreta and the degree of soil infestation with hookworm larvæ. Separation of these and other nematode larvæ from the soil is accomplished with the Baermann apparatus or the damp pad technic (see "TECHNICAL AIDS," page 439).

Control

Two major lines of attack are indicated, namely, (1) anthelmintic treatment of all infected individuals to reduce to a minimum the sources of soil infestation and (2) selective treatment of individuals showing evidence of hookworm disease and those whose egg counts indicate heavy worm burdens. Equally important is the sanitary disposal or sterilization of human feces, to prevent infestation of the soil.

Control also embodies improvement in the diet of hookworm communities to reduce the effects of malnutrition. Thus, it is evident that hookworm control must be made an integral part of comprehensive health projects, including medical care, sanitary improvements, health education, nutrition and improved agricultural practices.

OTHER BURSATE NEMATODES

Two species of nematodes belonging to the family Strongylidæ and found normally as intestinal parasites of simian hosts have been reported from man. They are *Ternidens deminutus* and *Œsophagostomum apiostomum*.

Ternidens deminutus (Railliet and Henry, 1905)
Railliet and Henry, 1909

This worm has been diagnosed from man in natives of Southern Rhodesia (50 to 65 per cent incidence, according to Sandground, 1931), Nyasaland and Mozambique. In size and shape it resembles human hookworms but is distinguished from the latter species by a terminal buccal capsule which is subglobose and is guarded internally by a double crown of stout bristles. The eggs are also like those of hookworms but are larger, averaging 84 by 51 microns. The third-stage larva is semirhabditoid rather than filariform and is not capable of penetrating the skin, hence it enters the body only by the oral route (Sandground, 1931).

T. deminutus is found throughout the intestinal tract, with its head inserted into the wall. It produces cystic nodules (Sandground, 1931) or small circumscribed, craterous ulcers, and at times causes perforation with peritonitis. The worms are hemophagous and heavy infections result in anemia (Amberson and Swarz, 1952). Anthelmintics employed in treating hookworm infection (page 255) are only moderately effective in eliminating *T. deminutus*.

Œsophagostomum apiostomum (Willach, 1891)
Railliet and Henry, 1905

This worm, a common parasite of monkeys in West Africa and the Philippines and China, has been reported from man in Northern Nigeria and in the vicinity of Lake Omo, East Africa. Although *Œ. apiostomum* is approximately the size of hookworms, like *T. deminutus* it has a terminal buccal capsule, beset with a crown of 12 pyramidal setæ. Infection probably results from swallowing third-stage semi-

17

rhabditoid larvæ, which pass down to the cecum, invade the wall and become encapsulated in a fibrous nodule, within which the worms grow. Then they break out of the capsule into the cecal canal, where they become attached to the mucosa and mature. The eggs measure 60 to 63 by 27 to 40 microns and are indistinguishable from those of hookworms.

The development of the tumors in the submucous and muscular coats of the cecum may be responsible for hypermotility in the area but the essential damage occurs when the emerging adolescent worms rupture the tissue capsule, with hemorrhage of nearby blood vessels and occasional perforation into the peritoneal cavity. During development within the nodule chemotherapy is ineffective but as soon as the worms emerge into the cecal canal they may be eliminated by administration of tetrachloroethylene as in hookworm infection (page 255).

The related *Œ. stephanostomum thomasi* was once recovered from the human intestine in Manãos, Brazil.

Syngamus laryngeus Railliet, 1899

Species of the genus *Syngamus* are relatively small-sized nematodes, in which the male and female worms are typically joined in permanent copula. They possess a thick-walled, cavernous buccal capsule, armed at its base with a number of small teeth. The male is only about one-third as long as the female. The outer shell of the ovoidal eggs consists of a large number of truncated prisms cemented together. Eggs of species parasitizing birds have a pair of polar caps; eggs of those parasitizing mammals lack these caps.

Several species of *Syngamus* have been described from mammals. Human infection, probably for the most part with *S. laryngeus* but possibly also with *S. nasicola*, has been reported 6 times from Puerto Rico, 7 times from Brazil (Amaral *et al.*, 1954), 4 times from Martinique, twice from St. Lucia (W. Indies), and once each from British Guiana, Trinidad and the Philippines (Andrade Lima and Simões Barbosa, 1951).

These worms reside as adults in the upper respiratory tract of their hosts, causing asthma, hemoptysis, and paroxysms of coughing and sneezing, during which the worms may be expelled from their attachment to the respiratory mucosa. Life history data have not been reported for species of *Syngamus* parasitizing mammals. Human infection is incidental; since the worms are probably always expelled during paroxysms of coughing no special therapeutic measures are indicated.

Species of Trichostrongylus

Species of *Trichostrongylus* are delicate thread-like nematodes lacking a buccal capsule and dental apparatus and possessing a relatively large copulatory bursa in the male. They are typically attached to the small intestine of ruminants and are incidental parasites of man; in some countries *T. orientalis* is more commonly found in man than in other mammals. Eggs of these worms (Fig. 125) are oval-elliptical, measure from 70 to 90 microns by 40 to 50 microns depending on the species, and are usually in the morula stage of development when evacuated in the stool. Under favorable conditions the eggs become fully embryonated and hatch in about 24 hours. The first and second stage larvæ are rhabditoid in type like those of hookworms but can be readily distinguished by a minute bead-like knob at the tip of the tail (Fig. 119, *C*). Transformation to the infective pseudo-filariform larva occurs usually on the 3rd or 4th day. This stage is very resistant to desiccation, is unable to penetrate skin but when ingested with grass burrows into the intestinal wall. About 4 days later it emerges and without a migration to the lungs inserts its anterior end deeply into the wall and develops into an adult. The prepatent period is about 3 weeks (Lie Kian Joe, 1947).

Generic diagnosis is made on the characteristic eggs (Fig. 125) recovered from the stools and their differentiation from hookworm eggs (Fig. 118, page 247). Specific diagnosis depends on study of the differential features of the copulatory bursa and spicules in the male (Fig. 126).

Trichostrongylus colubriformis (Giles, 1892) Ransom, 1911.—This cosmopolitan trichostrongyle has been recovered from sheep, goats, gazelles, antelopes, deer, camels, baboons, apes, squirrels and rabbits, and from man in Egypt, Iran, India, Armenia, Indonesia, Australia and once from a surgical appendix in New Orleans, U.S.A.

Trichostrongylus probolurus (Railliet, 1896) Looss, 1905.—This cosmopolitan species is a common parasite of sheep, gazelles and camels and has been reported from man in Egypt, Armenia and Siberia.

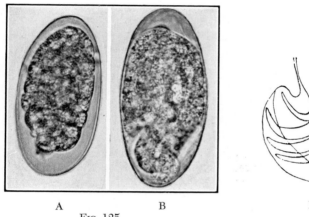

A   B   Fɪɢ. 126

Fɪɢ. 125

Fɪɢ. 125.—Eggs of *Trichostrongylus orientalis*. A, in freshly evacuated stools; B, with slightly immature, motile first-stage larva. × 500. (Photomicrographs by Dr. T. B. Magath, in Faust and Russell's *Clinical Parasitology*, Lea & Febiger, Philadelphia.)

Fɪɢ. 126.—Copulatory bursa of male *Trichostrongylus orientalis*. × 250. (From Faust's *Human Helminthology*, Lea & Febiger, Philadelphia.)

Trichostrongylus vitrinus Looss, 1905.—This cosmopolitan species is a parasite of oxen, sheep, goats and camels, and has been reported from man in Egypt, Armenia and Siberia.

Trichostrongylus orientalis Jimbo, 1914.—This species is a common parasite of man in Japan and Korea and has also been found in man and herbivorous animals in China, Formosa and Armenia. In man the commonly parasitized level of the digestive tract is the duodenum but worms have been found attached to the pyloric wall of the stomach and to the jejunum. The adults are grayish-white. The males measure 3.8 to 4.8 mm. in length and the females 4.9 to 6.7 mm.; the delicate heads measure only 7 and 9 microns in diameter respectively. The posterior end of the male is shown in Fig. 126. The eggs of *T. orientalis* (Fig. 125) measure 75 to 91 microns by 39 to 47 microns.

Other species of *Trichostrongylus* reported incidentally from man include: *T. instabilis* (Armenia, Siberia), *T. axei* (Armenia, Siberia, Mauritius, Java), *T.*

skrjabini (Armenia) and unidentified species from Tunisia, Belgian Congo, Southern Rhodesia, Iran, Chile, Hawaii and Fiji, and a Greek resident in United States. Human infection with *Trichostrongylus* sp. also occurs in Georgia (U.S.A.). Eggs of these several species have been frequently mis-diagnosed as those of hookworms.

Clinical Notes on Trichostrongyles in Man.—Light infections usually produce no symptoms but large numbers of worms cause intestinal disturbances. Transient eosinophilia has been observed (Lie Kian Joe, 1947), and in 2 cases severe diarrhea and very high eosinophilia (74%, 81%) were associated with the infections, at least one of which was contracted in the United States (Wallace *et al.*, 1956). Treatment to eradicate trichostrongyles is not satisfactory.

The metastrongyle *Angiostrongylus cantonensis* as an adult parasitizes species of the genus *Rattus* and utilizes land molluscs as intermediate host. Following exposure of the rat, the worm first invades the brain, then migrates to the lungs where it matures. Rosen *et al.* (1962) have demonstrated brain infection with *A. cantonensis* in a 50-year-old male Filipino, who died in an Hawaiian hospital. Mature male and female worms were dissected out of the brain tissue.

On a single occasion each of the following species of related bursate worms has been reported as an intestinal parasite from man: *Ostertagia ostertagi* and *O. circumcincta* (U.S.S.R.); *Hæmonchus contortus*, the sheep wireworm (Brazil), and possibly *Mecistocirrus digitatus* (Hongkong). In addition, *Metastrongylus elongatus*, the lung worm of hogs, has been found twice in the human respiratory tract and once in the human digestive tract of European subjects.

Strongyloides stercoralis (Bavay, 1876) Stiles and Hassall, 1902
(The human threadworm, causing strongyloidiasis)

The human *Strongyloides* was first observed in the diarrheic stools of French troops who had served in Indochina. At necropsy of 5 of these men minute nematodes were recovered from the wall of the ileum and from the biliary and pancreatic ducts. Bavay (1876) named those organisms recovered from the feces *stercoralis* and those from the intestine *intestinalis*, but the studies of Grassi (1879), Perroncito (1880) and Leuckart (1882) demonstrated the two were different stages in the life cycle of the same species. Askanazy (1900) provided evidence that the parasitic females inhabited and oviposited in the intestinal mucosa. Several investigators including Looss (1905) and Fülleborn (1914) proved that infective-stage filariform larvæ in the soil enter the skin and carry out a migration through the lungs similar to hookworms. Fülleborn (1926) demonstrated further that rhabditoid larvæ in the feces may at times transform to the infective stage on moist perianal skin and be capable of producing autoinfection without leaving the human body, while Nishigori (1928), Faust (1932–1940), Hartz (1946) and other investigators found that internal autoinfection may occur.

Strongyloides stercoralis is primarily a parasite of warm climates but it has been found sporadically in temperate and even cold regions. In parts of Brazil, Colombia and Panamá the incidence is much higher than in other countries in which careful parasitologic surveys have been conducted.

Morphology, Biology and Life Cycle

The Adult Worms of the Parasitic Generation.—Parasitic males of *Strongyloides stercoralis* have not been found in man. The parasitic females (Fig. 127*A*) are slender filiform worms, measuring up to 2.2 mm. in length by 30 to 75 microns in diameter. Reproduction is parthenogenetic. Upon maturing, 28 days or less following cutaneous exposure of the human host, each parasitic female *S. stercoralis* deposits in the intestinal mucosa several dozen eggs daily during the first few months of maximum fecundity.

Larvæ of the Parasitic Generation.—The eggs laid by the parasitic females are thin-shelled, ovoidal, and measure 50 to 58 microns by 30 to 34 microns. As the larvæ mature and hatch they migrate to the intestinal lumen and descend through the intestinal canal, they feed, grow, and in most infections may molt once, so that the stage evacuated in the stool is the first or second rhabditoid larva (Fig. 119*A*, 128*A*).

A day or two after the feces containing rhabditoid larvæ are deposited in a warm, moist, shaded site metamorphosis to the filariform stage (Fig. 128*B*) takes place. The larvæ enter exposed human skin and initiate a new infection.

Autoinfection.—This is an abbreviated type of the direct mode of development, in which metamorphosis to the infective (filariform) larval stage occurs within the intestinal canal or on the perianal skin, and reinfection takes place without the organisms leaving the host's body. This type of infection is probably more common than has been recognized or reported (Brown and Perna, 1958; Grove and Elsdon-Dew, 1958).

Free-living Generations.—The interpolation of a free-living generation is common in *S. stercoralis*. In a particular infection it may occur as the exclusive type or be associated with the more common, direct cycle type.

Both males and females of the free-living generation are rhabditoid forms. The male (Fig. 127*B*) is broadly cylindrical, with a rounded anterior end and a pointed caudal extremity curved conspicuously to the ventral side. It measures about 0.7 mm. long by 40 to 50 microns in diameter. The female (Fig. 127*C*) more closely resembles the rhabditoid larval stage with an attenuated posterior extremity beginning just behind the vulva and terminating in a sharply pointed tail. Free-living females require insemination before they lay fertile eggs.

The eggs of the free-living generation are laid in an early stage of embryonation, develop rapidly in well-aërated, warm, wet ground, and hatch. In 2 or 3 days, free-living rhabditoid larvæ have either developed into rhabditoid adults or have transformed into filariform larvæ.

Larval Migration from the Skin to the Intestine.—On contact with the skin (and occasionally the buccal mucosa) filariform larvæ of *S. stercoralis* (either direct or indirect mode of development) bore their way through the epidermis down to the small blood vessels, penetrate into the venules and are carried through the right side of the heart to the lungs. When they reach the pulmonary capillaries they break out into the alveoli, where they molt twice and transform into post-filariform and then adolescent worms (Faust, 1933).

In some individuals, the presence of the worms in the terminal respiratory passages provokes appreciable cellular infiltration. This may result in female worms entering the bronchial epithelium and developing to maturity in this location, but a majority ascend the respiratory tree to the

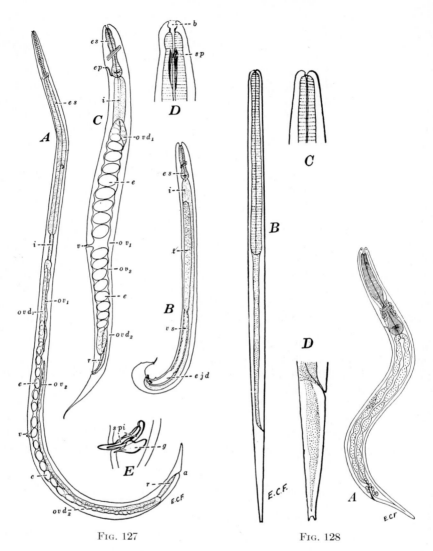

Fig. 127

Fig. 128

FIG. 127.—*Strongyloides stercoralis.* A, parasitic female, × 75; B, free-living male, × 160; C, free-living female, × 160; D, anterior end of free-living male, × 500; E, copulatory spicules and gubernaculum of male, greatly enlarged. a, anus; b, buccal chamber; e, uterine egg; ejd, ejaculatory duct; ep, excretory pore; es, esophagus; g, gubernaculum; i, midgut; ov₁ and ov₂, anterior and posterior ovaries; ovd₁ and ovd₂, anterior and posterior oviducts; r, rectum; sp, buccal spears; spi, copulatory spicules; t, testis; v, vulva; vs, seminal vesicle. (A, B, C, after Faust; D, E, adapted from Kreis; from Faust's *Human Helminthology*, Lea & Febiger, Philadelphia.)

FIG. 128.—Larval stages of *Strongyloides stercoralis.* A, rhabditoid larva, × 310; B, filariform larva, × 120; D, C, anterior and posterior ends of filariform larva, × 540. (A, after Looss; from Faust's *Human Helminthology*, Lea & Febiger, Philadelphia.)

epiglottis, and pass through the stomach to the small intestine, where they burrow into the mucosa, mature and begin to oviposit.

The life cycle of *Strongyloides stercoralis* is synoptically illustrated in Figure 129.

Location of Parasitic Females in the Intestine.—The most common level of the intestine parasitized by *S. stercoralis* is the duodenum, next is the jejunum. However, all levels of the digestive tract from the pyloric wall

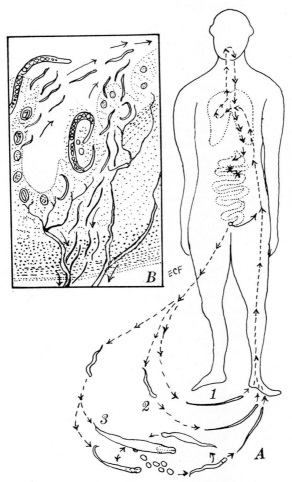

Fig. 129.—Life Cycle of *Strongyloides stercoralis* showing intrinsic and free-living phases. *A, free-living phases: 1,* filariform larva passed in the feces invades skin to initiate superinfection; *2,* rhabditoid larva passed in the feces transforms into filariform larva infective for man; *3,* rhabditoid larvæ passed in the feces develop into free-living adults, which produce one or more free-living generations before development of infective filariaform larvæ. *B, autoinfection* (insert, upper left): parasitic females oviposit in intestinal mucosa; larvæ hatched from eggs may escape into lumen or may pass into the submucosa and muscle layers, invade mesenteric venules and initiate internal autoinfection. (Original, Faust.)

of the stomach to the anus have been found invaded in both human and experimental hosts.

Almost without exception the parasitic females live among the epithelial and gland cells, or in the tunica propria, and under normal conditions do not penetrate the muscularis mucosæ into the deeper layers of the intestinal wall.

Pathogenesis and Symptomatology

The Skin Lesions.—No lesion has been described comparable to the "ground itch" of hookworm infection. Usually *Strongyloides* larvæ proceed rather rapidly from the sites of entry to the cutaneous blood vessels but some of them may temporarily become trapped in the dermis and possibly never reach their destination.

Larval Migration Through the Lungs.—On arrival in the pulmonary capillaries the larvæ produce hemorrhage at each site of escape into the alveoli, followed by a pronounced cellular infiltration into the invaded respiratory passages. Conspicuous among these cells are eosinophils, lymphocytes and epithelioid cells. If many larvæ are in transit through the lungs there will be small areas of consolidation in the terminal bronchioles.

The Adult Worms in the Intestine.—Not more than 28 days following invasion of the skin, a majority of the young worms will have arrived in the intestine, the females will have entered the mucosa, matured, begun to oviposit, the eggs will have hatched and active rhabditoid larvæ are for the first time present in the stools.

Unless large numbers of females are simultaneously entering the mucosa they cause relatively little irritation as they penetrate between epithelial cells to the base of the glands or into the tunica propria of the villi (Hartz, 1946). Damage to the invaded intestinal mucosa is cumulative, due to continued movements of the females within the tissues, the deposition and hatching of the eggs, and the active escape of first-stage rhabditoid larvæ out of the mucosa into the intestinal canal. There may be infiltration of eosinophils, epithelioid cells, occasionally giant cells, and fibroblasts. The affected tissue becomes increasingly non-functional and areas of 0.5 to 1.0 cm. diameter are at times sloughed off down to the muscularis mucosæ.

Systemic damage from the intestinal infection consists of sensitization and probably toxic reactions, varying in degree in different individuals and in different stages of the infection. As in ascariasis (page 239), these effects are potentially enhanced or reactivated by reinoculation or by auto-infection.

Symptoms.—Entry of the filariform larvæ of *S. stercoralis* from the surface of the skin to the cutaneous blood vessels produces a relatively mild needling sensation at each site of penetration and often is not specially noted by the patient. In transit through the lungs the young worms may cause symptoms suggesting bronchopneumonia, at times with consolidation of one or more lobules. In case female worms develop to maturity in the bronchial epithelium they may be responsible for chronic bronchial disease (Kyle, McKay and Sparling, 1948).

In a voluntary self-infection, Desportes (1944–1945) developed prodromal abdominal symptoms 26 days after skin inoculation, consisting initially of hunger pains, followed in a few days by profound lassitude and diffuse abdominal pain which increased in frequency and intensity up to 6 weeks, after which time it became less acute. Jones (1950) found that the most common complaint is abdominal pain which is rather sharply localized.

The blood picture at the beginning of the intestinal phase is typically one of leukocytosis, with a ratio of eosinophils to total white cells ranging from 5.0 to 68 or even 75%. In the chronic stage smaller percentages of eosinophils are characteristic.

In internal autoinfection the invasion of filariform (or rhabditoid) larvæ into the deeper layers of the intestinal wall and their migration by internal blood routes to the lungs may produce paralytic ileus (Nolasco and Africa, 1926), hepatitis, cholecystitis, myocarditis, pneumonia or tracheitis, with symptoms of abdominal pain, diarrhea alternating with constipation, tender liver, dyspnea, cough, hemoptysis and low-grade fever (Kyle, McKay and Sparling, 1948). Whitehall and Miller (1944) reported genito-urinary complication of intestinal infection in a male patient who gave a history of abdominal discomfort, nocturia, urinary incontinence and diurnal urgency to urinate, with the stools negative and the urine positive for *Strongyloides* larvæ. Redewill (1949) studied genito-urinary strongyloidiasis in a man and his wife, in whom there was severe urticaria of the preputia.

For the relationship of *S. stercoralis* to "creeping eruption" see "*Larva Migrans*," page 282.

Diagnosis

Since there is no well-defined clinical syndrome which is pathognomonic of strongyloidiasis, proof of the infection depends on demonstration of the organism. Routine diagnosis is made by recovery of active rhabditoid larvæ (Fig. 119*A*) in fecal films examined microscopically, but occasionally filariform larvæ (Fig. 128*B*) are found in such preparations, particularly if the feces have stood at laboratory temperature for a day or more before examination is made.

Many times an exhaustive examination of the stools of *Strongyloides* patients will be negative when duodenal aspiration will provide a positive diagnosis. Jones (1950) demonstrated active larvæ in 91% of 71 *Strongyloides* patients on whom duodenal aspiration was performed, in contrast to 27.4% positives of 952 stools and 80% of patients diagnosed by multiple stool examination. However, stools are sometimes positive when duodenal aspirates are negative. Occasionally larvæ of *S. stercoralis* are recovered from the sputum, urine or aspirates from body cavities.

Treatment

Dithiazanine is the most effective drug in the treatment of strongyloidiasis, although even with this drug failures are common, while nausea and vomiting are frequent side-effects. Treatment is given for one or two weeks. Cure rate is difficult to estimate since infections may relapse following a prolonged period of negative stools. Nevertheless patients with symptomatic strongyloidiasis are usually benefited by the treatment (see Table 7, page 416).

Prognosis

Cachectic patients with diarrhea and passing numerous *Strongyloides* larvæ have a poor prognosis. Such patients tend not to present an eosinophilia. They must be observed for electrolyte and fluid imbalance and anemia, which complications should be corrected, while treatment with dithiazanine should be attempted. Rarely strongyloidiasis may be the cause of death (Faust and De Groat, 1940). Yet in the vast majority of patients the prognosis is good.

Epidemiology

In some respects *S. stercoralis* behaves like human hookworms; in other ways it is quite different. Eggs laid by the parasitic females in the intestinal mucosa hatch before they escape into the intestinal canal, so that only rhabditoid larvæ are found free in the intestinal contents. The larvæ feed in transit down the bowel and usually may have transformed into the 2nd rhabditoid stage by the time they are evacuated in the stool. Under favorable conditions on the soil they mature into the infective filariform stage within 24 to 48 hours. On contact with human skin they burrow under epidermal scales or into hair follicles, enter cutaneous blood vessels and migrate through the lungs to the intestinal tract much like the hookworms. This *direct mode of development* is probably the most frequent type of life cycle of *Strongyloides*.

In warm climates with abundant rainfall rhabditoid larvæ evacuated in the feces onto favorable soil may develop into free-living rhabditoid males and females, which mate and produce eggs that hatch and give rise to a second generation of rhabditoid larvæ. Usually after a single generation of free-living adults the rhabditoid larvæ transform into the infective filariform stage. This is the *indirect mode of development*.

Strongyloides infection is more common in adults than in young children, and is particularly prevalent in mental hospitals and prisons in warm, moist climates.

Dogs are occasionally found infected with strains of *Strongyloides* indistinguishable from *S. stercoralis*, yet all reliable evidence indicates that man almost invariably begets his own *Strongyloides* infection, as a result of his careless personal hygiene.

Control

Control of human strongyloidiasis is concerned primarily with reduction of the sources of exposure, both extrinsically and in the individual. Since ground contaminated with *Strongyloides*-positive human stools will frequently contain infective-stage larvæ in one to two days, special precautions must be taken to prevent promiscuous defecation on the soil.

Rhabditoid Nematodes as Pseudoparasites of Man

Species of the genus *Rhabditis* and related free-living forms which are coprophagous in their mode of nutrition are from time to time seen in human stools and are diagnostically confused with the rhabditoid larvæ and free-living adult stages of *Strongyloides*, although some have a long acuminate tail. These pseudoparasites can be readily distinguished from the rhabditoid stages of *Strongyloides*, hookworms and *Trichostrongylus* by an examination of the esophagus. The species of *Rhabditis* have a median esophageal swelling (Fig. 119,*D,mb*) which is lacking in *Strongyloides*, hookworms and *Trichostrongylus* (Fig. 119 *A–C*).

The recovery of *Rhabditis* in fecal smears usually indicates a contamination of the specimen after it has been passed, but occasionally these nematodes may be ingested and survive passage through the digestive tract (*Rhabditis hominis, R. donbass, R. schachtiella*). Other species (*R. pellio, R. axei*) have been sporadically reported from vaginal secretions and urine, while *R. niellyi* was once recovered from an itching cutaneous papule.

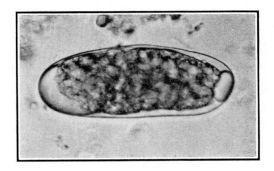

Fig. 130.—Photomicrograph of egg of *Meloidogyne javanica* (syn. *Heterodera marioni, H. radicicola*) from human stool. × 500. (Courtesy of Dr. T. B. Magath, from Faust and Russell's *Clinical Parasitology*, Lea & Febiger, Philadelphia.)

The vinegar eel (*Turbatrix aceti*), which grows in "mother of vinegar," has been diagnosed from the urine and vaginal secretions of women who used vinegar as a vaginal douche, and on one occasion from a contaminated (?) specimen of urine passed by a male patient.

Other nematodes which are natural parasites of plants are consumed in food. The enlarged underground roots of radishes, turnips, rutabagas and parsnips are particularly subject to infection with these nematodes. The species most frequently involved is *Meloidogyne javanica* (syn. *Heterodera marioni* or *H. radicicola*). The stage recovered in the stool is commonly the partially embryonated egg, which is thin-shelled, hyaline, elongate-ovoidal with rounded ends, and measures 82 to 120 microns by 24 to 43 microns (Fig. 130). These eggs may be confused with infertile *Ascaris* or hookworm eggs and, if they are somewhat flattened on one side, with those of pinworms.

SPIRUROID NEMATODES

These roundworms vary remarkably in their appearance: Some are delicate filiform objects, others are wiry and still others are stout and relatively short. All have a moderately slender esophagus lacking a posterior swelling. In most species the males have caudal wings (alæ). In all species for which the life cycle has been elucidated there is an arthropod intermediate host.

Gongylonema pulchrum Molin, 1857

This thread-like nematode is a cosmopolitan parasite of ruminants, and has also been found in pigs, bears, hedgehogs, monkeys, and occasionally in man, with the diagnosed human cases in Italy, Germany, Bulgaria, U.S.S.R., Ceylon, and the United States.

In ruminants the male worms reach a length of 62 mm. and a diameter of 0.15 to 0.3 mm., and the female worms, 145 mm. and 0.2 to 0.5 mm. respectively. The anterior end of the worm is provided with 8 longitudinal series of cuticular blister-like bosses, which converge anteriorly towards the small buccal cavity. The caudal end of the male is provided with an asymmetrical pair of wings, median ventral to which are several pairs of pre-anal and post-anal papillæ. The female lays fully embryonated eggs which are transparent, thick-shelled, broadly ovoidal and measure 50 to 70 microns by 25 to 37 microns.

When ingested by various species of dung beetles and cockroaches they hatch, burrow into the hemal cavity and become encapsulated. The definitive host is infected by swallowing the infected insect (Ransom and Hall, 1915; Baylis, Sheather and Andrews, 1925), the larvæ are freed and migrate up to the esophagus or mouth cavity, in the mucous and submucous membranes of which they develop into adult worms and in which the females oviposit.

In the reported human cases worms have been extracted from, or have spontaneously emerged from the lips, gums, hard and soft palate, tonsil and angle of the jaw, but never from the esophagus. The symptoms in human infection consist primarily of local irritation and nervousness, and in one case a pharyngitis and stomatitis. These manifestations disappear on removal of the worm. No chemotherapy is indicated.

Thelazia callipæda Railliet and Henry, 1910, and
Thelazia californiensis Kofoid and Williams, 1935

These nematodes most commonly reside in the conjunctival sac of the host. *T. callipæda* is Oriental in its geographic distribution and commonly parasitizes the dog, while *T. californiensis* has been reported from California, New Mexico, Oregon and Nevada. Workers in California have reported the cat, fox, coyote, dog, horse, rabbit, sheep, black bear and two species of deer parasitized with *T. californiensis*. Human infection with the former species has been described six times from China, twice from Korea and once from India. Six human infections with *T. californiensis* have been published (Lee and Parmelee, 1958).

The adult worms are wiry, creamy-white threads which measure 4.5 to 13 mm. by 0.25 to 0.75 mm. (males) and 6.2 to 17 mm. by 0.3 to 0.85 mm. (females). The posterior end of the male is strongly curved towards the ventral side. The vulva in the female opens midventrally a considerable distance in front of the equatorial plane. The female lays hyaline, thin-shelled ovoidal eggs. Intermediate hosts in California are flies (*Fannia* sp.) (Burnett, Parmelee, Lee and Wagner, 1957).

Thelazia causes considerable damage to the tissues of the eye, including inflammation of the conjunctival sac, excess lacrimation, and superficial scarification of the corneal conjunctiva as the worms migrate out of the conjunctival sac across the front of the eye and back again. They may be easily removed with eye forceps after the introduction of a few drops of novocaine into the conjunctival sac.

Physaloptera caucasica von Linstow, 1902

The natural hosts of this worm are African monkeys but the species has a considerably wider geographic range than tropical Africa. Infection or pseudo-infection with *Physaloptera* in the human intestinal tract has been reported from the Caucasus, tropical Africa, Southern Rhodesia, India, Panama and Colombia. The worms are relatively large, stout, creamy-white objects, which measure 14 to 50 mm. long by 0.7 to 1.0 mm. in diameter (males) and 24 to 100 mm. long by 1.14 to 2.8 mm. in diameter (females). Although they have a superficial resemblance to young ascarids, they may be distinguished by a cuticular collarette, a pair, rather than three, fleshy lips surrounding the mouth, and distinctive dental processes and papillæ just inside the mouth. The smooth, hyaline thick-shelled eggs are broadly ovoidal, measure 44 to 65 microns by 32 to 45 microns and are fully embryonated when laid. Various insects serve as intermediate hosts (Schell, 1952).

The adult worms live with their heads deeply buried in the wall of the digestive tract from the level of the esophagus to the mid-level of the ileum. Likewise the liver may at times be parasitized. Epidemiologic, clinical and preventive aspects of this infection have not been studied.

Gnathostoma spinigerum Owen, 1938, and
Gnathostoma hispidum Fedtschenko, 1872

Biological Data.—These nematodes are natural parasites of certain mammals which feed on fish or other cold-blooded vertebrates. Adults of *Gnathostoma spinigerum* are found in tumors of the digestive tract of the cat, wild cat, leopard, lion, tiger, racoon and dog from Japan to Indonesia and India, also Northern Rhodesia but not in U.S.A. Human infection with this species, almost invariably in an advanced larval stage in extra-intestinal sites, has been reported from Thailand, Malaya, Indo-China, China, Japan, Indonesia, India and Palestine. Adults of *G. hispidum* have been obtained from gastric tumors of hogs and wild hogs in Japan, China, India and other parts of Asia, Europe and Australia. Human infections with immature worms of this species in extra-intestinal sites have been described once each from Japan and China and twice from India.

The adult worms of both species are robust cylindroidal objects with rounded ends. In the tiger the adult males of *G. spinigerum* reach a length of 11 to 25 mm. and the females, 25 to 54 mm. They possess a subglobose cephalic swelling separated from the body proper by a distinct cervical constriction (Fig. 131 *B*). Both ends are curved ventrally and in the digestive tract the worms are tightly coiled within the tumor cavity. The head portion of the adults is provided with eight encircling rows of sharp curved hooklets (Fig. 131 *B*,*C*). The eggs deposited by the females in the tumor cavities are transparent, ovoidal, with a pitted outer shell and a mucoid plug at one end (Fig. 131 *G*). They measure 65 to 70 microns by 38 to 40 microns and are essentially unembryonated when evacuated in the feces of the cat.

The life cycle of *G. spinigerum* has been elucidated in Thailand, Japan, and the Philippines (Miyazaki, 1958). On dilution with water, eggs in the host's feces become fully embryonated within 1 week at temperatures of 27° to 31° C. and hatch. First-stage larvæ are eaten by fresh-water copepods (*Cyclops*), bore their way into the hemal cavity and in 10 to 14 days transform into second-stage larvæ. When the infected *Cyclops* is ingested by fresh-water fishes, the larvæ migrate into the flesh, become encapsulated and transform into the third stage. When infected fish are eaten by snakes, birds, and mammals other than the natural final hosts, the third-stage larvæ are not destroyed, nor are they able to complete their development; they merely migrate to the muscles of these transfer (*paratenic*) hosts and retain their infectivity. Consumption of the infected flesh by an appropriate host provides opportunity for completion of the cycle: The larva is dissolved out of the tissues finds its way into the stomach wall and develops to maturity in the cavity of the tumor, which has an opening into the lumen of the digestive tract through which eggs of the worm escape into the intestinal canal. However, even in the

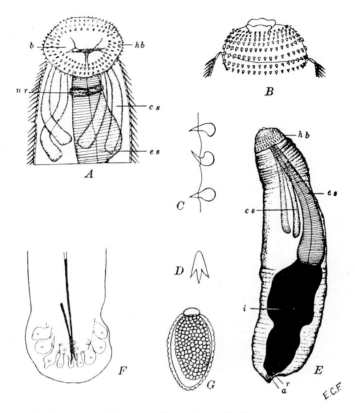

Fig. 131.—*Gnathostoma spinigerum*. *A*, anterior end of immature worm, ventral view, showing bulbous head (*hb*) with four rings of hooklets, two pairs of salivary glands (*cs*), nerve ring (*nr*) and esophagus (*es*), × 100; *B*, head of more mature worm, lateral view, with eight cephalic rings of hooklets, × 100; *C*, detail of head hooklets; *D*, detail of anterior body spine; *E*, immature worm, lateral view, showing head bulb (*hb*), esophagus (*es*), $\frac{1}{2}$ of 2 pairs of salivary glands (*cs*), midgut (*i*), rectum (*r*) and anus (*a*) × 40; *F*, posterior end of male, ventral view, showing peri-anal papillæ and copulatory spicules, × 40; *G*, egg from cat's feces, × 333. (*A–E*, after Morishita and Faust; *F*, after Baylis and Lane; from Faust's *Human Helminthology*, Lea & Febiger, Philadelphia.)

appropriate final host there is a period of normal migration and development in the liver before the worms enter the stomach wall, which apparently always is invaded from the serosal surface (Miyazaki, 1954).

Pathogenesis.—Species of *Gnathostoma* are not well adapted to man as the definitive host and hence, rarely if ever, reach maturity within tumor cavities of the digestive tract. Instead, the excysted third-stage larva digested out of the flesh of the fish host migrates from the intestinal canal to the cutaneous or subcutaneous and somatic muscular tissues, where it produces a picture of "larva migrans," a granulomatous lesion or a stationary abscess. The worms have been observed in tissues from practically all surface areas, including the breast and occasionally the eye (Sen and Ghose, 1945; Chang, 1949; Daengsvang, 1949). Toumanoff and Le Van-Phung (1947) have called attention to the high eosinophilia which is characteristically associated with human gnathostomiasis. (See *"Larva Migrans,"* page 284.)

Treatment.—This is concerned with removal of the larval or possibly the mature worms from the superficial tissues and is usually accomplished by excision.

Control.—Thorough cooking of fish or other second intermediate hosts intended for human consumption will prevent infection in man.

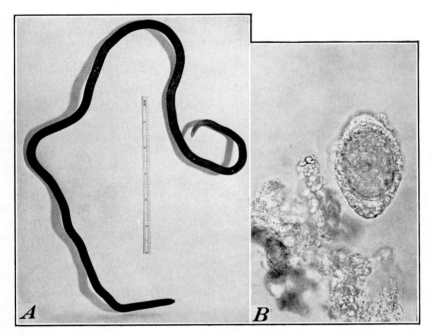

FIG. 132.—*Dioctophyma renale. A*, Mature female from kidney of a naturally infected dog; *B*, photomicrograph of egg, × 500. (Original, courtesy, Dr. T. B. Magath, Mayo Clinic.)

Dioctophyma renale (Goeze, 1782) Stiles, 1901
(Giant kidney worm)

This large roundworm is rather widely distributed throughout the world in fish-eating mammals, including the dog, wolf, *Canis jubatus*, cat, puma, glutton, raccoon, coati, mink, marten, skunk, weasel, otter and seal, and has also been reported from the ox and horse. Ten authentic human infections are on record.

The adult worms (Fig. 132*A*) are large cylindrical nematodes which are blood-red in color. The males measure 14 to 20 mm. in length by 4 to 6 mm. in diameter and at their posterior extremity have a bell-shaped copulatory bursa which is not supported by rays, as in the hookworms and their relatives, but on its inner aspect is covered with papillæ. The females measure up to 100 cm. in length by 5 to 12 mm. in diameter. The eggs (Fig. 132*B*) are ellipsoidal, dirty brown in color, have deep pittings in the shell except at the poles, and measure 64 to 68 microns by 40 to 44 microns. The normal habitat of the adults is in the parenchyma of the kidney, but they may be found in the peritoneal and thoracic cavities.

The life cycle of *D. renale* is incompletely known. Unembryonated eggs are passed in the urine and their development takes place in water. Fresh-water fishes apparently harbor the larval stage infective for mammals.

One to as many as eight adult *D. renale* have been recovered from infected mammals. In the kidney the worms gradually consume the parenchyma, finally leaving only the renal capsule. Animals or patients having the kidney infection discharge blood and pus in their urine, and suffer from acute renal colic. At times a worm migrates into the ureters and may escape through the urethra. All of the human infections have involved the kidneys. Diagnosis is made on microscopic demonstration of the typical eggs passed in the urine or on the spontaneous discharge of a worm *per urethram*. No chemotherapy has been developed for this disease.

Trichinella spiralis (Owen, 1835) Railliet, 1895
(Trichina worm, causing trichinosis)

This minute nematode was first observed in its coiled larval stage encapsulated in human striated muscle at necropsies in London, in 1828 and 1833. Two years later Paget (1835) found the same stage of the parasite post-mortem in a tuberculosis patient and referred the material to Richard Owen, who described the organism and gave it the specific name *spiralis*. Von Siebold (1844) and Dujardin (1845) suggested that the form was the undeveloped larval stage of a roundworm; in 1860 Leuckart and Virchow proved experimentally that this hypothesis was correct. Meanwhile pathologists in other European countries found trichina cysts in human muscle tissue, while Joseph Leidy (1846), in Philadelphia, first demonstrated their presence in domestic swine.

In 1860, Zenker provided evidence that this infection in man was responsible for serious and at times fatal consequences. This stimulated unusual clinical interest throughout Europe and resulted in intensive study of the epidemiology and pathogenesis of trichinosis in man, together with the institution in Germany of microscopic examination of diaphragms of all slaughtered hogs to determine if the pork was safe for human consumption.

Until recent decades, human infection with *Trichinella spiralis* was an important clinical and public health problem in the pork-eating populations of Europe; today the infection is still widely distributed in Germany, Poland, Spain, Hungary and the lower Danube countries. In contrast, it has come to be recognized as a widely disseminated, clinically important disease in the United States and parts of Latin America, with epidemic outbreaks in small or moderate-sized groups of the population.

Morphology, Biology and Life Cycle

The adult *Trichinella spiralis* is a delicate thread-like nematode (Fig. 134) hardly visible to the unaided eye. The male (Fig. 134*A*) measures 1.4 to 1.6 mm. in length by 40 to 50 microns in diameter; it is very slender anteriorly but somewhat more robust in its posterior half. The cloacal opening is terminal and is guarded by a pair of conspicuous conical papillæ. The female (Fig. 134*B*) is somewhat more than twice as long as the male and about one and a half times as large in diameter. The vulvar opening lies midventrally approximately one-fifth the body length from the anterior end.

When the excysted larvæ first invade the intestinal mucosa, typically at the level of the duodenum and adjacent segment of the jejunum, they enter the glandular crypts where they develop to maturity, copulate and the female proceeds to produce uterine eggs in not more than 5 days. The

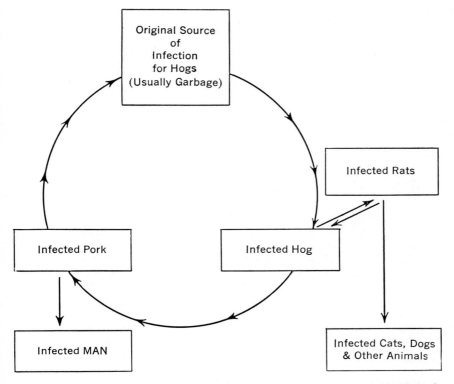

Fig. 133.—Diagram illustrating the common methods of exposure to trichinosis in the continental United States. (From Faust's *Human Helminthology*, Lea & Febiger, Philadelphia.)

males are rather rapidly dislodged from the mucosa, are swept down the bowel and are eliminated, but the females burrow more deeply into the mucosa. Soon they begin to larviposit (Fig. 134*B*). The little larvæ measure about 100 by 6 microns. At first many of them (Fig. 134) escape into the intestinal canal but as the mother worms become more deeply buried in the intestinal wall an increasing number of the larvæ reach the mesenteric venules or lymphatics and become distributed throughout the body. The females continue to produce progeny in limited numbers for 4 to 16 weeks or more, with a total output of many hundreds.

18

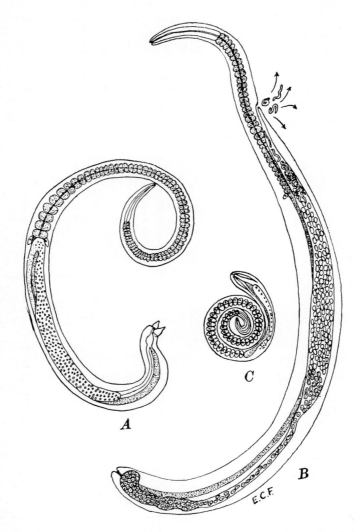

Fig. 134.—*Trichinella spiralis*. *A*, adult male, with tubular testis originating in the posterior region of the body, ascending anteriorwards to the equatorial plane, then bending abruptly and proceeding posteriorwards as the dilated vas deferens, which joins the delicate ejaculatory tubule that empties into the cloaca at the posterior end of the body; *B*, adult female with club-shaped ovary in the posterior part of the body, constricted oviduct and distended uterus which opens through the vulva in the anterior fifth of the body; *C*, larva recently deposited in muscle. *A*, *B*, × 90; *C*, × 660. (*A*, *B*, after Yorke and Maplestone; *C*, adapted from Staübli, from Faust's *Human Helminthology*, Lea & Febiger, Philadelphia.)

Between the 7th and 14th day after exposure most of the larvæ have entered the blood stream and have been filtered out in striated muscle.

Encapsulation begins about the 21st day, with the production of an ellipsoidal sheath around the tightly coiled larva (Fig. 135). These cysts have their long axis parallel to that of the muscle fibers. Muscles most heavily parasitized are the diaphragm, larynx, base of the tongue, abdomen, intercostals, biceps, psoas, pectoral, gastrocnemius and deltoid. As the larva grows to a length of 0.8 to 1.0 mm. within the cyst capsule, it provokes inflammation and degeneration of adjacent muscle fibers, with the forma-

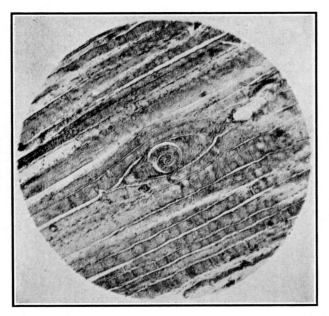

FIG. 135.—Encapsulated larva of *Trichinella spiralis*. (After Aldridge; from Faust and Russell's *Clinical Parasitology*, Lea & Febiger, Philadelphia.)

tion of a double-walled adventitious capsule. Although some encapsulated larvæ remain viable for many years, many of them become calcified between the sixth and twelfth month.

Figure 136 provides a synoptic diagram of the consecutive stages in the life cycle and their time relationship to the lesions produced and the cardinal symptoms.

Pathogenesis and Symptomatology

Pathogenesis.—The entry of the young excysted worms into the intestinal mucosa causes catarrhal inflammation and at times profuse hemorrhage due to irritative damage to host cells and acute eosinophilic cellular reaction around the invaders.

Once larviposition has begun and the larvæ are in migration through the tissues, their temporary lodgment in capillaries or perivascular sites provokes the same type of cellular response. This is particularly notable in the myocardium through which the larvæ migrate but in which they do not encyst, with necrosis and fragmentation of the muscle fibers followed by fibrocytic repair. Similarly, if they become temporarily trapped in the

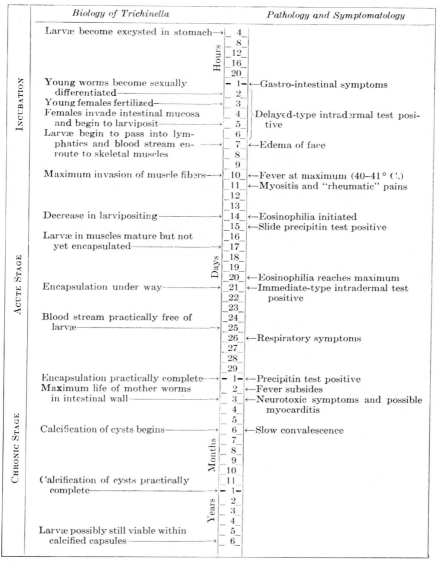

	Biology of Trichinella		Pathology and Symptomatology
INCUBATION	Larvæ become excysted in stomach→	*Hours* 4 8 12 16 20	
	Young worms become sexually differentiated—————	1 2	←Gastro-intestinal symptoms
	Young females fertilized————	3	
	Females invade intestinal mucosa and begin to larviposit————→	4 5	Delayed-type intradermal test positive
	Larvæ begin to pass into lymphatics and blood stream enroute to skeletal muscles ——→	6 7 8 9	←Edema of face
ACUTE STAGE	Maximum invasion of muscle fibers→	10 11 12 13	←Fever at maximum (40–41° C.) ←Myositis and "rheumatic" pains
	Decrease in larvipositing————→	14 15	←Eosinophilia initiated ←Slide precipitin test positive
	Larvæ in muscles mature but not yet encapsulated———————→	16 17	
		Days 18 19	
	Encapsulation under way————→	20 21 22 23	←Eosinophilia reaches maximum ←Immediate-type intradermal test positive
	Blood stream practically free of larvæ———————————→	24 25 26 27 28 29	←Respiratory symptoms
CHRONIC STAGE	Encapsulation practically complete→	1	←Precipitin test positive
	Maximum life of mother worms in intestinal wall—————→	2 3 4	←Fever subsides ←Neurotoxic symptoms and possible myocarditis
	Calcification of cysts begins————→	5 6	←Slow convalescence
		Months 7 8 9 10	
	Calcification of cysts practically complete————————→	11	
		Years 1 2 3 4	
	Larvæ possibly still viable within calcified capsules ————→	5 6	

FIG. 136.—Synoptic diagram illustrating (*on left*) the progressive biological stages of *Trichinella spiralis* and (*on right*) the parallel clinical picture. (After Cameron, from Faust's *Human Helminthology*, Lea & Febiger, Philadelphia.)

capillaries of the brain, eyes, lungs or other organs, an acute inflammatory reaction occurs around the invaders.

On invasion of striated muscle fibers from the adjacent capillaries, the larvæ become tightly coiled on themselves and produce an immediate inflammatory tissue change resulting in formation of an inner membrane within an adventitious capsule. The completed capsule is ellipsoidal with blunt ends (Fig. 135). As soon as complete encapsulation has been accomplished the larva is effectively isolated. Eventually the entire cyst including the larva becomes calcified.

In addition to the intense focal infiltration of eosinophils around adults and larvæ of *T. spiralis* in the tissues there is a characteristic hypereosinophilia in the circulating blood.

Symptomatology.—*The average case of trichinosis is not severe and causes no detectable symptoms*, although a history of digestive upset following consumption of infected meat and succeeded by muscular pains can at times be elicited in relatively asymptomatic cases.

During the invasion of the duodenal and jejunal mucosa by a large number of excysted trichina larvæ the symptoms mimic those of acute food poisoning. This syndrome lasts through the 7th day. Later larval migration is responsible for severe, and at times completely incapacitating myositis, producing difficulty in breathing, mastication, speech and use of the extremities. Dyspnea may be intense and edema, particularly of the face, is characteristic. There is fever of 39° to 40° C., occasionally 41° C., remittent in type. At times there are petechial hemorrhages of the skin and mucous membranes, in the conjunctivæ and in the retinal vessels. These symptoms are most prominent during the 2nd week but continue throughout the period of larviposition (1 to 3 months). An eosinophilic leukocytosis of 15 to 50% or higher develops during this period.

The third clinical stage is a culmination of the traumatic and toxic effects of the infection. The edema persists, especially around the eyes, sides of the nose, temples, hands, feet and conjunctivæ. There may be profound cachexia. If extensive migration of the larvæ takes place through the cerebral capillaries, grave motor and psychic disturbances may occur (Pearson, Borgoño and Salcedo, 1960), while the lesions in the myocardium may be responsible for a syndrome of congestive heart failure (Blumer, 1936). Fatal outcome or chronic invalidism is not infrequent in these heavy infections.

Diagnosis

Unless the physician obtains a clear picture of the typical symptoms in his patient, he must depend on laboratory evidence to support a clinical diagnosis of trichinosis. This can not usually be obtained until the larvæ produced by the female worms have migrated into striated muscles 14 to 21 days after exposure. Meanwhile severe illness and irreversible pathologic changes may have occurred.

There are two available methods of clinical laboratory diagnosis, namely, (1) biopsy of a small piece of muscle and its microscopic examination, either under compression or after artificial digestion in gastric juice and demonstration of larvæ, and (2) immunologic tests. The common immunologic tests are intradermal, flocculation and precipitin reactions (See "TECHNICAL AIDS," page 450.)

Treatment

There is no specific therapy for trichinosis, hence palliative and supportive treatment must be relied upon to carry the patient through the critical period. However, if the disease is suspected during the early intestinal phase the administration of saline purgatives may dislodge many of the female worms before they become deeply embedded in the intestinal mucosa, measurably reducing the number of larvæ produced, hence the damage resulting from their migration and encapsulation.

In patients critically ill due to allergic reaction to, or intoxication with, substances derived from the worms, administration of ACTH may ameliorate the crisis (Roehm, 1954; Sager *et al.*, 1955).

Prognosis

In heavy infections this is poor to grave, in lighter infections it is fair to good. In severe epidemics 0.5 to 30% of the patients succumb, with an average of about 3.0%.

Epidemiology

In nature trichinosis is an enzoötic disease, for the most part propagated between the black rat and the brown rat which are cannibalistic. Although all stages in the life cycle of *Trichinella spiralis* are developed in a single host, in order that the parasite may survive it is necessary that the infected flesh of one host be consumed by another. Almost all mammals are susceptible to infection.

Human trichinosis results for the most part from consumption of inadequately cooked pork, but at times from eating bear meat (northwestern United States, Alaska) or walrus flesh (Greenland). In the United States during 1949–1952 hogs fed on grain or forage were found to have considerably less than 1% infection, whereas hogs fattened on uncooked municipal garbage from Boston, New York and Philadelphia had an incidence of 3.5 to 11.21 per cent with recovery of 100 to 2,741 larvæ per gram by digestion technic (Schwartz, 1952, 1960). Intensive infections in the United States, including epidemic outbreaks, are almost invariably traceable to garbage-fed hogs, expecially those butchered on the farm for very limited consumption.

The common methods of exposure to trichinosis in the United States are diagrammatically illustrated in Figure 133.

On the basis of autopsy surveys of more than 10,000 persons in the United States it has been calculated that the average incidence of trichinosis is 12.3% (Sawitz, 1938), but Gould (1952) believes that more thorough examination would reveal about 30%. In the United States of the new cases developing each year 16,000 (4.6%) may be expected to have symptoms of clinical grade (Link, 1952). The incidence of trichinosis varies within wide limits in different parts of the United States (Faust and Russell,

1957). Although human trichinosis has been found to occur in all Latin American countries surveyed except Panamá and Puerto Rico, moderately high incidence has been reported only from Mexico and Chile. Alicata (1938), in Hawaii, found 15% of wild hogs infected with *Trichinella spiralis* and 7.4% of a random sampling of human diaphragms positive. Epidemics have occurred in recent years in the eastern, northern, western and south-western parts of the United States, Sweden, Greenland and Syria.

Control

Preventing Infection in Swine.—Although occasional human infection results from consumption of inadequately processed flesh of infected bears, whales and walruses, these sources are relatively incidental compared to domestic pork. In the United States within recent years high endemicity and at times epidemic outbreaks of trichinosis have occurred mostly in areas where raw municipal garbage constitutes a considerable part of hog food (Schwartz, 1952). Hence legislation in each state to require that all such garbage be thoroughly heated before it is fed constitutes a practical goal which has not been attained. This measure, consistently carried out throughout the entire country, would probably protect many consumers by providing trichina-free pork.

Condemning Infected Carcasses.—To be effective this requires not only gross inspection of pork for detection of trichina lesions but laborious microscopic examination of samples from the diaphragm and other infected muscles of each slaughtered hog. This is impracticable.

Sterilizing the Meat.—This can be accomplished by two practical methods, freezing and thorough cooking. Augustine (1933) demonstrated that refrigeration at minus 18° C. (minus 0.4° F.) for 24 hours provides essentially safe pork. Gould (1952) recommends storage of pork in deep-freeze units as a modern method which is simple, effective and is particularly applicable to rural areas. Thorough cooking of pork is always a safeguard but the danger lies in failure to heat the inside of the meat sufficiently to kill the trichina cysts even though the outside may be golden brown.

There is the possibility that irradiation may eventually provide a means of devitalizing trichina cysts in carcasses.

LARVA MIGRANS

Definition and General Remarks.—*Larva migrans* is a term applied to the migration of larval nematodes in unsuitable hosts. Unable to complete their normal migration, the young worms wander for a time in the host's tissues but in most instances are eventually encapsulated if they do not die or reach the outside of the body.

Larval nematodes which have developed in the soil to the filariform stage and employ the cutaneous mode of entry into the body (*e.g.*, hookworms) are responsible primarily for *cutaneous larva migrans* in the poorly adapted host. Those which are introduced onto the skin by blood-sucking insect intermediate hosts (*e.g.*, the filaria worms) at times cause creeping somatic lesions, at other times, visceral lesions. Those hatched from eggs in the small intestine and normally requiring a migration to the lungs (*e.g.*, ascarids) are responsible primarily for *visceral larva migrans*. The fourth type, ingested in an advanced larval stage in host tissues (*e.g.*, spiruroid nematodes) may migrate through the viscera or the subcutaneous tissues. The different types of larva migrans have been reviewed by Beaver (1956).

Cutaneous Larva Migrans

Historical Notes.—The clinical manifestations of this infectious process have been known since 1874, when Lee described a linear cutaneous eruption with an advancing end, but the etiology was not definitely demonstrated until 1926, when Kirby-Smith, Dove and White proved experimentally that a common causative agent in the southern United States is the canine or feline strain of the cat hookworm *Ancylostoma braziliense*.

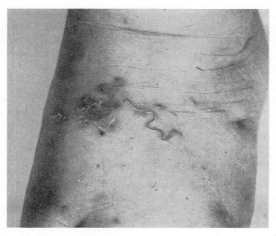

Fig. 137.—Cutaneous larva migrans, showing serpiginous linear lesion on foot. (After Drs. Alex J. Steigman and P. Hess, in Nelson's *Textbook of Pediatrics*, courtesy W. B. Saunders Co., Philadelphia.)

Geographical Distribution.—Cutaneous larva migrans resulting from exposure to *A. braziliense* has a widespread distribution throughout the sandy coastal areas of the United States from southern New Jersey to the Florida Keys on the Atlantic Coast and along the entire littoral of the Gulf of Mexico, extending inland in Texas as far as Dallas and San Antonio. The largest number of cases is found in the vicinity of Jacksonville, Florida. Creeping eruption has also been reported from many other subtropical and tropical coastal regions, including southern Brazil, Uruguay and Argentina, Spain, southern France, South Africa, India, the Philippines and Australia.

Other species of hookworms are also capable of producing cutaneous larva migrans in man, *viz.*, the cosmopolitan hookworm of dogs, *Ancylostoma caninum*, the European dog hookworm *Uncinaria stenocephala*, the human hookworms, *Necator americanus* and *A. duodenale*, and the hookworm of cattle, *Bunostomum phlebotomum*. However, cases resulting from natural exposure to the infective stage of these worms other than *A. caninum* are very few compared to *A. braziliense* (Beaver, 1956).

Pathogenesis and Symptomatology.—At each point where the filariform larva of *A. braziliense* invades the skin it produces an itching, reddish papule. In two or three days the larva has developed a serpiginous tunnel between the stratum germinativum as a roof and the corium as a floor. The lesion is at first erythrematous and soon becomes elevated and vesicular (Fig. 137). As the larva proceeds through the skin at a rate of several millimeters a day, the older portion of the tunnel becomes dry and crusty. The progressive movement of the worm and the tissue irritation which it produces are responsible for an intense pruritus which almost invariably leads to scratching. This opens the lesion to pyogenic organisms. Activity of the larva may continue for several weeks or months, resulting in extensive skin involvement (Fig. 138) and at times serious systemic illness.

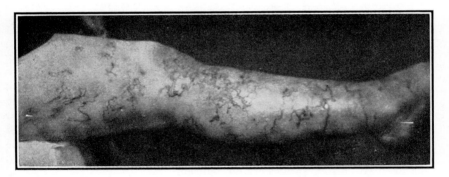

Fig. 138.—Late stage of multiple larva migrans of *Ancylostoma braziliense* origin. (After Kirby-Smith, in Stitt's Diagnostics, courtesy, P. Blakiston's Son & Co., from Faust's *Human Helminthology*, Lea & Febiger, Philadelphia.)

Diagnosis.—Dermatologists and general practitioners in endemic areas have come to recognize the classical picture of an advancing serpiginous tunnel in the skin with an associated intense pruritus as pathognomonic of cutaneous larva migrans, but the lesion may be atypical. Furthermore, creeping eruption of hookworm origin must be differentiated from that produced by fly larvæ (*Hypoderma* spp., *Gasterophilus* spp., *et al.*, see pages 390 and 391, and, in Oriental regions, from that due to *Gnathostoma* spp. see page 270).

Treatment.—Many types of treatment have been recommended for cutaneous larva migrans but usually without controls. Therapy may be directed towards removing or killing the worm, relieving symptoms or facilitating the deep migration of the worm. The most successful procedures result in removing the worm. This is done by producing a bleb by freezing the skin with ethyl chloride or solid carbon dioxide, or by burning it with caustic agents such as phenol. The larva, which is located in the superficial portion of the epidermis, is thus separated from the host by the vesicle fluid and eventually is lost with the epidermal slough.

Symptoms may be alleviated by anti-histaminics, anti-pruritics (*i.e.*, trimeprazine), sedatives and anesthetic or protective coatings. Cortico-steroids will inhibit the skin reaction but are recommended only in severe infections.

Possibly some of the treatments reportedly successful allow the larva to proceed with its migration. The action of promethazine, regarded as effective, is not known.

Epidemiology.—Exposure results from contact of the human skin with warm, moist sandy soil, containing filariform larvæ of hookworms originating from the excreta of dogs and cats. The sites of exposure to *A. braziliense* are found on bathing beaches and under houses where workers temporarily lie prone on the ground repairing exposed plumbing fixtures. In both of these epidemiologic situations extensive body surfaces are liable to exposure.

Control.—Unlike intestinal hookworm infection in man due to *Necator americanus* and *Ancylostoma duodenale*, in which man is solely responsible for pollution of the soil, with few exceptions the hookworms concerned in cutaneous larva migrans are intestinal parasites of domestic animals, almost exclusively dogs and cats. Control of the sources of exposure must therefore be directed towards reduction of hookworms in dogs and cats, including periodic de-worming of these animals and destruction of all vagrant dogs and cats.

Cutaneous Larva Migrans of Strongyloides Origin.—The studies of Napier (1949) Caplan (1949) and Sandosham (1952) on a type of creeping eruption associated with strongyloidiasis in non-native ex-prisoners-of-war in Siam and Burma, and the reported existence of the same clinical type of dermatitis in Indo-China (Galliard and Chabaud, 1952), Iraq and on the Mediterranean Coast, provide suggestive evidence that cutaneous larva migrans may result from perianal autoinfection in persons harboring *Strongyloides stercoralis* (see page 261).

Clinically the creeping cutaneous lesion in strongyloidiasis advances more rapidly than that following exposure to *Ancylostoma braziliense*, and the duration of the eruption is much shorter.

Cutaneous Larval Filariasis

This subject has been given almost no consideration as a type of larva migrans. It will be mentioned briefly here but is presented somewhat more adequately in Chapter 13 (Filaria Worms), page 293. Immature and larval filariæ, possibly all species belonging to the genus *Dirofilaria*, have been removed on several occasions from cutaneous and palpebral nodules of persons in Mediterranean countries, Thailand, Argentina, and Florida and Louisiana, U.S.A. It seems probable that mosquitoes are the intermediate hosts and vectors, and that human infection is only incidental to that of an as-yet-unknown reservoir.

Visceral Larva Migrans

Compared with cutaneous larva migrans, the visceral type has been recognized clinically for only a short time, while its nematode etiology has been demonstrated very recently (Wilder, 1950; Beaver *et al.*, 1952). As in the cutaneous type, the invading larvæ generally are of species naturally adapted to hosts other than man, and remain for long periods in the tissues. These lesions have been reported from the liver, the brain, and numerous other organs including the eye (Ashton *et al.*, 1960; Dugoid *et al.*, 1961; Woodruff *et al.*, 1961) (Fig. 139). Careful study of biopsied liver specimens by Beaver *et al.* (1952) and experimental studies by Smith and Beaver (1953) have lead to the conclusion that the larvæ involved most frequently are those of *Toxocara*, in most instances *T. canis*.

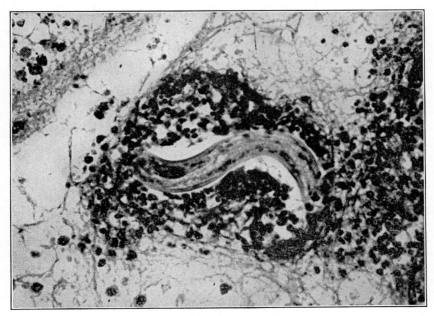

Fig. 139.—Larva of *Toxocara canis* (second stage) surrounded by eosinophils in vitreous chamber of human eye. × 220. (Wilder, courtesy of Armed Forces Institute of Pathology and Trans. Am. Acad. Ophth. and Otolaryng.)

Because *Ascaris lumbricoides* has at times been found as an intestinal infection in association with granulomatous lesions of the viscera, it has commonly been assumed that the latter are necessarily the result of visceral migration of human *Ascaris* larvæ. Aside from the morphologic differences between infective-stage *Ascaris* and *Toxocara* larvæ, several of the cases studied have been children who provided a history of eating dirt, which is as commonly seeded with eggs of *Toxocara* as with those of human *Ascaris* (Headlee, 1936), and some patients lived in areas where human ascariasis is not endemic.

In visceral larva migrans the clinical picture varies from asymptomatic, except for a persistent eosinophilia (Smith and Beaver, 1953), to a syndrome of chronic hypereosinophilia, hepatomegaly, moderate pulmonary infiltration, fever, cough, and hyperglobulinemia (Beaver *et al.*, 1952). The allergic reaction in the lungs may be so severe as to embarrass respiration. Clinical and pathological descriptions have been published of cases in which the eye (Irvine and Irvine, 1959) and various other organs were involved (Dent *et al.*, 1956). Severe myocarditis has been observed in one case (Friedman and Hervada, 1960).

Diagnosis of Visceral Larva Migrans.—This requires demonstration of the parasite in specimens obtained by biopsy or necropsy. In cases with liver involvement, biopsy of a small subcapsular nodule will usually provide the necessary evidence.

Treatment.—There is no specific therapy. In a majority of cases the prognosis is excellent, with complete recovery. If life is endangered by the asphyxia resulting from bronchiolar spasm or allergic pneumonia, corticosteroids may be indicated as a temporary measure, but they are not to be used in the usual case.

Control.—The high incidence of *Toxocara* infection in well-cared-for dogs emphasizes the need for ridding household pets of their intestinal parasites at frequent intervals in order to safeguard young children from contracting roundworm infections normally occurring in these animals (Beaver, 1959; Vaughn and Jordan, 1960).

Spiruroid Larva Migrans

Species of *Gnathostoma* (*G. spinigerum* and *G. hispidum*) have been recovered in an advanced larval stage from subcutaneous tissues. In Japan and Thailand, where *G. spinigerum* has been found on many occasions in the human host, exposure results from consuming uncooked fish which contain the encapsulated third larval stage of the worm. Unable to develop into the adult worm in the wall of the human stomach, the larva undertakes an extra-intestinal migration and is discovered in serpiginous tunnels in the skin, in abscess pockets in subcutaneous tissues, or occasionally in the eye, lungs and other sites.

Tropical Eosinophilia (Occult Filariasis?)

Filarial worms which normally live in other animals occasionally undergo partial development in man. *Dirofilaria* species, discussed briefly above and in a later section, develop to the immature adult stage in man and generally are found in nodules or abscesses under the skin. In the normal host, unknown at present, they may inhabit other tissues. In man they probably also occur in deeper tissues where they escape detection in most instances but may be discovered in the lungs by x-ray examination of the chest.

Tropical eosinophilia, also called "Eosinophilic Lung" and "Tropical Pulmonary Eosinophilia," has recently been placed under suspicion as a form of cryptic, zoönotic filariasis, although its exact nature and cause, or causes, are still not known. It was first described by workers in India where the disease is prevalent in the more southern areas. It is also prevalent in other areas of Southeast Asia. Since it resembles other diseases in which hypereosinophilia is prominent, reports of its occurrence in other parts of the world are questionable. It is essentially a respiratory disease in which cough and asthma usually are the presenting symptoms. The features which serve to distinguish it from other respiratory disorders associated with hypereosinophilia are (1) pulmonary shadows in the roentgenograms, (2) increased erythrocyte sedimentation rate and (3) prompt, marked clinical improvement upon the administration of either organic arsenicals or diethylcarbamazine (Hetrazan). Evidences that at least one variety of tropical eosinophilia is an occult form of filariasis are provided by four observations: (1) the filarial complement fixation test is positive in very high titers before treatment and becomes negative after successful treatment; (2) the response to treatment with diethylcarbamazine is much the same as in some types of filariasis; (3) the disease in essentially all of its clinical features has been experimentally produced twice in a human volunteer who was inoculated with a filaria which normally lives in monkeys, cats and other animals; and (4) in a number of autopsy and biopsy studies microfilariæ have been demonstrated in areas of eosinophilic infiltration in the lungs of individuals with typical symptoms of tropical eosinophilia but without demonstrable microfilariæ in the blood (Danaraj, 1958, 1959; Danaraj *et al.*, 1959) in Singapore; Buckley, (1958) in Malaya, and Webb *et al.*, (1960) in India.

SUMMARY

1. Roundworms (nematodes) are unsegmented and are typically elongate, cylindrical. They are covered with a cuticle secreted by a hypodermis, have a dermomuscular layer, a body cavity not lined with mesothelium and a complete digestive tract. With few exceptions they are diecious.

2. Although a majority of roundworms are free-living, a very large number have become adapted to parasitism. All species have the same fundamental stages in their life cycle, *viz.*, the parent worms, the egg and several successive larval stages.

3. The pinworm (*Enterobius vermicularis*) represents the simplest type of obligate parasitism among the nematodes. It is a cosmopolitan human parasite, which is particularly prevalent among children. The adult worms live free in the appendix and cecum. When the gravid female migrates down the intestine and out of the anus, she deposits almost fully embryonated eggs on the perianal and perineal skin. *Via* fingertips or in air currents they get into the mouth and are swallowed. On arrival in the intestine they hatch and develop into adult worms in 4 weeks or less.

The commonest symptom of pinworm infection is an itching of the perianal skin, resulting in scratching and scarification of the area. The infection is most satisfactorily diagnosed by use of the Scotch-tape anal "swab" to collect the characteristic eggs. Piperazine is satisfactory for eradicating this infection, provided all positive individuals in a community are diagnosed and are given full treatment simultaneously. In addition to successful treatment, control requires careful habits of personal and group hygiene.

4. The whipworm (*Trichuris trichiura*) is prevalent in warm moist climates. The adult worms live with their delicate anterior ends

securely threaded into the cecal mucosa. The females lay a few thousand eggs daily. These become infective in about 3 weeks on warm, moist, shaded soil. When taken into the mouth and swallowed the eggs hatch and in about 90 days develop into adult worms.

The infection may be inconsequential if only a few worms are present, but a heavy worm burden invariably produces diarrhea or dysentery, with measurable damage to the intestinal mucosa and systemic absorption of the worm's toxic metabolites. Diagnosis is based on recovery of the typical eggs in the feces. Dithiazanine is the most effective anti-*Trichuris* drug available for oral administration. Control consists in sanitary disposal of human excreta.

5. The large intestinal roundworm (*Ascaris lumbricoides*) is cosmopolitan and is particularly common in small children in the Tropics and warmer temperate climates. The adult worms live unattached in the small intestine. Each female lays about 200,000 eggs daily. When deposited on the ground, the eggs become infective within 2 to 3 weeks. When they are swallowed they hatch in the small intestine. The larvæ migrate *via* blood or lymphatic vessels to the lungs, then break out into the alveoli, and after 8 or 9 days of growth they move up the air passages, and are swallowed. On reaching the small intestine they develop into adults in about 8 to 12 weeks following exposure.

During larval migration through the lungs the larvæ produce pneumonitis and systemic sensitization. Later, in the intestine, the infection may be relatively benign, although it is commonly accompanied by colicky pains, indigestion and evidences of malnutrition. The worms may cause intestinal obstruction, or they may perforate the bowel wall, block the appendiceal lumen or the common bile duct, or enter the parenchyma of the liver. Diagnosis is made on recovery of the typical eggs in the feces. The worms may be expelled by oral administration of piperazine. Control consists of sanitary disposal of human excreta.

6. The two common human hookworms are widely distributed in the moist temperate and tropical regions of the world. *Necator americanus* is more abundant in warm climates, including the southeastern United States, and *Ancylostoma duodenale* more frequent in the north temperate zones of the Eastern Hemisphere. The adult worms are attached to the mucosa of the small intestine. Each female lays daily a few thousand eggs. When the eggs are deposited on warm, moist, sandy soil in a shaded location, they soon hatch and the escaping larvæ feed, grow, molt, then feed again and in 5 or more days transform into the infective stage. On contact with human skin they penetrate to the cutaneous blood vessels, are carried to the lungs, escape into the air passages, move up to the epiglottis, and are carried to the duodenum or jejunum, where they become attached and in 5 weeks or more develop into adults.

Hookworm disease results primarily from loss of blood due to the worms feeding from, and laceration of the intestinal mucosa. This is responsible for the anemia and hypoproteinemia, and indirectly for stunted physical and sexual growth, lethargy, and physical and mental retardation in hookworm-infected populations. Diagnosis is made on recovery of hookworm eggs in the feces. Treatment consists in oral administration of tetrachloroethylene in soft gelatin capsules to remove the worms, soluble iron to relieve the anemia and diets rich in protein to compensate for the hypoproteinemia. Control of human hookworms requires anthelmintic treatment, together with provision for sanitary disposal of human excreta.

7. In certain countries man is exposed to infection with hookworms and related nematodes of domestic animals, including *Ancylostoma ceylanicum*, *A. caninum*, *Ternidens deminutus*, *Œsophagostomum apiostomum*, *Syngamus laryngeus*, and several species of *Trichostrongylus*.

8. The human threadworm (*Strongyloides stercoralis*) is prevalent in warm, moist climates and occurs sporadically in temperate regions. The infection is more frequently found in adults than in children, and results from pollution of warm, wet, shaded sites with human excreta. The parasitic females live embedded in the mucosa of the intestine, usually at the duodenal level. Here they lay eggs which hatch, releasing a first-stage larva, which often molts and is passed in the feces as the second-stage larva. On favorable ground it becomes infective in 24 to 48 hours, or may pass through a free-living cycle before producing the infective filariform stage. On contact with human skin the filariform larva enters the cutaneous bloodvessels and migrates through the lungs before reaching the intestinal tract. The biological prepatent period is 28 days or less. At times filariform larvæ developing in transit down the intestine or at the anus produce autoinfection.

The most frequent symptoms of strongyloidiasis are diarrhea and pains in the pit of the stomach. Diagnosis is based on demonstration of larvæ in the stool or duodenal aspirate. Treatment with dithiazanine is helpful but is not always curative. Control in a community requires sanitary disposal of human excreta.

9. Spiruroid nematodes are normal parasites of domestic and wild mammals and occur infrequently in man. Ingestion of the encysted larva provides the means of exposure for the definitive host. Species reported from man include *Gongylonema pulchrum*, *Thelazia callipæda* and *T. californiensis*, *Physaloptera caucasica*, *Gnathostoma spinigerum* and *G. hispidum*.

10. The giant kidney worm (*Dioctophyma renale*) has a cosmopolitan distribution in fish-eating mammals. Ten human cases have been reported.

11. The trichina worm (*Trichinella spiralis*) is found in most countries of the world except in the Tropics. All stages in the life cycle are completed in one host but two hosts are required for continuation of the infection. Trichinosis is enzoötic among brown and black rats. Human infection results from consumption of uncooked or undercooked pork, occasionally bear or walrus meat, containing the encysted larvæ.

There are three clinical stages in the infection, *viz.*, (1) a food-poisoning syndrome during the biological incubation period; (2) symptoms of severe muscular rheumatism during larval migration, and (3) following encystation of the larvæ in muscle fibers, symptoms developing from cumulative traumatic, inflammatory and toxic damage.

A majority of cases are essentially asymptomatic. Specific diagnosis is made on recovery of the larvæ in biopsied muscle or on immunologic tests, none of which is positive until 21 days after exposure. There is no specific therapy. Control may be effected by subjecting pork to freezing for 24 hours or more, and thorough cooking of the meat.

12. "Larva migrans" is the migration of larval nematodes without development in inappropriate hosts. There are four principal categories, *viz.*, (1) cutaneous larva migrans produced by filariform larvæ of non-human hookworms; (2) cutaneous (and visceral) larva migrans due to larvæ of non-human filaria worms; (3) visceral larva migrans produced by larvæ of *Toxocara canis* hatched from eggs in the small intestine and migrating into liver, lungs, or other organs, and (4) visceral (or cutaneous) larva migrans due to immature spiruroid nematodes. Cutaneous larva migrans has also been reported as a sequela of perianal autoinfection in strongyloidiasis. Chemotherapy is relatively effective for hookworm-induced cutaneous larva migrans. Control of larva migrans requires primarily the periodic de-worming of dogs and cats.

13. Tropical eosinophilia, characterized by hypereosinophilia, eosinophilic pulmonary infiltration, cough and asthma, all of which respond favorably to treatment with arsenicals or diethylcarbamazine, is probably a form of occult zoönotic filariasis. It is most prevalent in India and Southeast Asia. Clinical diagnosis is confirmed by filarial complement fixation tests showing high titers which decline after successful treatment.

REFERENCES

ALICATA, J. E. 1938. A Study of *Trichinella spiralis* in the Hawaiian Islands. Pub. Health Repts., *53*, 384–393.

AMARAL, A. D. F., QUAGLIA, F. O., and INOUE, C. R. 1954. Sobre novo caso de singamose humana. Rev. de Med., *38*, 1–9.

AMBERSON, J. M., and SWARZ, E. 1952. *Ternidens deminutus* Railliet and Henry, a Nematode Parasite of Man and Primates. Ann. Trop. Med. & Parasitol., *46*, 227–237.

DE ANDRADE LIMA, L. I., and SIMÕES BARBOSA, F. 1951. Consideraçoes em tarno de um caso de singamose humana. Publ. Avulsas do Inst. Aggeu Malhães, Brasil, *1*, 27–34.

ASHTON, N. 1960. Larval Granulomatosis of the Retina Due to Toxocara. Brit. J. Ophthalm., *44*, 129–148.

AUGUSTINE, D. L. 1933. Effects of Low Temperatures upon Encysted *Trichinella spiralis*. Am. J. Hyg., *17*, 697–710.

BEAVER, P. C. 1949a. Methods of Pinworm Diagnosis. Am. J. Trop. Med., *29*, 577–587.

————. 1949b. Quantitative Hookworm Diagnosis by Direct Smear. J. Parasitol., *35*, 125–135.

————. 1950. The Standardization of Fecal Smears for Estimating Egg Production and Worm Burden. J. Parasitol., *36*, 451–456.

————. 1951. Hemoglobin Determination in Hookworm Disease Case-Finding. Am. J. Trop. Med., *31*, 90–97.

————. 1952. The Detection and Identification of Some Common Nematode Parasites in Man. Am. J. Clin. Path., *22*, 481–494.

————. 1956. Larva Migrans. In Parasitological Review Section, Exper. Parasitol., *5*, 587–621.

————. 1956. The Record of *Ancylostoma braziliense* as an Intestinal Parasite of Man in North America. Am. J. Trop. Med. & Hyg., *5*, 737–738.

————. 1959. Visceral and Cutaneous Larva Migrans. Pub. Health Repts., *74*, 328–332.

————. 1961. Control of Soil-transmitted Helminths. Pub. Hlth. Papers, Wld. Hlth. Org., No. 10, 44 pp.

BEAVER, P. C., and DANARAJ, T. J. 1958. Pulmonary Ascariasis Resembling Eosinophilic Lung. Am. J. Trop. Med. & Hyg., *7*, 100–111.

BEAVER, P. C., SNYDER, C. H., CARRERA, G. M., DENT, J. H., and LAFFERTY, J. W. 1952. Chronic Eosinophilia Due to Visceral Larva Migrans. Pediatrics, *9*, 7–19.

BECK, J. W., SAAVEDRA, D., ANTELL, B. J., and TEJEIRO, B. 1959. The Treatment of Pinworm Infections in Humans (Enterobiasis) with Pyrvinium Chloride and Pyrvinium Pamoate. Am. J. Trop. Med. & Hyg., *8*, 349–352.

BIOCCA, E. 1951. On *Ancylostoma braziliense* (de Faria, 1910) and its Morphological Differentiation from *A. ceylanicum* (Looss, 1911). J. Helminthol., *25*, 1–10.

BLUMER, G. 1936. Trichinosis, with Special Reference to Changed Conceptions of Pathology and Their Bearing on Symptomatology. New England J. Med., *214*, 1229–1235.

BROWN, H. W., and CHAN, K. F. 1955. Treatment of *Enterobius vermicularis* Infections with Piperazine. Am. J. Trop. Med. & Hyg., *4*, 321.

BROWN, H. W., and PERNA, V. P. 1958. An Overwhelming Strongyloides Infection. J. Am. Med. Assoc., *168*, 1648–1651.

UCKLEY, J. J. C. 1958. Tropical Eosinophilia in Relation to Filarial Infections (*Wuchereria* spp.) of Animals. Tr. Roy. Soc. Trop. Med. & Hyg., *52*, 335–336.

————. 1958. Occult Filarial Infections of Animal Origin as a Cause of Tropical Pulmonary Eosinophilia. East Afr. Med. J., *35*, 493–500.

BURNETT, H. S., PARMELEE, W. E., LEE, R. D., and WAGNER, E. D. 1957. Observations on the Life Cycle of *Thelazia californiensis* Price, 1930. J. Parasitol., *43*, 433.

CALLE, S. 1961. Parasitism by *Capillaria hepatica* Pediatr., *27*, 648–655.

CAPLAN, J. P. 1949. Creeping Eruption and Intestinal Strongyloidiasis. Brit. Med. J., *i*, 396.

CARR, H. P., PICHARDO SARDA, M. E., and NUÑEZ, N. A. 1954. Anthelmintic Treatment of Uncinariasis. Am. J. Trop. Med. & Hyg., *3*, 495–503.

CHANG, E. 1949. Uveitis of a Cantonese Caused by *Gnathostoma spinigerum* (Owen, 1836). Chinese Med. J., *67*, 166–168.

CORT, W. W., *et al.* 1921–1925. Investigations on the Control of Hookworm Disease. Am. J. Hyg., Vols. *1* to *5*. (34 Separate Papers.)

CRAM, E. B. 1943. Studies on Oxyuriasis. XXVIII. Summary and Conclusions. Am. J. Diseases Children, *65*, 46–59.

DAENGSVANG, S. 1949. Human Gnathostomiasis in Siam with Reference to the Method of Prevention. J. Parasitol., *35*, 116–121.

DANARAJ, T. J. 1958. The Treatment of Eosinophilic Lung (Tropical Eosinophilia) with Diethylcarbamazine. Quart. J. Med., *27*, 243–263.

————. 1959. Pathologic Studies in Eosinophilic Lung. Arch. Path., *67*, 515–524.

DANARAJ, T. J., DA SILVA, L. S., and SCHACHER, J. F. 1959. The Serological Diagnosis of Eosinophilic Lung (Tropical Eosinophilia) and its Etiological Implications. Am. J. Trop. Med. & Hyg., *8*, 151–159.

DARLING, S. T. 1922. The Hookworm Index and Mass Treatment. Am. J. Trop. Med., *2*, 397–447.

DEANE, M. P. 1950. Helmintos eliminados por um grupo de residentes da Amazonia, após um tratamento pelo hexilresorcinol. Rev. Serv. Especial Saúde Publica, *3*, 443–464.

DENT, J. H., NICHOLS, R. L., BEAVER, P. C., CARRERA, G. M., and STAGGERS, R. J. 1956. Visceral Larva Migrans—With a Case Report. Am. J. Path., *32*, 777–803.

DESPORTES, C. 1944–1945. Sur *Strongyloides stercoralis* (Bavay, 1876) et sur les *Strongyloides* de Primates. Ann. de Parasitol., *20*, 160–190.

DUGOID, I. M. 1961. Chronic Endophthalmitis Due to Toxocara. Brit. J. Ophthalm., *45*, 705–717.

FAUST, E. C. 1931. Human Strongyloidiasis in Panama. Am. J. Hyg. *14*, 203–211

————. 1933. The Development of *Strongyloides* in the Experimental Host. Am. J. Hyg., *18*, 114–132.

————. 1935. The Pathology of *Strongyloides* Infection. Arch. Path., *19*, 769–806.

————. 1949. *Human Helminthology*, 3rd ed., 744 pp. Lea & Febiger, Philadelphia.

FAUST, E. C., and DEGROAT, A. 1940. Internal Autoinfection in Strongyloidiasis. Am. J. Trop. Med., *20*, 350–375.

FOSTER, A. O., and LANDSBERG, J. W. 1934. The Nature and Cause of Hookworm Anemia. Am. J. Hyg., *20*, 259–290.

FRIEDMAN, S., and HERVADA, A. R. 1960. Severe Myocarditis with Recovery in a Child with Visceral Larva Migrans. J. Pediatrics, *56*, 91–96.

FRYE, W. W., SWARTZWELDER, C., LAMPERT, R., ABADIE, S. H., and CARSON, C. B., JR. 1957. An Effective Trichuricide Suitable for Oral Administration. Am. J. Trop. Med. & Hyg., *6*, 890–893.

GALLIARD, H., and CHABAUD, A. G. 1952. Anomalies, d' eteignant par passage chez le chien, d'une souche de *Strongyloides stercoralis*, isolée d'un cas d'urticaire migrant. Comparaison avec differentes souches normales étudiées au Tonkin. Ann. de Parasitol., *32*, 588–597.

GOODWIN, L., JAYEWARDENE, L. G., and STANDEN, O. D. 1958. Clinical Trials with Bephenium Hydroxynaphthoate against Hookworm in Ceylon. Brit. Med. J., *ii*, 1572–1576.

GOULD, S. E. 1952. Trichinosis in Man and Its Prevention. Proc. 1st Nat'l Conf. on Trinchinosis, Chicago, p. 53.

GROVE, S. S., and ELSDON-DEW, R. 1958. Internal Autoinfection with *Strongyloides stercoralis*. So. Afr. J. Lab. & Clin. Med., *4*, 55–63.

HARTZ, P. H. 1946. Human Strongyloidiasis with Internal Autoinfection. Arch. Path., *41*, 601–611.

HEADLEE, W. H. 1936. The Epidemiology of Human Ascariasis in the Metropolitan Area of New Orleans, Louisiana. Am. J. Hyg., *24*, 479–521.

HELLER, E. R. 1944. The Epidemiology of Enterobiasis. Med. Parasit. & Par. Dis., Moscow, *13*, 16–23. (Russian text.)

IRVINE, W. C., and IRVINE, A. R. 1959. Nematode Endophthalmitis: *Toxocara canis*. Am. J. Ophthalmol., *47* (Part 2), 185–191.

JACOBS, A. H. 1952. Enterobiasis in Children; Incidence, Symptomatology, and Diagnosis, with a Simplified Scotch Celluose Tape Technique. J. Pediatrics, *21*, 497–503.

JONES, C. A. 1950. Clinical Studies in Human Strongyloidiasis. I. Semeiology. Gastroënterol., *16*, 743–756.

JUNG, R. C. 1953. A Study of the Pneumonitis Due to Larval Ascaris Infection. Ph.D. Dissertation, Tulane Univ.

JUNG, R. C., and BEAVER, P. C. 1952. Clinical Observations on *Trichocephalus trichiurus* (Whipworm) Infestation in Children. Pediatrics, *8*, 548–557.

JUNG, R. C., and McCROAN, J. E. 1960. Efficacy of Bephenium and Tetrachlorethylene in Mass Treatment of Hookworm Infection. Am. J. Trop. Med. & Hyg., *9*, 492–495.

KIRBY-SMITH, J. L., DOVE, W. E., and WHITE, G. F. 1926. Creeping Eruption. Arch. Derm., Syph., *13*, 137–173.

KOINO, S. 1922. Experimental Infection of the Human Body with Ascarides. Japan Med. World, *2*, 317–320.

KYLE, L. H., McKAY, D. G., and SPARLING, H. J., JR. 1948. Strongyloidiasis, Ann. Int. Med., *29*, 1014–1042.

LEE, R. D. and PARMELEE, W. E. 1958. Thelaziasis in Man. Am. J. Trop. Med. & Hyg., *7*, 427–428.

LIE KIAN JOE. 1947. *Trichostrongylus* Infection in Man and Domestic Animals in Java. J. Parasitol., *33*, 359–362.

LINK, V. B. 1952. Trichinosis: A National Problem. Proc. First Nat'l Conf. on Trichinosis, Chicago, 3–7.

LOOSS, A. 1896. Notizen zur Helminthologie Ægyptens. I. 3. Die Lebensgeschichte des *Ancylostomum duodenale*. Centralbl. Bakt., *20*, 863–870.

————. 1897. II. Ibid., *21*, 913–926.

McNAUGHT, J. B., BEARD, R. B., and MYERS, J. D. 1941. The Diagnosis of Trichinosis by Skin and Precipitin Tests. Am. J. Clin. Path., *11*, 195–209.

MADSEN, H. 1945. Biological Observations upon *Enterobius vermicularis* (Pinworm). Acta Path., *22*, 392–397.

MENDHEIM, H., SCHEID, G., and SCHMIDT, J. 1952. Die selteneren Spulwurminfektionen beim Menschen. Zeitschr. f. Tropenm. u. Parastiol., *3*, 368–371.

MILLER, M. J. 1941. Quantitative Studies on *Trichocephalus vulpis* Infections in Dogs. Am. J. Hyg., *33* (Sec. D), 58–70.

MIYAZAKI, I. 1954a. Studies on *Gnathostoma* Occurring in Japan (Nematoda: Gnathostomidæ). I. Human Gnathostomiasis and Imagines of *Gnathostoma*. Kyushu Mem. Med. Sci., *5*, 13–27.

————. 1954b. II. Studies on *Gnathostoma* Occurring in Japan. II. Life History of *Gnathostoma* and Morphological Comparison of Its Larval Forms. Kyushu Mem. Med. Sci., *5*, 123–139.

————. 1958. Gnathostomiasis in Japan. Abstr. 6th Int'l Congr. Trop. Med. & Malaria, 57–58.

NAPIER, L. E. 1949. *Strongyloides stercoralis* Infection. Part II. Strongyloidiasis Among Ex-Prisoners-of-War. J. Trop. Med. & Hyg., *52*, 46–48.

PALMER, E. D. 1955. Course of Egg Ouput Over a 15 Year Period in a Case of Experimentally Induced Necatoriasis Americanus in the Absence of Hyperinfection. Am. J. Trop. Med. & Hyg., *4*, 756–757.

PEARSON, E., BORGOÑO, J. M., and SALCEDO, M. 1960. Síndrome meníngeo en triquinosis. Bol. chileno Parasitol., *15*, 70–72.

RANSOM, B. H., and CRAM, E. B. 1921. The Course of Migration of *Ascaris* Larvæ. J. Parasitol., *2*, 80–86.

REARDON, L. 1938. Studies on Oxyuriasis. XVI. The Number of Eggs Produced by the Pinworm, *Enterobius vermicularis*, and Its Bearing on Infection. Pub. Health Repts., *53*, 978–984.

REDEWILL, F. H. 1949. *Strongyloides stercoralis* Involving the Genito-urinary Tract. Urol. and Cut. Rev., *53*, 609–614.

RHOADS, C. P., CASTLE, W. B., PAYNE, G. C., and LAWSON, H. A. 1934. Hookworm Anemia: Etiology and Treatment, with Especial Reference to Iron. Am. J. Hyg., *20*, 291–306.

ROEHM, D. C. 1954. Trichinosis: Report of Case Manifesting Myocarditis, Encephalitis and Radial Neuritis; Response to ACTH. Review of Literature Regarding the Erythrocyte Sedimentation Rate. Ann. Int. Med., *40*, 1026–1040.

ROSEN, L., CHAPPELL, R., et al. 1962. Eosinophilic Meningoencephalitis Caused by a Metastrongylid Lung-Worm of Rats. J. Am. Med. Assn., *179*, 620-624

SAGAR, L. F., KASHTAN, H. A., and MILLER, P. B. 1955. Trichinosis with Myocarditis; Report of a Case Treated with ACTH. New Engl. J. Med., *252*, 397–398.

SANDGROUND, J. H. 1931. Studies on the Life-History of *Ternidens deminutus*, Nematode Parasite of Man, with Observations on Its Incidence in Certain Regions of South Africa. Ann. Trop. Med. & Parasitol., *25*, 147–184.

SANDOSHAM, A. A. 1952. An Investigation into the Association of Creeping Eruption with *Strongyloides* Infection Contracted in the Far East. J. Helmintho., *26*, 1–24.

SAWITZ, W. 1938. Prevalence of Trichinosis in the United States. Pub. Health Repts., *53*, 365–383.

SCHELL, S. C. 1952. Studies on the Life Cycle of *Physaloptera hispida* Schell (Nematoda: Spiruroidea), a Parasite of the Cotton Rat (*Sigmodon hispidus littoralis* Chapman). J. Parasitol., *38*, 462–472.

————. 1952. Trichinæ in Swine. Proc. 1st Nat'l Conf. on Trichinosis, Chicago, pp. 26–30.

SCHWARTZ, B. 1960. Trichinosis in the United States of America. Polskie Towarzystwo Parazytol., *6*, 303. (Abstract.)

SCOTT, H. H. 1943. The Influence of the Slave Trade in the Spread of Tropical Disease. Trans. R. Soc. Trop. Med. & Hyg., *37*, 169–188.

SCOTT, J. A. 1945. Hookworm Disease in Texas. Tex. Repts. on Biol. & Med., *3*, 558–568.

SEN, K., and GHOSE, N. 1945. Ocular Gnathostomiasis. Brit. J. Ophthalm., *29*, 618–626.

STOLL, N. R. 1947. This Wormy World. J. Parasitol., *33*, 1–18.

SVENSSON, R. M.   1925.   Observations on the Development and Longevity of Hookworm Larvæ in Different Temperature Conditions. China Med. J., *39*, 667–673.

SWARTWELDER, C., MILLER, J. H., and SAPPENFIELD, R. W.   1955.   Treatment of Ascariasis in Children with a Single Dose of Piperazine Citrate. Pediatrics, *16*, 115–117.

————.   1957.   The Effective Use of Piperazine for the Treatment of Human Helminthiases. Gastroenterol., *33*, 87–96.

SWARTZWELDER, C., MILLER, J. H., LAMPERT, R., PEÑA CHAVARRIA, A., ABADIE, S. H., ANTHONY, S. O., and SAPPENFIELD, R. W.   1957.   Dithiazanine, an Effective Broad-Spectrum Anthelmintic. J. Am. Med. Assoc., *165*, 2063.

VAN THEIL, P. H., KUIPERS, F. C., and ROSKAM, TH.   1960.   A Nematode Parasitic to Herring, Causing Acute Abdominal Syndromes in Man. Trop. & Geogr. Med., *12*, 97–113.

THORSON, R. E.   1956a.   Proteolytic Activity in Extracts of the Esophagus of Adults of *Ancylostoma caninum* and the Effect of Immune Serum on this Activity. J. Parasitol., *42*, 21–25.

————.   1956b.   The Effect of Extracts of the Amphidial Glands, Excretory Glands, and Esophagus of Adults of *Ancylostoma caninum* on the Coagulation of Dog's Blood. J. Parasitol., *42*, 26–30.

TOUMANOFF, C., and LE-VAN PHUNG.   1947.   Note au sujet d'un cas de gnathostomose humaine observée en Indochine, Bull. Soc. Path. Exot., *40*, 168–174.

VAUGHN, J. and JORDAN, R.   1960.   Intestinal Nematodes in Well-Cared-For-Dogs. Am. J. Trop. Med. & Hyg., *9*, 29–31.

VOGEL, H., and MINNING, W.   1942.   Beiträge zur Klinik der Lungen-Ascariasis und zur Frage der flüchtigen Eosinophilen Lungen-Infiltrate. Beitr. zur Klinik der Tuberkulose, *98*, 620–654.

WALLACE, L., HENKIN, R., and MATHIES, A.   1956.   Trichostrongylus Infestation with Profound Eosinophilia. Ann. Int. Med., *45*, 146–150.

WARD, R. L. and DENT, J. H.   1959.   *Capillaria hepatica* Infection in a Child. Bull. Tulane Med. Faculty, *19*, 27–33.

WEBB, J. K. G., JOB, C. K., and GAULT, E. W.   1960.   Tropical Eosinophilia. Demonstration of Microfilariæ in Lung, Liver and Lymph-Nodes. Lancet, April 16, 835–842.

WHITEHALL, R., and MILLER, M. H.   1944.   Infestation of the Genito-Urinary Tract by *Strongyloides stercoralis*. Bull. Johns Hopkins Hosp., *75*, 169–174.

WILDER, H. C.   1950.   Nematode Endophthalmitis. Trans. Am. Acad. Ophthalm., *55*, 99–109.

WINCKEL, W. E. F., and TREURNIET, A. E.   1956.   Infestation with *Lagochilascaris minor* (Leiper) in Man. Documenta Med. Geograph. et Trop., *8*, 23–28.

WINFIELD, G. F.   1937.   Studies on the Control of Fecal-borne Diseases in North China. I. Problems and Methods. Chinese Med. J., *51*, 217–236.

WOODRUFF, A. W., ASHTON, N., and STOTT, G. J.   1961.   *Toxocara canis* Infection of the Eye. Trans. R. Soc. Trop. Med. & Hyg., *55*, 13–14.

Chapter 13

The Filariæ

Introductory Remarks

THE true filariæ (Filarioidea) have a unique stage in their life cycle, the *microfilaria*, which distinguishes them as a group. This embryo or pre-larval form develops as a tightly coiled filiform object within the eggshell in the uterus of the mother worm. About the time of oviposition the embryo uncoils into a delicate snake-like form. In some species, the egg-shell becomes correspondingly elongated to accommodate itself to the uncoiled embryo and the microfilaria is referred to as "sheathed." In other species, the shell splits, allowing the naked embryo to escape as an "unsheathed" microfilaria.

From the site where they are deposited the microfilariæ enter blood (or lymphatic) vessels and reach the skin. In order to proceed with their development they must be picked up by an appropriate blood-sucking arthropod, in which they transform first into rhabditoid larvæ and then the infective filariform larvæ, which are discharged from the mouth parts of the arthropod at the time it is feeding on the skin of the definitive host. The young worms now enter the host's tissues and after a considerable period of migration settle down in a suitable location to develop into the adult worms.

Species of True Filaria Worms Parasitizing Man

There are 7 species of filariæ which utilize man as definitive host, *viz.*, *Wuchereria bancrofti, Brugia malayi, Onchocerca volvulus, Loa loa, Acantho-cheilonema perstans, A. streptocerca* and *Mansonella ozzardi*. Each species is transmitted by a particular type of blood-sucking insect (Fig. 140).

Wuchereria bancrofti (Cobbold, 1877) Seurat, 1921
(Bancroft's filaria, causing Bancroft's filariasis)

This infection was known to the ancient Hindus (600 B.C.), and the Persian physicians Rhazes and Avicenna referred to its chronic manifes-tations as elephantiasis arabicum. In 1863 Demarquay, in Paris, first found microfilariæ of this worm in hydrocele fluid of a patient from Cuba; in 1866 Wucherer, in Brazil, observed them in chylous urine, and in 1872 Timothy Lewis, in India, discovered them in peripheral blood. The adult females were first seen by Bancroft (1876–1877) and the adult males by Sibthorpe (1888), both recovered from lymphatic tissues in Australia. Patrick Manson, in Amoy, China demonstrated (1878) that the night-biting mosquito *Culex fatigans* ($=C.$ *quinquefasciatus*), was an essential intermediate host and described (1879) noctural periodicity of the microfilariæ in peripheral blood. Manson-Bahr (1912) and O'Connor (1923) showed that microfiliariæ of the strains of *W. bancrofti* in the South Pacific islands exhibited essentially no periodicity.

Bancroft's filariasis is widely distributed throughout the tropical areas of the world and in some regions extends well into subtropical areas (see map, Fig. 141). Until recent decades it was endemic in the southeastern United States. It seems probable that it did not occur in the Western Hemisphere until it was introduced from Africa with the slave trade.

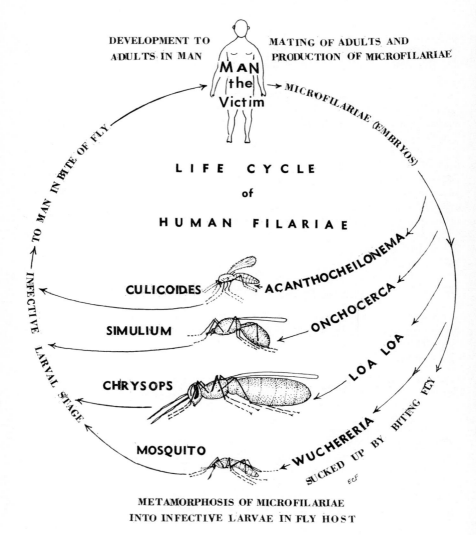

Fig. 140.—Life cycle of human filariæ. (Original, Faust.)

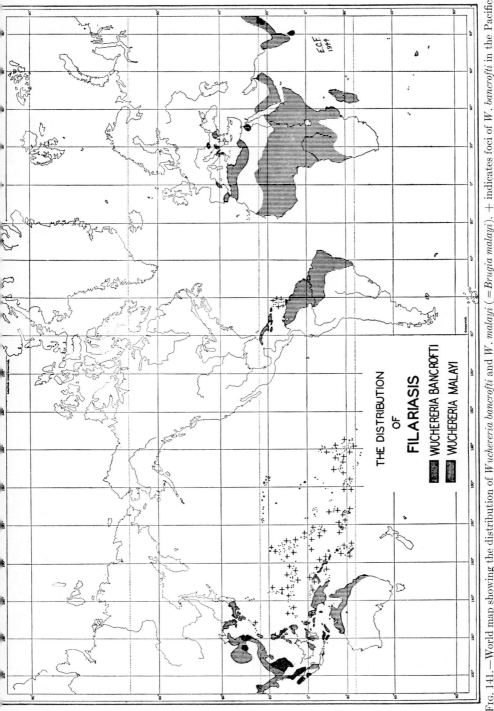

Fig. 141.—World map showing the distribution of *Wuchereria bancrofti* and *W. malayi* (= *Brugia malayi*). + indicates foci of *W. bancrofti* in the Pacific islands. (From Faust and Russell's *Clinical Parasitology*, Lea & Febiger, Philadelphia.)

THE DISTRIBUTION
OF
FILARIASIS

WUCHERERIA BANCROFTI
WUCHERERIA MALAYI

E.C.F.
1944

(295)

In parts of India and the South Pacific islands the incidence of Bancroft's filariasis is high. In other tropical areas there is wide endemicity but relatively low prevalence in the population.

Morphology, Biology and Life Cycle

The Adult Worms.—The adults of *W. bancrofti* (Fig. 106 *m*, page 223) are creamy white, elongated threads which taper at both ends and have a smooth cuticle. The head is slightly swollen and is unarmed. The male measures about 40 mm. in length by 0.1 mm. in cross section. Its caudal end is curved ventrally as much as 360 degrees. The female measures 80 to 100 mm. in length by 0.24 to 0.3 mm. in diameter. The vulva opens midventrally about 0.8 to 0.9 mm. from the anterior end.

The Microfilariæ.—In the inner portion of the two uteri the elongated embryos are tightly coiled within thin, transparent, ovoidal egg membranes, which measure about 38 by 25 microns. As the embryos are pushed along towards the outer ends of the uteri they uncoil and the membranes are stretched into "sheaths" that are somewhat larger than the microfilariæ.

On escape from the mother worm the microfilariæ may remain for some time in the lymphatic vessels or they may soon enter the blood stream. In most strains of *W. bancrofti* they circulate periodically, passing through peripheral blood at night and congregating in visceral blood, particularly the pulmonary capillaries, during the daytime (Hawking and Thurston, 1951). The mechanisms and stimuli involved in the periodicity of microfilariæ in the peripheral blood are still essentially unknown. In the South Pacific strains no particular periodicity is exhibited.

The microfilariæ of *W. bancrofti* (Fig. 142) as they actively circulate in the blood stream or lymph measure 244 to 296 microns in length by 7.5 to 10 microns in cross section. They are bluntly rounded at the anterior tip and attenuated posteriorly. In a wet blood film they move about gracefully, pushing the red blood corpuscles to one side. Internally they possess no digestive tract but a relatively solid column of cells with densely staining nuclei, among which certain specific anatomical landmarks may be discovered when the organisms are stained by intravital or permanent dyes. (For staining technics, see "TECHNICAL AIDS," page 433.) For differential diagnostic purposes it may be noted that the embryo is "sheathed," its caudal extremity is free of cells, its movement is graceful, and it exhibits nocturnal periodicity in peripheral blood in all geographic areas where other human filariæ are endemic.

The important diagnostic differences between the "sheathed" microfilariæ of *W. bancrofti*, *B. malayi* and *Loa loa* are provided in Table 4, while the more easily recognized structural features of the "sheathed" and "unsheated" microfilariæ of man are illustrated in Figure 143.

The Mosquito Phase of the Cycle.—In the mosquito each microfilaria which has just been ingested is found in the midgut ("stomach") within a "sheath." Soon the embryos lose their sheaths, invade the stomach wall and within 24 hours in a suitable mosquito host they migrate to the thoracic muscles and become relatively quiescent. During the next 2 to 7 days they transform into sausage-shaped rhabditoid larvæ (Fig. 144*A*), 225 to 300

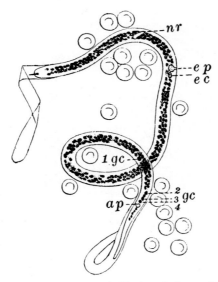

Fig. 142.—"Ensheathed" microfilaria of *Wuchereria bancrofti*. *nr*, nerve ring; *ep*, excretory pore; *ec*, excretory cell; 1, 2, 3, 4 *gc*, so-called "genital cells;" *ap*, anal pore. × 666. (From Faust's *Human Helminthology*, Lea & Febiger, Philadelphia.)

Table 4.   Differential Characters Between the Microfilariæ of *Wuchereria bancrofti*, *Brugia malayi* and *Loa loa*

Note.—Percentages indicate proportion of total length from anterior tip.

Character	*Mf. bancrofti*	*Mf. malayi*	*Mf. loa*
1. Periodicity	Usually nocturnal	Nocturnal	Diurnal
2. Length in microns (thick films)	244 to 296	177 to 230	250 to 300
3. Excretory cell and excretory pore	Small (30.75%), near excretory pore (28.95%)	Large (37.07%), far behind excretory pore (30.09%)	Similar (36.6%) to *Mf. malayi;* (31.6%)
4. "G" cells	Small, of similar size; G_1 (70.14%) far ahead of G_2–G_4	Larger than in *Mf. bancrofti;* G_1 (68.33%) relatively near and larger than G_2–G_4	Similar to those of *Mf. malayi;* G_1 (68.6%)
5. Anal pore	82.48%	82.28%	81.9%
6. Tail	Tapers to delicate point; no terminal nuclei	May be swollen at levels of 2 terminal nuclei	Tapers gradually; caudal nuclei continuous with those of trunk
7. Appearance	Moves in graceful, sweeping curves	Stiff, with secondary kinks	Similar to *Mf. malayi*
8. Pathogenesis	Lymphangitis of genitalia and lower extremities; later elephantiasis or varicose lymphatics	Lymphangitis and elephantiasis confined mostly to the extremities	Fugitive inflammation of subcutaneous tissues
9. Insect hosts	*Culex, Aëdes,* occasionally *Mansonia, Anopheles*	*Mansonia, Anopheles*	*Chrysops*

microns in length by 15 to 30 microns in cross section. Soon the worms transform into an active, elongated, filariform type (Fig. 144*B*), which migrates out of the thoracic muscles into the head of the mosquito and then down to the tip of the proboscis sheath, from which it enters the human host at the time of the next blood meal. The complete mosquito phase is accomplished in 10 to 40 days.

The Biological Incubation Period.—The route through which the infective larvæ enter the skin and migrate to the sites where they later develop into adults is not completely known. Yokogawa (1939) found that they

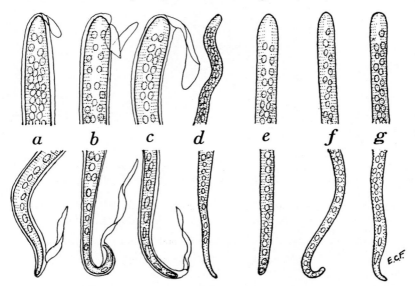

Fig. 143.—Differential characters of the head and tail ends of the microfilariæ of man. *a, Wuchereria bancrofti; b, B. malayi; c, Loa loa; d, Onchocerca vulvulus; e, Acanthocheilonema perstans; f, A. streptocerca; g, Mansonella ozzardi.* Greatly enlarged, drawn to scale. (From Faust and Russell's *Clinical Parasitology*, Lea & Febiger, Philadelphia.)

undertake invasion only if there is lymph exudate from the mosquito's puncture wound. Thereafter the successful individuals continue to migrate through lymphatic vessels, growing slowly; the adolescent worms tend to congregate in the groin glands and in the epididymis of the male and labial glands of the female. However, they may settle down in lymphatic varices, in nodular dilatations of the lymphatic vessels in the lower extremities, or may complete their development elsewhere. After maturing and mating they become coiled together and parturition is begun. Up to one year is often required from invasion of the skin until the worms have completed their development, but there are instances of much shorter incubation.

Pathogenesis and Symptomatology

The Acute Stage.—The symptoms resulting from Bancroft's filariasis are due primarily to local and systemic sensitization and tissue reactions to the invader. As long as the immature worms are in active migration they produce relatively little local reaction; but when trapped they tend to produce an acute tissue response, consisting of an accumulation of histiocytes, epithelioid cells, lymphocytes, giant cells and eosinophils in the lumen of the vessel around the worms, hyperplasia of the endothelium and perilymphatic cellular infiltration.

At times this is sufficient to strangulate the worms in migration months before maturity (Michael, 1944). Later, when the worms settle down and develop into adults, parturient females and microfilariæ may produce acute tissue reactions. These tissue changes tend to constrict the wall of the vessel and obliterate its channel (see Fig. 145).

Whenever such acute inflammatory reaction takes place there is a reddened, swollen, raised lymphatic tract immediately around and retrograde to the site of blockage. It is exquisitely tender, painful and there is at times a febrile reaction. King (1944) states that the earliest symptoms in young adult males develop 3 to 16 months after exposure; that the cardinal manifestations are lymphangitis, usually with an associated lymphadenitis, and only in 20% with fever of mild type and short duration. The lymphangitis may originate in an upper extremity, mostly epitrochlear, but eventually practically all of the lesions concentrate in the scrotum and consist of inflammatory involvement of the spermatic cord, epididymis, testis or entire scrotal organ. Relapses

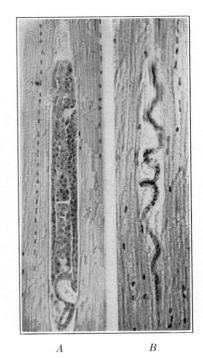

A   B

Fig. 144.—Photomicrographs of *A*, rhabditoid larva and *B*, filariform larva of *Wuchereria bancrofti* in thoracic muscles of *Culex pipiens*. × 300. (After Dr. C. U. Lee, from Faust's *Human Helminthology*, Lea & Febiger, Phila.)

of the acute syndrome are frequent. In lightly exposed white immigrants in Samoa, Webster (1946) found that bouts of lymphangitis with fever occurred annually. In natives of endemic areas this stage of the infection may be symptomless. Since first exposure is likely to take place early in childhood, the severe early involvement of the genitalia is usually lacking. Living worms may be present for years in dilated lymphatic channels (Fig. 146) without remarkable symptoms. These persons characteristically have microfilariæ circulating in their blood and constitute the usual source of infection for the mosquito.

The Chronic Stage.—The tissue changes shown in Figure 146 represent a mild form of the chronic stage. The advanced chronic stage may develop in highly sensitized reactors directly from the acute inflammatory condition of a lymphatic vessel containing the worms or may build up slowly from the milder fibrotic type. In either case reëxposure hastens the reaction. As a result of obliterative changes in the vessels, thrombi, and proliferative changes, the worms die and are absorbed or become calcified. This chronic process may not mature until many years after initial exposure.

The organs and tissues in which these changes occur are the groin, with the development of nodular groin-gland varicosities; the lower extremities, one or both of which become elephantoid with redundant skin and a dense fibrous subcutaneous matrix filled with islands of lymph, and the external genitalia.

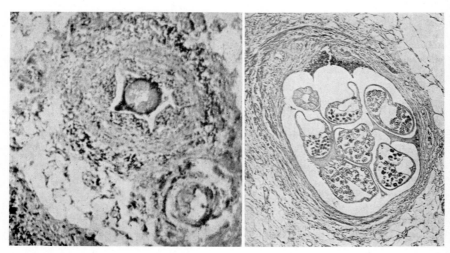

Fig. 145   Fig. 146

Fig. 145.—Section through a lymphatic vessel in the epididymis, showing early acute tissue reaction around *Wuchereria bancrofti*.   × 100. (Photomicrograph from preparation of Dr. F. W. O'Connor, Collection, Armed Forces Institute of Pathology, from Faust's *Human Helminthology*, Lea & Febiger, Philadelphia.)

Fig. 146.—Mild fibrotic tissue reaction around a living parturient female *Wuchereria bancrofti* in an inguinal lymph vessel.   × 66. (Photomicrograph by Faust from preparation by Conrad Bauer, from Faust's *Human Helminthology*, Lea & Febiger, Philadelphia.)

Diagnosis

Routine surveys to determine the incidence of Bancroft's filariasis in an area are based on (1) demonstration of the microfilariæ of *W. bancrofti* in blood films and (2) clinical evidence of the disease. In native populations in endemic regions these two types of information seldom coincide. A higher percentage of persons in the younger age groups have microfilaremia and a higher percentage in the older age groups have symptoms.

During the biological incubation period microfilariæ have not yet been produced, hence diagnosis must be based on history of exposure, lymphangitis and lymphadenitis compatible with Bancroft's filariasis and occasional demonstration of immature worms in an inflamed lymphatic focus (Michael, 1944). Intradermal tests, employing *Dirofilaria* antigen, will be positive in 90% of these cases (see "TECHNICAL AIDS," page 450).

Once microfilariæ are being discharged they can be recovered in blood films. In all areas except the South Pacific islands they are present in appreciable numbers in peripheral blood only at night, usually with greatest frequency between 10 P.M. and 2 A.M. Diagnosis is more commonly made with thick films. For preparation of these films and their staining the reader is referred to "TECHNICAL AIDS," pages 433–434.

After the parent worms die, microfilariæ soon disappear from the blood, and diagnosis must be made on the epidemiologic and clinical history. Care should be exercised to distinguish filarial lymphangitis and its sequelæ from similar clinical pictures resulting from non-filarial disease.

Treatment

Before patent infection with Bancroft's filaria has developed, specific chemotherapy is not likely to be considered. After the worms have died, it is probably useless. At times symptomatic treatment is successful in allaying pain and in case of bacterial complications the use of antibiotics may be helpful. Moreover tight bandaging of elephantoid extremities and surgical removal of redundant tissues may aid in directing lymph flow into collateral channels and thus reduce the amount of accumulated lymph. At times psychologic therapy is necessary for young adult males with scrotal involvement.

Specific Chemotherapy.—Until recent years chemotherapy in Bancroft's filariasis has been unsatisfactory. Certain antimonials and arsenicals may kill the circulating microfilariæ and after prolonged administration inhibit their production (Otto *et al.*, 1952). More rapid filaricidal results can be obtained with suramin sodium (Bayer 205) but this drug like the antimonials and arsenicals requires administration by needle.

The advent of Hetrazan (diethylcarbamazine) has provided the first anthelmintic of practical usefulness in the treatment of Bancroft's filariasis. The advantages of this drug are its oral route of administration, the relatively good tolerance of the patient for the drug and its relatively rapid beneficial clinical effects (Hawking, 1955). Most satisfactory results are obtained when Hetrazan is taken in the amount of 2 mgm. per kilo of body weight 3 times daily for 10 or more days. It quickly destroys the microfilariæ in circulating blood and (at times) kills the parent worms (see Table 7, p. 420).

Epidemiology

Man is the only known definitive host of *Wuchereria bancrofti* and female mosquitoes of the genera *Culex*, *Aëdes*, *Mansonia* and *Anopheles* are necessary intermediate hosts. The adult worms develop in the human lymphatic system and the microfilariæ enter the blood stream and reach the peripheral circulation. When picked up by the appropriate mosquito the microfilariæ transform into larvæ in the thoracic muscles, migrate to the tip of the proboscis and are transferred to a human host when the mosquito feeds. Under optimal conditions the mosquito phase of the cycle is completed in 10 or 11 days; in contrast, several months are usually required from the time the infective-stage larva enters the skin until microfilariæ of the next generation are recovered from peripheral blood.

All persons of all ages and racial groups are susceptible to infection with *W. bancrofti*. In areas of high endemicity children are exposed early in life. Conditions highly favorable for continued propagation of the infection consist of human carriers with microfilariæ in their blood and appropriate mosquitoes breeding near human habitations serving as vectors.

Control

Control of Bancroft's filariasis can be effected by (1) treatment of all microfilaria carriers in an endemic area and (2) elimination of the mosquito transmitters. Use of DDT as a larvicide and residual spray in and around habitations has been demonstrated to reduce infection in many communities, and when combined with Hetrazan therapy promises much in the control of the disease (March *et al.*, 1960).

Brugia malayi (Brug, 1927) Buckley, 1960
(Malayan filaria, causing Malayan filariasis)

The "sheathed" microfilaria of this species was first observed in blood films of natives of Sumatra by Lichtenstein (1927) who was unable to infect *Culex* mosquitoes with the living embryos. Brug (1927) designated the new organism *Filaria malayi*. Rao and Maplestone (1940), in India, and Bonne *et al.* (1941), in Indonesia, obtained and described the adult worms, while Buckley (1960) created the genus *Brugia* for this and two related species.

The geographical distribution of *B. malayi* is relatively extensive (Fig. 141, page 295), including Korea, Central and South China, Indo-China, the Philippines, Malaya, Sumatra, Celebes, Borneo, Ceram, New Guinea, Ceylon, and at least four states of India. In some of these countries *B. malayi* is coextensive with *W. bancrofti*, and undoubtedly some of the earlier records incorrectly reported *W. bancrofti* when they should have been *B. malayi*.

A series of studies by British workers in Malaya and East Africa have shown that *Brugia malayi* occurs in cats and monkeys, as well as man, and is closely related to two other species of filariæ which normally occur in other mammals but may be transmissible to man (Laing *et al.*, 1960). Since these three species are morphologically similar and differ in some important respects from *Wuchereria bancrofti* (Buckley, 1960), they have been placed in the new genus *Brugia*, viz., *B. malayi* (Brug, 1927) Buckley, 1960, *B. pahangi* (Buckley and Edeson, 1956) Buckley, 1960, and *B. patei* (Buckley, Nelson and Heisch, 1958) Buckley, 1960. These species of *Brugia* differ from *W. bancrofti* in the following respects: (1) the microfilariæ all have terminal caudal nuclei, whereas those of *W. bancrofti* do not; (2) the male's left spicule has a complex center section lacking in *W. bancrofti*; (3) its caudal papillæ are typically 11 in number (four pairs of ventrolaterals, one pair of post-anals and an unpaired pre-anal). whereas in *W. bancrofti* there are typically about 24, with the greater number in the ventrolateral group, and (4) the adult worms are much smaller than *W. bancrofti*. Like *W. bancrofti*, these species live in the lymphatics of the mammalian host.

B. *pahangi* has been found in wild and domestic cats, dog, tiger, loris and musang in Malaya. In a human volunteer experimentally inoculated with infective larvæ of this filaria no microfilariæ appeared in the blood but on two occasions the inoculations were followed by severe symptoms typical of tropical eosinophilia (Buckley, 1958a, 1958b). The mosquito vectors are species of *Mansonia* and *Armigeres*. B. *patei* has been found in the dog, cat and genet cat in East Africa. The vector mosquitoes are species of *Mansonia* and *Aëdes*.

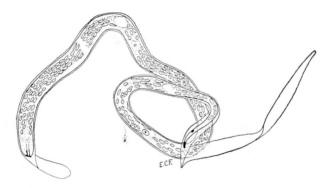

Fig. 147.—Microfilaria of *Brugia malayi*. × 666. (Original camera lucida drawing from blood film of Celebes carrier, Brug material, from Faust's *Human Helminthology*, Lea & Febiger, Philadelphia.)

Morphology, Biology and Life Cycle

The adults of *B. malayi* (Fig. 106 *l*, page 223) resemble those of *W. bancrofti* in most respects but are specifically distinguishable (Buckley and Edeson, 1956; Buckley, 1960). The males measure 22 to 23 mm. in length by 88 microns in cross section. Their posterior end is tightly coiled. The female measures 5 cm. long by 160 microns in cross section. The most distinctive morphologic character of *W. malayi* consists of the two cells in the tip of the tail of the microfilaria (Fig. 147 and Table 4, p. 297).

Although the microfilaria of *B. malayi* exhibits nocturnal periodicity in its migration through cutaneous blood vessels, this is not as absolute as in the periodic strains of *W. bancrofti*, and in some areas periodicity is more pronounced than in others (Wilson *et al.*, 1958).

Clinical Aspects

The discovery of two species generically related to *B. malayi* in Southeast Asia and East Africa has made generalizations concerning the clinical aspects of infection with this group inadvisable. Early reports (Lichtenstein, 1927; Brug, 1927) indicated that Malayan filariasis was associated with elephantiasis of the legs. More recently Turner (1959) has described a clinical course similar to that of Bancroftian filariasis manifested by lymphadenopathy, lymphadenitis and eventual elephantiasis, in which the lower limbs were primarily affected.

Specific diagnosis of Malayan filaria is based on demonstration of the characteristic microfilaria in night-time blood. Wilson (1950), Field (1951) and Turner (1959) have reported favorably on the value of *Hetrazan* (diethylcarbamazine) in the treatment of this disease (see Table 7, p. 420).

Epidemiology

B. malayi is transmitted by mosquitoes of the genera *Mansonia* and *Anopheles*. Species of *Mansonia* are intermediate hosts almost exclusively of *B. malayi* while certain species of *Anopheles* are equally good transmitters of *malayi*, *bancrofti* and malaria parasites. In areas where *Mansonia* is the vector Malayan filariasis is typically rural (Field, 1951); where an anopheline is involved the disease is essentially urban or suburban (Feng, 1936).

Control

In endemic areas of Malayan filariasis where species of *Anopheles* are the vectors, anti-larval spraying and residual spraying of homes with DDT will provide effective control as it does in malaria. In localities where *Mansonia* species are involved and the infection is rural, the problem is more complicated, since the larvæ of these mosquitoes obtain oxygen by inserting their breathing tubes into the hanging roots of water plants. Workers in Travancore (India), recommended periodic removal of these plants from the water as a practical control measure, and others have found this procedure effective in reducing the incidence of new infections. The use of 2-4-D (Weedone) has been effective in killing *Pistia* in Ceylon and has been accompanied by notable reduction in new cases of this disease. Treatment of carriers with Hetrazan renders the great majority free of microfilariæ but control programs based on periodic mass treatments have not proved completely effective due in part to difficulties in reaching scattered populations in endemic areas, to frequency of severe reactions to the treatment, and to the possible influence of reservoirs of infection in animals (Turner, 1959).

Onchocerca volvulus (Leuckart, 1893) Railliet and Henry, 1910
(Convoluted filaria, causing onchocercosis)

Historical and Geographical Notes

This species was first described by Leuckart (1893) from material removed from a native of the Gold Coast, West Africa. In 1915, Robles found the same worm in a native worker on a coffee plantation in Guatemala, on the western slope of the Continental Divide, and demonstrated its causal relationship to blindness. In 1926, Blacklock proved that a blackfly, *Simulium damnosum*, was an essential intermediate host and transmitter of the disease in Africa.

O. *volvulus* is distributed throughout extensive areas of tropical Africa. In the Western Hemisphere, to which it was probably introduced from Africa, it is established on the Pacific Coast of Guatemala, the adjacent Mexican states of Chiapas and Oaxaca, and in parts of Venezuela and nearby Dutch Guiana.

Morphology, Biology and Life Cycle

Adult Worms.—The adults of O. *volvulus* (usually as a mated pair) are intricately coiled up in the midst of a dense, fibrous, subcutaneous tumor but occasionally females have been found free in connective tissue. The nodules may develop on any part of the body but are frequently located near the junction of long bones or on the scalp. In most instances they can be seen or palpated but there are cases in which microfilariæ are present in the skin without evidence of nodules.

The worms themselves (Fig. 106 *n*, page 223) are wiry, creamy-white threads which are bluntly rounded at both ends. The males measure 19 to 42 mm. in length by 130 to 210 microns in cross section. They are tightly recurved ventrally at the posterior end. The females measure 33.5 to 50 cm. in length by 270 to 400 microns in cross section.

The Microfilariæ.—The embryos are coiled within a broadly ovoidal egg membrane in the inner end of the uterus but become uncoiled and elongated as they reach the outer end. On leaving the mother worm they escape from the eggshell, *i.e.*, they become unsheathed. They are of two sizes, 150 to 287 by 5 to 7 microns and 285 to 368 by 6 to 9 microns. The anterior and posterior ends of this microfilaria are illustrated in Figure 143, p. 298. The free microfilariæ remain in the superficial lymphatic vessels and connective tissue of the skin and rarely, if ever, get into the blood stream except accidentally.

The Insect Phase of the Life Cycle.—Although *Simulium* flies are blood suckers, they also imbibe tissue juices, otherwise they would not have an opportunity to pick up the microfilariæ of O. *volvulus*. The microfilariæ taken up by *Simulium* migrate from the dorsal food reservoir, rather than the midgut, directly to the thoracic muscles, where they are transformed into rhabditoid and then filariform larvæ with two molts of cuticle. This requires a minimum of 6 days, during which time there is a cytophysiological reaction on the part of the thoracic muscle fibers, leading to intrasyncytial localization of the larvæ (Lebied, 1961). Thereafter the larvæ proceed down to the tip of the fly's proboscis, ready to infect the next human host. The species of *Onchocerca* which parasitize horses and cattle are specifically distinguishable from O. *volvulus* in their microfilarial stage.

The Biological Incubation Period.—There is almost no specific information concerning this filaria from the time it invades the skin until it reaches maturity in a subcutaneous nodule. The worms mature slowly and may require as long as a year to reach full size, but occasionally *Onchorcerca* nodules have been detected in infants 3 to 10 months old. Some of the tumors appear on covered parts of the body not accessible to the fly, suggesting that the invading worms may have migrated some distance from the site of entry before they were trapped by host tissue infiltration. Yet an overwhelming majority are located on or near exposed areas of the skin.

Pathogenesis and Symptomatology

The Parent Nodules.—With relatively infrequent exceptions the presence of the maturing or adult *O. volvulus* causes a local cellular reaction of a fibrocytic nature; this results in encapsulation of the worms which lie tangled within the dense fibrous matrix (Fig. 148). Occasionally the tumor presents an abscessing center due to bacterial invasion and rarely the para-

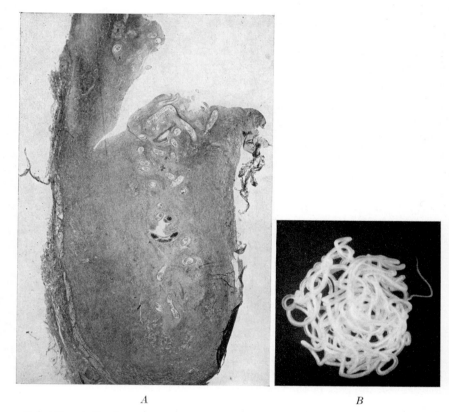

A   *B*

Fig. 148.—*A*, Section through *Onchocerca volvulus* tumor removed from the scalp of a Guatemalan patient, × 6. (Original photomicrograph, from Faust's *Human Helminthology*, Lea & Febiger, Philadelphia); *B*, Tangled pair of parent worms (female stouter, male more filiform) digested out of nodule, × 3. (Original, courtesy of Dr. Luis Maz-, zotti, Mexico, D. F.)

sites escape encapsulation and migrate through the tissues like *Loa loa*. There may be only a single nodule or the lesions may be numerous. In Guatemala and Mexico the number rarely exceeds 6 (Puig Solanes *et al.*, 1948). In Africans the nodules are more commonly found on the trunk, buttocks or elbows than on the head (Fig. 149). *S. damnosum* usually "bites" close to the ground. In native Americans nodules most commonly are on the scalp (Fig. 150). The parent nodule is typically painless and is benign.

Sensitization Reaction.—Almost invariably *O. volvulus* infection provokes an acute sensitization reaction, particularly noted in the skin, which may reveal pigmentation dermatitis, licheniform, eczematoid or erysipelatoid lesions (Goldman and Ortiz, 1946), or extreme dermatoglyphia in fair-skinned patients. There is typically a high eosinophilic leukocytosis, while there may be a tissue concentration of eosinophils, plasma cells and at times

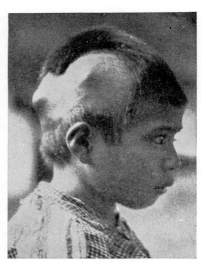

Fig. 149   Fig. 150

Fig. 149.—*Onchocerca volvulus* nodules in region of trochanter and at elbow of African patient. (After Blacklock, Ann. Trop. Med. & Parasitol., from Faust's *Human Helminthology*, Lea & Febiger, Philadelphia.)

Fig. 150.—*Onchocerca volvulus* nodules on scalp of a Guatemalan boy. The right eye shows evidence of partial blindness. (After Strong, in Onchocerciasis, 1934, courtesy of Harvard Univ. Press, from Faust's *Human Helminthology*, Lea & Febiger, Philadelphia.)

giant cells near the nodules. Moreover, the migration of microfilariæ through the connective tissue of the skin characteristically produces a severe pruritic dermatitis.

Ocular Lesions.—Beginning with Robles' original observations (1915) workers in Guatemala and Mexico, later in Africa and Venezuela, have noted the causal relationship of onchocercosis to ophthalmitis and loss of vision. The microfilariæ of *O. volvulus* invade all of the tissues of the eye, producing punctate, vascular or interstitial keratitis, iritis, chorioretinitis, congestion and punctate hemorrhage around the limbus of the eye, congestion and edema of the conjunctiva, exudation into the vitreous and later degenerative changes of the optic nerve. The first complaints are of impaired vision, then intense photophobia, partial loss of vision, and finally, in many instances, total blindness. Puig Solanes *et al.* (1948) have found that ocular damage is commoner in persons who have multiple *Onchocerca* tumors, and Noble (1952) has observed that in eastern Venezuela where the infection is relatively light the eye lesions are minimal. Extensive studies of the causes of blindness in West Africa have convinced Rodger (1959) that the inflammatory ocular lesions of onchocerciasis result from death of the microfilariæ in the tissues of the eye, with an underlying deficiency in vitamin A.

Diagnosis

Diagnosis can not be made from blood films since the microfilariæ of *O. volvulus* do not circulate through the blood stream. Routinely thin skin shavings about 0.5 cm. in diameter are removed with a sharp razor blade. If the microfilariæ are abundant a single biopsy from the small of the back will suffice; if they are scant in number it may be desirable to obtain specimens from each shoulder blade, posterior cervical triangle, intercostal area and ileal crest. The specimen is placed in a drop of tepid physiologic salt solution on a microscopic slide and mounted with a cover-glass. Microfilariæ will soon emerge from positive tissues and move about actively in the medium. Experienced clinicans working in endemic areas will also be able to demonstrate the organisms with the ophthalmic microscope.

While the intradermal test, employing filaria antigen, is diagnostically positive in about 90% of proven cases, skin biopsy is a more practical procedure.

Treatment

As soon as a subcutaneous nodule has been demonstrated to be an *Onchocerca* tumor the first and most important therapeutic task is to excise the nodule. This has a twofold clinical purpose, *i.e.*, (1) to forestall further opportunity for microfilariæ to damage the eye, and (2) to reduce the likelihood of hypersensitization when chemotherapy is instituted.

Suramin (Naphuride sodium, Bayer 205) is a very valuable drug in the treatment of onchocercosis, since it not only kills the circulating microfilariæ but also, somewhat more slowly, destroys the parent worms (Burch and Ashburn, 1951). This drug is fairly well tolerated, but its practical disadvantage consists in the route of administration, namely, by vein, which poses a serious problem for ambulatory clinics in endemic areas.

Hetrazan (diethylcarbamazine) has the advantage of oral administration, and is probably as effective in killing the microfilariæ in onchocercosis as it is in Bancroft's filariasis when full therapeutic dosage is attained, but difficulty is experienced with respect to allergic side reactions to a much greater degree in onchocercosis. Ruiz Reyes (1951) states that with a standard course of treatment, consisting of 2 mgm. per kilo body weight 2 or 3 times daily for 10 days, there are manifestations of intense pruritic dermatitis, edema, conjunctivitis, adenopathy, fever and intestinal colic for the first 4 days of treatment, after which these symptoms tend to subside.

He recommends three or four courses of treatment during the first year and two courses during each of the following years. Hawking (1955) suggests preliminary treatment with Hetrazan to kill the microfilariæ, and subsequent use of suramin sodium, which is more likely to be lethal to the adult worms (see Table 7, p. 420).

Prognosis

In untreated heavy infections, the prognosis is poor.

Epidemiology

Man is the only definitive host of *O. volvulus*, and species of *Simulium* are the intermediate hosts and transmitters. The flies breed in fast-flowing mountain streams above the coastal plains and the adults usually bite man and other animals close to their breeding places, but the flies may be carried in air currents and thus pick up, incubate and transmit the infection many kilometers distant from where they breed. Persons bathing or washing clothes in the clean mountain streams or drawing water from this supply are frequently bitten by the flies. In many endemic zones the disease is associated with coffee planting; laborers on these plantations are more commonly infected than supervisory personnel because of greater exposure. The flies do not enter well-shaded homes.

Control

In order to effect control of onchocercosis the attack should be carried out against (1) the human carrier and (2) the transmitter. Ruiz Reyes (1951) emphasizes the public health importance of periodic denodulization to prevent the development of new broods of microfilariæ and adequate Hetrazan therapy to kill circulating microfilariæ.

Vector control in onchocercosis is considerably more difficult than that presented in Bancroft's filariasis, because the transmitters breed in swiftly running mountain streams and do not ordinarily enter living quarters of the victims. Larvicides sprayed on the flowing water are rapidly dissipated and residual spraying of homes to kill the adult flies is ineffective since the flies seldom invade the living quarters. In the endemic areas of Mexico, it has been discovered (Vargas, 1952; Nettel, 1952) that the breeding places are much more circumscribed than the areas of human infection. Once the former have been mapped, the larvicidal application of DDT during the dry season when the streams are at pool stage, narrows the attack within practical limits.

Loa loa (Cobbold, 1864) Castellani and Chalmers, 1913
(The "eye worm," causing loaiasis)

The first authentic record of this worm was provided in 1770, by Mongin, who reported the extraction of a female specimen from the front of the eye of a Negress in St. Domingo, West Indies. Other cases among African slaves in the American Tropics continued to be described until 1844. The first indigenous observation from Africa is attributed to Guyot (1778). The worm was not specifically described until 1864, and another long interval elapsed before Connal and Connal (1921, 1922) conclusively proved Manson's hypothesis (1895) that the mango-fly, *Chrysops dimidiata*, is a necessary intermediate host and transmitter.

The endemic zone of loaiasis is limited to West and Central Africa, where the infection is widely distributed. Snijders (1935) found high prevalence (90%) in some villages of the former Belgian Congo, and Gordon *et al.* (1950) state that it is a common infection in the Cameroons and Southern Nigeria. Caucasians as well as natives in these countries contract the infection.

Morphology, Biology and Life Cycle

The Adult Worms.—The adults (Fig. 106 *i*, page 223) inhabit the subcutaneous tissues, through which the worms are continually migrating. They are thread-like, whitish, have a bossed cuticle, and taper gradually towards both ends. The head is unarmed. The male measures 30 to 34

FIG. 151.—Microfilaria of *Loa loa*. × 666. (After Fülleborn, from Faust's *Human Helminthology*, Lea & Febiger, Philadelphia.)

mm. in length by 0.35 to 0.43 mm. in diameter. Its caudal end is curved ventrally. The female measures 50 to 70 mm. in length by 0.5 mm. in diameter. The embryos develop as tightly coiled objects within ovoidal thin shells in the inner end of the two uteri but become uncoiled and elongated in the outer portion of the uteri. They retain their sheath when deposited by the mother worms.

The Microfilariæ.—The microfilariæ of *Loa loa* exhibit day-time (diurnal) periodicity in peripheral blood, displaying stiff, ungraceful but rapid movements among the red blood cells. These sheathed microfilariæ (Fig. 143, p. 298, Fig. 151) are relatively large, measuring 250 to 300 microns in length by 6 to 8.5 microns in mid-diameter, and have a core of nucleated cells which extend without interruption into the tip of the tail. The morphologic features which distinguish the microfilaria of this species from that of *Wuchereria bancrofti* and *B. malayi* are provided in Table 4 (page 297).

The Insect Phase of the Life Cycle.—When the microfilariæ of *Loa loa* are ingested by the day-biting *Chrysops dimidiata* or *C. silacea* feeding on a human carrier, they soon become exsheathed in the midgut of the fly and migrate to muscular and connective tissues, undergo transformation to the filariform larva (Connal and Connal, 1922), then migrate down to the tip of the fly's proboscis, ready to be transferred to the next human host about the tenth day after the infective meal. Gordon and Crewe (1953) state that these larvæ begin to leave the proboscis "as soon as, but not before, the labium of the insect begins to bend following the entrance of the fascicle into the host's tissues."

The Biological Incubation Period.—Very little is known concerning the development of *Loa loa* after it enters the human skin. Gordon and Crewe (*l.c.*) state that the invading larvæ migrate down to the muscular tissue. As in other filaria infections of man, the incubation period may require as long as 12 months. During this period and after maturity the females (and

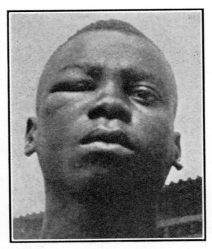

Fig. 152.—Unilateral palpebral edema in *Loa loa* infection at the time a female worm is migrating across the front of the right eye. In Dubois and van den Berghe's *Diseases of Warm Climates*, courtesy Grune & Stratton, from Faust and Russell's *Clinical Parasitology*, Lea & Febiger, Philadelphia.)

males?) migrate through the subcutaneous tissues of the body and periodically reach the head, crossing in front of the eyes under the corneal conjunctiva during each excursion. The life expectancy of the adult worms is at least 4 and as much as 15 years.

Pathogenesis and Symptomatology

In their migrations through various parts of the body the adult worms can be demonstrated in the extremities, trunk and head. The worms are more of a nuisance than a cause of severe local tissue reaction, although almost always there is a temporary inflamed tract ("fugitive swelling" or 'Calabar swelling") in the wake of each worm. Moreover, migration through the bulbar conjunctivæ is always troublesome and is attended with considerable pain and edema (Fig. 152).

Dubois and van den Berghe (1948) recognize three clinical types of loaiasis, *viz.*, (1) essentially symptomless carriers; (2) patients with demonstrable adult worms and microfilariæ who have allergic reactions, including edema, pruritus and eosinophilia, and (3) patients with allergic manifestations but without demonstrable adults or microfilariæ, possibly due to death of the worms before they reach maturity.

Diagnosis

After the end of the biological incubation period the microfilariæ of *Loa loa* can be found in day-time blood except in those cases in which the worms apparently fail to mature. For demonstration and differential diagnosis thick-blood films stained by the Giemsa technic are recommended (see "TECHNICAL AIDS," page 434). In case the organisms are not demonstrable but the patient's history and the clinical findings suggest loaiasis, intradermal testing with filaria antigen will almost always provide an immediate postive reaction in individuals who have the disease. (For this and other immunologic tests in loaiasis, see "TECHNICAL AIDS," pages 450–451.)

Treatment

The classical method of treatment consists of extracting the parent worm at the time it is migrating across the front of the eye. This requires experience and skill, to prevent damage to the corneal conjunctiva and the escape of the worm into the deeper tissues of the orbit.

Since the introduction of Hetrazan (diethylcarbamazine) in the treatment of loaiasis, with few exceptions the results with this drug have been consistently favorable, irrespective of the clinical type of the disease (see Table 7, page 420.) Ordinarily the use of this anthelmintic produces no serious side effects. (Compare with onchocercosis, page 308). Marked clinical improvement may be expected with Hetrazan therapy in symptomatic cases. Madell and Spingarn (1953) have reported success of suramin sodium and failure of Hetrazan in a case of thoracic loaiasis.

Prognosis

The prognosis is excellent with specific therapy.

Epidemiology

The distribution of *Loa loa* corresponds to that of the mango flies *Chrysops dimidiata* and *C. silacea*. They breed in relatively clear, flowing streams in high-canopied rain forests and come out to nearby clearings to bite man. In this way they pick up the microfilariæ from human carriers and later, after a period of incubation, inoculate other persons with the infective-stage larvæ.

Control

Reduction in the infection rate in native populations in endemic territories will depend on a two-pronged attack, *viz.*, (1) chemotherapeutic destruction of the microfilariæ in the human host and (2) use of larvicides to kill the breeding stages of the mango-flies which transmit the infection from person to person. Bites by these flies may be avoided for short periods of time by application of dimethyl phthalate to exposed areas of the skin.

Acanthocheilonema streptocerca (Macfie and Corson, 1922)
Faust (in Craig and Faust, 1951) and
Acanthocheilonema perstans (Manson, 1891) Railliet, Henry and Langeron, 1912

A. streptocerca was first described by Macfie and Corson (1922) from the microfilarial stage seen in skin biopsies of 45% of natives of a Gold Coast village, during a survey to determine the incidence of *Onchocerca volvulus*, *A. perstans* and other human filariæ. *A. streptocerca* has a wide distribution in the western, central and northeastern parts of the former Belgian Congo, with a high incidence in the central area. In 1946, Peel and Chardome for the first time discovered adult worms (females only), in the cutaneous connective tissue of chimpanzees (*Pan paniscus* and *P. satyrus*). The microfilariæ are unsheathed, taper at both ends and have a crooked posterior end (Fig. 143 *f*, page 298). They are somewhat shorter (180 to 240 microns long) and more slender (3 microns in diameter) than the microfilariæ of *Loa loa* and *Wuchereria* (Fig. 143 *a–c*). The biting gnat *Culicoides grahami* serves as intermediate host and vector. Most infected persons appear to be symptomless carriers but cutaneous edema and elephantiasis in some infected natives in the Congo may be due to this filaria. Diagnosis is made by skin biopsy deep enough to include dermal tissue, in which the microfilariæ will be found in positive cases. Chemotherapy and control measures have not been developed.

Mature worms of *A. perstans* were first found by Daniels (1898) in aborigines of British Guiana. They were identified by Manson as the definitive stage of microfilariæ which he had previously described from blood films of natives from the Congo, and for which he had proposed the species name "*perstans*" (1891). This worm has an extensive distribution on the east coast of South America from Panama to Argentina, in western and central Africa and is mildly endemic in Algeria and Tunis. Man is the important and possibly the only definitive host. The intermediate hosts and transmitters in Africa are the biting gnat *Culicoides austeni* (Sharp, 1928; Hopkins and Nicholas, 1953) and possibly *C. grahami*. The adults (Fig. 106, *f* page 223) live in body cavities. No pathogenicity has been demonstrated in persons who have this infection. Diagnosis is made on discovery in blood films of the unsheathed microfilariæ, which measure about 200 microns in length by 4.5 microns in diameter, and their differentiation from this stage of *A. streptocerca*, *Loa loa* and *Wuchereria bancrofti* in Africa, and *Mansonella ozzardi* and *W. bancrofti* in South America (See Fig. 143).

Mansonella ozzardi (Manson, 1897) Faust, 1929

This filaria was first obtained by Ozzard as a microfilaria in a blood survey of Carib Indians who lived inland in British Guiana, and was described as a new species by Manson (1897). It is indigenous to Latin America from northern Argentina to Yucatan and in the West Indies (Puerto Rico, St. Vincent, Dominica). The adults (Fig. 106 *k*, p. 223) live in body cavities, threaded into mesenteries or embedded in visceral fat. The microfilariæ are "unsheathed," delicate, graceful objects measuring 185 to 200 microns in length by 5 microns in diameter, and are non-periodic in their migration through peripheral blood. The biting gnat *Culicoides furens* has been found to be the intermediate host and transmitter in British Guiana (Buckley, 1934), and *C. paraënsis* is circumstantially suspected to be the vector in northern

Argentina (Romaña and Wygodzinsky, 1950). In the State of Amazonas, Brazil, Cerqueira (1959) has demonstrated *Simulium amazonicum* to be a good potential transmitter of this filaria. No symptoms have been attributed to this infection.

Dirofilaria conjunctivæ (Addario, 1885)
Desportes, 1939–1940

On a number of occasions immature filariæ have been removed from tumors or abscess pockets in various anatomical locations of the human body. Desportes (1939–1940) has provided evidence that they are assignable to the genus *Dirofilaria*. Some of the cases involved the palpebral conjunctivæ and other tissues of the eye; in one the filaria was obtained from the upper lip; in others from an arm, and in still others from the gastrosplenic ligament, the infra-mammary region (Faust *et al.*, 1952). The countries in which human infections have been discovered include France, Corsica, Italy, Sicily, Trieste, Hungary, Roumania, Macedonia, Turkey, India, Central Africa, Thailand, Argentina, Colombia, and southern U.S.A.

Man does not provide a suitable environment for these worms, since they are rarely able to reach maturity in the human host. Moreover, it is highly probable that this filaria is a relatively common parasite of some animal closely associated with man and that the infection has a cosmopolitan distribution.

Dracunculus medinensis (Linnæus, 1758) Gallandant, 1773
(The dragon worm, Medina worm or Guinea worm, causing dracunculosis or dracontiasis)

This worm has been known since the days of antiquity. Priests of ancient Egypt, the Hebrews, Greeks and Romans were all familiar with it. Fedtschenko (1869) first provided evidence that the infection required a species of "water flea" (*Cyclops*) as an intermediate host.

Dracunculus medinensis has a distribution throughout tropical Africa, Arabia, Transjordania, Iraq, Iran, Afghanistan, Turkestan, southeastern U.S.S.R., Pakistan, western India, Madras Presidency of India and parts of Indonesia. It apparently no longer occurs endemically in the Western Hemisphere. In reservoir hosts, *D. medinensis* is found in fur-bearing mammals in North America, in the dog in China and has also been reported from horses, cattle, leopards, polecats and monkeys in endemic areas of the Old World. One autochthonous human case has been recorded from Korea (Kobayashi, 1928).

Morphology, Biology and Life Cycle

Dracunculus medinensis is commonly referred to as a filaria. While it grossly resembles the true filaria worms (Filarioidea), it lacks a microfilarial stage and employs as intermediate host a primitive aquatic arthropod rather than one specialized in piercing the host's skin. Furthermore, the adult worms are distinctly different from the filariæ, *i.e.*, the females are very much larger than the males; in gravid females the vulva becomes atrophied, the vagina disintegrates and first-stage rhabditoid larvæ are discharged from a prolapsed segment of the uterus through a rupture in the body wall near the mouth.

The adults of *D. medinensis* are elongated cylindrical threads (males) or cords (females), which are bluntly rounded at the anterior end and curved ventrally. The male measures from 12 to 20 mm. in length by 0.4 mm. in diameter. The female measures from 70 to 120 cm. in length by 0.9 to 1.7 mm. in diameter. The worms develop to maturity in body cavities and visceral connective tissues. As soon as the female becomes gravid it migrates to the subcutaneous tissues and produces a papule in the dermis. Within one to a few days this changes to a blister, which ruptures. On immersion in fresh water a loop of the uterus is prolapsed and on contact with the water bursts open, discharging a swarm of delicate, wiry rhabditoid larvæ which have a long attenuated tail, a transversely striated cuticle and a pair of anal papillæ set into deep pockets.

The Extrinsic Phase of the Life Cycle.—The larva discharged into the water moves about stiffly, at times coiling on itself to produce the appearance of the Greek letter *alpha*. This apparently attracts Cyclops which ingest the larvæ. On arrival in the arthropod's midgut, the larva penetrates into the hemocele and, following one molt of cuticle, becomes infective in about 10 days. If the Cyclops is ingested by man or other suitable hosts the infection is successfully transferred. A considerable number of species of Cyclops have been incriminated as natural hosts of *D. medinensis*.

The Biological Incubation Period.—On arrival in the duodenum of the definitive host, the larvæ are digested out of the Cyclops and migrate through the intestinal wall to loose connective tissue, usually in a retroperitoneal location. Here they grow into adult worms over a period of 8 to 12 months.

Pathogenesis and Symptomatology

The biological incubation period is characteristically symptomless. Fairley and Liston (1925) state that a few hours preceding the appearance of the skin lesion there are pronounced systemic prodromata, consisting of erythema and urticarial rash, with intense pruritus, nausea, vomiting, diarrhea, severe dyspnea, giddiness and at times syncope, all resulting from the activation and migration of the gravid female. Then a reddish papule develops at the site where the head of the worm penetrates the dermis, with a vesicular center and indurated collar, and measuring 2 to 7 mm. in diameter. The lesion is most frequently found between the metatarsal bones (Fig. 153), or on the ankles or calf of the leg, but it may develop at a knee joint, on the hands, thighs, arms, trunk, buttocks, inguinal region, scrotum, shoulders, angle of the jaw, fronto-nasal area, or soft palate. If the worm fails to reach the body surface it dies and disintegrates, at times producing a sterile abscess, or it may become calcified (Jelliffe, 1950).

The blister is typically sterile before it bursts, and contains macrophages, eosinophils and neutrophils in a yellowish fluid. As soon as it ruptures, releasing the highly allergenic fluid, the patient's symptoms abate, but sepsis frequently develops in the worm's tunnel.

Although multiple *Dracunculus* infections are by no means rare (occasionally as many as 15 to 50), relatively few patients have more than 6 and the majority only 1. But reëxposure in highly endemic areas provides opportunity for reinfection, which is accepted fatalistically by native populations.

Diagnosis

There is no reliable means of diagnosing dracunculosis until the gravid female worm migrates to the skin and produces the typical blister, although in endemic regions the hypersensitization reaction which immediately precedes the patent infection can be regarded as a relatively certain prodrome of the fully developed infection. As soon as the worm projects its anterior extremity out of the skin, specific diagnosis can be made.

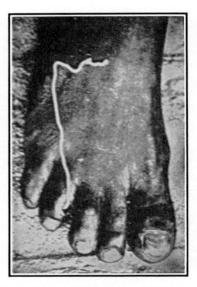

Fig. 153.—Female *Dracunculus medinensis* partially removed from a metatarsal lesion. (After Castellani and Chalmer's Tropical Medicine, from Faust's *Human Helminthology*, Lea & Febiger, Philadelphia.)

Treatment

Prompt administration of an anti-histaminic drug is indicated to relieve the prodromal symptoms and prevent possibly fatal anaphylatic shock.

From ancient times natives have learned to wind the emerging end of the worm on a small stick, an inch or two a day, using gentle traction to prevent breaking the worm in two within the cutaneous tunnel. In this way the complete worm is eventually extracted. Elliott (1942) successfully treated dracunculosis by instilling an emulsion of phenothiazine, lanolin and olive oil into the worm's tunnel and adjacent tissues.

Prognosis

Dracunculosis is temporarily disabling and occasionally results in chronic invalidism, but the prognosis is usually good.

Epidemiology

In all areas where man is involved the epidemiology is concerned solely or almost exclusively with the infection in the human host and species of *Cyclops*. *D. medinensis* is acquired from swallowing water containing the infected arthropod. Human customs of bathing, washing clothes and drawing water from open wells or ponds are responsible for propagation of this disease. Moreover, the incubation period in the human host corresponds to the annual visits of pilgrims, whose ablutions provide the inoculum for the Cyclops and at the same time new infection from drinking the infested water.

Control

Methods must be developed to prevent villagers from infesting wells and ponds with viable larvæ of the worm, so that their drinking water will be protected. Furthermore, the introduction of plankton-feeding fish into all bodies of water in which Cyclops breed will appreciably reduce the number of these intermediate hosts.

SUMMARY

1. True filaria worms have a *microfilaria* which distinguishes them from all other groups of nematodes. This is deposited by the mother worm, either with the eggshell stretched out to accommodate itself to the uncoiled embryo, *i.e.*, sheathed, or without the shell, *i.e.*, unsheathed. The microfilariæ migrate to the skin where they are found in bloodvessels, lymphatics or cutaneous connective tissue. When picked up by certain skin-piercing arthropods they transform into rhabditoid larvæ and then the infective filariform larval stage. When the arthropod next punctures the skin of the definitive host, the larvæ enter the skin and migrate to the site where they develop into mature worms.
2. Seven species of filariæ are important natural parasites of man. *Wuchereria bancrofti* and *Brugia malayi* reside in lymphatic vessels; *Onchocerca volvulus* is found in subcutaneous nodules; *Loa loa* migrates through the subcutaneous tissues; *Acanthocheilonema perstans* and *Mansonella ozzardi* live in body cavities, and *A. streptocerca* is adapted to the connective tissues of the skin.
3. *Wuchereria bancrofti* is most frequently found in lymphatic vessels in the region of the groin and pelvic organs. The "sheathed" microfilariæ get into the blood stream and migrate to the cutaneous circulation, in most geographical areas at night. Domestic and semi-domestic mosquitoes serve as intermediate hosts and transmitters. *W. bancrofti* has an extensive distribution in warm climates. The adolescent and mature worms provoke an acute lymphangitis and lymphadenitis around, and retrograde to the sites where the worms are trapped. Such reactions tend to recur. Fibrosis of the lymph channels and surrounding tissues causes varicose groin gland and elephantiasis of the genitalia and lower extremities. Bacteria have not been demonstrated in the

primary lesion. During the time of microfilaremia the embryos may be seen in peripheral blood at night. Hetrazan clears the blood of microfilariæ and more slowly kills the parent worms. Control consists in administering Hetrazan to carriers to prevent infection of the mosquito vectors and use of DDT to kill the mosquitoes.

4. *Brugia malayi* likewise inhabits the lymphatic vessels, and in most respects is comparable to *W. bancrofti*. Hetrazan is an effective therapeutic. *B. malayi* is widely distributed in countries bordering on the China Sea, in Indonesia, eastern India and Ceylon. The urban type, transmitted by anopheline mosquitoes, can be controlled by residual spraying of homes with DDT; the rural type, transmitted by *Mansonia* mosquitoes, is controlled by mass treatment with Hetrazan and the application of 2-4-D (Weedone) to destroy the aquatic plants from the underwater parts of which the larvæ obtain oxygen.

5. *Onchocerca volvulus* is confined in its maturing and adult stage to fibrous tumors in the subcutaneous tissues. The unsheathed microfilariæ migrate through connective tissue, including that of the skin. They are transmitted by the coffee-fly *Simulium* which breeds in rapidly flowing mountain streams and bites in the open. The infection has extensive distribution in tropical Africa, on the Pacific slopes of Guatemala and adjacent states of Mexico, eastern Venezuela and Dutch Guiana. The worm nodules are benign but the infection produces systemic and dermal sensitization. The microfilariæ migrate into the tissues of the eye and the optic nerve and are responsible for failing vision and eventual blindness. Specific diagnosis is made by recovering the microfilariæ from superficial skin biopsies. Treatment consists in enucleation of the nodules as soon as they appear, administration of Hetrazan to kill the microfilariæ and suramin to kill the adults. Control of the insect vector requires application of DDT to the breeding sites.

6. *Loa loa* is a filaria of West and Central Africa. The parent worms migrate through subcutaneous tissues and periodically cross the front of the eye. The sheathed microfilariæ exhibit diurnal periodicity in the cutaneous blood vessels. The mango-fly *Chrysops*, which breeds in flowing streams, is the transmitter. There are (1) relatively symptomless microfilaria carriers; (2) persons with demonstrable worms who have symptoms of an allergic nature, and (3) those who have symptoms but in whom the causative agent can not be demonstrated. Hetrazan is usually vermicidal and symptomatically beneficial.

7. *Acanthocheilonema perstans*, which has an extensive distribution in tropical Africa, Atlantic coastal areas of South America, and some of the West Indies, and *Mansonella ozzardi*, which is indigenous to tropical America, live in body cavities. Their unsheathed microfilariæ constantly circulate in peripheral blood. *A. streptocerca*, which inhabits the deeper cutaneous connective tissues, is endemic in parts of Central Africa. Its unsheathed microfilariæ are found in the dermal layer of the skin. These three species are transmitted by the biting gnat *Culicoides*.

8. *Dirofilaria conjunctivæ* is the name applied to immature filariæ, almost exclusively females, which have been recovered from nodules or abscess

pockets of persons in Europe, Asian countries, Africa, Argentina and southern United States. Most of the lesions have involved the conjunctivæ and other tissues of the eye, the nares, lips and superficial tissues of the upper extremities. Man is regarded as an unfavorable host of this filaria, which is a natural parasite of some animal associated with man.

9. *Dracunculus medinensis* is a common parasite of man throughout tropical Africa, the Middle East and India. The worms mature in visceral tissues, after which the gravid female migrates to the skin and produces a blister. On contact with fresh water active first-stage larvæ are discharged from the lesion into the water. When ingested by the "water flea" *Cyclops*, the larvæ mature and are ready for transfer to the human host. Intense allergic reactions characteristically develop during migration of the female to the skin. Natives extract the worm a few inches each day, so as not to break it in two in the tissues and produce an abscess. Practical control measures are required (1) to prevent infected persons from entering infested water for bathing, washing their clothes and drawing water, (2) and to kill the Cyclops in the water.

REFERENCES

BUCKLEY, J. J. C. 1958a. Tropical Eosinophilia in Relation to Filarial Infections (*Wuchereria* spp.) of Animals. Trans. Roy. Soc. Trop. Med. & Hyg., *52*, 335–336.
————. 1958b. Occult Filarial Infections of Animal Origin as a Cause of Tropical Pulmonary Eosinophilia. East Afr. Med. J., *35*, 493–500.
————. 1960. On *Brugia* gen. nov. for *Wuchereria* spp. of the *"malayi"* group, *i.e.*, *W. malayi* (Brug, 1927), *W. pahangi* Buckley and Edeson, 1956, and *W. patei* Buckley, Nelson and Heisch, 1958. Ann. Trop. Med. & Parasitol., *54*, (1): 75–77.
BUCKLEY, J. J. C., and EDESON, J. F. B. 1956. On the Adult Morphology of *Wuchereria* sp. (*malayi?*) from a Monkey (*Macaca irus*) and from Cats in Malaya, and on *Wuchereria pahangi* n.sp. from a Dog and a Cat. J. Helm., *30*, 1–20.
BURCH, T. A., and ASHBURN, L. L. 1951. Experimental Therapy of Onchocerciasis with Suramin and Hetrazan. Am. J. Trop. Med., *31*, 617–623.
CERQUEIRA, N. L. 1959. Sôbre a transmissão da *Mansonella ozzardi*. Jornal Brasil. Med., *1*, 900–914.
DESPORTES, C. 1939–1940. *Filiaria conjunctivæ* Addario, 1885, parasite accidental de l'homme, est un Dirofilaria. Ann. de Parasitol., *17*, 380–404, 515–532.
DUBOIS, A., and VAN DEN BERGHE, L. 1948. *Diseases of the Warm Climates. Their Clinical Features, Diagnosis and Treatment.* 445 pp. Grune & Stratton, New York.
ELLIOTT, M. 1942. A New Treatment for Dracontiasis. Trans. R. Soc. Trop. Med. & Hyg., *35*, 291–298.
FAUST, E. C., AGOSIN, M., GARCIA-LAVERDE, A., SAYAD, W. Y., JOHNSON, V. M., and MURRAY, N. A. 1952. Unusual Findings of Filarial Infections in Man. Am. J. Trop. Med. & Hyg., *1*, 239–249.
FIELD, J. W. (Editor). 1951. *The Institute for Medical Research 1900–1950.* Studies from the Institute of Medical Research, Federation of Malaya, Jubilee Volume, No. 25, Kuala Lumpur, 389 pp.
GOLDMAN, L., and ORTIZ, L. F. 1946. Types of Dermatitis in American Onchocerciasis. Arch. Derm. & Syph., *53*, 79–93.
GORDON, R. M., and CREWE, W. 1953. The Entrance of *Loa loa* into the Mammalian Host and the First Stage of Its Migration to the Deeper Tissues. Trans. R. Soc. Trop. Med. & Hyg., *47*, 6.
HAWKING, FRANK. 1955. The Chemotherapy of Filarial Infection. Pharmacol. Rev., *7*, (2), 279–299.
HAWKING, F., and THURSTON, J. P. 1951. The Periodicity of Microfilariæ. I. The Distribution of Microfilariæ in the Body. II. The Explanation of Its Production. Trans. R. Soc. Trop. Med. & Hyg., *45*, 307–340.

HOPKINS, C. A. and NICHOLAS, W. L. 1953. The Development of the Infective Stage. of *Acanthocheilonema perstans* in Bred *Culicoides austeni*. Trans. R. Soc. Trop. Med. & Hyg., *47*, 6–7.

JELLIFFE, D. B. 1950. Calcification of a Guinea-Worm. J. Trop. Med. & Hyg., *53* 210–211.

KING, B. G. 1944. Early Filariasis Diagnosis and Clinical Findings. Am. J. Trop. Med., *24*, 285–298.

LAING, A. B. G., EDESON, J. F. B. and WHARTON, R. H. 1960. Studies on Filariasis in Malaya: The Vertebrate Hosts of *Brugia malayi* and *B. pahangi*. Ann. Trop. Med. & Parasitol., *54* (1): 92–99.

LEBIED, B. 1961. Introduction a la theorie de l'evolution intrasyncytiale des Filariata. I. Sur la phagocytose des microfilaires *Onchocerca volvulus* par les fibres musculaires thoraciques chez *Simulium*. Riv. Parassitol., *22*, 107–136.

MADELL, S. H., and SPINGARN, C. L. 1953. Unusual Thoracic Manifestations in Filariasis Due to *Loa loa*. Am. J. Med., *15*, 272–280.

MARCH, H. N., LAIGRET, J., KESSEL, J. F., and BAMBRDIGE, B. 1960. Reduction in the Prevalence of Clinical Filariasis in Tahiti Following Adoption of a Control Program. Am. J. Trop. Med. & Hyg., *9*, 180–184.

MICHAEL, P. 1944. Filariasis among Navy and Marine Personnel. Report of Laboratory Investigations. U. S. Naval Med. Bull., *42*, 1059–1074.

NETTEL, F. R. 1952. Oncocercosis. Revisión del problema entomólogico de la oncocercosis y plan para erradicación de *Simulium ochraceum* Walker. Med. (Méx.), *32*, 438–441, 482–493.

NOBLE, B. R. 1952. Contribución al estudio de la oncocercosis en Venezuela. Lesiones oculares. IV Congr. Panam. de Oftalmol., pp. 3–18.

O'CONNOR, F. W. 1923. Researches in the Western Pacific. Being a Report on the Results of the Expedition Sent from the London School of Tropical Medicine to the Ellice, Tokelau and Samoan Islands in 1921–1922. London Sch. Trop. Med Research Mem. Ser. 6, *4*, 1–57.

OTTO, G. F., BROWN, H. W., BELL, S. D., JR., and THETFORD, N. D. 1952. Arsenamide in the Treatment of Infections with the Periodic Form of the Filaria, *Wuchereria bancrofti*. Am. J. Trop. Med. & Hyg., *1*, 470–473.

PEEL, E., and CHARDOME, M. 1946. Note préliminaire. sur des filaridés de chimpanzés *Pan paniscus* et *Pan satyrus* au Congo Belge. Rev. Travaux Sci. Méd. Congo Belge, May, No. 5, 244–247.

PUIG SOLANES, M., VARGAS, L., MAZZOTTI, L., GUEVARA ROJAS, A., and NOBLE, B. 1948. Oncocercosis. Univ. Nac. de Méx., 129 pp.

RODGER, F. C. 1959. *Blindness in West Africa*, 1st ed., 262 pp., H. K. Lewis & Co. Ltd., London.

RUIZ REYES, F. 1951. Tratamiento de la oncocercosis con Dietilcarbamazine. Med. (Méx.), *31*, 495–504.

TURNER, L. H. 1959a. Studies on Filariasis in Malaya. The Clinical Features of Filariasis Due to *Wuchereria malayi*. Trans. Roy. Soc. Trop. Med. & Hyg., *53*, 154–169.

————. 1959b. Studies on Filariasis in Malaya. Treatment of *Wuchereria malayi* Filariasis with Diethylcarbamazine in Single Daily Doses. Ann. Trop. Med. & Parasitol., *53*, 180–188.

VARGAS, L. 1952. Consideraciones sobre una campana contra la oncocerciasis. Med. (Méx.), *32*, 189–192.

WEBSTER, E. H. 1946. Filiariasis among White Immigrants in Samoa. U. S. Naval Med. Bull., *46*, 186–192.

WILSON, T. 1950. Hetrazan in the Treatment of Filariasis Due to *Wuchereria malayi*. Trans. R. Soc. Trop. Med. & Hyg., *44*, 49–66.

WILSON, T., EDESON, J. F. B., WHARTON, R. H., REID, J. A., TURNER, L. H., and LAING, A. B. G. 1958. The Occurrence of Two Forms of *Wuchereria malayi* in Man. Trans. Roy. Soc. Trop. Med. & Hyg., *52*, 480–481.

YOKOGAWA, S. 1939. Investigations on the Mode of Infection of *Wuchereria bancrofti*. Second Report. Japan J. Med. Sci., Pt. V, Path., *4*, 197–204.

Chapter 14

Other Helminths Parasitizing Man

THORNY-HEADED WORMS (ACANTHOCEPHALANS)

THESE worms comprise the Phylum Acanthocephala. In some respects they resemble the tapeworms, although in no way is there evidence of close kinship (Van Cleave, 1941, 1948.)

All species of acanthocephalans are parasitic throughout their life cycle except for the interval required for completion of embryonation of the eggs on the ground or in water. The sexes are separate. The designation "thorny-headed" refers to the armature of spines on the proboscis.

The adult acanthocephalans (Fig. 154) are elongated, somewhat flattened sacs, rounded posteriorly and provided anteriorly with a spinose proboscis which serves as an efficient organ for attachment to the host's intestinal wall. This organ may be introverted into a proboscis sheath located in the anterior part of the body proper. The living worms are chalky to milky white or light pink in color. They lack segmentation but may have superficial transverse constrictions (*Macrocanthorhynchus hirudinaceus*) or bead-like annulations (*Moniliformis moniliformis*). They vary in size from a few millimeters to several centimeters in length. They have no digestive tract, absorbing nutriment from their body surface (Bullock, 1958), and their body cavity lacks a mesothelium. They possess one or more pairs of very elongate, possibly glandular organs, called *lemnisci*. In some species primitive nephridial structures have been described. There is a central nerve mass in or on the internal margin of the proboscis sheath.

The males (Fig. 154 *A*) are considerably smaller than the females. The male genitalia consist of a *genital pore* at the posterior extremity, surrounded by a campanulate *bursa*; two ovoidal *testes*, each with a *vas efferens*; several *cement glands* opening into a *cement-gland receptacle*, and a *suspensory ligament* which anchors the male organs in the body cavity.

The females (Fig. 154 *B*) are likewise provided with a *suspensory ligament*. The primary genital organ consists of a number of ovarian follicles or floating *ovaries*, from which many eggs are produced and float in the body cavity. After 3 (or at times 4) egg envelopes have been provided, the eggs are withdrawn from the body cavity through a muscular bell-shaped structure, the *selective apparatus*, into the *uterus*. They pass into the *vagina* and are discharged through a terminal pore.

Acanthocephalans are parasites of the intestine of their definitive hosts. The eggs are evacuated in the feces and deposited on the ground or in water, where they complete embryonation. On being ingested by species of arthropods, including dung beetles and cockroaches, the eggs hatch in the midgut, whereupon the emerging larvæ migrate through the gut wall

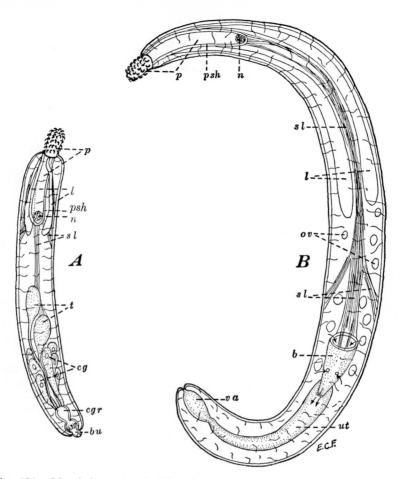

FIG. 154.—Morphology of male (*A*) and female (*B*) acanthocephalans. *b*, muscular bell; *bu*, bursa; *cg*, cement glands; *cgr*, cement gland receptacle; *l*, lemnisci; *n*, nerve mass; *ov*, floating ovaries; *p*, proboscis; *psh*, proboscis sheath; *sl*, suspensory ligaments; *t*, testes; *ut*, uterus; *va*, vagina. (Original, from Faust's *Human Helminthology*, Lea & Febiger, Philadelphia.)

into the hemal cavity and undergo development into *acanthor*, hatched from the egg; *acanthella*, the second larval stage, in which a rudimentary proboscis is developed, and *juvenile*, in which indications of adult structures may be found. When an appropriate vertebrate ingests an arthropod containing the juvenile forms, the young worms are digested out of their intermediate host, become attached to the definitive host's intestine, develop to maturity, mate, and egg-laying begins.

Two species of acanthocephalans have been reported as incidental parasites of man, viz., *Macracanthorhynchus hirudinaceus* and *Moniliformis moniliformis*.

to dark brown in color, intensely opaque and measure from 10 to 50 cm. in length. Their anterior ends are either somewhat elliptically pointed or bluntly rounded. The posterior end of the male is bifurcated behind the anus (Fig. 157, *B, G, I*) or at least grooved (Fig. 157, *D*), while that of the female is either entire or trifurcated.

The mature worms live in fresh water, where they slowly move about in a stiff, wiry fashion. Here they mate and the females discharge strings of eggs into the water. After a period of embryonation in water a larva breaks

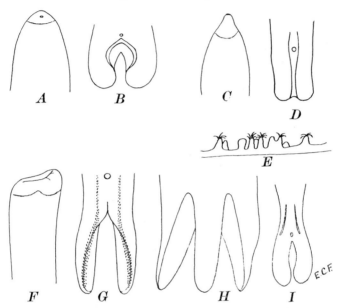

FIG. 157.—Diagnostic characters of some gordiid worms. *A*, anterior end and *B*, posterior end of male *Gordius villoti*, enlarged; *C*, anterior end and *D*, posterior end of male *Chordodes*, enlarged; *E*, section through cuticular papillæ and hairs of *Chordodes*, greatly enlarged; *F*, anterior end and *G*, posterior end of male *Paragordius varius*, enlarged; *H*, posterior end of female *P. varius*, enlarged; *I*, posterior end of male *Parachordodes*, enlarged. (*A, B, C, D, I*, adapted from Camerano; *E*, adapted from Römer; *F, G, H*, adapted from Stiles, from Faust's *Human Helminthology*, Lea & Febiger, Philadelphia.)

out of the egg shell. Provided with a beaked proboscis having retractile stylets and three rows of reversed spines, it bores into animal tissue. In a grasshopper, cricket or cockroach, it proceeds to the hemocele of this insect and transforms into a snake-like worm which is coiled back and forth on itself. As it approaches maturity the gordiid ruptures the body wall of the insect and becomes a free-living aquatic worm.

Human "Parasitism" with Gordiid Worms

There are many accounts of gordiid worms parasitic in man, including instances of passage of the living organisms in the vomitus or feces and of a few discharged *per urethram*. Infested water used as a vaginal douche may account for urethral discharge of mature gordiids from female subjects (Baylis, 1941; Carvalho, 1942;

Yeh and Jordan 1958) but no plausible explanation has been advanced in the case of several quite immature specimens passed *per urethram* on several occasions by an adult male patient in South Carolina (Faust and Russell, 1957, page 493). One male and one female gordiid have been removed from the external ear of a country girl in Colombia (Faust and Botero, 1960). Instances of gordiid worms evacuated from the human body have been reported from Europe, Africa, and North and South America, all lacking evidence of true parasitism or that the presence of a gordiid in the digestive tract produced serious harm. One instance of tissue invasion of man by a gordiid worm was reported from Florida by Sayad, Johnson and Faust (1936), in which an immature female worm was found in the midst of an inflammatory tumor on the lower border of the orbit of a white patient. The worm had caused considerable local host cell reaction, with dense infiltration of eosinophils, epithelioid and giant cells.

SUMMARY

1. The thorny-headed worms, or Acanthocephala, are elongated, somewhat flattened, sacculate organisms, measuring from a few millimeters to many centimeters in length, and are provided anteriorly with a spinose proboscis. They lack segmentation, a digestive tract and a mesothelial lining of the body cavity. The sexes are separate. The adults are intestinal parasites of vertebrates.
2. Eggs laid by the female worms are evacuated in the host's feces. When fully-embryonated eggs are ingested by a coprophagous arthropod they hatch, migrate to the hemocele and transform into larvæ infective for the definitive host.
3. Two species of acanthocephalans have been reported as human parasites, *Macracanthorhynchus hirudinaceus*, a large form commonly found as an adult in the pig and using dung beetles as intermediate hosts, and *Moniliformis moniliformis*, a parasite of rodents with larval stages in roaches.
4. Gordiid worms, or "hair snakes," Phylum Nematomorpha, superficially resemble the true roundworms (Nematoda) but differ in having their body cavity lined with mesothelium; lack of longitudinal cords; digestive tract atrophied in the mature worms; cloaca in the female as well as the male, and ovaries discontinuous with their ducts. Gordiid worms are parasitic only during their larval development.
5. The adult male and female gordiid worms are elongated, creamy-yellow to dark brown wiry objects which measure 10 to 50 cm. in length. The fertilized eggs embryonate in the water and give birth to larvæ that actively penetrate into the hemocele of grasshoppers; crickets and cockroaches, where they gradually metamorphose into the adult stage, following which they escape into water.
6. Human "parasitism" with "hair snakes" has been reported from many parts of the world. In most instances the worms have been spontaneously passed in the feces or have been vomited.

REFERENCES

Acanthocephala

Beck, J. W. 1959. Report of a Possible Infection with the Acanthocephalan *Moniliformis moniliformis* (syn. *M. dubius*). J. Parasitol., *45*, 510.

BRUMPT, E. 1949. *Précis de Parasitologie.* 6th ed. p. 1037. Masson et Cie, Paris.

BULLOCK, W. L. 1958. Histochemical Studies on the Acanthocephala. III. Comparative Histology of Alkaline Glycerophosphatase. Exp. Parasitol., *7*, 51–68.

GRASSI, B., and CALANDRUCCIO, S. 1888. Ueber einen Echinorhynchus welcher auch in Menschen parasitiert und dessen Zwischenwirth ein Blaps ist. Centralbl. Bakt., *3*, 521–525.

SITA, E. 1949. The Life-Cycle of *Moniliformis moniliformis* (Bremser, 1811), Acanthocephala. Current Sci. (India), *18*, 216–218.

VAN CLEAVE, H. J. 1941. Relationships of the Acanthocephala. Am. Naturalist, *75*, 31–47.

———. 1948. Expanding Horizons in the Recognition of a Phylum. J. Parasitol., *34*, 1–20.

Gordiid Worms

BAYLIS, H. A. 1927. Notes on Two Gordiids and a Mermithid Said to Have Been Parasitic in Man. Trans. R. Soc. Trop. Med. & Hyg., *21*, 203–206.

CARVALHO, J. C. M. 1942. Studies on Some Gordiacea of North and South America. J. Parasitol., *28*, 213–222.

FAUST, E. C., and BOTERO, R. D. 1960. Extraordinario hallazgo de una nueva especie de *Neochordodes* (Gordiácea) en Colombia. Homenaje al Dr. Eduardo Caballero y Caballero, Mexico, D. F., pp. 523–527.

SAYAD, W. Y., JOHNSON, V. M., and FAUST, E. C. 1936. Human Parasitization with *Gordius robustus.* J. Am. Med. Assn., *106*, 461–462.

YEH, L. S., and JORDAN, P. 1958. A New Gordiid Worm Parasitic in Man. Trans. R. Soc. Trop. Med. & Hyg., *52*, 11.

Chapter 15

The Leeches or Hirudineans

Introduction

THE leeches, Class Hirudinea of the Phylum Annelida, are predatory or parasitic invertebrates which have true segmentation but lack appendages. They have a very muscular body, which is elongated-ovoidal, and are provided with two suckers, one surrounding the mouth and one at the posterior end of the body (Fig. 158), by which they move like, "measuring worms." They are also good swimmers. Leeches utilize vertebrate blood as food and most species are avidly sanguivorous. Like ticks, leeches ingest a large quantity of blood, which they temporarily store in greatly distended ceca and later digest. Some leeches are aquatic, others are terrestrial in rain-forest areas and still others are amphibious.

Morphology, Biology and Life Cycle

Morphology.—Leeches vary in size from a few millimeters to several centimeters in length, and in shape from elongated cylindroidal to broadly ovoidal or pyriform objects. They have an antero-posterior axis, bilateral symmetry and are dorso-ventrally compressed, but frequently have a convex dorsum and a concave ventral side. There are a maximum of 34 true segments in the body, with a similar number of median ventral, paired nerve ganglia and a similar number of rows of sensory papillæ. Each segment has three to many external annulations.

A thin, smooth, tough cuticle covers the body. Seventeen paired nephridiopores are located in the median annulus of segments 7 to 23. On the dorsal face of each of the first 5 segments in most leeches there are minute pairs of "eye-spots" or light-sensitive end organs. Cuticular setæ are developed only in the genus *Acanthobdella*. Depending on the species, the surface of the leech may be essentially colorless, striped longitudinally or symmetrically patterned in colors.

The *digestive system* (Fig. 159) is provided anteriorly with a protrusile proboscis (Order Rhynchobdellida) or three very muscular jaws with marginal denticles (Order Gnathobdellida). The small mouth leads into a muscular pharynx, which is surrounded by many unicellular secretory glands that provide anticoagulin (*hirudin*) when the leech is taking a blood meal. Behind the pharynx there is a long, thin-walled median crop, with 11 pairs of distensible diverticula or ceca. The distal end of the crop joins the midgut, where digestion of the stored blood takes place. Further posteriorly there are first a short intestine and then a short rectum which opens through a small anal pore.

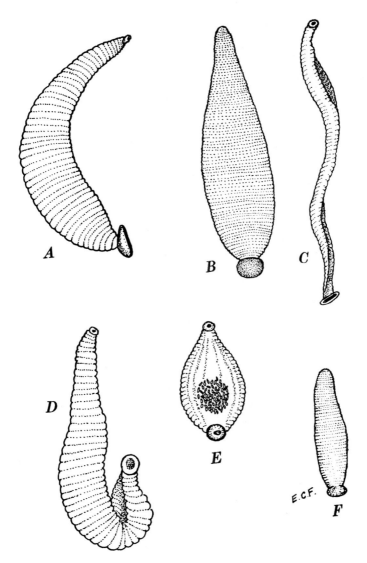

Fig. 158.—Habit sketches of leeches. × 1. *A, Limnatis nilotica* (adapted from Brumpt); *B,* dorsal view and *C,* lateral view of extended specimen of *Hirudo medicinalis* (adapted from Schmidt); *D. Hæmopis sanguisuga* (adapted from Blanchard); *E, Placobdella parasitica,* ventral view, with brood of attached young (adapted from Hemingway in Nachtrieb); *F, Hæmadipsa zeylanica,* dorsal view (adapted from Brumpt).

The *blood-vascular system* is composed of bloodvessels with muscular walls and two blood sinuses (one dorsal and one ventral) which represent the greatly reduced body cavity. Branches and capillaries extend to all parts of the organism.

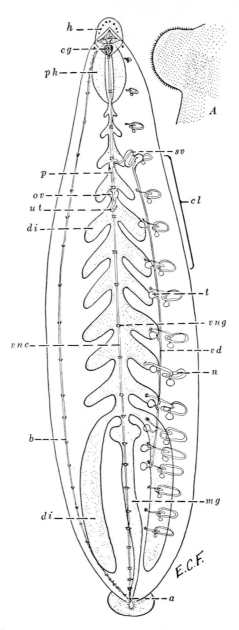

FIG. 159.—Internal anatomy of the "medicinal leech," *Hirudo medicinalis* Bilaterally symmetrical nephridia and male genitalia are shown only on the right side, the lateral blood vessel only on the left side. *a*, anus; *b*, blood vessel; *cg*, cephalic ganglion or "brain;" *cl*, clitellar metameres; *di*, diverticula of the crop; *h*, head with "eye-spots;" *mg*, midgut; *n*, nephridium; *ov*, ovary; *p*, penis; *ph*, pharynx; *sv*, seminal vesicle; *t*, testis; *ut*, uterus; *vd*, vas deferens; *vnc*, ventral nerve cord; *vng*, ventral nerve ganglion. × 2. *A*, detail of one of the 3 hammerhead jaws with marginal denticles, greatly enlarged. (Original adaptation, from Faust's *Human Helminthology*, Lea & Febiger, Philadelphia.)

The *nervous system* (Fig. 159) consists of a pair of median ventral, partially fused ganglia for each segment, with connecting longitudinal twinned nerve cords, and at the anterior end a large cephalic ganglion.

The *reproductive organs* of both sexes are found in the same worm. Each organism (Fig. 159) possesses 1 to 10 (or more) pairs of small spherical *testes*, each with a *vas efferens*; paired *vasa deferentia, seminal vesicles, prostate glands, ejaculatory ducts* and muscular *penial organs*; one pair of *ovaries* with *oviducts* which unite and join a muscular *uterus* that opens through a short *vagina* one segment behind the male genital pore.

Life Cycle.—Insemination is characteristically accomplished by cross-fertilization, either by reciprocal copulation or by implantation of a horny spermatophore containing the spermatozoa of one onto the cuticle of another. Fertilization always precedes oviposition. In some groups the eggs are deposited soon after fertilization; in other groups (Fig. 158, *E*) even the hatched young are carried for some time in a cocoon. As soon as the little leech is able to suck blood, it leaves its parent and fends for itself.

Medical Importance of Leeches

Since the days of early Greek medicine the "medicinal leech" (*Hirudo medicinalis*) has been employed by physicians to extract blood from patients (Fig. 158, *B*, *C*). It is still dispensed in some pharmacies of Europe and Latin America.

Leeches Injurious to Man.—Leech infestation is known as *hirudiniasis*. Aquatic forms are responsible for internal, at times external, and terrestrial species for external hirudiniasis.

Internal Hirudiniasis.—Small, unengorged leeches, which get into the mouth in unfiltered or unstrained drinking water, reach the posterior pharynx, the larynx, epiglottis and esophagus, or may wander into the nasopharynx, become attached and suck blood. They increase greatly in size, cause congestion and inflammatory swelling of the area, at times producing occlusion of the respective passages. They produce intense pain and tenderness of the affected region. If the leech is attached to the posterior pharynx or the larynx, sudden deep inhalation of air may carry it into the trachea or a bronchus, producing blockage of the air passage and at times suffocation.

Internal hirudiniasis involving the pharynx and upper respiratory tract has been widely reported from southern Europe, northern Africa, and Asian countries extending from the Mediterranean coast to India and China. In many of these regions the leech is *Limnatis nilotica* (Fig. 158, *A*), which is so small as to be hardly noticed in clear water of quiet brooks, pools, ponds or lakes; but after attachment to mucous membranes and engorgement it may reach a length of 8 to 12 cm. and a width of 1 to 1.5 cm. near the posterior end. *L. maculosa, L. africana, L. mysomelas,* and *L. granulosa* are other species with similar proclivities. *Dinobdella ferax* is a common culprit in India, Burma, southern China and Formosa (Chin, 1949).

Internal hirudiniasis may also occur as a result of bathing, swimming or standing waist-high in leech-infested fresh water, with involvement of the vagina, labium majus, or male urethra.

Leeches lodged in the nasal passages may be visualized with a speculum. If the worm is located in the nares, naso-pharynx or upper pharynx, the area may be injected with procaine and the intruder removed with a probe having a sharp hook on its inner end (Salzberger, 1928). If the leech has become attached to the posterior pharynx, larynx, trachea or bronchus, the patient should be placed in the Trendelenburg position before attempts are made to remove it. For leech infestation of the genito-urinary tract, strong saline irrigation is advised by Indian physicians to evacuate the worm.

All drinking water from areas where aquatic leeches are known to occur should be boiled, filtered or strained through several layers of cheese cloth.

External Hirudiniasis.—Leech infestation of the skin is a relatively common occurrence among persons who travel through tropical rain-forests. Moreover, it has been reported from the Chilean Andes, Australia and Micronesia. A considerable number of terrestrial leeches have been incriminated, including the notorious *Hæmadipsa zeylanica* of India, Ceylon and Burma.

Travelers through leech-infested tropical rain-forests are frequently plagued by these worms, which are able to get inside closely-woven pants or insinuate themselves into tightly laced, stout, knee-length leather boots.

Although the leech's puncture of the skin is essentially painless, there may be a serous discharge from the wound for some time, due to secretion of hirudin into the puncture site. Healing is slow and is frequently complicated by invasion of pyogenic organisms. Leeches found attached to the skin should not be pulled off without first applying a few drops of brine or procaine to the worm or touching it with a match flame, after which it can be removed by gentle traction. The wound should then be staunched and covered with an aseptic dressing. As a prophylactic, dimethyl phthalate, when applied to clothing, and to the tongue, lace holes and neck of shoes or boots, repels terrestrial leeches up to 6 days (Ribbands, 1946), and other repellents in a Tween-80 emulsifier, when impregnated into field clothing, protect the wearer under tropical rain-forest conditions (Audy and Harrison, 1954; Walton, Traub and Newson, 1956).

SUMMARY

1. Leeches (Class Hirudinea, Phylum Annelida) are aquatic or terrestrial invertebrate forms, predatory or parasitic and typically blood-sucking in their habits. They have true segmentation but are provided with three or more superficial annulations for each metamere. They vary in size from a few millimeters to several centimeters in length, are elongated, bilaterally symmetrical, dorso-ventrally compressed, and have a sucker at the anterior and posterior extremities. The species of medical importance have three muscular jaws with marginal denticles.

2. Leeches have a complete digestive tract, with 11 pairs of distensible diverticula from the thin-walled crop, capable of storing a considerable amount of blood. They are hermaphroditic but cross-fertilization is characteristic.

3. Leeches are injurious to man by internal or external attachment.

Aquatic species may be accidentally taken into the mouth and become attached to the mucous lining of the pharynx or upper respiratory passages, producing painful inflammatory swellings and at times blockage of the respiratory passages, or may enter the urethra. Other species in tropical rain-forests fasten themselves to the skin of persons passing along jungle paths, frequently getting under clothing or within leather boots, where they suck blood and produce relatively painless swelling of the affected areas.

4. In internal hirudiniasis of the pharynx or upper respiratory passage the worm should first be visualized, anesthetized by injection of procaine into the parasitized area, then skillfully removed with a hooked probe. For urethral infestation irrigation with strong salt solution is usually effective. In external hirudiniasis a few drops of procaine or strong salt solution or a match flame should be applied to the worm to cause its partial relaxation, after which it may be removed by gentle traction. The bleeding is then staunched and the wound dressed aseptically.

5. Prophylaxis in internal hirudiniasis of the pharynx or respiratory organs consists in drinking only boiled or filtered water. Impregnation of clothing with repellents is usually effective in preventing external hirudiniasis.

REFERENCES

AUDY, J. R., and HARRISON, J. L. 1954. Field Tests of M-1960 against Leeches Med. J. Malaya, *8*, 240–250.

CHIN, T. H. 1949. Further Note on Leech Infestation in Man. J. Parasitol., *35*, 215.

RIBBANDS, C. R. 1946. Experiments with Leech Repellents. Ann. Trop. Med. & Parasitol., *40*, 314–319.

SALZBERGER, M. 1928. Leeches as Foreign Bodies in the Upper Air Passages in Palestine. Laryngoscope, *38*, 27–32.

WALTON, B. C., TRAUB, R., and NEWSON, H D. 1956. Efficacy of the Clothing Impregnants M-2065 and M-2066 against Terrestrial Leeches in North Borneo. Am. J. Trop. Med. & Hyg., *5*, 190–196.

SECTION IV

Arthropods as Agents and Vectors

Chapter 16

Arthropods and Human Disease

INTRODUCTION

ARTHROPODS (Phylum Arthropoda) constitute the largest group of related organisms in the Animal Kingdom. They are segmented invertebrates which are bilaterally symmetrical, have an anterio-posterior axis, are provided with an exoskeleton and have paired jointed appendages. In the ancestral arthropod (Fig. 160) all of the segments (metameres) were separated from one another, with a twinned nerve ganglion and a pair of jointed appendages of similar type for each body segment; but as evolutionary

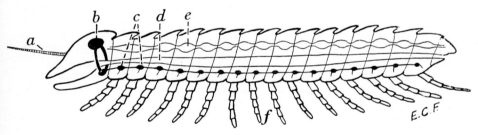

FIG. 160.—An ancestral arthropod (lateral view). *a*, antenna; *b*, brain; *c*, ventral nerve cord with twinned ganglion for each segment; *d*, digestive tract; *e*, dorsal blood vessel. (Adaptation by Faust, from Faust and Russell's *Clinical Parasitology*, Lea & Febiger, Philadelphia.)

changes developed, the 5 (or 6) anteriormost segments became consolidated into a head portion, and the head appendages became modified into sense organs (*antennæ*), jaws (*mandibles*), piercing organs (*cheliceræ*), etc., while those of the remainder of the body became transformed in terrestrial species into *walking legs* and in aquatic species into biramous paddle-like *swimming appendages*.

The Adult.—All arthropods possess a *digestive tract* divided into three portions, *viz.*, (1) a foregut lined with chitin, divided successively into a mouth cavity, a muscular pharynx, esophagus and proventriculus, for the

(335)

ingestion and trituration of food; (2) a non-chitinized midgut or "stomach," in which nutriment is digested and from which it is absorbed, and (3) a chitinized posterior portion, consisting of hindgut and rectum for the accumulation and elimination of excreta.

The *excretory organs*, present in all but a few arthropods, consist of the Malpighian tubules, usually 2 or more in number, which lie freely in the hemocele and open into the hindgut near its junction with the midgut. They serve to collect liquid wastes, which are then discharged into the hindgut.

There is a *blood vascular system* consisting of a dorsally situated pumping organ (heart), aorta and paired vessels, and a hemal cavity (hemocele) which extends into all parts of the body and communicates with the heart. The blood consists of plasma and corpuscles and is usually provided with hemocyanin rather than hemoglobin.

The *respiratory system* has been developed into one or the other of two main types, *viz.*, gills for aquatic species and a tracheal system for terrestrial forms. The "book lungs" of scorpions and spiders constitute a special adaptation of gills to a non-aquatic environment.

The *central nervous system* consists of a dorsally-situated "brain" composed of 5 or 6 fused cephalic ganglia, circum-esophageal commissures to the median ventral paired nerve trunks, and twinned ganglia for each postcephalic body segment. Nerve fibers extend from the central nervous system to all important organs and tissues. In many groups there are light-sensitive organs in the head, either individual "eye-spots" (ocelli) or compound eyes (ommatidia).

Arthropods have no trace of a ciliated epithelium. The musculature which is mostly striated is highly developed in many species, particularly in the organs of locomotion.

The sexes are separate and are frequently distinguishable by external morphologic differences.

There is suggestive evidence that species differentiation among arthropods may be demonstrated by hemolymph electrophoresis (van Sande and Karcher, 1960).

The Life Cycle.—The simplest type of life cycle consists of egg, one or more larval stages resembling the adult except for smaller size and lack of sex organs, and the adult. Some groups have one or more nymphal stages between larva and adult, while others have a much more complicated development, with the interpolation of a pupal stage between the last larva and the adult. In the latter type there is little resemblance between the larva and the adult, so that during the pupal period complete internal and external reörganization is required. During each stage of growth the entire exoskeleton as well as the chitinous lining of the foregut and hindgut are shed and a new exoskeleton is secreted.

Biology of Arthropods.—There is agreement among entomologists that arthropods were originally aquatic. Groups like the copepods and the larger crustaceans have continued to inhabit the water and respire through gills. Many species have become terrestrial and as a result have developed a tracheal type of respiration. Others which are aquatic during their larval and pupal stages and aërial during their adult life employ tracheal respiration during both immature and sexually mature stages. House (1958) has presented a comprehensive review of the specific nutritional requirements of the larval and adult stages of arthropods which have developed parasitic habits.

Medical Importance of Arthropods.—Some types of arthropods are beneficial to man; others produce great economic loss, and still others are themselves harmful in causing disease, in serving as intermediate hosts of parasites or in transmitting pathogenic microörganisms.

Classification of Arthropods.—The species of medical importance belong to the following groups.

CRUSTACEA (mostly aquatic). Examples: copepods (*Cyclops* and *Diaptomus*); decapods (crabs and crayfishes). [Intermediate hosts.]

CHILOPODA (terrestrial). Example: centipedes. [Venomous.]

ARACHNIDA (terrestrial). Examples: scorpions, spiders, ticks and mites. [Venomous, biological vectors, intermediate hosts.]

PENTASTOMIDA (strictly endo-parasitic). Examples: the tongue worms. [Parasitic.]

INSECTA (Aquatic, terrestrial or parasitic during larval development; terrestrial, aërial or parasitic in adult stage). Examples: sucking lice, true bugs, beetles, bees, wasps and ants, moths, flies and gnats, fleas. [Venomous, biological and mechanical vectors, intermediate hosts, parasitic.]

ARTHROPODS AS AGENTS OF HUMAN DISEASE

Many arthropods are agents of disease when the adult or larval stage of the organism feeds on the skin or underlying tissues, withdrawing blood, producing traumatic or necrotic damage, or causing sensitization. And in a few groups the arthropod introduces a potent venom into the skin of the victim, producing local, systemic and neurotoxic injury.

CENTIPEDES (CHILOPODA)

Adult Morphology.—Centipedes (Fig. 161) are elongated terrestrial forms ranging from 5 to 25 cm. or more in length, with one pair of jointed appendages and one pair of tracheal openings (spiracles) for each body segment behind the head. The genital pores are found ventrally on the penultimate body segment. The head appendages consist of a pair of long, many-jointed antennæ, a pair of stout mandibles, an anterior pair of biramous maxillæ, and a posterior pair of leg-like maxillæ. A pair of poison claws arise from the first body segment just ventro-lateral to the mouth. The terminal joint of each claw is a strong, sharply-pointed, incurved, piercing fang, with a subterminal pore for secretion from the poison gland which is situated in the base of the claw. The opalescent discharge consists of venom and a much larger amount of digestive enzymes. Centipedes are carnivorous and at times cannibalistic (Bücherl, 1959).

Clinical Notes.—The size of the centipede, its activity and the time which has elapsed since the last "bite" are usually related to the amount of venom introduced into the skin of the victim. Many centipedes have

22

considerable difficulty in piercing the skin of the human finger (Baerg, 1929) and at most produce intense pain at the site of inoculation, with local swelling, but with complete recovery in a few days (Cloudsley-Thompson, 1958). No human deaths have been reported as a result of uncomplicated centipede bites.

On a number of occasions small centipedes have been found to be accidental invaders of the human nares, frontal sinuses, digestive tract and urethra, causing temporary painful congestion or occlusion of the organ.

Millipedes (Diplopoda), the "thousand-legged worms," which typically have two pairs of jointed appendages for each body segment, are relatively harmless, but may produce burning sensation at the site of skin contact.

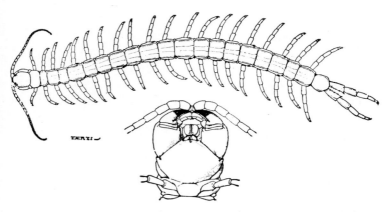

Fig. 161.—The centipede *Scolopendra morsitans*. *Above,* dorsal view of entire centipede; *below,* anterior view of head. (After Castellani and Chalmers, from Faust and Russell's *Clinical Parasitology*, Lea & Febiger, Philadelphia.)

SCORPIONS (SCORPIONES)

Adult Morphology.—Scorpions, like crabs and crayfishes, have their body divided externally into a fused, unsegmented cephalothorax and an abdomen with distinct evidence of segmentation. True scorpions (Fig. 162) have a long anterior pair of pinchers (pedipalps) with their conspicuous terminal claws, 4 pairs of long, sprawling, cephalothoracic legs behind the pinchers, and the division of the abdomen into a broad anterior, 7-segmented portion and a much narrower, 5-segmented posterior portion with a terminal segment (the telson) which is modified into a sting apparatus. The male can be distinguished from the female because of broader claws in the pedipalps and a longer posterior abdomen. (Whip scorpions, which are harmless, have a uniformly broad abdomen which ends in a long, whip-like caudal extremity.) Between the bases of the pinchers there are a pair of small jaws or cheliceræ. Also at the anterior end of the scorpion there are a pair of conspicuous median compound eyes and 2 to 10 lateral "eye-spots." Just behind the base of the last pair of legs on the ventral side there are a pair of comb-like tactile organs.

Bionomics.—Scorpions lurk in dark places, where they may be resting, or they may move about actively. Characteristically the stinger is curved over the back or to one side. They are found under rocks, old logs, piles of sand, dark corners of earthen floors, the underside of mattresses, crevices of walls or between floor boards. Many species of scorpions live in hot arid regions, but they can not survive dryness or intense heat. This is why they migrate into houses or under cool moist covering during midday. Other species live in moist tropical climates.

The preferred food of the scorpion consists of the water roach (*Blatella germanica*), small spiders or beetles. But they will eat centipedes or other scorpions, provided their prey has just molted and has a soft cuticle (Stahnke, 1949).

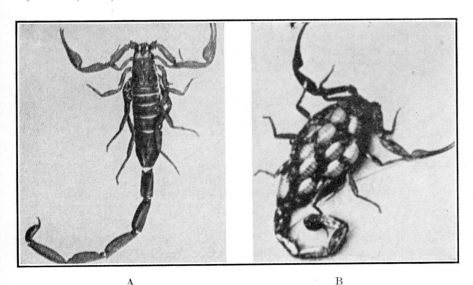

A   B

Fig. 162.—*A*, male *Centruroides*, × 1 (after Dr. C. C. Hoffman); *B*, female *C. sculpturatus* with newly born young, × 1 (after Stahnke). (From Faust and Russell's *Clinical Parasitology*, Lea & Febiger, Philadelphia.)

The Life Cycle.—Scorpions are viviparous. Following several months of intra-uterine development, the young are born with an embryonic envelope which facilitates parturition. Immediately after birth the mother removes the membrane with her pedipalps and the little scorpions crawl onto her back, where they remain for some time (See Fig. 162 *B*).

Venenation.—Human beings come in contact with scorpions by accidentally stepping on them with bare feet or by bringing the hand or forearm in contact with them, usually in dark places inside habitations. But scorpions may be found in vegetation near homes, inside dwellings near water containers, or concealed inside boots or shoes, clothing or any other damp dark object.

Scorpion venom is elaborated in two glands which lie in the swollen portion of the telson, and is discharged through the hollow, sharp, curved tip. It is a clear, colorless toxalbumin, containing hemorrhagic, hemolytic, neurotoxic fractions and adenosine triphosphatase (Cloudsley-Thompson, 1958). Small species of scorpions are less likely to pierce human skin than larger forms, but once the stinger has penetrated, the amount of the different toxic components in the venom determines the type and severity of the reaction. If the venom consists primarily of hemorrhagin the lesion will be mostly local at the site of its introduction; if it consists primarily of neurotoxin, the reaction will be systemic. Species of *Centruroides* of Mexico and southwestern United States, *Buthus* of southern Europe, the eastern Mediterranean, northern Africa and Manchuria, *Androctonus* and *Buthacus* of northern Africa, *Buthotus* of Israel, *Parabuthus* of Bechuana-land, *Scorpio maurus* of northern Africa, *Tamulus* of India and *Tityus* of Trinidad and South America, all belong to the latter group. The most venomous are the species of *Buthotus*, *Buthus*, *Androctonus* and *Tytius* (Weismann and Shulov, 1959).

Children of preschool age are most liable to venenation and the highest mortality occurs in this age group. During the 20-year period 1929–1948, there were 64 deaths reported in Arizona from scorpion sting, all due to species of *Centruroides* (*C. sculpturatus* or *C. gertschi*). These constituted 68% of all deaths from venomous animals (Stahnke, 1949).

Pathogenesis and Symptomatology.—At the site of the sting there is a single, small puncture wound, accompanied by sharp, aching, local pain. In many instances the essential toxic fraction is hemorrhagin, which causes an erythematous swelling at the site, frequently with induration, with a small area of hemorrhage. This may involve a forearm if the sting was on a finger, or the ankle and lower part of the leg if the sting was on the foot, with swelling of the member but rarely extending further than the axial or popliteal lymph nodes respectively. But unless the wound becomes secondarily infected, the symptoms subside in a few hours or at most in one or 2 days.

Scorpions which inject neurotoxic venom produce systemic manifestations, which do not produce a swelling or discoloration at the site of the sting. There is an immediate, intense, aching local pain, a radiating, burning sensation, and inflammation of the nearby lymph nodes, followed by rapid development of generalized numbness, throbbing and spastic twitching of the muscles, with convulsive attacks. There may be vomiting, continuous rhinorrhea and profuse frothy salivation; extreme thirst, urinary incontinence or anuria, tachycardia, weak shallow respiration and a fever up to 40° C. (104° F); hypertension (Patterson, 1960); respiratory and bulbar paralysis with fatal termination.

Diagnosis.—In a scorpion-infested region, clinical diagnosis may be made from the patient's local or systemic symptoms, history of contact with a scorpion, and demonstration of a small reddened local wound having a single point of skin puncture. This type of venenation must be differentiated from spider bite (page 343), tick paralysis (page 347) and bee sting (page 364).

Treatment.—Therapeutic measures should be undertaken at the earliest possible moment. A tight tourniquet should be placed proximal to the site to isolate it from the body, but this must be released every 20 to 30 minutes so as not to embarrass blood and lymphatic flow. If an ice-pack is available it should be placed over the puncture wound; or in a hospital ethyl chloride may be sprayed over the immediate area (Stahnke, 1953). Special medical care is indicated for patients under school age, those who have a history of cardiac symptoms, in cases of multiple stings on different parts of the body or on the external genitalia, and whenever there are severe neurotoxic symptoms. Supportive treatment includes parenteral administration of glucose, amino acid solutions and blood plasma, sodium phenobarbital for irrational patients. Antivenin should be reserved for persons manifesting systemic intoxication. This is available in most Pasteur institutes in scorpion-infested countries, but is not produced commercially in the United States (Keegan, 1956, page 428). The outcome is favorable in cases of sting with scorpions which inject only hemorrhagic venom; grave to equivocal in cases of neurotoxic venenation unless effective medical care is rapidly made available.

Control.—Eradication of scorpions over wide areas is impractical. Residual spraying of BHC (Gammexane) in and around homes in Brazil has greatly reduced scorpion accidents (de Souza *et al.*, 1954).

SPIDERS (ARANEÆ)

Adult Morphology.—Spiders are arachnids which have a cephalothorax and an abdomen separated by a conspicuous constriction (the pedicle). They lack external evidence of segmentation (Figs. 163, 164), although at times there is a cervical groove or furrow between the head and the thorax. The exoskeleton is relatively thin but tough; it may be smooth or be provided with hairs or setæ. Several simple "eye-spots" are present on the front of the head. The mouth parts consist of a pair of poison jaws (cheliceræ) just above the mouth, an upper lip (labrum), a median epipharynx immediately ventral to the labrum, a median lower lip and a pair of pedipalps. The poison jaws have a short, broad, basal segment and a clawed

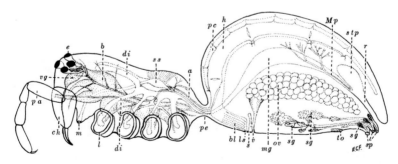

Fig. 163.—Diagram of female spider, showing external and internal organs on left side. *a*, aorta; *b*, brain; *bl*, book lung; *ch*, chelicera; *di*, diverticulum of midgut; *e*, eyespot; *h*, heart; *l*, thoracic leg attachment; *ls*, lung slit; *m*, mouth; *mg*, midgut; *Mp*, Malpighian tubule; *ov*, ovary; *pa*, pedipalp; *pc*, pericardial cavity; *pe*, pedicle; *r*, rectum; *s*, opening of spermatheca; *sg*, silk gland; *sp*, spinnerets; *ss*, sucking stomach; *stp*, stercoral pocket; *to*, tracheal opening (spiracle); *v*, vagina; *vg*, venom gland. (Original adaptation from Comstock.)

terminal segment through the tip of which the poison gland opens.   In the males the pedipalps are greatly modified for transfer of seminal fluid to the female.   There are 4 pairs of walking legs arising from the ventral side of the thorax.   The abdomen is sacculate and is much larger than the cephalo-thorax.   Typically there are 1 or 2 pairs of slits on the ventral side of the abdomen which are the openings of primitive book lungs.   Most species of true spiders also have a pair of spiracles leading into a tracheal system of respiration.

Fig. 164.—Female black-widow spider (*Latrodectus mactans*) with cocoon containing eggs.   (After G. H. Needham, from Faust and Russell's *Clinical Parasitology*, Lea & Febiger, Philadelphia.)

Bionomics.—Spiders are provided with spinning organs, usually 3 pairs of glands, which open ventrally near the posterior end of the body.   All spiders are carnivorous and many are cannibalistic.   They trap their victims, including flies and other relatively small, soft-bodied insects or their own kind, then pounce on them and render them helpless by injecting venom through the tips of their poison jaws, after which they proceed to suck out the body juices.   All true spiders employ this method of obtaining food but relatively few species are capable of piercing tough cuticle.

Spiders live in a variety of locations on the ground, under fallen trees, in piles of rocks, or outside and within human habitations.   They require moisture and during long dry seasons will migrate considerable distances from an arid to a moist habitat.

The Life Cycle.—The fertilized eggs are laid in masses, usually within a spun cocoon.   The eggs soon hatch, but the 8-legged spiderlings usually remain within the cocoon for weeks or months.   To permit growth they shed their cuticle repeatedly and possibly never outgrow this habit.

Spiders Harmful to Man.—Relatively few spiders are medically important.   Those which attack man do so accidentally when the hand or other exposed part of the body comes in contact with the spider or its web.

Pathophysiologically spiders belong to two groups, namely, (1) those responsible primarily for a local necrotizing ulcer and (2) those causing primarily systemic symptoms.

Necrotic Arachnidism.—Species of *Loxosceles* have in recent years come to be recognized as agents of a serious type of disease which is referred to as *loxoscelism*. One species, *Loxosceles laëta*, is widely distributed in southern South America; most clinical reports have come from Uruguay (Mackinnon and Witkind, 1953) and Chile (Schenone, 1953; Prats and Schenone, 1957). An additional species, *L. rufipes*, appears to be responsible for similar necrotizing lesions in Argentina. Another species of *Loxosceles*, *L. reclusus*, and possible a close relative, *L. marylandicus*, are the agents of the same type of necrotism produced in patients in Missouri and midwestern United States (Atkins *et al.*, 1958). These spiders are medium-sized (0.9 to 1.5 cm. long), yellowish to medium-brown or dark-brown in color, somewhat

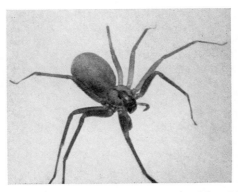

FIG. 165.—*Loxosceles reclusus* Gertsch and Mulaik, female. (Atkins, J. A. *et al.*, Amer. Journal of Tropical Medicine and Hygiene, 7, 1958). Engraving produced one-fourth size from photograph generously provided by Professor Curtis W. Wingo, Dept. of Entomology, Univ. Mo., Columbia, Mo.

pubescent, with a distinct constriction between cephalothorax and abdomen (Fig. 165). They are almost exclusively domestic in their habits, spinning their webs in dark places in and around the home, including clothes closets and within garments hanging in the closets, or behind picture frames on the wall.

On contact with the face, arm or neck, the spider bites the victim, producing cutaneous necrosis at the site, with local pain and swelling of the member. If the introduced venom is small in amount and weak in potency there may be only mild systemic reactions; but if the venom is large in amount or of high potency, the systemic reactions may be severe (James *et al.*, 1961), at times with fatal termination in a few days (Schenone *et al.*, 1959). In mild loxoscelism the cutaneous lesion heals slowly, leaving a disfiguring cicatricial scar which may be several centimeters in diameter; in the more severe cases the toxic products produce hemorrhage and erosion in all mucous membranes, hematuria usually within 24 hours, high fever and cardiac failure.

Loxoscelism has occurred in all age groups but is more common in young women because of greater exposure when putting on garments infested with *Loxosceles*. If the patient sees a physician within a few hours after the accident the parenteral administration of corticosteroids may not only ameliorate the condition and control the systemic toxemia but in milder cases will facilitate rapid healing of the cutaneous lesion and reduce the amount of scarring (see Table 7, page 422). DDT, chlordane or preferably BHC (Gammexane), sprayed in locations where *Loxosceles* females spin their webs and deposit their eggs, will reduce their number and consequently the likelihood of *Loxosceles* envenenation.

Latrodectism.—Many species of spiders throughout the world produce *systemic arachnidism*. There are the large hairy, ferocious-looking tarantulas of the Tropics, which are less harmful than their size would suggest, and the dangerous smaller forms with potent venom. The latter include several species of *Latrodectus*, among them the "black widow" (*L. mactans*), distributed in the Americas from southern United States to Chile; the "brown widow" (*L. geometricus*), found in Florida, U.S.A.; *L. curacaviensis*, common in Canada and New England; *L. hasselti*, from New Zealand to India; *L. tredecimguttatus*, in the Mediterranean area; *L. indistinctus*, in Africa; *L. hystrix*, in the Yemen, and *L. pallidus*, in Palestine, Asia Minor and southern U.S.S.R. Other species venomous for man include: *Atrax robustus* and *A. formidabilis* of Australia; *Sericopelma communis* of Panama and species of *Lycosa* and *Ctenus* of Brazil. These spiders are not primarily domestic in their habits but during severe droughts will be found under stone walls or lumber piles and on the under-side of outdoor privy seats, where the web comes in contact with the external genitalia of persons using the privy (Levi, 1958; Wiener, 1956).

The venom of *L. mactans* and probably of related species contains a transparent, lemon-colored, oily thermolabile toxalbumin and digestive enzymes (D'Amour, Becker and Van Riper, 1936). That of *L. mactans* is about one-third as potent as rattlesnake venom, while that of *L. indistinctus* is at least as toxic as Cape cobra venom. The poisonous fraction is a neurotoxin. Toxicity varies with seasonal temperatures (Wiener, 1956).

At the site of the bite produced by *Latrodectus* there is an immediate sharp pain but little swelling; later the wound may become reddened and edematous. The bitten member burns and aches. The venom will soon reach the lymphatics and then the circulating blood, with the development of motor disturbances, including weakness, cramps, and spastic contraction of the muscles, particularly those of the abdomen. Gajardo-Tobár (1941) reported marked clonic and tonic motor disturbances, exaggerated reflexes, rapid shallow respiration, early tachycardia and incredibly high arterial pressure. Convulsions may occur in small children, and delirium, stupor, complete prostration or shock in all age groups. Death from respiratory failure is not uncommon when diagnosis and treatment are delayed. Venenation caused by *Latrodectus* and other spiders of this group must be differentiated from scorpion sting or cobra-type venenation, as well as from perforated intestinal ulcer, appendicitis, peritonitis and intussusception (Schenone, 1959). The history of a spider in contact with the skin, and the early demonstration of two small punctures close to one another will suggest spider bite. Vasodilatation, cholinesterase inhibition with neostigmine and sedation are frequently indicated and specific antivenin should be administered, if available, as soon as possible following the accident (see Table 7, page 422). DDT and BHC (Gammexane) are effective in killing all types of spiders when these insect toxicants are sprayed in a kerosene medium or dusted onto active webs and sites where the spiders reside. Children should be warned not to reach with unprotected hands into old piles of lumber or under stones.

TICKS AND MITES (ACARI)

Adult Morphology and Bionomics.—These arthropods are more or less broadly oval, without distinct superficial separation between cephalothorax and abdomen and with no external evidence of segmentation. They have 4 pairs of legs arising from the ventral side of the thorax, the front 2 pairs extending anterolaterally and the hind 2 pairs posterolaterally. The head structures (capitulum) consist of a median hypostome situated below the mouth and a pair of cheliceræ (both arising from a capitular base), together with an outer pair of palps. The cheliceræ open an incision for the hypostome to penetrate into softer tissues so that the animal may then suck tissue juices. Salivary gland secretions may aid in the procurement of this nutriment. Most acarids do not enter the host tissues but a few species (*e.g.*, mange mites and demodectic mites) are parasitic in the skin.

The Life Cycle.—The females lay their eggs singly or in batches, depending on their egg-producing capacity. After embryonation and hatching the emerging active 6-legged larva feeds and grows, then sheds its cuticle and becomes an 8-legged nymph, which resembles the adult except that it lacks sexual organs. There is a second-stage nymph in some groups of mites, and a few species of mites have 3 nymphal stages. The last nymphal stage transforms into the 8-legged adult.

Ticks (Ixodoidea)

Definition.—Ticks are large mites which have a leathery integument, a large hypostome beset with recurved teeth, a furrowed ventral side, and tracheæ which open externally through a pair of spiracular (stigmal) plates near the bases of the third and fourth legs. All ticks feed on vertebrate blood during each of their active stages. There are two families (Fig. 166), the Argasidæ or soft-bodied ticks (Fig. 167), which lack a hard dorsal shield, have their mouth parts under the anterior extremity of the body and like bedbugs hide in cracks during the daytime and feed intermittently at night, and the Ixodidæ or hard-bodied ticks (Fig. 168), which have a shield covering the entire dorsum of the male but only the anterior part of the female, have mouth parts visible in front of the body and in most species remain on the host for a prolonged period to take blood. Like the leeches (page 330) ticks have several distensible diverticula of the crop to accommodate a big meal. During engorgement the tick swells up to many times its fasting size.

Ticks as Causative Agents.—Ticks produce two types of damage to their

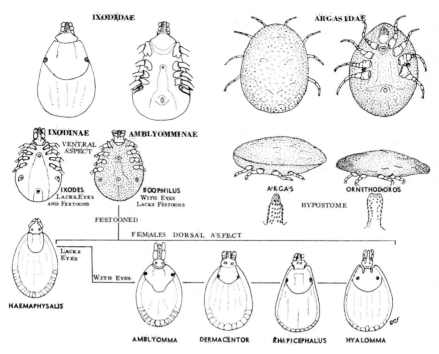

FIG. 166 —Diagram illustrating the differential characteristics of the families, sub-families and genera of ticks. (Original, Faust.)

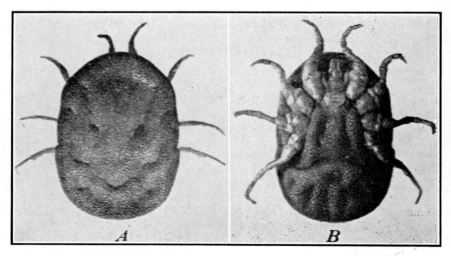

FIG. 167 —Soft-bodied tick (*Ornithodoros moubata*). *A*, dorsal view; *B*, ventral view. × 6⅔. (After Professor O. Jírovec, Prague, from Faust and Russell's *Clinical Parasitology*, Lea & Febiger, Philadelphia.)

hosts, *viz.*, (1) local traumatic and inflammatory at the site of attachment and (2) systemic.

Local traumatic and inflammatory damage is produced by all ticks when they puncture the skin and suck blood. The large hypostome with its recurved teeth serves as an effective anchoring organ in the skin after the sharply toothed cheliceræ cut an opening through the epidermis. The palps do not enter the wound but serve as a counter-anchor. Through a tubular stylet lying within the mouth cavity blood is sucked into the muscular pharynx. Secretion into the wound from a pair of salivary glands prevents coagulation of blood. The combined mechanical and digestive action provokes an inflammatory reaction in the perivascular tissues of the corium, with local hyperemia, edema and hemorrhage, together with a thickening of the stratum corneum.

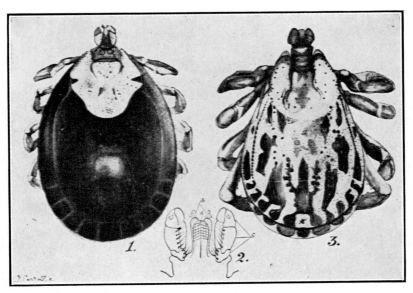

Fig. 168.—Hard-bodied tick (*Dermacentor andersoni*), dorsal views. *1*, female; *2*, head showing hypostome (a), cheliceræ (b) and palps (c); *3*, male. Enlarged. (From Stitt's Diagnostics, Prevention and Treatment of Tropical Diseases, in Faust and Russell's *Clinical Parasitology*, Lea & Febiger, Philadelphia.)

Systemic damage may consist solely in a sensitization reaction to the salivary secretions of the tick. Much more serious is *"tick paralysis,"* which is characterized by an ascending flaccid motor paralysis, with generalized intoxication, elevation of temperature to 40° C. (104° F.), difficulty in swallowing and respiration, and at times fatal termination. This syndrome may appear rapidly or be delayed for 5 days or more following the bite, depending principally on whether the site of the tick's attachment is on the neck at the base of the skull, further down the spinal cord or on a more distant site. Young children are particularly apt to develop tick paralysis.

The cause of the paralysis is some fraction of the tick's saliva introduced into the skin, with "failure in the liberation of acetylcholine at the neuro-muscular junction because of a conduction block in the somatic motor fibers produced by the tick 'toxin'" (Murnaghan, 1960). Most cases of tick paralysis in North America have been associated with bites of the hard-bodied Rocky Mountain wood tick, *Dermacentor andersoni* and the Eastern dog tick, *D. variabilis*. Other ticks have produced similar symptoms in Europe, South Africa and Australia.

Tick paralysis (Landry's type) requires differentiation from poliomyelitis, encephalomyelitis and ascending motor paralysis resulting from venenation of other arthropods or snakes having neurotoxin in their venom. There is no specific treatment but palliative and supportive therapy is helpful. Dusting of DDT inside the shoes and pants will serve as a partial prophylaxis in preventing the tick from attaching to the skin. Children or adults who walk through tick-infested areas should remove all clothing as soon as they return to their home or camp and all attached or crawling ticks should be removed at once to minimize danger.

For a consideration of ticks as vectors of pathogenic agents, please consult Chapter 18, pages 396–415.

MANGE MITES (SARCOPTOIDEA)

Morphology and Bionomics of Sarcoptes scabiei.—Several species of mange mites parasitize the skin of mammals. *Sarcoptes scabiei* commonly produces human disease.

S. scabiei was first described and incriminated by Renucci in 1834. This minute, broadly oval mite (Fig. 169) superficially resembles a microscopic turtle with the head organs and the 4 pairs of legs protruding from the main portion of the body. The anterior 2 pairs of legs have delicate, terminal, stalked sucking pads; in the female the posterior 2 pairs end in bristles, while in the male the 3rd pair is provided with bristles and the 4th pair with sucking pads. On the dorsal surface of the body there are many more or less transverse, parallel ridges, except medially, just behind the head and also numerous tooth-like and finger-like spines as well as bristles, all of which are important in identifying the species. *S. scabiei* lacks special respiratory organs. The females are somewhat larger than the males, *i.e.*, 330 to 450 microns by 250 to 350 microns and 200 to 240 microns by 150 to 200 microns respectively.

These mites live in slightly serpiginous cutaneous burrows. The gravid female is usually found at the inner, blind end of the tunnel, where she deposits one to a few large, broadly ovoidal eggs daily for 4 to 5 weeks. The males reside in lateral burrows. Three to 5 days after oviposition a 6-legged larva escapes from the egg shell. It either produces a lateral tunnel or crawls out of the mouth of the tunnel, starts a new one by burrowing down a hair follicle or develops a molting pocket under epidermal scales. In 2 or 3 days the larva molts and becomes a first-stage nymph. After a second nymphal period the mite becomes sexually mature. A complete life cycle requires 8 to 17 days.

Pathogenesis and Symptomatology.—The cutaneous lesion may be only a few millimeters or several centimeters in length, and is most frequently located between the fingers, on the back of the hands, at the elbows, axillæ, groin, or on the breast. The tunnel lies in the deeper part of the epidermis and is slightly lower at its inner end. As the mites feed on the tissues they deposit microscopic fecal pellets, which are responsible for the vesiculations and the associated pruritus. The itching is intensified by warmth and moisture. The first objective evidence is the small, reddish, slightly raised track in the skin, with a minute vesicle at the inner end. Scratching opens the tunnels and produces a bloody-serous exudation, permits bacteria to enter the lesion and frequently spreads the parasites to

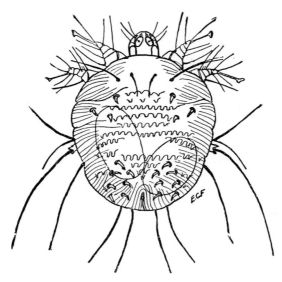

Fig. 169.—Human mange mite (*Sarcoptes scabiei*), gravid female (dorsal view), containing 2 immature eggs. Greatly enlarged. (After Faust in Brennemann's Practice of Pediatrics, from Faust and Russell's *Clinical Parasitology*, Lea & Febiger, Philadelphia.)

other skin areas. The chronic stage consists of multiple lesions with vesicles, papules, pustules and excoriation, and a weeping eczema of the area.

Diagnosis.—The physician can make a relatively satisfactory diagnosis on the basis of the clinical picture. Sarcoptic mange must be differentiated from the dermatomycoses, various types of cutaneous larva migrans and several other dermatitides.

Treatment.—The most satisfactory treatment consists in the application of 2 ounces of lindane ointment ($\frac{1}{2}\%$ gamma isomer of benzene hexachloride in vanishing cream) to all parts of the body below the head following a soaking hot soapy bath. After 24 hours the patient takes a second bath and puts on clean clothes. Occasionally a second treatment may be required. Lindane kills the eggs as well as the active stages of the mite (see Table 7, page 420).

Epidemiology of Human Sarcoptic Mange.—Exposure to sarcoptic mange is due almost exclusively to contact with infested persons, their clothing, bed linen, towels or other fomites contaminated with gravid females of *S. scabiei* or their offspring.

Control.—Sarcoptic mange tends to be hyperendemic in jails, armies, among school children and families who do not practice good personal and group hygiene. Prescription of specific therapy in dispensaries and by visiting nurses in schools and homes provides a method of practical control

Follicular Mites (Demodicoidea)

Demodex folliculorum and Follicular Mange.—Although related species infest dogs and other domestic mammals, *D. folliculorum* is the only follicular mite of man. The adult is an elongated, vermiform organism, having a length of 0.1 to 0.39 mm. It is provided with a small, inconspicuous hypostome, a pair of stylet-like chelicerae and a pair of relatively large palps each with a terminal claw. There are 4 pairs of short, stumpy, thoracic legs having a sucking cup and 2 claws on the terminal joint, a long median genital slit in the female between the last pair of legs, and many parallel transverse striations on the abdomen.

Clinical Notes—Follicular mites burrow into the hair follicles and sebaceous glands where they provoke a fibrous tissue reaction, causing a mild pruritus, possibly an acne-like dermatitis or localized keratosis, and providing an opportunity for bacteria to enter the skin. Application of lindane ointment to the affected area, following a thorough cleansing with hot soapy water to open the pores, constitutes specific treatment.

PARASITOID MITES (PARASITOIDEA)

Adult Morphology and Bionomics.—Members of this group (Fig. 170) are small macroscopic mites, oval or pyriform in contour, which are more closely related to the ticks than to other mites. Like other mites they have an unarmed, sharply pointed hypostome and are considerably smaller and more delicate than ticks. The legs have a sucking pad and 2 claws on the terminal joint. The species of particular medical interest belong to the genera *Bdellonyssus*, *Allodermanyssus* and *Dermanyssus*. The chelicerae of *Bdellonyssus* are spear-like and have a terminal joint apposed to the end portion of the subterminal one, while in the other two genera the chelicerae have a single needle-like termination. The species which attack man most frequently are the rat mite (*Bdellonyssus bacoti*), the mouse mite (*Allodermanyssus sanguineus*) and the chicken and pigeon mite (*Dermanyssus gallinæ*). *B. bacoti* not only infests rats but is also found on squirrels. *A. sanguineus* is found on domestic mice and other small rodents in the eastern and southwestern United States, Egypt and elsewhere in the Eastern Hemisphere. *D. gallinæ* is a cosmopolitan pest in chicken houses and dove cotes. These mites attack man when opportunity is provided (Williams, 1958).

Life Cycle.—Parasitoid mites typically have a larval stage hatched from the egg followed by two nymphal stages, then the adult. Under optimum conditions of 24 to 26° C. and 47% relative humidity the life cycle of *B. bacoti* is completed in 11 to 16 days, the adults survive 62 days and the females each lay 99 eggs (Skaliy and Hayes, 1949).

Medical Importance.—All three species of parasitoid mites mentioned above are biological vectors of pathogenic microörganisms which affect man. This subject is considered in Chapter 18 (pages 396–415). These mites all produce an aggravating dermatitis.

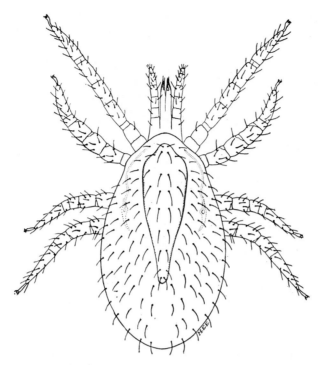

Fig. 170.—Adult parasitoid mite, *Bdellonyssus bacoti*, dorsal view. Greatly enlarged. (After Ewing, from Faust and Russell's *Clinical Parasitology*, Lea & Febiger, Philadelphia.)

B. bacoti feeds only on blood and drops off its host after a full meal. It takes at least 4 blood meals, one for each active stage. It infests persons working in places commonly frequented by rats. The dermatitis consists of urticarial wheals, papules and vesicles which develop at the site where each mite has fed. The intense itching frequently leads to scratching, with opportunity for secondary infection.

A. sanguineus and *D. gallinæ* probably do not suck blood but depend for their nourishment on tissue juices sucked out of the lower epidermis. They, too, produce a severe dermatitis and papular eczema due to the very toxic salivary secretions which they introduce into the skin.

Diagnosis of parasitoid mites is based on a history of contact with premises which harbor the natural hosts of these mites, and on demonstration of the particular mite recovered from the body of the victim. Treatment is topical and palliative in nature. Control consists in dusting chlordane or BHC (benzene hexachloride) in infested localities, such as chicken houses, rat runs and basements of homes, and campaigns to reduce domestic rodents.

CHIGGERS, HARVEST MITES, RED MITES, "RED BUGS" (TROMBIDOIDEA, Family TROMBICULIDÆ)

Adult Morphology and Bionomics.—The common names applied to this group refer to the larval stage which sucks tissue juices from man and a large variety of vertebrate hosts. The adults (Fig. 171) are about 1 mm.

long and figure-8-shaped. Both body and legs are covered with dense, velvety, pilose hairs. The cheliceræ have a blade-like distal joint provided dorsally with a row of saw teeth. There is a well-marked constriction of the body between the 2nd and 3rd pair of legs. The food of the nymphs and adults consists of eggs or the juices which these predators extract from other arthropods.

Life Cycle.—The eggs of trombiculid mites are laid on the ground and on the lower stems and leaves of grass or bushes. Upon maturity a 6-legged larva (Fig. 172) emerges from the egg shell and usually crawls upon a small rodent but may become attached to any terrestrial vertebrate including

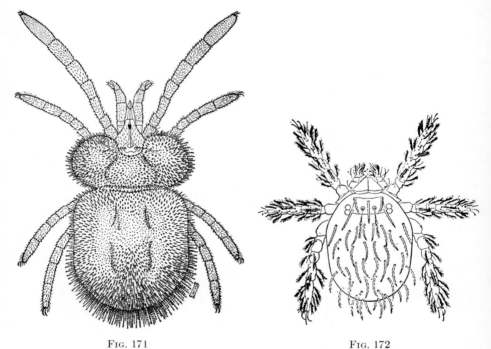

Fig. 171   Fig. 172

Fig. 171.—Adult red mite, *Trombicula alfreddugèsi*, dorsal view. Greatly enlarged. (After Ewing, from Faust and Russell's *Clinical Parasitology*, Lea & Febiger, Philadelphia.)

Fig. 172.—Larval stage of *Trombicula akamushi*, dorsal view. Greatly enlarged. (After Nagayo, *et al.* from Faust and Russell's *Clinical Parasitology*, Lea & Febiger, Philadelphia.)

larger rodents, domestic mammals or persons who enter infested vegetation. The larval mite sinks its cheliceræ and hypostome into the skin and proceeds to suck tissue juice until engorged. Then it releases its attachment, crawls down to the ground, transforms into a nymphochrysalis, then into a nymphal stage. Following an imagochrysalis stage the mite becomes sexually mature. North American species require a minimum of 55 to 71 days to complete a cycle.

The common species of trombiculids in the United States are *Trombicula* (*Eutrombicula*) *alfreddugèsi, T. (E.) splendens* and *T. (E.) batatas*; in Australia, *T. (Eutrombicula) sarcina*; in New Guinea, species of *Schöngastia*; in Europe, *T. (Neotrombicula) autumnalis*; in Japan, *T. (Leptotrombidium) akamushi*; in Malaya, *Ascoschöngastia malayensis.* The cuticle of the larva is usually red, hence the designation "red mite" or "red bug," but in some species it is practically colorless.

Medical Importance.—*Trombicula akamushi, T. deliensis, T. fuji* and *Ascoschöngastia indica* have been incriminated as reservoir hosts and biological vectors of *Rickettsia tsutsugamushi*, etiologic agent of scrub typhus. This subject is considered in Chapter 18 (pages 396–415). The larvæ of *Trombicula* and *Schöngastia* and probably other related genera produce a type of dermatitis in man. While some infested persons are relatively immune, others develop a severe local reaction which is first noted several hours after the mite has become attached and has begun to feed, accompanied by an almost insufferable pruritus. Soon a wheal forms around the site, frequently with hemorrhage. Scratching causes scarification and bleeding. The regions most frequently attacked are the ankles and legs, external genitalia and groin, the waistline, axillæ and breasts.

Treatment and Prophylaxis.—Topical application of phenolated camphor in mineral oil materially relieves the pruritus. Dusting of DDT into clothing, particularly socks and trouser cuffs provides considerable temporary protection. If persons find it necessary to travel through red mite-infested areas the impregnation of clothing with dimethyl phthalate or other repellent will greatly reduce the likelihood of bites. Cutting of high grass in the infested regions is an important control measure. Continued residence in the region usually provides tolerance to the bites.

Predaceous Mites (Tarsonemoidea)

Adult Morphology and Bionomics.—Members of this group have a distinct separation between cephalothorax and abdomen, with external evidence of segmentation on the abdomen. The cheliceræ are stylet-like and the palps are inconspicuous. Several species are predaceous on insects which infest grain crops. *Pediculoides (Pyemotes) ventricosus*, frequently referred to as the grain itch mite, is of medical importance.

Life Cycle.—*Pediculoides ventricosus* is produced viviparously and is mature at birth. The male immediately fertilizes the female, which then looks for a suitable host, piercing its skin to suck tissue juices. As it feeds the abdomen becomes greatly swollen. Eggs are produced, become mature and hatch within the distended sac, then the mites pass through larval and nymphal stages before emergence.

Clinical Notes.—When persons handle mite-infested grain, straw or hay during harvest time, the mites avidly attack the skin, become attached but are unable to penetrate. A wheal develops at each site of attachment to the skin, causing an intense pruritus. The lesion is a whitish raised area surrounding a central vesicle. Rubbing or scratching aggravates the condition. Systemic symptoms mimicking serum sickness may develop in cases of heavy infestation or in particularly sensitive individuals. Diagnosis can be made by obtaining the occupational history or habits of the patient, together with the character of the dermatitis and at times by recovery of the female mites from the skin. Scabies (page 349), pediculosis (page 367) and allergic dermatitis must be ruled out. Treatment consists first of all in topical application of a mild anti-pruritic, accompanied or followed by an antiseptic lotion.

Epidemiology.—*P. ventricosus* is cosmopolitan in its distribution in grain-raising regions of the world. Epidemic dermatitis due to this mite occurs seasonally in Italy, the Balkans, Egypt, Algeria, India, South Australia, the north-central plains area of the United States and adjacent Canada.

Control.—Little or no immunity is developed to this infestation. Persons may be attacked several times during one harvest season. Use of sulfur or other insect toxicant in infested granaries to kill the insects on which the mites normally feed, together with burning of the stubble in grain fields, will reduce exposure.

Food Mites (Tyroglyphoidea)

Adult Morphology and Bionomics.—The small, stout body is separated into a cephalothorax and an abdomen by a transverse groove but there is no external evidence of segmentation on the abdomen. The surface of the body is smooth and glistening, without transverse parallel lines. The legs typically have terminal claws and lack stalked suckers. Males have a sucking pad on each side of the genital opening. The adults are never true predators or parasites but feed on cheeses or cereals and a variety of organic substances.

Life Cycle.—The following stages are recognized: egg, larva, 2 (or 3) nymphal stages, adult female, and normal or heteromorphic male. If there are 3 nymphal stages, the second one is provided with suckers or claspers for grasping insects, allowing the mite to be dispersed to other localities.

Clinical Notes.—Dermatitis results when the skin of the hands or other body areas comes in contact with infested plant products. The mites crawl under epidermal scales or enter cracks in the skin, where they lodge and produce a temporary pruritus, *e.g.*, "copra itch," "grocer's itch," "vanilla worker's itch," etc. Almost invariably this is an occupational disease which must not be confused with scabies. Tyroglyphoid mites may temporarily lodge in the intestinal crypts and produce irritation of the mucous membrane, or may be breathed in and be expelled in the sputum or lodge temporarily in a bronchiectasis (Kao *et al.*, 1956; Liu *et al.*, 1957). In the lungs they may provoke bronchial asthma with an associated eosinophilia (Carter and D'Abrera, 1946; Soysa, 1949).

Treatment of cutaneous food-mite infestation consists in thoroughly cleansing the affected skin with soap and water and application of lindane ointment (0.5% gamma isomer of benzene hexachloride in vanishing cream). Intestinal infestation can usually be eliminated by saline purgation. Pulmonary infestation may possibly respond to arsenical treatment.

Epidemiology.—The group has very extensive distribution. Accidental human infestation results from handling or eating infested plant products. The more common mites which infest the skin are *Tyroglyphus siro*, from handling vanilla pods and beans, or cereal flour provided for human and animal consumption (Arru, 1960); *T.longior* var. *castellanii*, from contact with copra; *Glyciphagus prunorum*, concentrated in grocery stores, and *Rhizoglyphus echinopus*, associated with flower bulbs. If infested cheeses and other foods are eaten they provide a means for the mites to get into the alimentary tract.

Control.—No practical control measures have been developed.

"TONGUE WORMS" (PENTASTOMIDA)

Adult Morphology and Biology.—The adults of this group are elongate, linguiform or moniliform objects which have superficial annulations that do not correspond to the internal segments (metameres). They are legless, but near the mouth there are 2 pairs of hollow, curved, retractile hooklets (rudimentary appendages), which have basal glands that produce digestive and possibly hemolytic secretions. There is no external separation into head, thorax and abdomen. The males are somewhat smaller than the females. The adults are endoparasitic in the mouth, esophagus or respiratory organs of vertebrates, where they feed on blood and mucosal cells.

Life Cycle.—In the genus *Linguatula* (*L. serrata*), which is tongue-shaped, the females deposit their eggs in the posterior nares of the mammalian host. In the nasal secretions they are voided in the feces, and on reaching moist vegetation complete embryonation. When ingested by herbivorous mammals, the eggs hatch in the digestive tract, the emerging larvæ migrate through the intestinal wall and lodge in the liver or other viscera. There they transform in about 5 to 6 months into nymphs which lie within a capsule of host tissue. If the infected larval host is eaten by carnivorous animals, the nymphs are digested out of the tissue and migrate to the nasal passages where they develop into adults. The common larval hosts are rabbits, sheep and goats; the common definitive host is the dog.

In the genera *Armillifer* (*A. armillatus*, *A. moniliformis*) and *Porocephalus*, which superficially resemble a string of beads, the females live and deposit their eggs in the respiratory passages of pythons and other snakes. Animals which consume infected raw snakes, or ingest the "worm's" eggs that have been discharged in nasal secretions into water or on vegetation, serve as intermediate hosts in which the larval and nymphal stages develop.

Clinical Notes.—*Linguatula serrata* has been found as a human parasite in Africa, Germany, Switzerland, Greece, Panama, Colombia, Brazil, Chile, and United States of America. Species of *Armillifer* and *Porocephalus* have been recovered in immature stages from man in various anatomical sites, including the anterior chamber of the eye (Hunter and Higgins, 1960), in tropical Africa, Egypt, India, Java, and China. In most cases the "worms" produce no demonstrable symptoms and are incidental autopsy findings. Rarely multiple infection provokes marked inflammation of the intestinal wall or the liver. Diagnosis is almost invariably post-mortem. No satisfactory treatment has been developed.

Control.—This requires discontinuance of the custom of eating raw flesh and refraining from drinking raw water or eating polluted raw vegetation in enzoötic areas.

SUMMARY

1. Arthropods (Phylum Arthropoda) are characterized by bilateral symmetry, true segmentation, an exoskeleton and paired jointed appendages.
2. The adults have a complete digestive tract, an excretory system, a blood vascular system, a respiratory system (in most species), a central nervous system and male or female genitalia.
3. The life cycle of arthropods may be very simple, with only egg, larval and adult stages; it may be somewhat more complex, or it may have complete metamorphosis during a pupal stage between larva and adult.
4. Originally all arthropods were aquatic. Many groups have become adapted to a terrestrial life; some are either aquatic or terrestrial during their immature stages and terrestrial or aërial as mature forms.
5. Species of arthropods of medical importance may serve as intermediate hosts or vectors of other organisms pathogenic for man; or they themselves may produce human illness as parasites, or as a result of their venomous and salivary secretions.

6. Centipedes (Chilopoda) are elongated forms having one pair of jointed appendages for each body segment. On the head there are 1 pair each of antennæ and mandibles and 2 pairs of maxillæ. The first post-cephalic appendage bears a pair of poison jaws with a terminal fang.

7. Scorpions (Scorpiones) have a fused dorsal exoskeleton covering the head and thorax, and separate abdominal segments. They have long, clawed pedipalps and inconspicuous jaws on the head, four long cephalothoracic legs, and a broad anterior and narrow posterior portion of the abdomen ending in a curved caudal sting apparatus. Scorpions live in warm climates and shun extreme dryness and sunlight. Their natural food is soft-bodied insects but they also venenate larger animals as a protective mechanism. The venom of some scorpions produces only localized reaction. In other species the venom is primarily neurotoxic, resulting in an ascending motor paralysis. Insect toxicants sprayed within and around homes provide considerable protection.

8. Spiders (Araneæ) have a cephalothorax separated from a much larger abdomen by a conspicuous constriction, and 4 pairs of long thoracic legs. The mouth parts include a pair of poison jaws with a hollow termination, through which digestive enzymes and venom are secreted.

   All spiders which venenate man belong to two groups, one (*Loxo-sceles* spp.) having secretions which produce a local indolent ulcer (necrotic arachnidism) and the other (*Latrodectus* spp. *et al.*) causing ascending motor paralysis (systemic arachnidism). Residual spraying of DDT or benzene hexachloride (Gammexane) where the spiders live provides effective control.

9. Ticks and mites (Acari) are 8-legged arthropods which are usually broadly oval in contour and have no external separation between cephalothorax and abdomen. They possess a head portion with a well-developed median hypostome below the mouth, a pair of cheliceræ and a pair of palps. The life cycle includes the egg, a 6-legged larval stage, one or more 8-legged nymphal stages and the adult.

10. Ticks are large mites with a leathery integument and a conspicuous hypostome provided with sharp recurved hooklets. They have one larval and one nymphal stage between the egg and the adult. All ticks feed on vertebrate blood during each active stage. The soft-bodied forms (Argasidæ) feed intermittently and the hard-bodied forms (Ixodidæ) take a prolonged feeding.

    Ticks are medically important (1) as biological vectors of microör-ganisms pathogenic for man, (2) as the agents of painful cutaneous wounds, and (3) as the cause of tick paralysis resulting from the injection of their salivary secretions into the punctured skin. Dusting of DDT into socks and trouser cuffs will materially reduce the liability of tick infestation.

11. Mange mites are true tissue parasites in the skin. The species which infests man (*Sarcoptes scabiei*) is a very small macroscopic object, broadly oval, with a head projecting forward like a turtle's, 2 pairs of anteriorly-projecting legs and 2 pairs of posteriorly-projecting legs. The female lives at the inner end of a tunnel, where she lays a few large eggs each day for 4 to 5 weeks.

Human sarcoptic mange is almost always contracted from close contact with infested persons or their clothing. The female burrows into the deeper epidermis producing vesiculation at the inner end of the tunnel and causing intense pruritus. Scratching results in spread of the mite's progeny to other areas. Treatment consists in thorough soaking of the lesions with warm soapy water, then application of lindane ointment.

12. The follicular mange mite (*Demodex folliculorum*) is a microscopic vermiform object which invades the hair follicles and sebaceous glands, producing an inflammatory reaction of an acniform type, accompanied by moderate pruritus.

13. Parasitoid mites (*Bdellonyssus, Allodermanyssus* and *Dermanyssus*) are small macroscopic forms which commonly infest rodents or birds. All are biological vectors of pathogenic microörganisms and also produce a pruritic dermatitis. Control consists in dusting insect toxicants into infested locations and campaigns against domestic rats and mice.

14. Chiggers or red mites (family Trombiculidæ) are small macroscopic mites, having adults which obtain food from small invertebrates and larvæ which infest vertebrate hosts to suck tissue juices. A few species in the Orient are biological vectors of scrub typhus. Several species are aggravating pests of man, producing severe local reaction, with intense pruritus. Dusting of DDT into socks and clothing provides temporary protection from the mites.

15. Predaceous mites commonly prey on insects which infest cereal crops. *Pediculoides ventricosus* is a serious human pest, particularly at harvest time.

16. Food mites are small forms which infest the skin of persons who handle green grocery stocks and other infested objects. Rarely they may be inhaled and cause bronchial asthma.

17. "Tongue worms" (pentastomes) are worm-like arthropods with superficial annulations. They require two hosts to complete a life cycle. The immature stages are found in the visceral organs, the mature stage in the upper respiratory passages of the host. Man occasionally serves as intermediate host.

REFERENCES

ARRU, E. 1960. *Tyroglyphus siro* (Linnæus, 1758) causa di malattia nell' uomo e negli animali. Parassitol., *2*, 3–6.

ATKINS, J. A., WINGO, C. W., SODEMAN, W. A., and FLYNN, J. E. 1958. Necrotic Arachnidism. Am. J. Trop. Med. & Hyg., *7*, 165–184.

BAKER, E. W., and WHARTON, G. W. 1952. *An Introduction to Acarology*, 465 pp., Macmillan Co., New York.

BÜCHERL, W. 1959. Scorpion Venoms. Clin. Excerpts, Bayer (Leverkusen), No. 4, pp. 63–70.

CARTER, H. F., and D'ABRERA, V. ST. E. 1946. Mites (Acarina)—a Probable Factor in the Aetiology of Spasmotic Bronchitis and Asthma Associated with High Eosinophilia. Trans. R. Soc. Trop. Med. & Hyg., *39*, 373–396.

CLOUDSLEY-THOMPSON, J. L. 1958. *Spiders, Scorpions, Centipedes and Mites*, 228 pp., Pergamon Press, New York, London, etc.

D'AMOUR, F. E., BECKER, F. E., and VAN RIPER, W. 1936. The Black Widow Spider. Q. Rev. Biol., *11*, 123–160.

HOUSE, H. L.   1958.   Nutritional Requirements of Insects Associated with Animal Parasitism. Exp. Parasitol., *7*, 555–609.

HUNTER, W. S., and HIGGINS, R. P.   1960.   An Unusual Case of Human Porocephaliasis. J. Parasitol., *46*, 68.

JAMES, J. A., SELLARS, W. A., AUSTIN, O. M., and TERRILL, B. S.   1961.   Reactions Following Suspected Spider Bite. Am. J. Dis. Child., *102*, 395–398.

KAO, C. M., LIU, M. H., and WEI, P. H.   1956.   *Tyroglyphus* in the Sputum of Patient with Respiratory Disease: Report of a Case with Observations on Life History and Resistance of the Mite. Nat'l Med. J. China, *42*, 1048–1052.

KEEGAN, H. L.   1956.   Antivenoms Available for Treatment of Envenomation by Poisonous Snakes, Scorpions, and Spiders, in *Venoms*, pp. 413–438, Am. Assn. Adv. Sci., Washington, D.C.

LEVI, H. W.   1958.   Number of Species of Black-Widow Spiders (Theridiidæ: *Latrodectus*). Science, *127*, 1055.

LIU, M. H., KAO, C. M., and WEI, P. H.   1957.   Occurrence of Mites in Bronchiectasis Sputum. Chinese Med. J., *75*, 578–584.

MACKINNON, J. E., and WITKIND, J.   1953.   Arachnidismo necrótico. An. Fac. de Med., Montevideo, *38*, 75–100.

MURNAGHAN, M. F.   1960.   Site and Mechanism of Tick Paralysis. Science, *131*, 418–419.

PATTERSON, R. A.   1960.   Physiological Action of Scorpion Venom. Am. J. Trop. Med. & Hyg., *9*, 410–414.

PRATS, F., and SCHENONE, H.   1957.   Mordeduras de arañas. Nuevas consideraciones sobre Loxoscelismo. Bol. Chileno Parasitol., *12*, 7–9.

VAN SANDE, M., and KARCHER, D.   1960.   Species Differentiation of Insects by Hemolymph Electrophoresis. Science, *131*, 1103–1104.

SCHENONE, F. H.   1953.   Mordeduras de arañas. Bol. Inform. Parasit. Chilenas, *8*, 35–36.

SCHENONE, H.   1959.   Aspectos prácticos en la clínica del síndrome del latrodectismo y su tratamiento con Neostigmina (Prostigmina). Bol. Chileno de Parasitol., *14*, 80–82.

SCHENONE, H., SEMPREVIVO, L., and SCHIRMER, E.   1959.   Consideraciones a propósito de dos casos de Loxoscelismo cutáneo-visceral. Bol. Chileno Parasitol., *14*, 17–19.

SKALIY, P., and HAYES, W. J.   1949.   The Biology of *Liponyssus bacoti* (Hirst, 1913). (Acarina, Liponyssidæ). Am. J. Trop. Med., *29*, 759–772.

DE SOUZA, J. C., MACHADO DE BUSTAMANTE, F., and BICALHO, J. C.   1954.   Novos dados sobre o combate aos escorpiöes em Belo Horizonte com o hexoclorociclohexana. Rev. Brasil. de Malariol. e Doenças Trop., *6*, 357–361.

SOYSA, E.   1949.   The Eosinophilic Respiratory Syndrome. J. R. Army Med. Corps, *92*, 1.

STAHNKE, H. L.   1949.   Scorpions. 23 pp. Tempe, Arizona.

————.   1953.   The L–C Treatment of Venomous Bites or Stings. Am. J. Trop. Med. & Hyg., *2*, 142–143.

WEISMANN, A., and SHULOV, A.   1959.   Investigations on the Venom of the Scorpion *Buthotus (Buthus) judiacus*. E. Sim. Arch. l'Inst. Pasteur d'Algerie, *37*, 202–217.

WIENER, S.   1956.   The Australian Red-back Spider (*Latrodectus hasselti*). II. Effect of Temperature on the Toxicity of the Venom. Med. J. Australia, *i*, 331–334.

WILLIAMS, R. W.   1958.   An Infestation of a Human Habitation by *Dermanyssus gallinæ* (De Geer, 1778) (Acarina: Dermanyssidæ) in New York City, Resulting in Sanguisugent Attacks upon the Occupants. Am. J. Trop. Med .& Hyg., *7*, 627–629.

Chapter 17

Arthropods as Agents of Human
Disease (*Concluded*)

INSECTS

INSECTS (Class Insecta) are the most numerous of the arthropods and comprise about 70% of all the known species of animals. Both economically and medically insects constitute the most important group in the Animal Kingdom.

Adult Morphology.—All adult insects have 3 pairs of thoracic legs, hence the frequent reference to this class as "hexapods." Moreover, insects have three distinct portions of the body, *i.e.*, head, thorax and abdomen (Fig. 173).

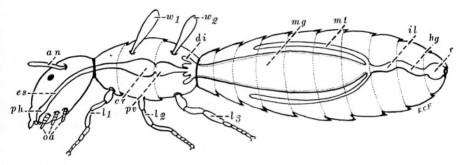

FIG. 173.—Schematic representation of an insect, viewed from the left side. *an*, antenna; *cr*, crop; *di*, food diverticulum; *es*, esophagus; *hg*, hindgut; *il*, ileum; *l₁, l₂, l₃*, thoracic legs; *mg*, midgut; *mt*, Malpighian tubule; *oa*, oral appendages; *ph*, pharynx; *pv*, proventriculus; *r*, rectum; *w₁, w₂*, wings. (Original adaptation.)

The *head* is developed from 6 fused segments. The paired appendages are all highly modified from the jointed legs of the primitive arthropod (Fig. 160, page 335). The anteriormost pair are the antennæ. The mouth parts consist of 1 pair each of palps, mandibles and maxillæ and a posteriormost fused pair, the labium or lower lip (Fig. 174). In the grasshopper, cockroach and beetles, these are adapted for chewing, whereas in sucking lice, bugs, moths and butterflies, flies and fleas they have been transformed into a tubule adapted for lapping or for piercing and sucking.

The *thorax* contains 3 segments, prothorax, mesothorax and metathorax, each with a pair of walking legs (Fig. 173). Most insects also have wings. The full number of wings consists of 2 pairs, 1 pair each on the mesothoracic

(359)

and metathoracic segments.   Flies have retained only the mesothoracic pair.

The *abdomen* consists of 12 original segments, a majority of which can be seen on external examination of the insect, although the first two are not apparent, and the distalmost ones are modified as external genital organs.

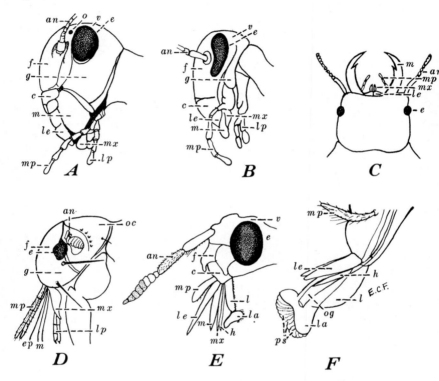

Fig. 174.—Representative head appendages of several insects. *A, B, C,* chewing types; *D, E, F,* sucking types. *A,* grasshopper; *B,* cockroach; *C,* lucanid beetle; *D,* human flea; *E,* deer fly; *F,* calliphorid fly. *an,* antenna; *c,* clypeus; *e,* compound eye; *ep,* epipharynx; *f,* frons; *g,* gena (cheek); *h,* hypopharynx; *l,* labium; *la,* labellum; *le,* labrum or labrum-epipharynx; *lp,* labial palp; *m,* mandible; *mp,* maxillary palp; *mx,* maxilla; *o,* ocellus (eyespot); *oc,* occiput; *og,* oral groove; *ps,* pseudo-tracheæ; *v,* vertex. (Original adaptations, *A,* from Folsom, *B,* and *C* from Comstock, *D* from Fox, *E* and *F* from Imms.)

The digestive tract with its component organs is shown in Figure 173.

Life Cycle.—In the ancestral insect the stage hatched from the egg was essentially adult in character.   Some present-day groups, such as the chewing and sucking lice, have only an inconspicuous metamorphosis between larva and adult.   Others, like the true bugs, resemble the ticks and mites in having larval and/or nymphal stages before transformation to the adult. In still other groups, *e.g.,* beetles, ants, butterflies and fleas, the larva is worm-like and has chewing mouth parts.   In these insects, following the last larval stage there is a pupal period during which a profound reorganization of internal and external structures takes place before the adult emerges from the pupal skin or cocoon.

Insects as Causal Agents of Disease

From a medical point of view, emphasis is usually focused on the insect as host and transmitter of pathogenic microörganisms. This subject is considered in Chapter 18, p. 396. But many insects are likewise important causal agents of disease. The types of injury which they produce may be classified as follows:

1. VESICATING, *i.e.*, discharge of body fluids which produce blisters on the skin or mucous membranes. Example: Blister beetles.
2. URTICATING, *i.e.*, nettling from poison "hairs" which come in contact with the skin or mucous membranes. Example: Certain caterpillars.
3. VENENATING, *i.e.*, introduction of poison fluid into the skin as a protective mechanism of the insect. Examples: Bees, wasps, hornets and ants.
4. SENSITIZING, *i.e.*, introduction of salivary or other secretions into the skin with resultant sensitization phenomena. Examples: Bloodsucking insects (sucking lice, true bugs, flies and fleas).
5. TISSUE-INVADING, *i.e.*, specific or accidental invasion of the skin by the larval or adult stage of the insect. Examples: Myiasis-producing flies, the chigœ flea, certain beetles.

These topics will be considered in sequence.

1. Vesicating Insects

Insect vesication is confined to a few families of beetles (Order Coleoptera), in which the adults have chewing mouth parts. There are 2 pairs of wings, of which the first pair are thickened to form a protective covering (elytra) over the membraneous second pair when the wings are at rest over the abdomen.

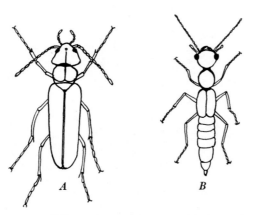

FIG. 175.—Vesicating beetles. *A, Lytta vesicatoria* ("Spanish fly"); *B, Pæderus sabæus* (rove beetle). (Original adaptations from Smart.)

The most notorious of the vesicating beetles belong to the Family Meloidæ, the adults of which produce cantharidin, a substance present in all body tissues but most concentrated in the genitalia. The effective principle is a volatile fluid of pungent odor and weakly acid taste. The commonest cantharidin-producing species is *Lytta* (*Cantharis*) *vesicatoria* ("Spanish fly"). When this beetle (Fig. 175 A) is accidentally crushed on the skin, an epidermal blister develops, in which histamine-like substances can be demonstrated.

A more potent vesicating fluid (not containing cantharidin) is elaborated by adults of certain rove beetles (Family Staphylinidæ), including species of the cosmopolitan genus *Pæderus* (Fig. 175 B). Both of these types of fluids cause intensely painful blisters when they come in contact with the skin or conjunctiva.

If a vesicating beetle alights on the skin, it is much safer to blow it off rather than to crush it. Tetracaine applied at the site partly alleviates the burning pain caused by the vesicating fluid.

2. Urticating Insects

Urtication among insects is a protective mechanism of the larval stages (caterpillars) of one family of butterflies and several families of moths (Order Lepidoptera). The adults typically have 2 pairs of membranous wings covered with overlapping patterned scales and maxillæ adapted to sucking juices such as the nectar of flowers. The females oviposit on or near vegetation which is used as food by the larval stages. The larvæ feed ravenously and develop into successively larger larval instars, then form a horny case or spin a cocoon which houses the pupal stage. After a period of weeks or months, metamorphosis is completed and the adult emerges from the pupal covering.

The specialized mechanism for urtication is confined to certain hairs or spines. These organs (Fig. 176) originate in the hypodermis and project through the cuticle. They are of two main morphologic types, primitive and modified (Gilmer, 1925). In the former, each seta is connected with a single unicellular poison gland at its base, which has a minute duct extending into the center of the hair. In the latter, the seta has a bulbous base lined or filled with a number of poison-producing cells. Poison setæ may be widely distributed over the larva's body or may be confined to tufts, easily seen or concealed among longer non-poisonous, silky hairs. The more common urticating caterpillars include a few butterflies, flannel moths, slug caterpillars, processionary caterpillars, tussock moths, tiger moths, owlet moths and giant silkworms.

All larval stages of poisonous species have urticating hairs. Accidental contact with the living caterpillar causes urtication. Poison hairs incorporated into the cocoon may become attached to the emerging adults and be carried to persons who accidentally brush against the moths; or residual hairs may be blown in air currents and make contact with unprotected human skin and mucous membranes.

The sharp poison setæ readily penetrate into tender skin, the conjunctivæ, nasal or buccal mucosa. The poison appears to be neither cantharidin nor formic acid and has a hemolytic constituent.

Pathogenesis and Symptomatology.—The amount of injury and the severity of symptoms in caterpillar urtication depend on the species of caterpillar and its type of poison, the number of setæ which have pierced the body surface, the age of the patient and the individual sensitivity of the victim.

At the time the poison is introduced, there is a local burning, stinging sensation, the affected area becomes erythematous, then elevated and whitish, with a reddish border extending radially as much as 2.5 centimeters and a peripheral reddish macular zone 2 cm. beyond. Occasionally urticarial wheals may develop over the entire body, accompanied by systemic manifestations suggesting a neurotoxic syndrome (Lucas, 1942).

Treatment.—There is no satisfactory treatment other than topical application of palliative lotions, tetracaine ointment, elixir of diphenhydramine (Benadryl), and occasionally codeine sulfate to relieve the pain (Randel, 1956). Usually there is no ulceration and the reaction subsides in a few hours.

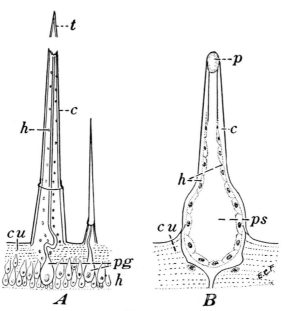

FIG. 176.—Primitive (*A*) and modified (*B*) types of urticating hairs of caterpillars. *c*, chitinous covering of spine; *cu*, cuticle; *h*, hypodermis; *p*, canal plug; *pg*, poison gland cell; *ps*, poison sac; *t*, tip of spine. (Adapted from Beyer and from Foot, in Faust and Russell's *Clinical Parasitology*, Lea & Febiger, Philadelphia.)

Control.—Area control of moths is indicated, both as an economic measure and as a potential disease preventive. Several insect toxicants are valuable when power-sprayed over affected outdoor areas. DDT and chlordane require no special precautions but dieldrin and thiocyanates, and particularly parathion, which are probably more effective, are so very toxic that there must be special protection for man and higher animals in the area.

3. Venenating Insects

Specific insect venenation is confined to the bees, wasps, hornets and ants (Order Hymenoptera). These insects have 2 pairs of membranous wings, mouth parts adapted to sucking or lapping nectar (bees), or for lancing and chewing (ants). In the worker (a modified female) the ovipositor at the caudal extremity is transformed into a sting apparatus. Metamorphosis in these insects is complete.

The Sting Apparatus.—As described for the honey bee, the venenating mechanism (Fig. 177) consists of a pair of tubular acid glands, the contents of which are conducted through a long duct into a venom receptacle, a single alkaline gland which opens at the base of the sting cavity, a strong chitinous bulb below the venom receptacle, and the chitinized sting, consisting of a dorsal sheath, a pair of ventro-lateral lancets and a pair of lateral palps. The puncture is made by the sheath and lancets, then a mixture of the poison secretions is injected into the wound. All species of bees, hornets, wasps and several species of ants have an efficient sting mechanism and potent venom.

Venenation.—The workers of the honey bee and of some wasps leave the posterior tip of their abdomen, including the entire sting mechanism, in the victim's

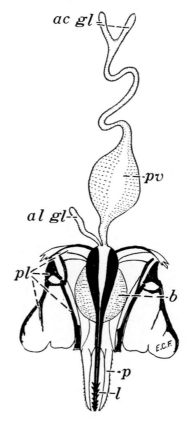

Fig. 177.—Venenating mechanism (modified ovipositor) of honey bee. *ac gl*, acid venom glands; *al gl*, alkaline venom gland; *b*, bulb; *l*, lancet; *p*, palp; *pl*, chitinized plates, *pv*, acid venom receptacle. (Adapted from Patton and Evans, in Faust and Russell's *Clinical Parasitology*, Lea & Febiger, Philadelphia.)

skin. Muscle attachments continue to contract for some time, forcing the sting more deeply into the wound and setting additional venom free. None of these individuals is able to sting again. Bumble bees retain their sting and produce less severe trauma.

The active venom fraction, *apitoxin*, is present in the acid gland secretion. Electrophoretic separation has demonstrated histamine, toxins, hyaluronidase as the spreading factor, and other active protein components in bee venom, also 5-hydroxytryptamine in wasp and hornet venom (Neumann and Habermann, 1956.)

Pathogenesis and Symptomatology.—In some individuals the sting of hymenopterans produces only a temporary local swelling with moderate pain which disappears in a few hours. In other persons the entire member becomes swollen and systemic symptoms of considerable or even profound nature develop. Subsequent venenation may have a rapid, fatal outcome.

Ants which produce particularly painful wounds are the large aggressive species found in the Tropics, such as the tucandeira (*Paraponera clavata*) of South America, which at times literally sting their victims to death. The "fire ant" (*Solenopsis sævissima* var. *richteri*), a relatively small species recently introduced from South America into the southern United States, is a vicious stinger. Its venom, having strong hemolytic property, produces a vesicle at the site of skin puncture, with a peripheral reddish macule which may become necrotic, and in some individuals may give rise to systemic reaction probably of an allergic type (Adrouny, Derbes and Jung, 1959).

Treatment.—Honey-bee sting is extracted by use of a sharp needle or knife blade. Local injection of an antihistaminic drug will ease the pain resulting from the accumulation of histamine-like substances at the wounded site. In cases of anaphylactic reaction, epinephrine, or preferably ethylnorepinephrine (Shaffer, 1961), should be administered hypodermically as promptly as possible. Ice packs and palliative lotions applied topically to bumble-bee, wasp, hornet and ant venenation may be helpful in reducing the swelling and relieving the pain.

Control.—Accidental sting by bees, wasps and hornets is sometimes unavoidable. However, sensitized persons should avoid exposure by wearing protective clothing, gloves, and nets for face and neck when they approach swarms or active hives. Hypersensitized individuals should receive desensitizing treatment carried out with honey-bee venom extract, which is group-specific. Sprinkling of powdered chlordane (6% in inert powder) on ant nests in the ground followed by wetting, to allow penetration of the toxicant into the soil, is effective against ants.

4. Salivary Sensitization

Introduction

Sensitization phenomena result from the injection of salivary secretions into the human skin by sucking lice, hemophagous bugs, blood-sucking flies and fleas. These secretions usually contain only digestive enzymes or related foreign proteins but the reniform salivary glands of sucking lice apparently produce a special toxic principle.

SUCKING LICE (ANOPLURA)

Adult Morphology.—Lice are small macroscopic, wingless, dorsoventrally flattened insects which have 3- to 5-jointed stubby antennæ and 3 pairs of conspicuous legs each ending in a sharp curved claw. The "biting lice" (Mallophaga) have chewing mouth parts, a head broader than the thorax and feed on feathers, hairs and epidermal scales of birds and mammals but do not infest man. In contrast, the sucking lice (Anoplura) have mouth parts adapted to piercing and sucking, their head is narrower than the thorax, their legs terminate in claws used for clinging to hairs or fibers, and they are restricted to an ectoparasitic life on mammals (Fig. 178).

The anteriormost portion of the head is the clypeus, which is prolonged into an upper lip (labrum), below which is the sucking apparatus (haustellum). In preparation for taking blood the louse applies its haustellum to the skin surface, inserts its teeth into the epidermis, then introduces the stylets and hypopharynx, deposits a drop of saliva, and by alternate contraction and distention of the pharynx pumps blood through the mouth funnel into the esophagus and midgut.

Externally neither the head nor the thorax exhibits evidence of segmentation but several of the abdominal segments are distinct. The abdomen of the male is narrower than that of the female and is rounded posteriorly, while the caudal extremity of the female is provided with a pair of blunt

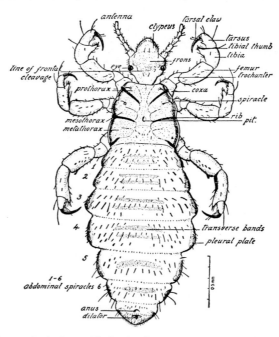

Fig. 178.—Human body louse (*Pediculus humanus* var. *corporis*), male, dorsal view, enlarged. (After Nuttall in Matheson's Medical Entomology, from Faust and Russell's *Clinical Parasitology*, Lea & Febiger, Philadelphia.)

processes (cerci) for grasping a hair or fiber onto which an egg is then attached. Blood and possibly cutaneous cell fluids constitute the food of adult sucking lice.

Life Cycle.—The female begins to oviposit in a day or two after she has matured and has been fertilized. Head lice (*Pediculus humanus* var. *capitis*) characteristically cement their eggs to the hair of the head or back of the neck; body lice (*P. humanus* var. *corporis*), to the fibers of body clothing; pubic lice (*Phthirus pubis*), to the hairs of the pubic region, chest, axilla, eyebrows and eyelashes. These eggs, the so-called "nits" (Fig. 179), hatch in 4 to 14 days at body temperature, with emergence of the first nymphal stage, which feeds, molts and passes through a second and third nymphal stage before becoming adult 12 to 28 days after oviposition. The adults live about 30 days, during which time each female produces 5 to 10 eggs daily.

Bionomics.—Lice are host-species specific. The three kinds of lice found on man are exclusively human parasites. Their nymphs and adults depend on man for food and warmth but actively transfer from one person to another. Body lice engorge at frequent intervals, discharging relatively large pellets of dark red excrement as they feed.

Infestation with lice is most common among groups in crowded quarters or those with poor personal hygiene. The body louse (*P. humanus* var. *corporis*) is usually found on individuals in cold climates who wear heavy clothing and seldom bathe. The head louse (*P. humanus* var. *capitis*) is more often found on long-haired girls and women than on males with short hair. The pubic louse (*Phthirus pubis*) is named because it is usually associated with the pubic hairs; it is also called the crab louse because of its

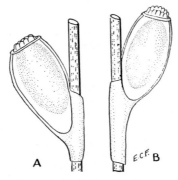

Fig. 179.—Eggs of human lice. *A*, *Pediculus humanus* var. *capitis*; *B*, *Phthirus pubis*. (Original adaptations, from Faust and Russell's *Clinical Parasitology*, Lea & Febiger, Philadelphia.)

superficial resemblance to a crab. Like the head louse, it is more intimately associated with the body hairs and takes a more prolonged feeding than the body louse, which lives among the wool or cotton fibers of clothing except when it is feeding on the skin.

Louse-bite.—Louse infestation is referred to as *pediculosis*. The local lesion produced by human body lice develops at any site on the body where the numphs or adults are feeding. Head lice may feed on any hair-covered area of the scalp. Pubic lice frequent the pubic or other hairy regions of the body.

Saliva introduced by the louse into the puncture wound results in the development of a roseate elevated papule, accompanied by intense pruritus. Involuntary scratching of the lesion causes an eczematous dermatitis, striated scarring from use of the fingernails and at times induration and bronzing of the area. Topical application of soothing lotions relieves the pruritus and allows the lesions to heal.

For consideration of lice as transmitters of pathogenic microörganisms please see Chapter 18, pages 406, 407 and 411.

Control.—For persons infested with head or pubic lice, lindane ointment ($\frac{1}{2}\%$ benzene hexachloride in vanishing cream) rubbed into the parasitized skin is a practical, specific measure. For body lice, dusting of the body and clothing with 2% DDT in pyrophyllite has proved most effective as a control measure except where resistance to DDT has developed (Barnett and Knoblock, 1952; Hurlbut *et al.*, 1954; Perry and Buckner, 1958). Chlordane is possibly the most effective, safe alternative. All clothing and other fomites of infested persons should be sterilized by fumigation with methyl bromide, using necessary precautions.

TRUE BUGS (HETEROPTERA)

Adult Morphology.—Members of this order of insects typically have 2 pairs of wings, of which the anterior pair are thickened basally and membranous distally and the posterior ones are entirely membranous. Bedbugs have only wing buds which never develop into functional organs. The most conspicuous external feature of the true bugs is the hinged proboscis, which lies under the head and thorax when at rest but is directed ventrally at right angles to the body when engaged in piercing and sucking.

The head appendages consist of a pair of 3-jointed antennæ and the proboscis with its enclosed structures. Palps are lacking. The protective portion of the proboscis is the sheath (lower lip or labium), a relatively long, 3- or 4-jointed, flexible tube which is almost completely closed on its anterior face. Covering the basal portion of the proboscis there is a short, rhomboidal, upper lip (labrum). Within the proboscis sheath there are a pair each of long, terminally-toothed, bristle-like mandibles and slightly larger, grooved maxillæ that form the food canal. Below the maxillæ there is a minute hypopharynx. (See Geigy and Kraus, 1952.)

The prothorax occupies the greatest part of the thoracic region. The legs are 5-jointed and terminate in 2 small claws.

The digestive tract of true bugs conforms for the most part to that of insects as a whole (Fig. 173, pages 359, 360).

Life Cycle.—Metamorphosis is incomplete and almost as inconspicuous as it is in the sucking lice. Following the hatching of the eggs there are several larval (or nymphal) stages, then the sexually mature males and females.

Bionomics.—In the bedbugs (Family Cimicidæ) the adults and immature stages hide in dark cracks and crevices within human habitations during the daytime and come out to suck blood from their victims at night. Each female lays about 100 to 500 glutinous eggs in batches over a period of several weeks. The female requires 4 to 12 minutes to become engorged. The two bedbugs which commonly attack man are *Cimex lectularius* (temperate zone) and *C. hemipterus* (tropical). The former is more urban, the latter more rural in its habitat. Both species are shiny, mahogany brown in color, with a body about 5 mm. long and 3 mm. broad, flattened dorso-ventrally; they lack wings, are covered with many hair-like spines and have conspicuous compound eyes (Fig. 180).

The assassin or cone-nosed bugs (Family Triatomidæ) and their relatives of the Superfamily Reduvidoidea are more elongated and considerably larger than the bedbugs (Fig. 181). They have conspicuous, well-developed wings, a pair of compound eyes, and immediately postero-dorsal to each eye a small "eye-spot." Seen from above, the head is roughly diamond-shaped but from a lateral view it is more or less conical. The abdomen is elongated-ovoidal and is not conspicuously flattened. Assassin bugs which are medically important reside in warm regions. Some species, such as *Triatoma infestans, Panstrongylus megistus* and *Rhodnius prolixus* of South America are primarily domestic in their habits and lay their non-glutinous eggs in cracks and crevices of poorly constructed adobe and thatched homes, from which the active stages sally forth at night to feed on sleeping victims.

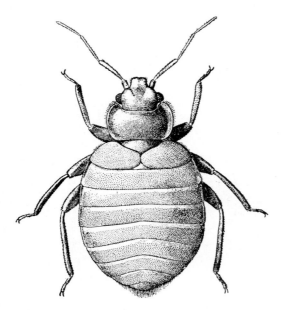

Fig. 180.—Bedbug (*Cimex lectularius*), adult female, dorsal view. × 10. (After MacGregor, in Byam and Archibald's Practice of Medicine in the Tropics, from Faust and Russell's *Clinical Parasitology*, Lea & Febiger, Philadelphia.)

Bedbug and Assassin-Bug "Bite."—All of these species are avid blood suckers. Bedbugs are usually more annoying than they are injurious, but in some persons their "bites" are responsible for a swollen, inflamed, cutaneous lesion with an indurated circumference at the site of each puncture, occasionally accompanied by systemic sensitization. Some species of assassin bugs inflict painful wounds, with local swelling, induration, oozing of blood and serum from the puncture site and generalized urticaria. *Reduvius personatus* has a potent salivary toxin which produces intense local pain when introduced into the skin. Other species like *Panstrongylus megistus* expertly puncture the skin and withdraw blood almost painlessly from the victim. The common location of their "bites" is the face, particularly on the

24

lips and outer angle of the eyes. Topical application of soothing lotions, ointments, or antihistaminic drugs relieves the dermatitis.

The importance of bugs as vectors of pathogenic microörganisms is considered in Chapter 18, page 399.

Control.—Since bedbugs which suck human blood are domestic in their habits, their control is limited to human dwellings. The most satisfactory method of control consists in spraying a 2% emulsion of chlordane in kerosene with $\frac{3}{10}$% Triton X-45 emulsifier into cracks and crevices of walls, bedbug-infested mattresses, beds, or other furniture. In old plastered walls the potency of chlordane deteriorates rapidly because of the lime content of the plaster, so that several applications may be required to kill all of the bugs.

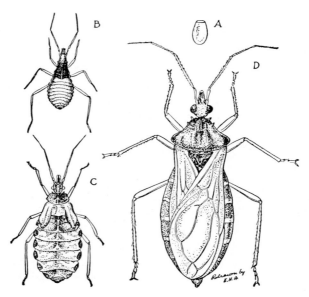

Fig. 181.—Stages in the life cycle of an assassin bug, *Panstrongylus megistus*. *A*, egg; *B*, one-day-old larva hatched from egg; *C*, 3-months-old larva; *D*, adult female. (Adapted rom Pinto, in Shattuck's Diseases of the Tropics, Appleton-Century-Crofts, Inc., N.Y.)

Assassin bugs are domestic and wild, depending on the particular species. The practical problem is limited to eradication of those which inhabit homes. The most efficient insecticide for this purpose is benzene hexachloride (Gammexane), employing an emulsion consisting of 5% technical grade gamma isomer in kerosene with $\frac{3}{10}$% Triton X-45 emulsifier. The emulsion is sprayed on inside walls and into the thatch or other roof covering of the home. In dry climates the residual effect is prolonged for at least 6 months, considerably less in moist climates.

Both types of bug infestation are commonly associated with homes of the low economic segment of a population. The fundamental preventive measure consists in the construction or rebuilding of domiciles free of wall cracks and with a roof which does not attract the breeding of bugs.

FLIES (DIPTERA)

Introduction

Flies are insects which as adults typically have a single pair of membranous wings arising from the dorso-lateral angle of the 2nd thoracic segment. In place of a 2nd pair of wings on the 3rd thoracic segment there are a pair of minute club-shaped "balancing organs" (halteres). The mouth parts of flies are adapted to sucking or lapping liquid or fine particulate nutriment, and in several families to piercing the skin in order to obtain a meal of blood or tissue juice. All flies have complete metamorphosis, with egg, several larval instars, pupa and adult.

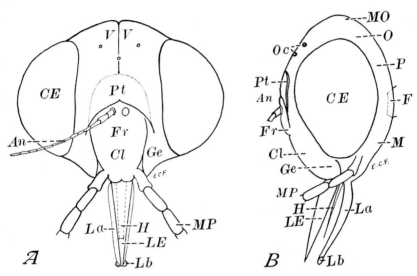

FIG. 182.—Schematic representation of the head of a fly. *A*, frontal view; *B*, lateral view. *An*, antenna; *CE*, compound eye, *Cl*, clypeus; *F*, foramen between head and thorax; *Fr*, frons; *Ge*, gena (cheek); *H*, hypopharynx; *La*, labium; *Lb*, labellum; *LE*, labrum-epipharynx (upper lip); *M*, metacephalon; *MO*, mid-occiput; *MP*, maxillary palp; *O*, occiput; *Oc*, ocelli (eyespots); *P*, paracephalon; *Pt*, ptilinum; *VV*, vertex. (Original adaptation, from Faust and Russell's *Clinical Parasitology*, Lea & Febiger, Philadelphia.)

Adult Morphology.—Some flies, *viz.*, mosquitoes, sandflies and midges, are delicate forms, while others, *viz.*, horse flies, flesh flies and warble flies, are relatively large and quite robust.

The Head.—This is a relatively large, moveable part of the body, connected with the thorax by a constriction, and covered with several well-defined chitinous plates (sclerites). From frontal or lateral view (Fig. 182) the most conspicuous feature is the compound eyes, which are usually separated from one another (dichoptic) by a median frontal plate but in some males are essentially contiguous (holoptic). The antennæ have a remarkable variety of forms. The maxillary palps are attached to the lower lateral angles of the clypeus. The mouth parts are developed into a sucking proboscis, which is short and stout in some groups and long and slender in others. It is composed of the unpaired labrum-epipharynx, the deeply troughed labium or lower lip, and internally between the labrum-epipharynx and labium, the hypopharynx with its salivary duct. Food passes through this channel into the digestive tract.

The house fly (*Musca domestica*) feeds by lapping and sucking; the lower portion of the proboscis is modified into a haustellum, with an expanded terminal portion adapted for adhesion to surfaces and provided with minute channels (pseudo-tracheæ) for directing nutriment centrally into the food canal (Fig. 174, *F*, p. 360). Species which feed by piercing and sucking, as the female mosquito, have a sharply-pointed labrum-epipharynx and hypopharynx.

The Thorax.—The second segment bears the single pair of thin, membranous wings, usually naked but in some groups covered with hairs, setæ or scales. The vein patterns of the wings are important in classification of flies. Each of the 3 pairs of legs has 5 distinct portions, with a terminal pair of claws, sucking pads (pulvilli) and at times a median bristled or feathered empodium.

The Abdomen.—The first two segments are atrophied or greatly reduced. In some but not all groups segments 3 through 11 can be distinguished. In the female, segments 7 to 10 are modified into an ovipositor; in the male, segments 9 and 10 form the complicated external genitalia (hypopygium). Adult flies have no abdominal leg-like appendages. Table 5 provides a key for the identification of the adults of the common domestic flies.

Table 5.—Key for Identification of the Adults of the Common House Flies. (Adapted from Dr. Luis Vargas, 1959)

1*a*. Body lacking metallic sheen; black, gray or brown 2
1*b*. Body having metallic sheen 7
2*a*. Small size . . . . Family Drosophilidæ, *Drosophila* spp.
2*b*. Medium to large size 3
3*a*. Wings twice as long as abdomen . . . . Family Anthomyidæ, *Fannia* spp.
3*b*. Wings only a little longer than abdomen 4
4*a*. Abdomen with numerous conspicuous black spots; thorax with 3 dark
    longitudinal stripes . . . . . . Family Sarcophagidæ, *Sarcophaga* spp.
4*b*. Abdomen lacking conspicuous black spots . . . . . . Family Muscidæ 5
5*a*. Proboscis long and slender, tapering to distal end, non-retractile . *Stomoxys calcitrans*.
5*b*. Proboscis short, enlarged distally, retractile 6
6*a*. Wings with 4th vein strongly angled . . . . *Musca* spp.
6*b*. Wings with 4th vein only slightly curved . . . . *Muscina* spp.
7*a*. Small; both thorax and abdomen with metallic sheen; 4th vein not
    angled . . . . Family Anthomyidæ, *Ophyra* spp.
7*b*. Medium to large; 4th vein angled. Family Muscidæ, Subfamily Cal-
    liphorinæ 8
8*a*. Abdomen (only) with bluish metallic sheen . . . . *Calliphora* spp.
8*b*. Thorax and abdomen with metallic sheen of same color 9
9*a*. Color predominantly green; thorax with 3 dark longitudinal stripes;
    lower part of cheeks yellowish . . . . *Callitroga* spp.
9*b*. Thorax without longitudinal stripes; cheeks dark 10
10*a*. With greenish, greenish-yellow or greenish-bronze sheen; thoracic
    bristles prominent; wings not overlapping . . . *Phænicia* spp., *Lucilia* spp.
10*a*. With bluish-black sheen; thoracic bristles very small; wings usually
    overlapping . . . . *Phormia* spp.

Internal Anatomy.—In most respects the digestive tract is similar to that of other insects (see Fig. 173, page 359).

Life Cycles.—A majority of flies are oviparous but flesh flies, tsetse flies and the Pupipara are viviparous. There are 3 or more larval instars, then a pupal stage and the adult. The larvæ are more or less worm-like, with 12 or fewer distinct body segments, have a head (*e.g.*, mosquitoes) or lack a definite head (*e.g.*, house fly, flesh flies, etc.). They have chewing rather than sucking mouth parts.

The last larval skin becomes the pupal case, as in the house-fly, or it is shed and the pupa forms its own protective cuticle. Following complete metamorphosis during the pupal stage the adult emerges from the pupal covering.

While adult flies are adapted to life in the air, they obtain their food from sources on the ground. The female deposits her eggs or living young on the ground, on the bodies of vertebrate animals, in excreta or in water, depending on the adaptations of the particular species.

Classification of Flies

Taxonomic Classification.—The main division is into two sub-orders, *viz.*, the ORTHORRHAPHA ("straight-seamed flies"), in which the adults emerge from a T-shaped split in the dorsal cuticle of the mid-thoracic segment of the pupa, and the CYCLORRHAPHA ("circular-seamed flies"), in which emergence is through a circular opening in the anterior portion of the dorsal covering of the pupa.

Medical Classification.—From a medical viewpoint it is convenient to classify flies corresponding to their rôle in the production of injury and disease, *viz.*, (1) as biological or mechanical vectors of pathogenic organisms; (2) in the causation of sensitization, and (3) in the production of myiasis. The first of these topics is presented in Chapter 18, pages 396–415.

Flies as Sensitizing Agents

All flies which puncture human skin for the purpose of sucking blood introduce droplets of saliva consisting primarily of digestive enzymes, which may produce local reaction and in some individuals systemic sensitization. The flies which pierce the skin and suck blood belong to four major groups, *viz.*, (1) the Nematocera, *i.e.*, mosquitoes (Culicidæ), "moth" flies (Psychodidæ), midges (Chironomidæ), and coffee-flies (Simuliidæ); (2) the Brachycera, which include horse flies, gad flies and deer flies (Tabanidæ); (3) "circular-seamed" flies, represented by the biting *Stomoxys calcitrans*, of the family Muscidæ, and the tsetse flies (Glossinidæ), and (4) all of the Pupipara, which are commonly ectoparasitic on mammals and birds.

THE MOSQUITOES (CULICIDÆ)

Adult Morphology.—Mosquitoes are slender, delicate flies which have a cosmopolitan distribution and number several thousand species. The antennæ are long, 15-jointed and are provided with whorls of hairs at the nodes, which are plumose in the male, scantier in the female. The mouth parts are long and in the female of most species (but not the male) are adapted to piercing and sucking blood (Fig. 183).   The head is subglobose and the compound eyes are conspicuous.   The maxillary palps in the male (except in the tribe Sabethini) are nearly as long as the proboscis; the palps in female anophelines are equally long while those in female culicines are short.   The thorax is elongate-ovoidal or rectangular and is covered almost completely by the mesothoracic plate (mesonotum).   The legs

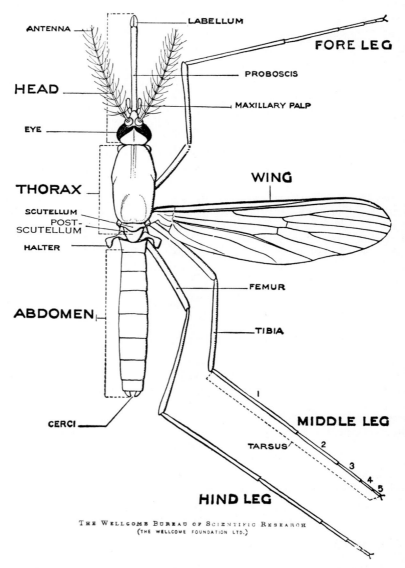

Fig. 183.—Diagram of a female culicine mosquito, dorsal view.   (After MacGregor, from Faust and Russell's *Clinical Parasitology*, Lea & Febiger, Philadelphia.)

which are long and slender terminate in 2 tarsal claws. The wings are long and narrow and frequently have species-distinctive scale patterns. When at rest they lie one on the other over the abdomen. Of the 10 functional abdominal segments 8 are clearly visible.

In many species insemination of the females occurs during or immediately following a prenuptial swarming, soon after emergence of the adults from their pupal case. The males are able to suck only plant juices and probably die soon after mating but the females survive for several weeks.

Life Cycle.—Egg production and egg laying are typically dependent on a previous blood meal. Most females oviposit in a wet or moist location.

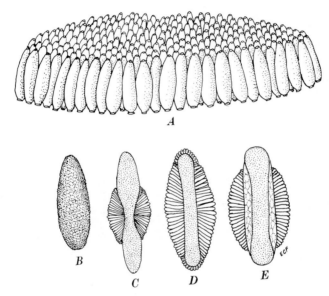

Fig. 184.—Mosquito eggs. *A*, raft of *Culex* eggs; *B*, egg of *Aëdes;* *C*, *D*, *E*, eggs of 3 different species of *Anopheles*. (Original, Faust.)

Eggs are laid singly until a complete brood has been discharged. *Anopheles* and *Aëdes* eggs remain isolated on the surface of the water but those of *Culex* become aggregated into floating rafts (Fig. 184*A*). Most mosquitoes utilize fresh water during their aquatic stages but a few are adapted to brackish water. Under favorable conditions of moisture and temperature the eggs hatch in 24 to 48 hours. At the moment of hatching the egg breaker, a chisel-shaped organ on the top of the head of the first-stage larva, produces a slit in the shell and the larva emerges into the water.

The larva has a head, thorax and abdomen, with a siphon tube (culicines) or much shorter stigmal apparatus (anophelines), bearing the openings of 2 tracheal tubes, arising from the 8th abdominal segment. Culicines feed at an angle below the water surface while anophelines must lie parallel to the surface and obtain their food close to the surface, usually with their head turned as much as 180° from its normal position (Fig. 185, *A*, *B*, *C*).

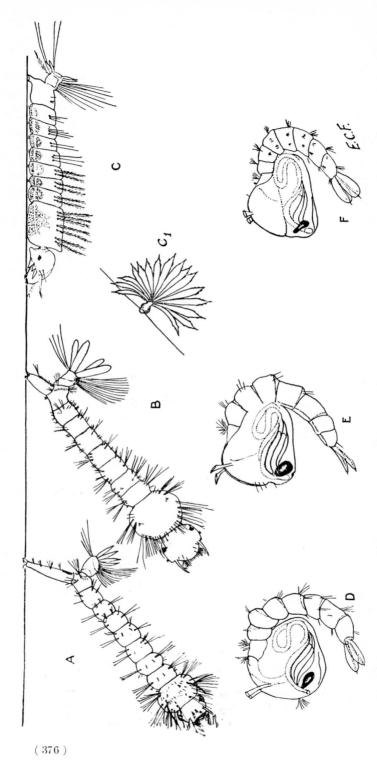

Fig. 185.— Larvæ (*A, B, C*) and pupæ (*D, E, F*) of *Culex pipiens, Aëdes ægypti* and *Anopheles quadrimaculatus* respectively, showing breathing position of larva and resting position of pupæ. *C₁*, palmate hair tuft from dorsum of 3rd abdominal segment of *A. quadrimaculatus*. (Original, in Faust and Russell's *Clinical Parasitology*, Lea & Febiger, Philadelphia.)

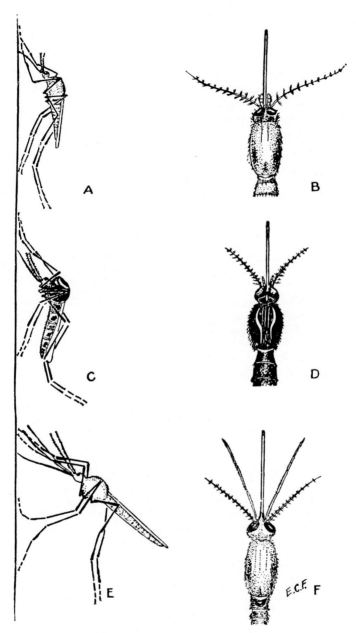

Fig. 186.—Adult resting position, and dorsal view of head and thorax of *Culex pipiens* (*A*, *B*), *Aëdes ægypti* (*C*, *D*) and *Anopheles quadrimaculatus* (*E*, *F*). (Original, in Faust and Russell's *Clinical Parasitology*, Lea & Febiger, Philadelphia.)

These larvæ have chewing mouth parts with which they crush small particulate food that the mouth brushes introduce in currents of water. Following four larval instars, the mosquito transforms into a megalocephalic pupa, which is strongly curved ventrally and has a pair of thoracic breathing trumpets (Fig. 185, *D, E, F*). As it matures the pupa becomes darker and more buoyant. When metamorphosis is complete the thoracic cuticle splits, and the thorax, head and finally the abdomen emerge. Meanwhile the wings have unfolded and the legs have stretched out, and in 5 to 10 minutes the body is dried so that the mosquito is ready for flight.

Figure 186 illustrates the characteristic appearance of the adult *Culex pipiens, Aëdes aegypti* and *Anopheles quadrimaculatus* when resting on a surface, together with the dorsal view of head and thorax of the females.

Bionomics.—The females of some species of mosquitoes have a preference for human blood. Many other species will feed without preference on the most available vertebrate.

Mosquito "Bite" and Sensitization.—After the female mosquito's proboscis penetrates beneath the epidermis it probes persistently and rapidly until a blood supply is tapped; feeding may be directly from the bloodvessel or from the pool of extravasated blood. The intensity of the tissue reaction to the "bite" depends on the sensitivity of the individual, the species of mosquito and the duration of the feeding.

Application of anesthetic ointment to the affected skin is palliative.

The role of mosquitoes in the transmission of pathogenic microörganisms is presented in Chapter 18, pages 396–415.

Control.—Control measures which have been employed include attack on the breeding sites by naturalistic methods and larvicides, use of DDT or other chlorinated hydrocarbon as a residual spray to kill adults in homes and out-buildings, and protection of persons by screening, bednets, etc. In so far as these mosquitoes cause sensitization, control can be effective. Area control of pest mosquitoes by periodic fogging of residential areas with insect toxicants provides considerable relief but does not appreciably affect their breeding.

SAND-FLIES (Psychodidæ)

Adult Morphology and Bionomics.—All of the blood-sucking members of this family belong to the genus *Phlebotomus, i.e.,* "vein cutters," which have widespread distribution in warm and temperate climates. The adults (Fig. 187) are small, hump-backed, tawny in color, with conspicuous black compound eyes, a pair of long delicate antennæ, long, narrowly obovate wings which form a V-shaped outline above the thorax when the fly is resting on a surface, long, straggling legs, and many delicate tawny hairs on the body, wings and legs. Sand-flies prefer to hop rather than fly and ordinarily are not found more than 5 meters above the ground or far from their breeding sites. Only the females puncture skin and take a blood meal. Sand-flies feed at night and hide in dark places in the daytime.

Life Cycle.—Long ovoidal eggs are laid in batches of about 50 in moist dark sites, under decaying leaves on the ground, in damp mossy places in rank vegetation or in hollow tree trunks. They hatch in 9 to 12 days and the emerging worm-like larvæ, carrying a pair of long caudal bristles, feed on organic débris and the excreta of lizards, but never in a strictly aquatic medium. There are 4 larval instars and a naked pupal stage. Thirty to 40 days after oviposition the cycle is completed.

Sand-fly Sensitization.—The "bite" of a female sand-fly produces a local, frequently indurated inflammation, at times with a wheal 1 to 2 cm. in

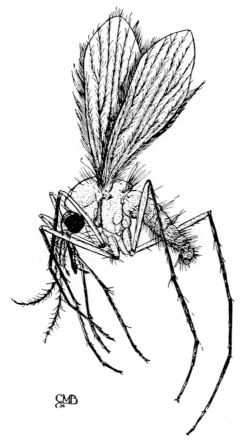

Fig. 187.—Adult female sand-fly (*Phlebotomus chinensis*). Greatly enlarged. (Original in Faust and Russell's *Clinical Parasitology*, Lea & Febiger, Philadelphia.)

diameter. This is accompanied by a needling pain, which may be followed by an irritating local pruritus lasting hours or weeks. Some persons develop a severe allergic reaction, with swelling of the bitten member, fever, nausea and general malaise. Topical application of phenolated camphor in mineral oil or anesthetic ointment alleviates the local pruritus.

For transmission of pathogenic microörganisms by *Phlebotomus* see Chapter 18, pages 404 and 408.

"BITING" MIDGES (Chironomidæ)

Adult Morphology and Bionomics.—The species of medical importance belong to the genus *Culicoides*. The adult *Culicoides* is a small dark fly, with long delicate antennæ, moderately long maxillary palps, humped thorax, a pair of short, broadly obovate wings, and moderately long legs. The hairs on the body, wings and legs are short and relatively scanty compared with those of *Phlebotomus*.

Life Cycle.—Eggs are laid in decaying vegetation in water, in tree holes, crab holes, in the scum of a wet sand bed or even in piles of wet manure. Some species breed in brackish water. The larvæ are delicate worm-like objects, which have caudal gills and hooks. The pupa is elongate, chrysalis-like, and has a pair of conspicuous breathing trumpets.

Culicoides Sensitization.—Swarms of these minute midges attack man or mammals, usually at dusk when there is little or no breeze, producing lesions which may cause only temporary needling pain, but in some persons produce severe local pruritus which lasts several days. Topical application of phenolated camphor in mineral oil or anesthetic ointment is palliative.

For a consideration of *Culicoides* as transmitter of filaria infections please consult Chapter 13, pages 313–314.

Control.—Ordinary screens and bednets will not prevent unfed females from reaching the skin of persons inside dwellings. DDT residual spraying inside homes and periodic area spraying with this insecticide will greatly reduce the annoyance caused by these midges.

BLACK FLIES, BLACK GNATS, COFFEE FLIES (Simuliidæ)

Adult Morphology and Bionomics.—The adults are small, stout, hump-backed forms, with relatively short, stout legs, moderately short, 11-jointed antennæ, outwardly curved maxillary palps, conspicuous eyes (holoptic in the male, dichoptic in the female), and a pair of large unpatterned wings. These gnats are not found at great distances from their breeding grounds unless they are carried in currents of air. Only the females suck blood. They usually take their blood meals in bright light. All members of the family belong to the genus *Simulium* (*sensu lato*). Some species are black but others are yellowish-brown or metallic in color.

Life Cycle.—The females lay batches of minute, triangular-shaped eggs in running, well-oxygenated water, at or just below the water surface, where they are glued to bare rocks, dead branches of trees, or stems of aquatic grass. In 4 to 12 hours the eggs hatch, and the larvæ emerge and become attached to objects in the water by a caudal hooked disc. There are 7 larval instars, requiring 13 or more days before the mature larva spins an incomplete cocoon around itself. The pupa has a pair of conspicuous, branched external breathing tubes. Following a period of metamorphosis lasting several days the adult fly emerges from the pupal case and takes to the air.

Simulium Sensitization.—Swarms of female *Simulium* attack man and domestic animals throughout the year in warm climates and during warm months in cooler climates. The "bite" itself is not particularly painful, but frequently it produces an intensely pruritic raised lesion. Typically a little pool of extravasated blood produced by the puncture remains in the skin for days or weeks until it is resorbed. Individuals who are repeatedly "bitten" may develop hypersensitization with swelling of an arm or face, generalized urticaria, fever and malaise. Application of anesthetic ointment to the affected skin will temporarily relieve the pruritus.

For the role of *Simulium* in the transmission of onchocerciasis consult Chapter 13, pages 304–310.

Control.—This requires surveys to determine the exact breeding places of the *Simulium,* then larvicidal treatment of the water at pool stage during the dry season with concentrates of DDT. Dimethyl phthalate or other insect repellent, when rubbed on the exposed skin, is frequently temporarily effective in preventing black-fly bites.

HORSE FLIES, GAD FLIES, DEER FLIES, MANGO FLIES (Tabanidæ)

Adult Morphology and Bionomics.—All of these flies are much larger and more robust than mosquitoes and other gnats, and in size and appearance more nearly resemble the house-fly, stable-fly and warble-fly. Tabanids have prominent irridescent eyes and rather dull-colored bodies which are relatively free of bristles. They have a pair of very powerful wings, a head which is broader than the thorax, short, stout, 3-segmented antennæ, a proboscis which is short in *Tabanus,* medium-long in *Chrysops* and very long in *Pangonia.* Only the females have mouth parts adapted to piercing and sucking blood.

Life Cycle.—The females lay batches of 100 or more elongated-ovoidal eggs which are attached to plants or rocks over clear, frequently running water. In 5 to 7 days the larvæ hatch, drop into the water, where they feed and pass through 7 larval instars in the course of a year, then migrate to dry ground to pupate. The chrysalis-like pupæ are completely quiet for one to 3 weeks, after which the adults emerge and soon mate.

Tabanid "Bites."—The relatively large proboscis produces an ugly puncture wound, which is painful and heals slowly. Sensitization occasionally develops from saliva secreted into the wound but the trauma produced is frequently more serious. At times surgical dressing of the puncture sites is required.

For the role of tabanids as transmitters of pathogenic microörganisms consult Chapter 13, pages 304–309, 393, and Chapter 18, page 411.

Control.—No effective control measures have been formulated.

BLOOD SUCKING MUSCID FLIES (Muscidæ)

Adult Morphology and Bionomics.—Muscid flies, of which the common house-fly, *Musca domestica,* is the best known example, are medium-sized, stout individuals, frequently of a general dusky-gray color. The blood-sucking species which commonly "bites" man and has a cosmopolitan distribution is *Stomoxys calcitrans.* It somewhat resembles *M. domestica* but can be distinguished by its long, stabbing proboscis, which projects con-

spicuously in front of the mouth.   Both males and females are vicious
"biters" and blood suckers.

Life Cycle.—The whitish ovoidal eggs are laid one at a time in manure,
decaying straw or rotting vegetation.   The maggot-type larvæ hatch in
one to 3 days, feed, and after passing through 3 larval instars in 11 to 30
days, crawl to a drier location and pupate.   After 6 to 20 days the adults
emerge from the pupal case and soon mate.

Stomoxys "Bites."—*Stomoxys* readily attacks man, stabbing into exposed skin, and like tabanid females produces sharp pain at the time of the
puncture.   A small pool of blood characteristically wells up over the wound.
Although this fly is an aggravating pest, it seldom produces serious local
or systemic sensitization.

For the rôle of *S. calcitrans* in myiasis please refer to page 393; and as a
disease transmitter, see Chapter 3, page 45.

Control.—This can best be obtained by preventing the breeding of the
fly.   Concrete drains under manure piles, power-spraying of DDT or other
insect toxicants into piles of rotting straw and area-spraying of DDT on
rotting vegetation constitute important control measures.

TSETSE FLIES (Glossinidæ)

Adult Morphology and Bionomics.—These flies, which are limited in
their natural distribution to the tropical belt of Africa, are about the size of
the common house-fly but are honey-brown in color.   When at rest they
may be readily recognized by the position of the proboscis extended in front
of the head and the way in which the wings are folded over one another
straight across the back of the abdomen (Fig. 188).   The piercing and penetrating parts of the proboscis are similar to those of *Stomoxys*, although
during the act of feeding they are flexible like those of mosquitoes.   Tsetses
not only suck blood from cutaneous capillaries but also that which wells up

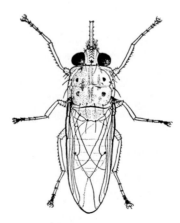

Fig. 188.—Adult tsetse-fly (*Glossina* sp.) in resting position.   (From Matheson's
Medical Entomology, in Faust and Russell's *Clinical Parasitology*, Lea & Febiger,
Philadelphia.)

from the wound onto the surface of the skin (Gordon and Crewe, 1949). Both males and females are efficient "biters" and voracious blood suckers.

The adults are hardy, long-lived and fly considerable distances but are indigenous to (1) tropical rain-forests, especially *Glossina palpalis* and (2) the high savannas of East Africa, *viz.*, *G. morsitans*.

Life Cycle.—Eggs produced by the females hatch *in utero*, where 3 successive larval stages feed on "milk" secreted by special intra-uterine glands. After 9 to 12 days the mature 3rd-stage larvæ are deposited on the ground one at a time and transform into pupæ by a hardening of the last skin. Metamorphosis to the adult requires 21 to 60 days, depending on the species.

Tsetse "Bites."—In nature tsetse flies have an abundance of wild mammals from which they secure blood. Man is "bitten" when he builds his villages near breeding grounds or enters the areas to fish, hunt or cut wood during the daytime. They are primarily important as the vectors of trypanosomiasis to man and domestic mammals (see Chapter 3, pages 56, 59).

Control.—Because tsetse flies have an abundance of wild mammals which serve as a ready source of food, control is difficult. Clearing of the bush around native villages, fords and boat landings, planned grass fires in certain areas, trapping of the flies in game preserves, and fumigation of vehicular transportation are useful in one area or another, but no single control program is thoroughly effective.

HIPPOBOSCIDS AND SHEEP KEDS (Pupipara)

These flies have a tough, leathery cuticle, are flattened dorsoventrally, have an efficient skin-piercing proboscis and as adults are more strictly ectoparasitic than other flies. They are larviparous and like tsetse flies the larvæ pupate soon after they are deposited by the females. Species of *Hippobosca* have a pair of functional wings; these flies parasitize dogs, cattle, horses and other large mammals. *Melophagus ovinus*, the sheep ked, has lost its wings as a result of its parasitic habits. None of the Pupipara is anthropophilous but they readily attack persons associated with infested domestic animals, become attached to the hair, particularly at the back of the neck, and voraciously suck blood. The puncture produces considerable pain and hemorrhage. Control involves spraying of effective insect toxicants on the natural mammalian hosts.

FLEAS (Siphonaptera)

Adult Morphology.—Fleas are small, wingless, medium- to dark-brown, shiny insects, which are compressed from side to side. They are provided with long legs for hopping and jumping, and both sexes have a proboscis adapted for piercing the skin and sucking blood (Fig. 189). Compound eyes are present in some species, lacking in others. Each of the pair of antennæ is situated in an oblique groove connected with a stricture separating the side of the head into two distinct parts. The following mouth parts can be demonstrated: an anterior pair of jointed maxillary palps, a posterior pair of jointed labial palps, a pair of minutely barbed, needle-like mandibles, a pair of blade-like maxillæ, and a single, stylet-shaped labrum-epipharynx, which with the mandibles forms the food channel. The 3 thoracic segments, each bearing a pair of 5-jointed legs terminating in 2 claws, are easily recognized. The abdomen is composed of 10 segments, of which the last 3 are modified into external genital structures. The 9th segment contains a dorsal prominence, the pygidium, which is considered to be sensory in function.

The digestive tract resembles that of most insects (Fig. 173, page 359); however, the proventriculus is provided with particularly long chitinous teeth.

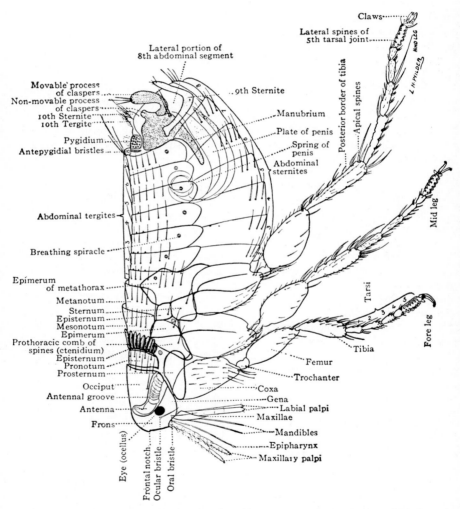

Fig. 189.—External anatomy of a male rat flea (*Nosopsyllus fasciatus*). (From Fox's *Insects and Diseases of Man,* in Faust and Russell's *Clinical Parasitology,* Lea & Febiger, Philadelphia.)

Bionomics.—Unlike lice, fleas are not host-specific although they are usually found on certain hosts. A majority of species of fleas are ectoparasites of rodents. A few of these such as *Xenopsylla cheopis* and *Nosopsyllus fasciatus* of domestic rats have as widespread distribution as their hosts, but most rodent fleas have rather limited geographic distribution. The

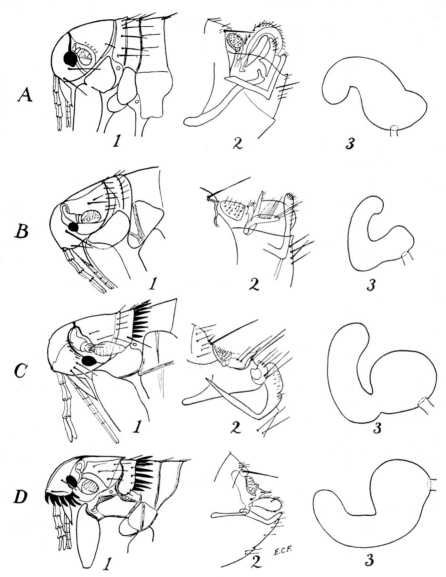

FIG. 190.—Head (*1*), caudal extremity of male (*2*) and seminal receptacle (*3*), of common fleas. *A, Pulex irritans; B, Xenopsylla cheopis; C, Nosopsyllus fasciatus; D, Ctenocephalides canis.* (Original adaptations, from Faust and Russell's *Clinical Parasitology*, Lea & Febiger, Philadelphia.)

25

human flea (*Pulex irritans*), the dog flea (*Ctenocephalides canis*) and the cat flea (*C. felis*) are cosmopolitan.

Life Cycle.—The minute, ovoidal, glistening white eggs are usually deposited on the ground or in infested nests. The larvæ are delicate, wormlike organisms with long delicate setæ. They have chewing mouth parts but feed mostly on bloody dejecta of the parent fleas. There are 3 larval instars, following which the mature larva spins a cocoon around itself and pupates. The larval period may require only a week in a warm climate or as much as 3 months in a cool climate; the pupal period may be as short as a week or as long as a year. The adults survive for a year or more under favorable conditions.

Species-diagnostic characteristics of the 4 fleas commonly infesting man are illustrated in Figure 190.

The Chigœ Flea.—Unlike other fleas which puncture the skin of man and other mammals to obtain blood, the chigœ, *Tunga penetrans*, invades the skin. The chigœ may be distinguished from other fleas by the sharp upper angling of the front portion of its head (the frons), the long, stiff, barbed mandibles, the lack of a distinct suture from the antennal groove to the top of the head and the foreshortened thoracic segments. The female sucks juices from cutaneous tissues and develops a tremendous distension of its abdomen. It lays eggs in the tissues or on the ground. Occasionally both males and hatched larval stages may be found in the lesions. This flea is a common parasite of the feet of hogs and dogs throughout tropical and subtropical America and parts of tropical Africa. Barefooted persons who walk on ground polluted from infested animals are liable to become parasitized by chigœs. Clinical consideration of chigœ infestation of man is provided on page 393.

Flea Sensitization.—Many persons are not seriously inconvenienced by the "bites" of fleas. In other individuals a local sensitization reaction develops at the puncture site. The lesion is roseate, raised, frequently edematous and indurated. It is intensely pruritic, and becomes inflamed and scarified as a result of scratching.

For a consideration of fleas as transmitters of pathogenic microörganisms, see Chapter 18, pages 406, 409.

Control.—Dogs, cats and domestic rodents provide the common sources for fleas which get on human skin and produce flea dermatitis. Periodic dusting of dogs with DDT, as well as the rugs and cushions in the home on which dogs and cats walk or lie, will greatly reduce the flea population within the house. DDT dusting of courtyards and lawns is also effective prophylaxis. Similar dusting of basements, rat runs and nests will help to prevent the breeding of rodent fleas around the home. The wearing of stout leather shoes will prevent most human infestation with the chigœ.

5. Tissue-Invading Insects

Three groups of insects are involved as intentional or accidental invaders of human and other animal tissues. These are the flies, beetles and the chigœ flea (*Tunga penetrans*).

FLIES (DIPTERA) AND MYIASIS

Myiasis is infestation of the body with the larvæ (maggots) of flies. With rare exceptions, as in the "biting" stable fly (*Stomoxys calcitrans*), none of the adults of the myiasis-producing flies have mouth parts able to puncture skin and suck blood, although most of them will avidly lap up blood when opportunity is afforded (Herms, 1932). Myiasis is (1) *specific*, resulting from obligate selection of living tissues by the mother fly as a source of nourishment for the larvæ; (2) *semi-specific*, in which oviposition or larviposition in tissues is stimulated by foul or fetid odors emanating from purulent discharges or contaminated wounds, and (3) *accidental*, in which the larvæ or the eggs by chance are deposited in superficial sites or contaminate the gastrointestinal or urinary passages.

The flies which cause myiasis belong to a number of families, of which some of the more important species (Fig. 191) will be presented as examples.

The larva of myiasis-producing species is armed with a pair of sharp, curved mandibular hooks for abrading and entering tissues. Mature maggots of a number of species are illustrated in Figure 192.

Specific Myiasis

Flesh Flies (Sarcophagidæ).—*Wohlfahrtia vigil.*—This medium-sized grayish fly (Fig. 191, *1*) is found in northern United States and adjacent Canada. The females are larviparous, the larvæ mature in 7 to 9 days, the pupal stage requires 10 to 12 days and females begin to deposit their young in 11 to 17 days after they emerge from the pupal case. The adults have well-developed mouth parts but apparently feed solely on nectar of wild flowers.

The larvæ are deposited in masses on exposed, undamaged body surfaces but usually migrate some distance before entering tender unbroken skin. Human infestation is confined to young infants left out of doors without protection of mosquito nets. Once under the epidermis the maggot produces a small raised abscess in the subcutaneous tissues with an opening to the surface. The head is at the inner end and the caudal extremity nearest the external pore. The reported symptoms include irritability, fever, dehydration and loss of weight. Early diagnosis will prevent the entrance of pyogenic bacteria as well as extensive mutilation. Under aseptic precautions the maggots may be squeezed out by slight pressure, the wounds cleaned and then covered with surgical dressing. These flies are not attracted by fetid odors and do not feed on dead flesh. Unscreened infants should not be left out of doors during the summer months when the flies are larvipositing.

Screw-worm Flies (Calliphoridæ).—*Callitroga hominivorax* (Syn. *C. americana*) (Primary Screw-worm Fly).—This bluish or bluish-green fly (Fig. 191, *3*) is widely distributed throughout the Americas from the southern half of the United States to Chile and Argentina. The female is oviparous, gluing her eggs in masses to clean skin near a wound. The eggs hatch in 11 to 21 hours and groups of the young maggots penetrate in pockets down to the underlying tissues. After 4 to 8 days of voracious feed-

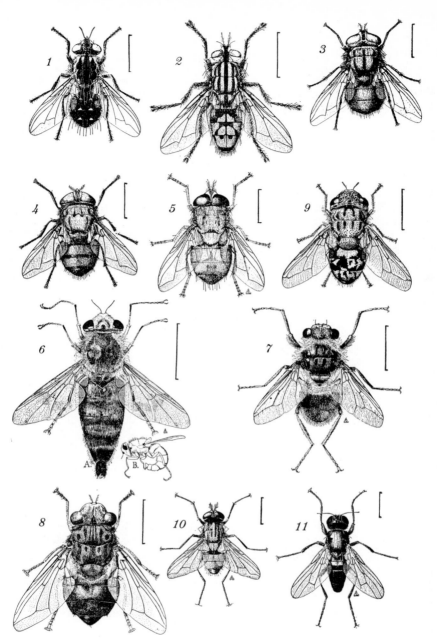

FIG. 191.—Adults of several important or relatively common myiasis-producing flies. *1, 3–9*, involved in specific myiasis (*1, Wohlfahrtia vigil*, female; *3, Callitroga hominivorax*, female; *4, Chrysomya bezziana*, female; *5, Cordylobia anthropophaga*, male; *6, Gasterophilus intestinalis*, female; *7, Hypoderma lineatum*, female; *8, Dermatobia hominis*, female; *9, Œstrus ovis*, female. *2*, involved in semi-specific myiasis (*Sarcophaga hæmorrhoidalis*, male). *10, 11*, involved in accidental myiasis (*10, Musca domestica*, male; *11, Piophila casei*, female). The line adjacent to each drawing indicates the natural size of the fly. (All figures from James' *The Flies That Cause Myiasis in Man*, courtesy Bureau of Entomology and Plant Quarantine, U. S. Dept. Agriculture.)

(388)

ing, the mature maggots drop to the ground and pupate. Seven to 54 days later the adults emerge and feed on manure, meat and serous or purulent exudates, but the maggots require clean flesh for their nourishment.

This maggot is the most important member of the screw-worm family affecting livestock and man. The hatched larvæ enter scarified, bruised,

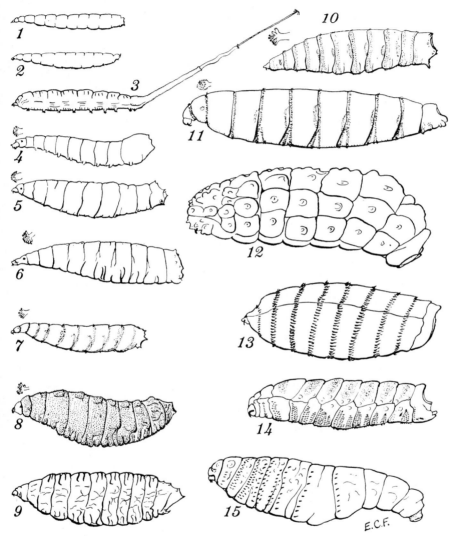

Fig. 192.—Appearance of the mature larvæ of several myiasis-producing flies, lateral view. *1, Sepsis* sp.; *2, Piophila casei; 3, Tubifera tenax; 4, Musca domestica; 5, Phænicia sericata; 6, Calliphora vicina; 7, Chrysomya bezziana; 8, Cordylobia anthropophaga; 9, Auchmeromyia luteola; 10, Callitroga hominivorax; 11, Wohlfahrtia magnifica; 12, Hypoderma bovis; 13, Gasterophilus intestinalis; 14, Œstrus ovis; 15, Dermatobia hominis.* × 3⅓. Anterior spiracle at upper left of *4, 5, 6, 7, 8, 10* and *11*. (Original adaptations, from Faust and Russell's *Clinical Parasitology*, Lea & Febiger, Philadelphia.)

inflamed or even undamaged skin and may tunnel deeply into the viscera. They also infest the vagina, the nasal and frontal sinuses, eyes, ears and mouth. The furuncular lesions which they produce are extremely painful and characteristically become secondarily infected, so that extensive mutilation commonly results. The more serious human cases terminate fatally. This species requires differentiation from its close relative, *C. macellaria*, the larva of which is typically saprozoic rather than an obligate parasite. Control can be effected by distribution of irradiated sterile males among females to prevent breeding of the progeny (Knipling, 1959).

Chrysomya bezziana (Old World Screw-worm Fly).—This fly (Fig. 191, *4*) has an extensive distribution through southern Asia and in Africa south of the Sahara. The female glues batches of eggs to dry, unbroken skin, either within the edge of a wound, over bruises or abscesses, or on surface membranes exuding purulent serum or blood. The larvæ hatch in 24 hours and at first feed near the surface, then burrow deeply into the flesh, causing a liquefaction necrosis. On the 6th day they have matured and emerge from the lesion to pupate on the ground. After a varying period, depending on the season, the adults come out of the pupal case and start a new cycle. There are 8 or more generations per year, each with a potential of several hundred eggs.

C. bezziana maggots attack open wounds in large numbers, and produce deep mutilation. In man they most frequently infest the scalp but have been reported from the nasal and frontal sinuses, ears, eyes and mouth, as well as exposed genitalia. The infestation may cause the loss of an eye or an ear, or erosion of the entire nares, at times with fatal outcome.

Cordylobia anthropophaga (Tumbu-Fly).—This yellowish-colored fly (Fig. 191, *5*), is widely distributed throughout Africa except on the Mediterranean coast. The adults deposit their eggs on dirt soiled with excrement, including the floors of native huts. Hatching occurs in 48 hours and the young maggots enter the skin of man, dog or rat which comes in contact with the infested ground, producing indurated furuncles in the dermis. The mature larva emerges on the 8th or 9th day, buries itself in the soil and pupates. Twelve to 14 days later the adult breaks out of the pupal case, soon mates and a new cycle is started. Natives expel the maggots by firm pressure between thumb and finger. Control requires thorough washing and ironing of all contaminated clothing and bedding, and sterilization of floors of native huts.

Auchmeromyia luteola (Congo Floor-Maggot).—The adult closely resembles *C. anthropophaga* (Fig. 191, *5*). It frequents shady places, including native huts in the African tropics. The maggot attacks human victims who sleep directly on the floors, voraciously sucks blood like a tick or bedbug, and is more of a nuisance than a true parasite. Control consists in sterilization of the floors of huts and use of raised platforms for sleeping.

Warble or Bot Flies (Gasterophilidæ, Hypodermatidæ, Cuterebridæ, Œstridæ).— *Gasterophilus intestinalis* (Common Horse-Bot).—This brownish-yellow fly (Fig. 191, *6*), 12 to 17 mm. long, looking more like a bee than a fly, is widely distributed in North America, Europe, Africa, Asia, Australia New Zealand and Hawaii. The horse is the usual host, on which eggs are glued to the body hairs. The horse bites the area with his lips, causing the eggs to hatch. The little spinose maggots adhere to the lips, penetrating below the surface. When mature the maggots emerge from the lips or tongue and either crawl out and drop to the ground to pupate, or are swallowed and pass out in the feces.

The larvæ of *G. intestinalis*, *G. hæmorrhoidalis* and *G. nasalis* from time to time infest the human skin and mucous membranes, causing a swelling at the site of entry and later a raised serpiginous tunnel just superficial to the stratum germinativum, in which the maggot travels several mm. daily for a period of several months, causing intense pruritus. Macroscopically the lesion resembles that of cutaneous larva migrans produced by *Ancylostoma braziliense* (Chapter 11, page 281), with which it is coëxtensive in distribution. Differential diagnosis can readily be made by massaging mineral oil over the invaded skin and demonstrating as many as 8 or 9 transverse bands of dark scales which are present at the anterior end of most body segments (see Fig. 192, *13*). Once identified the maggot can be removed with a sharp needle introduced into the head of the tunnel. Human infestation is usually on the extremities but there is one report of internal myiasis of the eye due to *G. intestinalis* (Anderson, 1935). Control is primarily a veterinary problem, requiring the treatment of infested horses with appropriate insecticides to kill the maggots as they hatch. Addition of the phosphate insecticide Dimethoate to grain in non-toxic amounts provides considerable promise (Drudge *et al.*, 1959).

Hypoderma bovis (Northern Cattle-Bot-Fly).—James (1947) refers to the adult of this species as "a dark, rather robust bumblebee-like fly, about 12 mm. in length." It has extensive distribution in the cooler parts of North America, Europe and Asia, and is frequently carried on cattle to other areas. The related species, *H. lineatum* (Fig. 191, *7*), is somewhat less robust and hirsute. The adult flies take no food. As the eggs are laid they are glued to the hairs of the legs or abdomen of cattle. On hatching 3 to 7 days later the young larvæ burrow into the skin, and migrate to the back of the animal, where they produce subcutaneous pockets (warbles). When the larvæ are mature, they perforate through the skin, drop to the ground and pupate. A year is required for a complete cycle, most of which is in the tissues of the host. Persons associated with infested cattle may become parasitized by *H. bovis* or *H. lineatum* (common cattle-grub or heel-fly).

The skin lesion in man is furuncular rather than serpiginous. The larva lives in the subcutaneous tissues, producing considerable inflammation and pain; and it often migrates some distance from the site where it entered the skin. There are also several reports of internal myiasis of the eye resulting from infestation with *H. bovis* and *H. lineatum* (Anderson, 1935). If there is a justifiable suspicion of *Hypoderma* infestation, after local procaine anesthesia the lesion should be incised and the larva, if present, removed while still alive, so that an abscess will not develop from a sequestered dead maggot. Control is almost exclusively a veterinary problem, including spraying of cattle with insecticides which will kill the young larvæ as soon as they hatch and before they enter the skin.

Dermatobia hominis (Tropical Warble-Fly).—This robust fly (Fig. 191, *8*), about 12 mm. long, resembles the common blue-bottle fly (*Calliphora vomitoria*). The adults, which do not feed, live in forests in tropical America and rarely venture far afield. They transport their eggs to distant vertebrate hosts by cementing batches of eggs to the abdomen of certain mosquitoes, to *Stomoxys calcitrans*, less often to ticks and assassin bugs; or they may oviposit on wet laundry hung out of doors near a forest. When the arthropod vector settles on the skin or when persons put on egg-infested garments, the eggs of *D. hominis* soon hatch and the young larvæ bore down to the subcutaneous tissues where each produces an inflamed pocket with a pore to the surface so that the posterior end of the larva may from time to time come out to breathe. After several weeks the mature larva emerges and drops to the ground to pupate. Following 14 to 24 days on the soil the adults emerge from the pupal case, copulate, and the females oviposit, possibly only once.

In man the lesions develop most often on the hands, wrists, ankles, neck and face. The invasion of the tissues is perpendicular to the surface, and never serpiginous in type. At first a small itching pimple appears. The area becomes inflamed, hyperemic and its surface is tightly stretched so that there is intense, throbbing pain. Considerable skill is required to extract the larva intact. No effective control program has been developed.

Œstrus ovis (Sheep-Bot or Gad-Fly).—The yellowish head of this fly (Fig. 191, *9*) has prominent pock-like pits between and below the eyes. This fly, which does not feed as an adult, deposits maggots in the nares or conjunctiva, where they feed on mucous membranes, then emerge and drop to the ground to pupate. It has a cosmopolitan distribution where domestic sheep and goats are raised.

Human infestation with *Œ. ovis* is often encountered in Italy, Palestine, North Africa, Cape Verde Islands, U.S.S.R. and less frequently in the western United States. The young larva on the conjunctiva may migrate into the lacrimal duct, or work its way deeply into the orbit, rarely into the eyeball. Superficial infestation is very irritating and painful; deep penetration may cause the loss of the eye. Nasal and oral myiasis produced by this fly is encountered mostly in Mediterranean countries, causing painful congestion similar to internal leech infestation (Chapter 15, page 331). Removal of the maggot at an early stage of its development usually assures rapid, uncomplicated recovery. Control measures are primarily concerned with periodic spraying or dipping of sheep and goats with larvicidal toxicants.

Semi-specific Myiasis

A majority of the flesh flies and screw-worm flies deposit their young or eggs in carrion which constitutes the source of nutriment for the growing maggots, but foul-smelling open wounds provide an equally favorable attraction and source of food. The maggots proceed to liquefy and consume the diseased tissues and often invade adjacent undamaged flesh or bone.

The most notorious of the flesh flies is *Sarcophaga hæmorrhoidalis*.

The adults (Fig. 191,*2*) have a cosmopolitan distribution and feed on decaying meat and flesh, or on feces. The females are larviparous and deposit their young on foul-smelling media or at times on the anus of persons sitting on outdoor latrines. Or the maggots may be ingested in contaminated cold meat. They develop through 3 larval instars, then drop or crawl to drier surroundings on the ground and pupate.

The maggots of *S. hæmorrhoidalis* ingested in infested cold food are capable of producing severe gastrointestinal disturbances, with griping abdominal pain, nausea, vomiting and fever, due sometimes, as Bryan demonstrated sigmoidoscopically (1937), to ulceration produced by the maggots which became attached to the intestinal wall. This fly is capable of completing its entire larval development within the human intestinal tract.

The common screw-worm fly, *C. macellaria*, is essentially saprozoic rather than parasitic. Other species of this group which are scavengers but may invade injured human tissues are: the black blow-fly (*Phormia regina*), the green-bottle flies (*Lucilia cæsar, Phænicia cuprina, P. sericata*), and the blue-bottle flies (*Calliphora vomitoria, C. vicina*). In most instances the damage produced by these maggots is traumatic, *i.e.*, extension of preëxisting wounds, but there are several records of at least temporary parasitism in the nares, adjacent sinuses and buccal cavity, intestinal tract and external ear.

Accidental Myiasis

Almost any fly that oviposits or larviposits in manure, decaying vegetation or other feeding site for its larval stages provides the opportunity for accidental myiasis in case the eggs or maggots are carelessly ingested in contaminated food or get into the bladder or vagina of persons who are unclean in their personal hygiene.

Larvæ of tabanids, including *Chrysops* sp., in paddy fields of Japan during the planting season, attack workers whose hands and feet are in contact with the mud, producing puncture of the wet skin, with intense pruritus (Otsuri and Ogawa, 1959).

BEETLE INFESTATION (Canthariasis)

There are numerous records of infestation of man by eggs, larvæ and adults of several species of beetles (Théodoridès, 1948). Most of these cases involve the intestinal and urinary tracts, in which the larvæ or adults have become accidentially and temporarily lodged, with mild or severe disturbances in digestion or urination.

CHIGŒ FLEA INFESTATION

The distinguishing morphologic characters of the chigœ flea (*Tunga penetrans*) have been described earlier in this chapter (page 386). Both males and females suck blood but only the females burrow into skin, where they become engorged until they may swell up to the size of a pea. The common sites of infestation are the soles of the feet and spaces between the toes, but no body surface is exempt from invasion. The pocket developed by the females may extend deeply into the dermis, causes great pain and inconvenience, and characteristically becomes secondarily infected. The female is carefully teased out of the wound with a sharp needle, then the wound is cleansed and provided with surgical dressing. The most satisfactory prophylaxis consists in wearing good stout leather shoes.

SUMMARY

1. Insects have a distinct separation into head, thorax and abdomen. The head of the adult has a pair of antennæ and mandibulate type of mouth parts. The thorax is composed of 3 segments, each with a pair of 5-jointed legs. Typically there are wings on the 2nd and 3rd segments. The abdomen has 12 original segments, of which the distalmost ones are modified as genital structures. Larval stages of insects are more or less worm-like and have chewing mouth parts.
2. The life cycle of insects varies from one in which the larva hatched from the egg is hardly distinguishable from the adult, to a very complex type in which a complete metamorphosis occurs during the pupal stage between the larva and the adult.
3. In the rôle of causal agents of disease, insects may be classified as (1) vesicating, (2) urticating, (3) venenating, (4) sensitizing and (5) tissue-invading.
4. Vesication is produced by certain familes of beetles, which have a fluid that causes blisters when it comes in contact with the skin and mucous membranes.
5. Urtication is produced by the nettling hairs of the caterpillars of one family of butterflies and several families of moths. In contact with the skin or mucous membranes, these hairs penetrate or break off, releasing a poison-gland secretion which causes urticaria.
6. Venenation is due to the introduction into the skin or mucous membranes of the venom of bees, wasps, hornets and ants, which produces local reaction and in hypersensitized individuals an anaphylactic reaction which may cause death.
7. Sensitization is produced by insects which have mouth parts adapted for piercing the skin and sucking blood. The introduction of salivary secretions into the puncture wound results in a local tissue reaction in many individuals and intense systemic symptoms of an allergic type in some persons.
8. Tissue invasion on the part of insects is due to specific, semi-specific or accidental entry of an immature or adult stage of the insect into the skin or mucous membrane of man or other animals. The most common agents are flies, which deposit living young (maggots) or eggs on undamaged or injured tissues. The larvæ penetrate into the tissues, on which they feed, produce severe, at times mutilating damage, and occasionally cause death.

Larval and adult stages of beetles have been found temporarily lodged in the digestive tract or urinary bladder.

The chigœ flea (*Tunga penetrans*) produces a dermatitis usually on the sole of the foot or between the toes. Only the females burrow deeply into the skin and produce a painful swelling.

REFERENCES

ADROUNY, G. A., DERBES, V. J., and JUNG, R. C. 1959. Isolation of a Hemolytic Component of Fire Ant Venom. Science, *130*, 449.

ANDERSON, W. B. 1935. Ophthalmomyiasis. Am. J. Ophthalm., *18*, 699–705.

BARNETT, H. C., and KNOBLOCK, E. C. 1952. Chemical and Biological Studies on DDT Resistance of Lice. U. S. Armed Forces Med. J., *3*, 297–304.

BRYAN, W. J., JR. 1937. Myiasis. J. Am. Med. Assn., *109*, 573–574.

DUDGE, J. H., LELAND, S. E., JR., WYANT, Z. N., and ELAN, G. W. 1959. Critical Tests on the Organic Phosphate Insecticide, Dimethoate®, against *Gastrophilus* spp. in the Horse. J. Parasitol., *45*, (Sec. 2), 56.

GEIGY, R., and KRAUS, C. 1952. Rüssel und Stechakt von *Rhodnius prolixus*. Acta Tropica, *9*, 272–276.

GILMER, P. M. 1925. A Comparative Study of the Poison Appratus of Certain Lepidopterous Larvæ. Ann. Entomol. Soc. Am., *18*, 203–239.

GORDON, R. M., and CREWE, W. 1949. The Mechanism by which Mosquitoes and Tsetse Flies Obtain Their Blood Meals. Ann. Trop. Med. & Parasitol., *42*, 356.

HERMS, W. B. 1932. Non-bloodsucking Flies as Vectors of Pathogenic Microörganisms. Ann. Entomol. Soc. Am., *25*, 623–628.

HERTIG, M. 1949. *Phlebotomus* and Residual DDT in Greece and Italy. Am. J. Trop. Med., *29*, 773–802.

HURLBUT, H. S., PEFFLY, R. L., and ABDEL, AZIZ SALAH. 1954. DDT Resistance in Egyptian Body Lice. Am. J. Trop. Med. & Hyg., *3*, 922–929.

JAMES, M. T. 1947. The Flies that Cause Myiasis in Man. U. S. Dept. Agr. Misc. Publ., No. 631. Washington, D. C. 175 pp.

KNIPLING, E. F. 1959. Sterile Male Method of Population Control. Science, *130* 902–904.

LUCAS, T. A. 1942. Poisoning by *Megalopyge opercularis* ("Puss Caterpillar"). J. Am. Med. Assn., *119*, 877–880.

MATHESON, R. 1950. *Medical Entomology.* 2nd ed., 612 pp. Comstock Publishing Co., Ithaca, N. Y.

NEUMANN, W., and HABERSMANN, E. 1956. Paper Electrophoresis Separation of Pharmacologically and Biochemically Active Components of Bee and Snake Venom, pp. 171–174, in *Venoms*, Am. Assn. Adv. Sci., Washington, D C.

OTSURI, M., and OGAWA, S. 1959. Observations on the Bite of the Tabanid Larvæ in Paddy Fields (Diptera, Tabanidæ). Acta Med. et Biol., *7*, 37–50.

PERRY, A. S., and BUCKNER, A. J. 1958. Biochemical Investigations on DDT-Resistance in the Human Body Louse, *Pediculus humanus humanus.* Am. J. Trop. Med. & Hyg., *7*, 620–626.

RANDEL, H. W. 1956. Caterpillar Urticaria in the Panama Canal Zone: Report of Five Cases, pp. 11–116, in *Venoms*, Am. Assn. Adv. Sci., Washington, D. C.

SHAFFER, J. H. 1961. Stinging Insects—A Threat to Life. J. Am. Med. Assn., *177*, 473–479.

THÉODORIDÈS, J. 1948. Les coleopteres parasites accidentels de l'homme. Ann. de Parasitol., *23*, 348–363.

Chapter 18

Arthropod Vectors of Human Disease

ARTHROPODS play a very significant role as vectors of many pathogenic microörganisms from man or reservoir hosts to man. Hence intensive and continued study of the biology and ecology of these vectors is necessary for control of the diseases which they transmit. This vector relationship may be entirely mechanical or the arthropod may be essential in completing the life cycle of the agent (*i.e.*, a biological vector).

ARTHROPODS AS MECHANICAL VECTORS

Characteristically the arthropod as mechanical vector obtains the pathogen from human or reservoir feces, blood or superficial ulcers. The contamination may be solely on the surface of the arthropod but more often the menstruum is ingested and then voided in vomit drops or in the excreta.

Disease Agents Mechanically Transmitted by Arthropods.—The most common are the enteric bacteria, transmitted by the common house-fly (*Musca domestica*) and other filth flies which breed in human excreta. Among these pathogens the typhoid organism (*Salmonella typhosa*), other species of *Salmonella*, the colon bacillus (*Escherichia coli*) and *Shigella dysenteriæ* (Richards *et al.*, 1961) are the most usual and most important. In areas of endemicity or of epidemic outbreaks cholera is also frequently spread by these flies (Napier, 1946). Likewise the house roach *Blatella germanica* and even the larger cockroach *Periplaneta americana* may occasionally serve as vectors of enteric pathogens (Janssen and Wedberg, 1952; Jung and Shaffer, 1952).

Species of eye-gnats of the genus *Hippelates* have been involved in epidemics of acute conjunctivitis in California and southeastern U.S.A., and species of *Siphunculina* are believed to contribute to the hyperendemicity of conjunctivitis in Egypt and India. *Hippelates* and *Aëdes ægypti* have also been incriminated on epidemiological grounds of the mechanical transmission of the agent of yaws (*Treponema pertenue*) from an open lesion of an infected person to a clean individual.

Domestic flies are incidental vectors of the bacterial agents of tuberculosis, anthrax, plague, tularemia and brucellosis, and experimental tests indicate that mosquitoes, deer flies, tabanids, bedbugs, body lice and ticks will discharge viable bacteria in their dejecta after feeding on some of these organisms. However, when maggots of filth flies ingest enteric bacteria, very few survive through pupal transformation to the adult fly (Greenberg, 1959). Ticks and bedbugs may occasionally transmit the virus of yellow fever in their excreta following a blood meal on an infected subject.

Among the animal parasites of man, filth flies and cockroaches are potential mechanical transfer agents of the cysts of intestinal protozoa, including *Entamœba*

(396)

histolytica, from human excreta to clean food. Likewise cockroaches, ants, wasps and dung beetles working in fecal deposits on the ground disseminate eggs of intestinal roundworms and tapeworms extensively through the top soil. The blood-sucking fly *Stomoxys calcitrans* is an efficient mechanical vector of *Leishmania tropica* (page 45) and the tsetse flies (*Glossina* spp.) at times transfer *Trypanosoma gambiense* and *T. rhodesiense* from person to person during an interrupted blood meal (page 59).

ARTHROPODS AS BIOLOGICAL VECTORS

A summary of important arthropod biological vectors, the pathogens which they transmit and the role played by the arthropod in the life cycle of the pathogen is presented in Table 6. This table is arranged according to the taxonomic classification of the vectors. The etiologic agents are considered separately in the following pages.

In recent years the viruses biologically transmitted by arthropods (*i.e.,* the arthropod-borne viruses) have come to be called the "arbor viruses." Nearly 100 distinct types have been distinguished (Casals, 1961). These organisms are ultramicroscopic, filtrable, obligate parasites of host cells. A majority utilize mosquitoes as their only natural vectors. The most important are those which produce yellow fever, dengue, the encephalitides, Colorado tick fever and sandfly fever.

Yellow Fever.—The virus of this disease measures 17 to $28\mu\mu$ in diameter. It is thermolabile, dies in 2 to 3 hours at room temperature, is destroyed by standard disinfectants but survives for years in the frozen state. In man it is typically viscerotropic but it may become neurotropic (Theiler, 1951). Its natural mammalian hosts are monkeys and occasionally in South America one or more species of mar-supials; its arthropod hosts are sylvatic, semi-domestic and domestic mosquitoes.

Geographical Distribution, Biology and Life Cycle.—Yellow fever is established in the tropical rainforests of Africa and America, where the enzoötic cycle involves primarily native monkeys and tree-canopy mosquitoes. In South America day-biting wild mosquitoes and in West Africa mostly night-biting forest mos-quitoes are the vectors from simian to simian host. Man is exposed when he enters the enzoötic area or when infected monkeys leave the jungle and cause infection in domestic mosquitoes, which, in turn, inoculate persons in nearby clearings or villages. In East Africa human exposure is different. Marauding monkeys leave the tree tops to steal bananas and other cultivated food in the nearby clearings, where they infect semi-domestic mosquitoes. In both types the enzoötic cycle (jungle yellow fever) is the basic one and human involvement is secondary. Since the virus is recoverable from the blood of the mammalian host for only a few days and remains viable in the tissues of the mosquito through its life time, the infected mosquito is both reservoir and vector (Strode, 1951).

From time to time enzoötic yellow fever reaches urban centers. If the susceptible domestic mosquito (*Aëdes ægypti*) is breeding in the town, epidemic yellow fever will develop. In past centuries the disease broke out periodically in seaports of West Africa and on the east coast of Latin America from Brazil to Mexico, and from there was transported to the West Indies and to temperate-zone cities, where it caused decimating epidemics. Walter Reed and associates conclusively demon-strated in Cuba (1900) that *Aëdes ægypti* is the urban transmitter, thus providing a method for control. Measures to eradicate this mosquito in yellow fever-plagued ports had by 1925 convinced public health authorities that they had conquered

Table 6.—*Arthropods as Biological Vectors of Important Pathogens of Man*

Taxonomic Group	Species	Pathogenic Agent (and Disease)	Role of Arthropod	Method of Human Exposure	Page Rf.
CRUSTACEA COPEPODA ("water fleas")	*Diaptomus* spp. *Cyclops* spp.	*Diphyllobothrium latum* (fish tapeworm infection)	1st intermediate host; no multiplication of larval tapeworm	Man eats infected fish (2nd intermediate host)	203
	Cyclops spp.	*Diphyllobothrium*, subgenus *Spirometra* (sparganosis)	Idem.	Man swallows infected cyclops	216
	Cyclops spp.	*Dracunculus medinensis* (dracontiasis)	Idem.	Idem.	314
	Cyclops spp.	*Gnathostoma spinigerum* (gnathostomiasis)	Idem.	Man eats infected fish (2nd intermediate host)	269
DECAPODA	Freshwater crabs and crayfishes	*Paragonimus westermani* (lung fluke infection)	2nd intermediate host; no multiplication of larval fluke	Man eats infected crustacean	156
ARACHNIDA ACARI (ticks and mites)	Hard- and soft-bodied ticks	*Rickettsia rickettsi*, *R. conori*, *R. australis* (spotted fever)	Rickettsia multiplies in midgut of tick; congenital transmission in tick	"Bite" of infected tick	405
	Hard-bodied ticks	*Coxiella burneti* (Q fever)	Rickettsia multiplies in midgut of tick	Idem.	408
	Hard-bodied ticks	Virus complex (Far Eastern Spring-Summer encephalitis)	Virus multiplies in tick	Idem.	404
	Hard-bodied ticks	*Pasteurella tularensis* (tularemia)	Bacillus multiplies in midgut of tick	Idem.	411
	Soft-bodied ticks	*Borrelia duttoni et al.* (tick-borne relapsing fever)	Spirochete multiplies in extra-intestinal tissues; congenital transmission in tick	Idem.	411

Vector	Pathogen (disease)	Development in vector	Method of transmission	Page
Trombicula spp. (red mites)	*Rickettsia tsutsugamushi* (scrub typhus)	Rickettsia multiples in gut of mite; congenital transmission in mite	"Bite" of larval mite	407
Allodermanyssus sanguineus (mouse mite)	*Rickettsia akari* (rickettsialpox)	Rickettsia multiplies in gut of mite	"Bite" of mite	405
Dermanyssus gallinae (chicken mite)	Virus of St. Louis and Western encephalitis	Virus multiplies in gut of mite; congenital transmission in mite	Idem. (uncommon)	403
INSECTA **ANOPLURA** (sucking lice)				
Pediculus humanus var. *corporis* (body louse)	*Rickettsia prowazeki* (epidemic typhus fever)	Rickettsia multiplies in wall of louse's midgut	"Bite," feces or crushing louse on skin	406
Pediculus humanus var. *corporis*	*Rickettsia quintana* (trench fever)	Rickettsia multiplies in louse's midgut	Idem.	411
Pediculus humanus var. *corporis*	*Borrelia recurrentis* (epidemic relapsing fever)	Spirochete multiplies in extra-intestinal tissues	Crushing louse on skin	62
HETEROPTERA (true bugs)				
Triatomid bugs	*Trypanosoma cruzi* (Chagas' disease)	Trypanosome multiplies in midgut of bug	Rubbing infected excreta on mucous membranes or into skin	102
DIPTERA (flies)				
Anopheles spp. (mosquitoes)	*Plasmodium* spp. (malaria)	Plasmodia complete sexual cycle and produce sporozoites	"Bite" of infected mosquito	293
Culex, Aedes, Anopheles spp.	*Wuchereria bancrofti* (Bancroft's filariasis)	Embryo matures to infective-stage larva	Idem.	
Mansonia, Anopheles	*Brugia malayi* (Malayan filariasis)	Idem.	Idem.	302
Aedes, Culex, Mansonia spp.	Virus of yellow fever, dengue, encephalitis, etc. (arbor viruses)	Virus multiplies in tissues of mosquito	Idem.	397–404
Culicoides spp. (gnats)	*Acanthocheilonema* spp., *Mansonella ozzardi* (filariasis)	Embryo transforms to infective-stage larva	Idem.	313

Table 6.—Arthropods as Biological Vectors of Important Pathogens of Man (Continued)

Taxonomic Group	Species	Pathogenic Agent (and Disease)	Role of Arthropod	Method of Human Exposure	Page Ref.
DIPTERA (concluded)	Simulium spp. (coffee flies)	Onchocerca volvulus (filariasis)	Idem.	Idem.	304
	Chrysops spp. (mango flies)	Loa loa (loaiasis)	Idem.	Idem.	309
	Chrysops spp., Tabanus spp.	Pasteurella tularensis (tularemia)	Bacillus multiplies in gut of fly	Idem.	409
	Phlebotomus spp. (sandfly)	Leishmania spp. (leishmaniasis)	Flagellate multiplies in midgut of sandfly and migrates to proboscis	Idem.	40
	Phlebotomus spp.	Bartonella bacilliformis (bartonellosis)	Pathogen multiplies in body of sandfly	Idem.	408
	Phlebotomus spp.	Virus of sandfly fever	Virus multiplies in tissues of fly	Idem.	404
	Glossina spp. (tsetse fly)	Trypanosoma rhodesiense, T. gambiense (African trypanosomiasis)	Trypanosome multiplies in midgut and salivary glands, then migrates to proboscis of tsetse fly	Idem.	52
SIPHONAPTERA (fleas)	Xenopsylla cheopis et al. (rodent fleas)	Pasteurella pestis (plague)	Bacillus multiplies in gut of fleas	"Bite" and feces of flea	409
	X. cheopis et al.	Rickettsia typhi (murine typhus)	Rickettsia multiplies in wall of flea's midgut	Idem.	406
	X. cheopis et al.	Hymenolepis diminuta (rat tapeworm infection)	Embryo matures to infective-stage larva in hemocele of flea	Swallowing infected flea	199
	Ctenocephalides canis, C. felis (dog and cat fleas)	Dipylidium caninum (dog tapeworm infection)	Idem.	Idem.	199

the disease but at that time they were unaware of the enzoötic source of the infection. Discovery of this cycle (Strode, 1951) constitutes one of the most important contributions to disease epidemiology. Once an epizoötic has passed, with death of many monkeys, the simian survivors are immune for life; similarly in epidemics the human survivors have permanent immunity. New generations of non-immune simian or human hosts in the presence of susceptible mosquitoes permit new outbreaks of the disease, as in recent years in Central America and on the island of Trinidad. This two-fold (*e.g.*, sylvatic and urban) cycle is diagrammatically illustrated in Figure 193 for the American and West African infections. *Aëdes ægypti*, which is prevalent in Eastern Asia and Australia, and *A. pseudoscutellaris* in the South Pacific islands, are susceptible vectors but the disease has never been reported east of Africa (Philip, Hughes and Darrow, 1958).

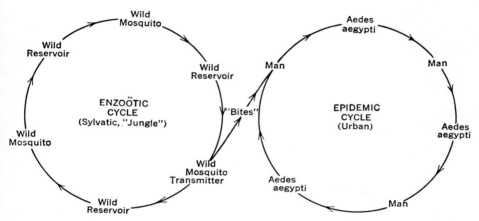

Fig. 193.—The enzoötic and epidemic transmission cycles of yellow fever. (Original from Faust and Russell's *Clinical Parasitology*, Lea & Febiger, Philadelphia.)

In the mammalian host the virus circulates in the blood during the last 6 to 10 hours of the incubation period and for 3 to 4 days thereafter. To become infected the susceptible mosquito must obtain the virus during this period. Eight to 14 days are required for incubation in the mosquito, after which the mosquito can transmit the virus for the remainder of its life.

Pathogenesis and Symptomatology.—The characteristic lesions are early mid-zonal necrosis and fatty degeneration of the liver, followed by extensive hemorrhages in the viscera and toxic nephrosis. The incubation period of 3 to 6 days, occasionally longer, is followed by a sudden onset of symptoms, including profound malaise, intense headache, myalgia and fever (39° to 40° C.). In 2 to 4 days the symptoms partly subside but they return because of profound intoxication, with decreased pulse rate (Faget's sign). If the fever gradually subsides and there are no grave complications such as extensive vomiting of blood and peptonuria, slow convalescence results (Strode, 1951). With the complications mentioned the prognosis is grave. Small children typically have asymptomatic or mild infection and develop permanent immunity.

Diagnosis.—This must be made on the epidemiologic history and characteristic symptoms. In suspected epidemics postmortem liver biopsy may provide the first specific diagnostic evidence.

Treatment.—This is exclusively symptomatic and palliative.

26

Epidemiology.—Today urban epidemics are uncommon and occur when one or at most a few persons become infected from wild mosquitoes in or near enzoötic jungle foci (Bugher *et al.*, 1944), or from monkeys breaking out of the jungle into inhabited areas, especially during periodic epizoötics (Kerr, 1958). In 1954, for the first time, an individual traveling by air during the incubation period developed symptomatic infection after his arrival at his destination (in Caracas, Venezuela). Technics to provide information on immunity in an exposed population include complement fixation, hemagglutination and mouse protection tests.

Control.—Eradication of jungle yellow fever is not feasible but persons liable to exposure will obtain protection for years, possibly for life, if they are immunized several weeks beforehand with attenuated neurotropic yellow fever virus. This prophylactic method was employed successfully in terminating the northern advance of the disease which broke loose from an enzoötic focus in Panama in 1949. An even more important control measure is the *Aëdes ægypti* eradication program which has been waged by the Pan American Sanitary Bureau of WHO in tropical Latin America for more than two decades. This campaign has been primarily responsible for the few epidemics which have developed within that period. Most countries require certification of yellow fever vaccination for immigrants and tourists entering from a country having enzoötic yellow fever.

Dengue.—The virus of dengue belongs to the same immunologic group as yellow fever (Casals, 1961). The disease is endemic in native populations and epidemic in non-immunes in many warm climates throughout the world. The virus is transmitted from person to person by *Aëdes ægypti* and related species of this genus prevalent in an area (and by *Armigeres obturbans* in Taiwan). Man is the only known natural vertebrate host, although monkeys are susceptible. First described as a clinical entity by Benjamin Rush in Philadelphia in 1780, dengue was proved to be caused by a filtrable virus by Ashburn and Craig in 1907, and to be transmitted by *Aëdes ægypti* by Siler, Hall and Hitchens in 1926. The mosquito obtains the virus from the patient only during the first 3 days of his illness (period of viremia), then requires 8 to 11 days incubation before becoming infective for life.

In the infected individual dengue virus lives in cells of the parenchymatous organs and endothelial lining of bloodvessels, in which it causes necrosis and hemorrhage. After an incubation period of 4 to 10 days there is characteristically an abrupt onset, with chills, extreme pain in the joints, loins, epigastric and postorbital regions, flushed swelling of the face, and fever of 39.5° to 40° C. lasting for 4 to 7 days, with increased pulse rate and often extreme prostration. There is a sudden short remission, with reduced temperature and profuse sweating, followed by a return of fever (the characteristic "saddle-back" fever curve), extreme malaise, nervous depression and terminal rash lasting for 2 or 3 days, then pruritic desquamation and slow convalescence. Previously exposed native populations may develop none of the characteristic symptoms of dengue, due to partial immunity. Diagnosis is made on the sequence of clinical manifestations, the characteristic leukopenia with a shift to the left in the Schilling count. Treatment is exclusively symptomatic and palliative. Dengue *per se* never ends fatally.

The epidemiology of the disease involves man and mosquitoes, most often *Aëdes ægypti*. Endemically it is more often rural than urban, but epidemically seaports are most frequently affected (Sabin, 1955). Man is exposed from "bites" of infected mosquitoes. At least four immunologic strains of the virus have been distinguished (Casals, 1961). Detection of endemicity is made on immunologic tests. Control depends exclusively on eradication of the mosquito transmitter in the area.

The Arbor Encephalitides.—An increasing number of arthropod-transmitted neurotropic viruses are being discovered yearly in different areas of the world, primarily as a result of immunologic tests of populations (Casals and Brown, 1954;

Causey and Theiler, 1958; Smith, 1958; Casals and Whitman, 1960). Among the better known members of this group are St. Louis, Japanese B, Venezuelan, Eastern (U.S.A.), Western (U.S.A.), and West Nile. St. Louis, Japanese B and West Nile belong to the yellow fever-dengue group, Eastern, Western and Venezuelan to a second immunological group.

St. Louis encephalitis has extensive distribution in the U.S.A. from west of the Appalachian Mountains to the Pacific Coast, and has been isolated in Trinidad and Panamá. Basically it is an infection of fowls, with transmission by the chicken mite *Dermanyssus gallinæ*. It spreads to horses and to man through infected *Culex tarsalis et al.*, *Aedes* spp., *Anopheles* spp., and *Culiceta* spp. Following human exposure and a variable incubation period, there is a sudden onset with severe headache, high fever, muscular rigidity and tremors lasting up to 10 days, then rapid recovery in the average case; but in epidemics some fatalities occur. No effective control measures have been undertaken.

Japanese B encephalitis has extensive distribution in the Far East from the Maritime Provinces of Siberia through Japan, China, Taiwan and the Philippines to India and the Southwest Pacific Islands. The life cycle of the virus involves birds (especially herons and egrets), domestic mammals and man on the one hand, and mosquitoes on the other. In nature *Culex tritæniorhynchus*, *C. pipiens* var. *pallens* and *Aëdes togoi* are the most important transmitters. The disease is enzoötic in the avian hosts; domestic mammals and man become secondarily involved. In Japan, where an intensive epidemiologic study was conducted in 1956–1957 during an outbreak of the disease in the Tokyo area (Scherer, Buescher *et al.*, 1959), exposure occurred at the height of *C. tritæniorhynchus* density; practically all of the swine became infected and served as a major source of infection for the mosquito vectors. Periodically extensive epidemics have developed, characteristically in a 3-year cycle, at times with high mortality. The symptoms are often severe, with nuchal rigidity, disorientation and other evidences of cerebellar involvement. The acute stage may pass into a subacute or chronic one, at times with permanent facial paralysis or other neurologic manifestations. Treatment is exclusively symptomatic. Control consists in preventing the breeding of the mosquito transmitters.

Venezuelan (equine) encephalitis is prevalent in the West Indies and Venezuela, and has been found in immunologic tests in Brazil, Ecuador and Colombia. The virus is transmitted in nature by species of *Aëdes*, *Anopheles* and *Mansonia*. Horses and man are highly susceptible. Clinically the disease resembles influenza rather than a neurotropic infection.

Eastern and Western encephalitis are closely related entities which practically cover the United States of America in their distribution (Eastern, east of the Appalachian Mountains, Western, from the Appalachians to the Pacific Coast). Both have also been found in South America and in Western Canada and Mexico. Species of *Aëdes*, *Culex*, *Culiceta* and *Mansonia* are the mosquito vectors for the former infection, *Culex*, *Culiceta*, *Aëdes* and *Anopheles* for the latter (Beadle, 1959; Brody and Murray, 1959). The most important of these for both virus types is *Culex tarsalis*. Eastern encephalitis produces epizoötics in horses, occasionally affects man. Birds are the reservoirs. Western encephalitis is primarily a bird-*C. tarsalis*-bird infection, with man as an important secondary victim. In epidemics the onset of the disease is sudden and symptoms are typically severe, with high fever, convulsions, twitching and signs of high intracranial pressure. Severe infection may terminate fatally, and survivors may have neurological sequelæ.

West Nile encephalitis has extensive distribution throughout Africa and the Middle East as far as India. In Egypt it is rural, in Israeli urban. It is probably transmitted in nature by species of *Culex* and *Aëdes*. The disease course is mild and no deaths have been reported.

Many other arbor viruses have been studied epidemiologically or immunologically. A majority of these are mosquito-transmitted and immunity tests in human populations indicate that some of these viruses originally discovered in the Eastern Hemisphere are also present in South America. At times the tests demonstrate the presence of several distinct viral immune bodies in the same population (Causey and Theiler, 1958; Smith, 1958; Groot *et al.*, 1959).

Tick-transmitted arbor virus has been demonstrated to be the cause of Colorado tick fever in man in extensive areas of the northwestern United States of America and on Long Island (N.Y.). The pathogen is transmitted principally by *Dermacentor andersoni* (western) and *D. variabilis* (eastern), and is congenital in the tick, passing through the egg to the offspring (Eklund *et al.*, 1955). After 4 to 5 days incubation following the "bite" of the infected tick there is a sudden onset, myalgia, bitemporal headache, malaise, chills and fever, followed by 1 to 2 days of lowered temperature, then return of initial symptoms with marked leukopenia. The disease is temporarily incapacitating but not fatal, and recovery results in partial immunity.

Far-Eastern Spring-Summer Encephalitis Complex.—This disease is caused by a group of viruses (Casals, 1961) having identical or quite similar antigenic characteristics; they are transmitted in nature to rodents or birds by several genera of ticks (*Ixodes, Dermacentor, Hyalomma, Hæmaphysalis*, etc.), which are congenitally infected (Hoogstraal, 1961). The enzoötic areas include forests of Central Europe, U.S.S.R., Central Asia, Siberia, Maritime Provinces, Korea, China, Malaya, and the Kyasanur Forest, India (Sabin, 1958). In these widely separated areas both the disease and the epidemiologic patterns differ remarkably (Hoogstraal, 1961). In the U.S.S.R. man is exposed upon entering enzoötic areas during the spring when hibernating ticks become reactivated and throughout the short summer season. Man may also be exposed from drinking raw milk of infected goats (Smorodintesev and Ilienko, 1958).

Sand-fly Fever.—This disease is endemic in the Mediterranean, Middle East and portions of southern U.S.S.R. (Henderson and Taylor, 1960). The virus is transmitted to man, the only known mammalian host, by indigenous species of sand-flies, most often *Phlebotomus papatasii*, hence the designation "pappataci fever." It develops epidemically following summer rains and the emergence of new broods of sand-flies (Sabin, 1955).

After inoculation by the sand-fly and an incubation period of $2\frac{1}{2}$ to 6 days, during which the virus becomes generally distributed throughout visceral as well as somatic tissues, the onset of symptoms is sudden, with a chilly sensation, rise in temperature usually lasting only 2 to 4 days, then gradual defervescence. Rarely a second febrile period develops, in which case the disease may be confused with dengue (page 402). There is typically a syndrome of severe frontal headache, generalized pain and stiffness in all of the visceral and somatic tissues, anorexia, flushed face and neck, but no rash. Profuse sweating follows defervescence, then intense fatigue and weakness. Convalescence leads to normal well-being and confers moderate immunity. Diagnosis is made on epidemiologic evidence and clinical findings. Treatment is entirely symptomatic.

The reservoir of the virus during the late fall, winter and early spring is not known (Sabin *et al.*, 1944). There is no acceptable evidence that the microörganism is congenitally transmitted in the sand-fly but this is a possibility. The disease characteristically occurs epidemically in non-immune persons but it probably appears asymptomatically in previously exposed native populations. As in sandfly-transmitted leishmaniasis in some of the same localities, sandfly fever can be prevented by residual spraying of DDT around and within human habitations (Hertig and Fairchild, 1948; Hertig, 1949).

THE RICKETTSIOSES

The rickettsiæ are microscopic, pleomorphic, Gram-negative, usually non-filtrable organisms intimately associated with their hosts (Zinsser, 1937). Many species are non-pathogenic symbionts of arthropods but others are highly pathogenic for man and domestic animals. Rickettsiæ are classified in two family groups, the RICKETTSIACEÆ and the BARTONELLACEÆ. In the Rickettsiaceæ the species of medical importance belong to the genera *Rickettsia* and *Coxiella*. The only member of the Bartonellaceæ known to produce infection in man is *Bartonella bacilliformis*.

Tick-borne Typhus Fevers.—The etiologic agents are three morphologically similar but immunologically distinct rods or oval rickettsiæ measuring about 0.3 microns in length. *Rickettsia rickettsi* is responsible for tick-transmitted fever in extensive regions of the western U.S.A. and adjacent Canada, where *Dermacentor andersoni* is the principal vector, and of the eastern United States, where *D. variabilis* is the common transmitter (Calhoun and Alford, 1955); likewise in other enzoötic-endemic areas in Mexico, Colombia and Brazil. *R. conori* is the agent of tick typhus in the Mediterranean Basin, South and East Africa (Gear, 1954), Siberia and India (Hoogstraal, 1961), and *R. australis* in North Queensland, Australia.

These rickettsiæ invade the nucleus as well as the cytoplasm of mammalian host cells, particularly the endothelial lining of bloodvessels, first near the site of inoculation by the tick, then in miliary foci throughout the body. They produce mural thrombi and provoke vascular infiltration, at times resulting in gangrene (Lillie, 1941). After 2 to 14 days of incubation there are prodromal malaise and chills, then typically rigors, intense headache, arthralgia, hyperesthesia, photophobia and a fever which may reach 41° C. In many cases of *R. conori* infection a persistent dark button-like eschar is seen at the site of the tick's "bite," hence the clinical designation *"fièvre boutonneuse."*

In tick typhus there is characteristically a roseate macular rash of a petechial type, which develops at the onset of symptoms, proceeding from the hands and feet to all cutaneous areas and adjacent mucous membranes (Woodward, 1959). Severe cases exhibit delirium, stupor and coma, usually with fatal outcome. On the average the fever declines or becomes remittent after the second week of illness and prolonged convalescence ensues. Diagnosis is based on epidemiologic evidence of exposure, particularly the presence of a tick attached to the skin in an infected area, positive agglutination of Proteus OX 19 and OX 2, and complement fixation for specific diagnosis (Bengtson, 1944). Treatment is primarily with such drugs as chloramphenicol and tetracycline drugs, which are rickettsiostatic.

In nature tick typhus rickettsiæ are maintained by congenital transmission from one tick generation to another; secondarily, small mammals provide blood meals for the larval ticks, and larger mammals such as sheep for the nymphs and adult ticks. Human infection, although numerically appreciable in hyperenzoötic areas (Cawley and Wheeler, 1957), is incidental to the natural cycle of the pathogen, for which there is no known practical control. Man may escape exposure by avoiding tick-infested enzoötic areas, by removing ticks from his body soon after they become attached, by dusting DDT into his clothing before entering infested areas, and by biennial immunization with specific vaccine.

Rickettsialpox.—This disease, caused by *Rickettsia akari*, has been found in urban housing areas in the Eastern U.S.A., *viz.*, New York City, Boston, Hartford (Conn.) and Cleveland (Ohio). Immunologically it is closely related to the tick typhus group of rickettsial diseases. The life cycle involves the parasitoid mite *Alloder-*

manyssus sanguineus as vector and mice and rats as the natural mammalian hosts. Rodent infestation of homes provides opportunity for infected mites to infect human beings. At the site of inoculation there is an initial vesicle or pustule, followed by mild symptoms including fever, sweating, regional adenopathy and a maculate rash mimicking that of chickenpox. Presumptive diagnosis is made on the type of rash and evidence of rodent infestation, confirmed by the complement fixation test. Chloramphenicol and tetracycline drugs hasten convalescence. Children are more often exposed and more often become infected than do adults. Control consists in residual spraying of infested quarters with DDT and in rodent eradication.

Louse-borne and Flea-borne Typhus Fevers.—The etiologic agents of these two diseases are short rods or coccus-like rickettsiæ measuring 0.3 to 0.5 microns in length, which are obligate cytoplasmic parasites of the mammalian host. *Rickettsia prowazeki*, the louse-borne species, is specifically adapted to man and is transmitted by human lice, commonly the body louse, *Pediculus humanus* var. *corporis*. *R. typhi*, the agent of murine typhus, is transmitted by rodent fleas to rats and mice and secondarily to man. The louse-borne type is epidemic in character; the rodent flea-borne type is enzoötic, but in man it develops sporadically or may become mildly epidemic. Rodent flea-borne typhus is considered to be the parent strain. It does not injure the infected flea and the pathogenicity in the rodent is not remarkable. The louse-borne type is lethal for the louse within 12 days after it acquires the infection, and human infection is typically severe.

Following cutaneous or mucous-membrane inoculation of *R. prowazeki* or *R. typhi* the organisms invade the cytoplasm of the endothelial cells of the bloodvessels where they cause inflammation, provoke mural thrombi, perivascular infiltration and extravasation of blood. In the epidemic type the incubation period is 5 to 7 days, in the rodent type in man, 4 to 14 days. There is a prodromal malaise, followed by a sudden onset of symptoms, with chills and fever up to 40° C. lasting a week, then remission of the fever. Patients suffer from severe headache, flushed cheeks, congested conjunctivæ, severe aching in the back and legs, hyperesthesia, and in the epidemic type tremors and twitching, mental lethargy, frequently delirium and prostration. In both types of the disease an ecchymotic rash appears on the fifth day. In the epidemic type gangrene may develop on the tips of the fingers, toes and nose. Diagnosis may be made presumptively on clinical and epidemiological grounds, confirmed by the Weil-Felix test (Proteus OX 19) and by specific complement fixation which distinguishes *R. prowazeki* from *R. typhi*, as well as from the tick-typhus group of rickettsiæ. The fluorescent antibody technic also distinguishes murine from epidemic typhus. The prognosis in murine typhus is much better because of the usually milder course of the disease. Symptomatic treatment is supplemented by administration of chloramphenicol and the tetracyclines, which control multiplication of the rickettsiæ.

Brill's disease is recrudescence of epidemic typhus in persons who had the acute infection years earlier and recovered symptomatically but carried a latent infection (Murray and Snyder, 1951).

The epidemiology of the two types of typhus fever is typically quite different. The man-louse-man cycle of *R. prowazeki* develops epidemically in crowded communities, in which customs of the population or lack of sanitation and personal hygiene favor louse infestation. The murine type caused by *R. typhi* is enzoötic in rats which infest seaports, along wharves and in shops, and from these areas may migrate inland. Man is exposed when infected rat fleas take a blood meal, introducing the rickettsiæ during defecation. Control of epidemic typhus requires mass delousing measures, including sterilization of clothing, thorough bathing of all exposed or louse-infested persons and body dusting of DDT or other insecticide to which the strain of lice is not resistant (Barnett and Knoblock, 1952; Hurlbut *et al.*, 1954; Perry and Buckner, 1958). Control of murine typhus requires community destruction of rats preceded by use of DDT or other effective insecticides in rat nests and burrows to kill the rodent fleas and thus to prevent transfer of the fleas to human hosts (Love and Smith, 1960).

Louse-borne Trench Fever.—Trench fever is produced by *Rickettsia quintana*, which is indistinguishable morphologically from *R. prowazeki* but is immunologically distinct. Epidemics of this relatively mild but highly incapacitating disease have occurred in Europe during past decades under conditions of trench warfare in which louse infestation became general. More recently it has been reported as endemic in Mexico (Varela, 1955). When a person is exposed to infected lice, an asymptomatic incubation period of 10 to 30 days is followed by a sudden onset, with symptoms similar to, but less severe than in epidemic typhus fever. The trench fever curve is remittent about every 5 days, hence the name "quintana." There is often a roseate macular rash. Diagnosis is based presumptively on clinical and epidemiological grounds. Treatment with chloramphenicol and tetracyline drugs hastens clinical recovery. Lice become infected from sucking blood of the patient beginning with the first day of symptomatic infection and for a long period thereafter. After 5 to 9 days incubation the louse becomes infective. The rickettsiæ multiply on the surface of the louse's gut wall and not within the intestinal epithelial cells. There are no proven reservoir hosts. Control is similar to that for epidemic typhus fever (see above).

Scrub Typhus.—Scrub typhus, or Japanese river fever, is produced by *Rickettsia tsutsugamushi*, which is morphologically similar to *R. prowazeki* (page 406). The disease has an extensive distribution from Japan and Korea, through the China Sea areas to Burma, India and Ceylon; it is also enzoötic in Queensland, Australia. The life cycle in nature requires trombiculid mites (most frequently *Trombicula akamushi* or *T. deliensis*) as vectors and wild rodents as the usual mammalian hosts (Audy, 1958). The rickettsia is transmitted congenitally in the mite, which feeds on mammalian tissue juices only during its larval stage and transfers the pathogen only during this period.

On introduction by an infected larval mite into the skin of man, the rickettsiæ multiply locally, at times producing a reddish-black eschar. Then they become extensively distributed throughout the body, especially damaging the endothelial lining of the bloodvessels, including those in the brain, myocardium and lungs. After one to two weeks of incubation there is a sudden onset of symptoms, with chills, headache, dizziness and a fever of 40° C. or more within 2 to 3 days, after which the temperature returns to normal in 2 or 3 days. With defervescence there is a petechial rash, first on the head, then extending to the trunk and extremities, fading about a week later. Seriously ill patients have a long convalescence and without good nursing care may not survive. Natives who have been exposed repeatedly may show no symptoms. Diagnosis is made presumptively on clinical and epidemiological grounds and is confirmed by agglutination of Proteins OX K (and not OX 19 or OX 2) by patient's serum and specific complement fixation test (Bengtson, 1946). Treatment with chloramphenicol or the tetracycline drugs is clinically very effective but does not eradicate the rickettsiæ, which survive until they are destroyed by specific antibodies.

Human infection results from contact with larval trombiculid mites in enzoötic regions, especially in rank grass where the mites and their wild rodent hosts abound. Protection consists in destroying such vegetation around campsites, and in wearing DDT-impregnated garments. Suppressive treatment with chloramphenicol is temporarily effective during field operations but active infection may be anticipated after withdrawing treatment. Moderate to fast immunity may develop following infection of clinical grade.

Q Fever.—This disease is produced by *Coxiella burneti*. It has a cosmopolitan distribution, including the southwest region and Pacific Coast of the United States of America. In the basic life cycle the pathogen is transmitted by ticks feeding on infected cattle but man is usually exposed from air-borne or milk-borne sources.

C. burneti is a short rod, measuring 0.4 to 1.0 microns in length, which attacks the cytoplasm of the endothelial lining of the bloodvessels and fixed histiocytes in all organs and tissues. Hypertrophy of the reticulo-endothelial organs results from inflammation of these cells and an increase in their number. Q fever frequently produces a severe pneumonitis due to pulmonary infiltration of mononuclear leukocytes. Following a short but variable incubation period, there is an acute onset, with fever of 39.5° to 40° C. of 6 to 24 days duration, but with slow pulse; severe headache, chills, then sweating, photophobia, malaise, anorexia and pain in the back and legs. There is no associated rash. The outstanding clinical characteristic is pneumonia which develops during the first week. A long period of convalescence may be anticipated. Deaths have occurred, but probably most human infections are asymptomatic. Presumptive diagnosis is based on clinical and epidemiological grounds, confirmed by agglutination of tissue-grown suspensions of *C. burneti* by patient's serum. Treatment consists primarily in the administration of chloramphenicol or tetracycline drugs (Clark and Lennette, 1952), supplemented by symptomatic care.

Q fever is primarily an occupational disease among stockmen, herders, slaughterhouse attendants and others exposed to air-borne infection from diseased animals, and by consumers of raw milk of infected cattle and goats. Human exposure directly from infected ticks is uncommon. In one year as many as 50,000 persons in the Los Angeles, California area were infected (Marmion, 1954). Prevention requires protective measures to guard against direct or indirect contact with infected animals, including transmission of the pathogen by air, fomites or in milk.

Bartonellosis (Carrion's Disease, Oroya Fever, Verruga Peruana).—This disease is casued by a minute pleomorphic intracellular rickettsia-like organism, *Bartonella bacilliformis*. The infection exists in a few mountain valleys in Peru, Ecuador and Colombia, where species of the sand-fly *Phlebotomus* breed and transfer the pathogen from one person to another.

On introduction into the skin *B. bacilliformis* first invades and multiplies in the circulating red blood cells, causing an anemia and systemic intoxication. Thereafter the organisms enter the reticuloendothelial system, likewise the endothelial lining of the bloodvessels and lymphatics, producing verrucous eruptions. The incubation period of 10 to 21 days or more is followed by an insidious onset, with toxic manifestations, thirst, anorexia and prostration, low-grade septic fever lasting for a few days to several weeks, and an associated hemolytic anemia, but typically no leukocytosis. During this first period there may be hemorrhage from mucous membranes. Once the fever has abated the primary symptoms are less pronounced but verrucous lesions begin to appear in the skin and subcutaneous tissues, most prominently over bony prominences and joints. They are hemangiomatous and have a tendency to break down. This condition may last for weeks or months and the eruptions may eventually be absorbed. Once healing has begun, recurrence of the verruga is uncommon. Diagnosis is made on epidemiological and clinica findings and demonstration of the microörganisms first in red blood cells, later in the eruptive lesions. Administration of chloramphenicol or the tetracyline drugs provides rapid clinical improvement.

A single night's exposure to "bites" of sand-flies in the endemic areas may result in infection, and repeated exposure practically guarantees infection. Man is the only known mammalian host. Sand-flies may acquire infection either from feeding on infected blood or open lesions of the victim. Native populations may have asymptomic infection, then develop immunity. Protection is provided by residual sprays of DDT in and around human habitations to destroy the adult *Phlebotomus* (Hertig and Fairchild, 1948).

BACTERIA AND BACTERIAL INFECTIONS

Plague.—Plague is produced by the Gram-negative bacillus *Pasteurella pestis*, which is non-motile, pleomorphic, bipolar, does not form spores but usually is encapsulated. This disease is probably much older than man himself, being transmitted from rodent to rodent by rodent fleas. Historical records of human plague indicate its decimating capacity in Asia and Europe up to the present century, then its introduction into the Americas at the beginning of the 20th century (Haas, 1959). Yersin (1894) first isolated the bacillus of plague in Hongkong, while Simond (1898), Bautier and Raybaud (1902) and Liston (1905) demonstrated the role of rodent fleas in its transmission. Although no devastating plague epidemics have occurred in recent years, the disease persists enzoötically in many foci in Asia, Africa, the Americas and in Hawaii.

When infected fleas feed on an infected rodent, the fleas may transmit the plague bacillus to man (1) by regurgitating the bacilli into the skin after an interrupted feeding; (2) by evacuating the bacilli in the feces after the bacilli have multiplied in the flea's midgut; (3) by proboscis transfer of the bacilli into the skin by a flea which has developed a proventricular "block," or (4) when "blocked" fleas contaminate the puncture wounds made successively in a number of uninfected persons. The domestic tropical rat flea *Xenopsylla cheopis* "blocks" readily (Eskey, 1938; Munshi, 1960) and is the most common transmitter of plague from domestic rats to man (Meyer, 1957). The several pathways through which plague bacilli are propagated are illustrated in Figure 194.

In *bubonic plague*, the usual portal of entry of the pathogen is through the puncture site made by the flea. The typical lesion develops in the nearest lymph node, where the characteristic bubo appears as a raised, very tender abscess with a blood-stained cheesy center containing a colony of multiplying *P. pestis*, surrounded by a hemorrhagic zone and then an outer one of blood-tinged serum. Rarely the lesion becomes localized by encapsulation. In 60% of human cases the bubo is in the groin. From the original site the bacilli usually get into the bloodstream, in which they continue to multiply (*septicemic plague*) or may become filtered out in the lungs (*pneumonic plague*). Once a patient acquires pneumonic plague the disease becomes contagious from droplet spray containing the organisms. During the first 3 to 5 days of the developing primary bubo there occur local aching, generalized malaise, mental apathy and manifestations of profound intoxication, chills and fever of a remittent type, rapid pulse and rapid shallow respiration. Septicemic cases are seriously affected and those who develop pneumonic plague are in grave danger (Pollitzer, 1954).

Presumptive *diagnosis* is made in a plague area on the character of the primary bubo with attendant symptoms, but in an incipient epidemic the first plague case(s) may not be suspected. Confirmation is made from smears and cultures of the contents of a bubo, of the blood in septicemic plague and of bloody sputum in the pneumonic type, and the inoculation of guinea pigs with material from these menstrua. Ground-up pooled specimens of rodent fleas may be inoculated into guinea pigs, to discover by symptoms and pathological findings whether rodent plague is present in the area. *Treatment* of plague has undergone a remarkable evolution since the advent of sulfa drugs and antibiotics. Streptomycin provides a 100% favorable prognosis, if the patient is diagnosed and treated early in the disease (Hirst, 1953). Chloramphenicol and the tetracyclines are also very effective drugs.

The *epidemiology* of plague involves primarily the enzoötic cycle of rodent-rodent flea-rodent (Meyer, 1957), the so-called "sylvatic" or "campestral" plague of wild rodents, and does not involve domestic rats (Macchiavello, 1959). By migration

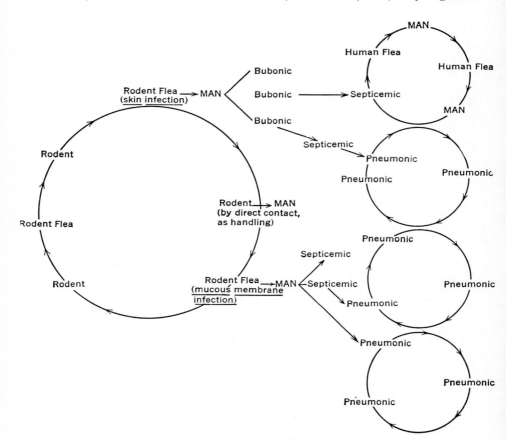

Fig. 194.—The transmission cycles of rodent and human plague. (Original, from Faust and Russell's *Clinical Parasitology*, Lea & Febiger, Philadelphia.)

and contact of wild rodents with domestic rats the infection often becomes epizoötic in urban areas. From infected rats the infected rat fleas transmit the disease to man. In practically all present-day plague areas the sylvatic or campestral foci are the sources from which urban rodent and human infection are derived. Measures to control the disease are directed toward eradicating rats in urban areas (Link and Mohr, 1953) and killing their fleas with DDT and other effective insecticides to which the fleas have not become resistant (Busvine, 1957). In regions of potential epidemics periodic vaccination with highly virulent killed *P. pestis* or with avirulent living organisms has had considerable prophylactic value. No practical method to eradicate the extensive areas of enzoötic plague has been developed. The danger of these foci was illustrated in 1957 when a victim exposed in Colorado traveled to Texas before she developed the disease and succumbed. Within the past half century human plague has been transformed from a decimating disease to a relatively minor cause of death.

Other Bacterial Infections.—Tularemia, produced by *Pasteurella tularensis*, and other bacterial diseases are at times transmitted to man from zoönotic sources by ticks, fleas, deer flies and mosquitoes (Jellison, 1959).

SPIROCHETAL DISEASES

Relapsing Fevers.—Tick-borne and louse-borne relapsing fevers are transmitted by arthropods as biological vectors. The tick-borne type is caused by the *Borrelia duttoni*-complex and the louse-transmitted type by the *B. recurrentis*-complex. These two groups of spirochetes are morphologically indistinguishable (Fig. 195). They are elongated threads with relatively sharp ends, measure 30 to 50 microns in length, have 8 to 10 undulations along their body, and divide by longitudinal binary fission. Different varieties or subspecies of the tick-borne spirochete are associated

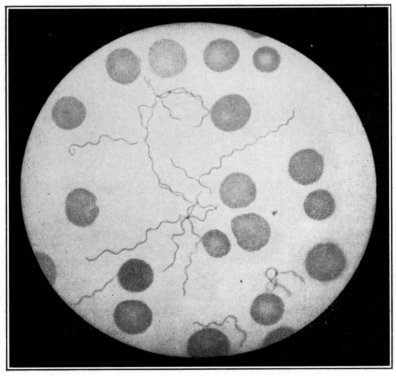

FIG. 195.—Tick-borne relapsing fever spirochetes (*Borrelia duttoni*) in peripheral blood during a clinical attack. (After Dr. S. B. Wolbach, in Shattuck's *Disease of the Tropics*, Appleton-Century-Crofts, Inc.)

with different species and species complexes of the tick *Ornithodoros*, which is the vector (Davis and Hoogstraal, 1954). Transmission is congenital in the tick, in which the organisms are developed in all tissues of the body; likewise in the louse the spirochete develops in all of the insect's tissues.

After being deposited in the human skin by the blood-sucking vector the spirochete circulates and multiplies in the bloodstream and tissue fluids but does not penetrate undamaged cells. Toxic metabolites cause necrosis of the parenchyma cells of the liver and spleen, degenerative changes of the bone marrow and kidneys and of the endothelial lining of the small bloodvessels, where multiplication takes place. The organisms are found in peripheral blood only during the primary and recurrent clinical attacks; at other times they are concentrated in the viscera. Following 4 to 8 days of incubation there is typically a sudden onset of symptoms, with a shaking chill and fever of 40° to 41° C., severe headache, pain in the back, legs and joints, tender liver and spleen, hemorrhage from smaller bloodvessels in the skin and mucous membranes and epistaxis, and at times nervous prostration. Four to 5 days later the temperature drops by crisis to normal, with sweating and weakness but relief from pain. Several relapses occur at intervals of 5 to 15 days, each of which is typically less severe than its predecessor. Successive clinical episodes are due to separate strains of the spirochete. *Diagnosis* is made on discovery of the organism in peripheral blood at the time of the clinical attack. *Treatment* is both symptomatic and specific. Administration of penicillin at any stage in the disease will usually terminate the symptoms and eradicate the infection.

Tick-transmitted relapsing fever is a zoönosis between wild mammals such as rodents and monkeys and *Ornithodoros* which infests them. Man is an accidental host in the cycle. In contrast, louse-transmitted relapsing fever is exclusively a man-louse-man disease in which the human body louse *Pediculus humanus* var. *corporis* is the vector. It develops epidemically under conditions of crowding and poor personal and group hygiene, as in louse-borne typhus fever (page 406). In areas of the tick-borne type of relapsing fever, impregnation of clothing with an arthropod repellent and DDT or BHC residual spraying of *Ornithodoros*-infested homes will reduce the likelihood of exposure. In louse-borne infection intensive campaigns to eradicate human body lice constitute the effective control technic. (See page 406, under Epidemic Typhus Fever.)

OTHER ARTHROPOD-TRANSMITTED DISEASES

The protozoan diseases which are transmitted by arthropods as biological vectors have been discussed earlier under their respective subject headings, *viz.*, malaria (pp. 105, 106, 108), the leishmaniases (pp. 41–51), the African trypanosomiases (pp. 52–60), *Trypanosoma rangeli* infection (p. 60) and Chagas' disease (pp. 60–65). The helminthic diseases involving arthropods have also been considered in previous chapters, *viz.*, tapeworm infections (pp. 198, 200), spiruroid and filarial infections (pp. 267–271, 293–317).

SUMMARY

1. Arthropods serve important roles as mechanical and biological vectors of disease-producing organisms.
2. As mechanical vectors, filth flies and other arthropods are common carriers of enteric pathogens, such as the Salmonellæ, Shigella and the cholera vibrio. Less commonly they have been incriminated in the epidemic spread of the agents of tuberculosis, plague, tularemia, brucel-

losis, anthrax, acute epidemic conjunctivitis, yaws, protozoan and helminthic infections.

3. Arthropod-borne (arbor) viruses, in which arthropods are biological vectors, include mosquito-transmitted yellow fever, dengue and the viral encephalitides (St. Louis, Japanese B, West Nile, Eastern, Western, and Venezuelan, as well as several other less known types), sandfly-transmitted pappataci fever, and Colorado tick-borne fever, likewise tick-transmitted Far-Eastern Spring-Summer Encephalitis Complex. Man is the only demonstrated vertebrate host of dengue and sandfly fever; all or a great majority of the other arbor viral diseases have reservoir hosts.

4. Arthropods are biological vectors of the following rickettsiæ which produce disease in man: *Rickettsia rickettsi, R. conori* and *R. australis*, tick-transmitted, producing three types of spotted fever; *R. akari*, mouse mite-transmitted, producing rickettsialpox; *R. prowazeki*, causing louse-borne typhus fever, and *R. typhi*, producing rat flea-transmitted murine typhus; *R. quintana*, producing louse-transmitted trench fever; *R. tsutsugamushi*, causing trombiculid mite-transmitted scrub typhus, and *Coxiella burneti*, tick-transmitted in nature, causing Q fever. In addition, the related *Bartonella bacilliformis*, which is sandfly-transmitted, causes bartonellosis (Carrion's disease). All of these rickettsioses except louse-borne typhus fever, trench fever and bartonellosis have known reservoir mammalian hosts.

5. Rodent fleas are biological vectors of the bacillus of plague from rat to rat and rat to man. Several blood-sucking arthropods are at times biological vectors of the bacillus of tularemia.

6. Arthropods are biological vectors of the spirochetes of relapsing fever; *Borrelia duttoni* causing tick-borne relapsing fever, which is transmitted by species of *Ornithodoros* from wild reservoirs to man, and *B. recurrentis* producing epidemic infection, which is transmitted from man to man by human body lice.

7. Protozoan and helminthic agents of human disease, *viz.*, of malaria, the leishamaniases, the African trypanosomiases, Chagas' disease, tapeworms, spiruroids and the filariases, have been considered in Sections II and III of this text.

REFERENCES

ASHBURN, P. M., and CRAIG, C. F. 1907. Experimental Investigations Regarding the Etiology of Dengue Fever, with a General Consideration of the Disease. Philippine J. Sci., *2*, 93–152.

AUDY, J. R. 1958. The Localization of Disease with Special Reference to the Zoönoses. Trans. R. Soc. Trop. Med. & Hyg., *52*, 308–328.

BARNETT, H. C., and KNOBLOCK, E. C. 1952. Chemical and Biological Studies on DDT Resistance of Lice. U. S. Armed Forces Med. J., *3*, 297–304.

BEADLE, L. D. 1959. Status of Mosquito-Borne Encephalitis in the United States. Pub. Health. Rept., *74*, 84–90.

BENGTSON, I. A. 1946. Complement Fixation in Tsutsugamushi Disease (Scrub Typhus). Pub. Health Repts., *61*, 895–900.

————. 1944. Complement Fixation in the Rickettsial Diseases—Technic of the Test. Pub. Health Repts., *59*, 402–405.

BRODY, J. A. and MURRAY, W. A. 1959. Arthropod-Borne Encephalitis in the United States. Pub. Health Repts., *74*, 461–468.

BUGHER, J. C., BOSHELL-MANRIQUE, J., ROCA-GARCIA, M., and OSORNO-MESA, E. 1944. Epidemiology of Jungle Yellow Fever in Eastern Colombia. Am. J. Hyg., *39*, 16–51.

BUSVINE, J. R. 1957. Insecticide Resistant Strains of Insects of Public Health Importance. Trans. R. Soc. Trop. Med. & Hyg., *51*, 11–31.

CALHOUN, E. L., and ALFORD, H. I. 1955. Incidence of Tularemia and Rocky Mountain Spotted Fever among Common Ticks in Arkansas. Am. J. Trop. Med. & Hyg., *4*, 310–317.

CASALS, J. 1961. Procedures for Identification of Arthropod-borne Viruses, Bull. Wld. Hlth. Org., *24*, 723–734.

CASALS, J., and BROWN, L. V. 1954. Hæmagglutination with Arthropod-Borne Viruses. J. Exp. Med., *99*, 429–449.

CASALS, J., and WHITMAN, L. 1960. A New Antigenic Group of Arthropod-Borne Viruses. The Bunyamera Group. Am. J. Trop. Med. and Hyg., *9*, 73–77.

CAUSEY, O. R., and THEILER, M. 1958. Virus Antibody Survey on Sera of Residents of the Amazon Valley, Brazil. Am. J. Trop. Med. & Hyg., *7*, 36–41.

CAWLEY, E. P. and WHEELER, C. E. 1957. Rocky Mountain Spotted Fever. J. Am. Med. Assn., *163*, 1003–1007.

CLARK, W. H., and LENNETTE, E. H. 1952. Treatment of Q Fever with Antibiotics. Ann. New York Acad. Sci., *55*, 1004–1018.

DAVIS, G. E., and HOOGSTRAAL, H. 1954. The Relapsing Fevers: A Survey of the Tick-borne Spirochetes of Egypt. Pub. Health Assn. (Egypt), *29*, 139–143.

EKLUND, C. M., KOHLS, G. M., and BRENNAN, J. M. 1955. Distribution of Colorado Tick Fever and Virus-carrying Ticks. J. Am. Med. Assn., *157*, 335–337.

ESKEY, C. R. 1938. Recent Developments in Our Knowledge of Plague Transmission. Pub. Health Repts., *53*, 49–57.

GEAR, J. 1954. The Rickettsial Diseases of South Africa. S. Afr. J. Clin. Sci., *5*, 158–175.

GREENBERG, B. 1959. Persistance of Bacteria in the Developmental Stages of the Housefly. III. Quantitative Distribution in Prepupæ and Pupæ. Am. J. Trop. Med. & Hyg., *8*, 613–617.

GROOT, H., KERR, J. A., *et al.* 1959. Antibodies to Yellow Fever and Other Arthropod-Borne Viruses in Human Residents of San Vincente de Chucuri, Santander, Colombia. Am. J. Trop. Med. & Hyg., *8*, 175–189.

HAAS, V. H. 1959. When Bubonic Plague Came to Chinatown. Am. J. Trop. Med. & Hyg., *8*, 141–147.

HENDERSON, J. R., and TAYLOR, R. M. 1960. Phlebotomus (Sandfly) Fever Virus in Tissue Culture. Am. J. Trop. Med. & Hyg., *9*, 32–36.

HERTIG, M. 1949. *Phlebotomus* and Residual DDT in Greece and Italy. Am. J. Trop. Med., *29*, 773–802.

HERTIG, M., and FAIRCHILD, G. B. 1948. The Control of *Phlebotomus* in Peru with DDT. Am. J. Trop. Med., *28*, 207–230.

HIRST, L. F. 1953. *The Conquest of Plague. A Study of the Evolution of Epidemiology*, 478 pp. Oxford Univ. Press, London.

HOOGSTRAAL, H. 1961. Ticks and Tickborne Diseases: Some International Problems and Cooperation in Their Study. Int'l Rev. Trop. Med., *1*, 247–267.

HURLBUT, H. S., PEFFLY, R. L., and ABDEL AZIZ SALAH. 1954. DDT Resistance in Egyptian Body Lice. Am. J. Trop. Med. & Hyg., *3*, 922–929.

JANSSEN, W. A., and WEDBERG, S. E. 1952. The Common House Roach *Blatella germanica* Linn., as a Potential Vector of *Salmonella typhimurium* and *Salmonella typhosa*. Am. J. Trop. Med. & Hyg., *1*, 337–343.

JELLISON, W. L. 1959. Fleas and Disease, in *Annual Review of Entomology*, Vol. 4, pp. 389–414. Stanford Univ. Press.

JUNG, R. C., and SHAFFER, M. F. 1952. Survival of Ingested *Salmonella* in the Cockroach *Periplaneta americana*. Am. J. Trop. Med. & Hyg., *1*, 990–998.

KERR, J. A. 1958. Los métodos utilizados en el estudio de la fiebre amarilla selvática. Bol. Ofic. San. Panam., *44*, 1–9.

LILLIE, R. D. 1941. Pathology of Rocky Mountain Spotted Fever. Nat'l Inst. Health Bull. No. 177, Washington, 59 pp.

LINK, V. B., and MOHR, C. O. 1953. Rodenticides in Bubonic Plague Control. WHO Bull., Geneva, *9*, 585–596.

LOVE, G. J., and SMITH, W. W. 1960. Murine Typhus Investigations in Southwestern Georgia. Pub. Health Repts., *75*, 429–440.

MACCHIAVELLO, A. 1959. Estudios sobre peste selvática en el America de Sur. V. Peste selvática en Bolivia. Bol. Ofic. San. Panam., *46*, 509–524.

MARMION, B. P. 1954. Q Fever. II. Natural History and Epidemiology of Q Fever in Man. Trans. R. Soc. Trop. Med. & Hyg., *48*, 197–207.

MEYER, K. F. 1957. The Natural History of Plague and Psittacosis. Pub. Health Repts., *72*, 705–719.

MUNSHI, D. M. 1960. Micro-anatomy of the Proventriculus of the Common Rat Flea *Xenopsylla cheopis* (Rothschild). J. Parasitol., *46*, 362–372.

MURRARY, E. S., and SNYDER, J. C. 1951. Brill's Disease. II. Etiology. Am. J. Hyg., *53*, 22–32.

NAPIER, L. E. 1946. *The Principles and Practice of Tropical Medicine*, 917 pp. Macmillan Co., New York.

PERRY, A. S., and BUCKNER, A. J. 1958. Biochemical Investigations on DDT-Resistance in the Human Body Louse, *Pediculus humanus humanus*. Am. J. Trop. Med. & Hyg., *7*, 620–626.

PHILIP, C. B. 1959. Some Epidemiological Considerations in Rocky Mountain Spotted Fever. Pub. Health Repts., *74*, 595–600.

PHILIP, C. B., HUGHES, L. E., and DARROW, D. I. 1958. Experimental Transmission of Yellow Fever Virus by Oriental Mosquitoes. Proc. 10th Internat'l Congr. Entomol., Vol. 3, 587–592.

POLLITZER, R. 1954. Plague. WHO Monogr., Ser. No. 22, 698 pp., Geneva.

RICHARDS, C. S., JACKSON, W. B., DeCAPITO, T. M., and MEIER, P. P. 1961. Studies on Rate of Recovery of Shigella from Domestic Flies and from Humans in Southwestern United States. Am. J. Trop. Med., & Hyg., *10*, 44–48.

SABIN, A. B. 1955. Recent Advances in Our Knowledge of Dengue and Sandfly Fever. Am. J. Trop. Med. & Hyg., *4*, 198–207.

———. 1958. Present Status of Knowledge and Problems in Field of Arthropod-Borne Virus Infections. Abstracts, 6th Internat'l Congr. Trop. Med. & Malaria, Lisbon, page 159.

SABIN, A., PHILIP, C. B., and PAUL, J. R. 1944. Phlebotomus (Pappataci or Sandfly) Fever. A Disease of Military Importance. Summary of Existing Knowledge and Preliminary Report of Original Investigations. J. Am. Med. Assn., *125*, 603–606; 633–699.

SCHERER, W. F., BUESCHER, E. L., *et al.* 1959. Ecologic Studies of Japanese Encephalitis Virus in Japan. Am. J. Trop. Med. & Hyg., *8*, 644–722.

SILER, J. F., HALL, M. W., and HITCHENS, A. P. 1926. Dengue. Its History, Epidemiology, Mechanism of Transmission, Etiology, Clinical Manifestations, Immunity, and Prevention. Manila, 476 pp.

SMITH, C. E. G. 1958. The Distribution of Antibodies to Japanese Encephalitis, Dengue and Yellow Fever Viruses in Five Rural Communities in Malaya. Trans. R. Soc. Trop. Med. & Hyg., *52*, 237–252.

SMORODINTSEV, A., and ILIENKO, V. 1958. Epidemiological Variants of Tick-borne Spring-Summer Encephalitis Infections in European U.S.S.R. Abstracts, 6th Congr. Trop. Med. & Malaria, Lisbon, pages 165–166.

STRODE, G. K., Editor. 1951. *Yellow Fever*, 710 pp. McGraw-Hill Book Co., New York.

THEILER, M. 1951. The Virus, pp. 43–136, in *Yellow Fever*, G. K. Strode, Editor. McGraw-Hill Book Co., New York.

VARELA, G. 1955. Nuevas rickettsiasis encontradas en la República Mexicana. Fiebre Q y fiebre de las trincheras. Gac. Méd. de Mexico, *85*, 275–279.

WOODWARD, T. E. 1959. Rickettsial Diseases in the United States. Med. Clinics N. Am., *43*, 1507–1535.

ZINSSER, H. 1937. The Rickettsial Diseases: Varieties, Epidemiology and Geographical Distribution. Am. J. Hyg., *25*, 430–463.

Table 7.—Selected List of Therapeutic Procedures for Important Diseases of Man Caused by Animal Agents

Disease	Therapeutic	Posology (Adult Dosage)	Comments	Page Ref. in Text
I. PRODUCED BY PROTOZOA				
Giardiasis	Quinacrine (0.1 Gm. tablets)	One *orally*, t.i.d., for 5 days	Effective, usually well tolerated	34
Trichomonas vaginitis	Diiodohydroxquin			38
	(a) (0.65 Gm. tablets)	(a) One *orally*, t.i.d., for 20 days;	Moderately effective, well tolerated	
	(b) (suppositories)	(b) One suppository inserted nightly into posterior fornix of vagina		
Leishmaniasis Cutaneous	(1) Stibophen (6.3% aq. sol.)	Infiltrate each sore with the solution every 3 or 4 days. Multiple sores require intramuscular administration.	Moderately specific, fairly well tolerated	44
	(2) Berberine bisulfate (2% aq. sol.)			
	(3) Glucantime (N-methylglucamine antimonate)	0.1 Gm. per kilo body weight *i.m.* daily for 15 to 20 days.	Well tolerated; suitable for children	44
Mucocutaneous	(1) Stibophen, as above. (2) Glucantime, as above.	Infiltrate primary lesions, as above	Mucocutaneous secondary lesions often fail to heal or recrudesce	47
Visceral (kala-azar)	(1) Ethylstibamine (5% aq. sol. in ampules)	2 ml.→4 ml.→6 ml. daily, *i.v.*, then 6 ml. daily until 48 to 80 ml. has been given	Moderately effective fairly well tolerated	50
	(2) Hydroxystilbamidine isethionate (5% aq. sol.)	150 mg. *i.v.*, slowly every day or two until 1.5 Gm. has been administered	For cases refractory to antimonials; usually effective without producing trigeminal neuropathy	50
Trypanosomiasis Rhodesian	(1) Suramin sodium (10% aq. sol. in ampules)	One Gm. *i.v.* once or twice a week, to maximum of 10 Gm.	Effective only in early stage of disease; melarsen oxide often helpful in more advanced stage	55
	(2) Melarsen oxide (Mel B)	3.6 mgm./kilo body weight *i.v.*, daily for 4 days. Repeat after 2 weeks.		55

Disease	Drug	Dosage	Remarks	Page
Gambian	(1) Tryparsamide (20% aq. sol. in ampules)	5 ml.→10 ml.→15 ml., i.v., weekly, then 15 ml. weekly up to maximum of 24 to 80 Gm.	Discontinue immediately if optical neuritis develops	59
	(2) Suramin sodium as in Rhodesian		Employed when tryparsamide is not tolerated or effective	59
	(3) Melarsen oxide (Mel B) or a diamidine as in Rhodesian		Employed when tryparsamide is not tolerated or effective	59
American (Chagas' disease)	No effective therapy known			64
Amebiasis Intestinal, dysenteric	(1) Tetracycline hydrochloride (0.25 Gm. capsules)	one to 2 Gm. *orally*, daily, for 3 or 4 days	Effective, usually well tolerated	81
	(2) Emetine hydrochloride (6% aq. sol.)	One mgm./kilo body weight up to maximum of 65 mgm., *i.m.*, daily, for 3 to 4 days	Precaution: myocardial toxicant; not curative	81
Non-dysenteric	(1) Diiodohydroxyquin (0.65 Gm. tablets)	One tablet orally, daily, for 20 days	No reported side effects	82
	(2) Glycobiarsol (0.50 Gm. tablets)	1 tablet each *orally*, t.i.d., for 7 days	Usually well tolerated	82
Hepatic	(1) Emetine hydrochloride (as above)	Dose as above but for 10 days	Often curative	82
	(2) Chloroquine phosphate (0.25 Gm. tablets)	2 tablets *orally*, twice daily for 2 days then 1 tablet twice daily	Usually well tolerated	82
Cutis	Tetracycline hydrochloride (0.25 Gm. capsules)	As in intestinal amebiasis (above) and topically	Requires eradication of primary foci of infection. Clinically effective, at times curative	82
Balantidiasis	(1) Tetracycline hydrochloride (0.25 Gm. capsules)	As in intestinal amebiasis (above)	Clinically effective	92
	(2) Carbarsone (0.25 Gm. tablets)	2 to 3 tablets *orally*, daily, for 10 days	Clinically effective	92
Malaria (all types) Therapeutic (treatment of attack)	(1) Chloroquine phosphate (0.25 Gm. tablets)	4 tablets *orally*, stat., 2 tablets 6 hours later, then 2 daily for 2 days	Clinically effective (all species); eradicates falciparum	118
	(2) Amodiaquin hydrochloride (0.25 Gm. tablets)	3 tablets *orally*, stat., followed by 2 tablets for 4 days	Idem.	118

27

Table 7.—*Selected List of Therapeutic Procedures for Important Diseases of Man Caused by Animal Agents (Continued)*

Disease	Therapeutic	Posology (Adult Dosage)	Comments	Page Ref. in Text
Suppressive	(1) Chloroquine phosphate (0.25 Gm. tablets)	2 tablets *orally*, twice weekly, beginning 2 weeks before and continuing 1 month after exposure period	Eradicative for falciparum infection	118
	(2) Amodiaquin hydrochloride (0.25 Gm. tablets)	As with chloroquine	As with chloroquine	118
Prophylactic	Primaquine phosphate (26.3 mgm. tablets)	One tablet *orally*, daily, for 14 days in conjunction with curative doses of chloroquine	Eradicates vivax, ovale and quartan parasites from exoerythrocytic foci. May cause hemolysis.	118
Toxoplasmosis	No curative therapy demonstrated		Pyrimethamine with sulfa drugs may be suppressive and clinically helpful	127
II. PRODUCED BY HELMINTHS				
Fasciolopsis infection	Hexylresorcinol (0.1 and 0.2 Gm. pills)	One Gm., in single dose, *orally*, on empty stomach	Safe, usually effective; treatment may be repeated after one week	138
Echinostome and Heterophyid infections	(1) Idem. (2) Tetrachloroethylene (0.5 and 1.0 ml. gelatin capsules)	(1) Idem. (2) 3 ml. in one dose, *orally*, on empty stomach	(1) Idem. (2) Well tolerated, usually effective	140, 143, 144
Fascioliasis	Emetine hydrochloride (6% aq. sol. in ampules)	10 mgm. *subcutaneously*, daily, for 8 days	Usually curative	147
Clonorchiasis and Opisthorchiasis	No effective therapy known			152, 154
Paragonimiasis	Bithionol (2.2-thiobis [4.6-dichlorophenol])		Clinical tests show promise of efficacy	157

Disease	Treatment	Dosage	Remarks	Page
Schistosomiasis	Potassium antimony tartrate (0.5% aq. sol., freshly prepared, filtered)	Administer slowly, *i.v.*, 8 ml. first day, then increasing by 4 ml. on alternate days to 20 ml., and continuing with 20 ml. until 320 ml. has been given	Moderately effective in early infections; poorly tolerated and less valuable in advanced cases	171
Schistosome Dermatitis	No specific therapy		Topical application of palliatives may be helpful.	182
Tapeworm Infections Intestinal	Quinacrine hydrochloride (0.1 Gm. tablets)	0.5 to 1.2 Gm. *orally*, in one dose, preceded 30 minutes earlier by adm. of chlorpromazine or other anti-emetic	Usually effective; post-treatment purgation required	193
Extra-intestinal (cysticercosis, echinococcocosis sparganosis)	No effective chemotherapeutic; surgical removal indicated when feasible			207, 213, 217
Enterobiasis (oxyuriasis)	Piperazine hexahydrate, as piperazine citrate syrup; (100 ml. syrup contains contains 10 to 12 Gm.)	1.5 Gm. *orally*, daily for 7 to 10 days	Highly effective, well tolerated	230
Trichuriasis	Dithiazanine iodide (50 mgm. coated tablets)	100 to 200 mgm., *orally*, 2 to 3 times daily for 7 days	Effective; frequently causes nausea, vomiting and diarrhea	235
Ascariasis	Piperazine citrate syrup (as above)	3 to 4 Gm. in a single dose, *orally*, repeat in 2 days.	Highly effective, well tolerated	241
Hookworm infections (intestinal)	Tetrachloroethylene (0.5 and 1.0 ml. gelatin capsules)	5 ml. in one dose, *orally*, on empty stomach, without purgation	Moderately effective, usually well tolerated	255
Strongyloidiasis	Dithiazanine iodide (50 mgm. coated tablets)	As in trichuriasis (above)	Moderately effective, may cause nausea, vomiting and diarrhea	266
Trichinosis	No specific therapy			278

Table 7.—Selected List of Therapeutic Procedures for Important Diseases of Man Caused by Animal Agents (Continued)

Disease	Therapeutic	Posology (Adult Dosage)	Comments	Page Ref. in Text
Larva migrans Cutaneous	Ethyl chloride or solid carbon dioxide	Freeze skin in most advanced end of lesion	Treatment of secondary infections in the lesion may be required	281, 284
Visceral				
Filariasis (Bancroft's, Malayan, Onchocerciasis, Loaiasis)	No specific therapy (1) Diethylcarbamazine citrate (Hetrazan) (0.1 Gm. tablets)	2 mgm./kilo body weight, orally, three times daily for 10 days or more	Microfilaricidal; (may produce moderate to severe side effects from byproducts of dying worms); allergic phenomena may be noted	301, 304, 308, 312
	(2) Suramin sodium (10% aq. sol. in ampules)	As in Rhodesian trypanosomiasis (above)	May produce severe allergic side effects in onchocerciasis	308
	(3) Removal of onchocerca nodules as soon as they appear		Reduces likelihood of allergic reactions	308
Dracunculosis	Gradual extraction of worm		Antibacterial treatment may be needed	316
Hirudiniasis Internal	Remove leech with hooked probe	Procaine anesthesia in nasopharynx may facilitate removal	Precautions needed to prevent leech from reaching trachea or bronchi	331
External	Strong salt solution or procaine	Apply to site of attachment to facilitate removal	Cauterize open wound and apply sterile dressing	332
III Produced by Arthropods				
Mange: Sarcoptic and Demodectic	Benzene hexachloride (Gammexane), $\frac{1}{2}$% in ointment base	Apply ointment after bathing; leave overnight; change clothes next day; repeat treatment in 6 to 10 days	Sterilization of all clothes and bed linen in contact with infested areas is essential	349

(420)

Condition	Agent	Application	Remarks	Page
Chigoe infestation	Tincture of iodine or merthiolate	Remove flea from lesion with sharp needle; treat lesion with iodine or merthiolate	Remove chigoes from between toes of infested dogs to prevent re-exposure	394
Myiasis	Surgical removal	After removal of maggots, and debridement if required, irrigate with antiseptic solution and apply sterile dressing	Early surgical intervention will prevent serious disfigurement	387–393
Hymenopteran (Bee, wasp, and hornet) sting	Remove honey bee sting with sharp knife			365
Anaphylaxis from insect sting	Epinephrine (1:10% aq sol)	Introduce 0 5 mgm epinephrine *subcutaneously* at site of sting	Desensitization may be required	365
Caterpillar urtication	(1) Local anesthetic (2) Antihistaminic	Apply (1 and 2) topically or (2) systemically		363
Beetle Vesication	Idem	Idem	Idem	362
"Bites" by ticks, mites, lice, bugs, bloodsucking flies, gnats and fleas	Idem	Idem	Idem	348, 351, 353, 354, 368, 370, 378, 379, 380, 381
Pediculosis (louse infestation) caused by				
Body lice	DDT (2% powder in inert base)	Dust body and infested clothing	Mass treatment of entire infested community is desirable	367
Head and pubic lice	Benzene hexachloride (Gammexane), ½% in ointment base	Rub into all infested areas of skin and hairs; leave over-night, then wash out; repeat if necessary	Treat all contacts simultaneously, if possible	368

Table 7.—*Selected List of Therapeutic Procedures for Important Diseases of Man Caused by Animal Agents (Continued)*

Disease	Therapeutic	Posology (Adult Dosage)	Comments	Page Ref in Text
Spider poisoning produced by Black widow (*Latrodectus*)	Specific antivenin	Administer *i.m.*	Calcium gluconate (10% sol.) introduced slowly *i.v.* may be a helpful adjuvant	345
Brown house spider (*Loxosceles*)	Corticosteroids (Cortisone acetate) (250 mg. in 10 ml. sterile aq. suspension)	Administer *i.m.*, 100 mgm. daily for 3 or 4 days	To prevent systemic effects of venom and to reduce local necrosis and scarring	344
Scorpion Venenation	Univalent or polyvalent antivenin	Administer *i.m.*	Glucose (10% sol.) introduced slowly *i.v.*, may be helpful; sedatives to relieve pain and respiratory stimulants may be indicated	340

SECTION V

Technical Aids

Chapter 19

Parasitologic Diagnosis

Introduction

In order that the clinical and public health implications of parasites and vectors may be properly evaluated, it is necessary that the organisms involved be accurately diagnosed. Throughout the preceding chapters of this book emphasis has been placed on laboratory diagnosis as an essential component of the diagnostic problem, and in many instances as the *sine qua non* of accurate etiologic diagnosis. Thus, adequately trained personnel and suitable laboratory facilities are indispensable, whether the focus is on the individual patient or on epidemiologic surveys of population groups.

Parasitologic Equipment and Supplies

Unless the laboratory is devoted exclusively to parasitology, provision must be made in the general laboratory, preferably in a separate room, for performing the essential technics of coprologic, hematologic and other parasitologic diagnosis.

There must be one good compound microscope for each person doing parasitologic diagnosis. For study of macroscopic specimens such as helminths, surgical biopsies or entomological material, it is desirable to have at least one binocular dissecting microscope, with a series of paired oculars and objectives. Additional microscopic equipment should include a micrometer disc to be placed in the eyepiece and a micrometer slide to calibrate the divisions in the micrometer disc for the particular microscope and for each of the eyepieces and objectives employed. If a micrometer slide is not available the units in a hemacytometer slide may be substituted in making the calibration. There should be at least one good incubator, a drying oven, and one or more International clinical centrifuges, and a steam sterilizer. Reagent bottles, petri dishes, staining dishes, pyrex-type beakers, flasks, test tubes (25 × 75 mm.) and pipettes of graded sizes, graduate cylinders, microscope slides, and coverglasses (22× 22 mm.) must be available in good supply. A suitable type of specimen container is a 2-oz. glass bottle with a screw top, which can be used for samples of stools, urine and sputum. For shipment it should fit into a mailing cylinder of heavy cardboard having a metal screw top. In addition, there is need for clear glass cylindrical jars with plastic tops for preservation of parasite objects.

For routine fresh fecal films each diagnostician requires conveniently placed dropping bottles of physiologic salt solution and iodine. For concentration technics there should be at hand large bottles of the principal reagents. For fixation of fecal films Schaudinn's fluid is most frequently employed. Other reagents are described later in this chapter. For fixing tissues, 10% formalin is recommended. For staining of fecal films the iron-hematoxylin technic is probably the most satisfactory. For blood films the routine stain is one of the Romanowsky eosin-methylene blue combinations. Best results are usually obtained with the Giemsa stain. For culturing protozoa there are several satisfactory types of media which will be considered in Chapter 20 (p. 441). For culturing helminth larvæ finely granulated charcoal is useful.

COPROLOGICAL EXAMINATION

Collection of the Specimen

A normal stool consists almost exclusively of *feces* but in the diseased intestine a portion of the stool may consist of blood and mucus, or there may be a considerable amount of cellular exudate and sloughed tissue. At times these portions of the stool provide evidence of parasitic infection when the feces are negative. Similarly *Ascaris*, *Enterobius* and proglottids of *Tænia* and *Dipylidium* may be passed without the presence of their eggs in the fecal part of the specimen. It is therefore important that the material submitted for examination be sufficient for dependable diagnosis. Gross inspection of the specimen should always precede microscopic examination.

Collection should be made in a clean container without contamination with water or urine. The specimen must be free of oil, magnesia, aluminum salts or barium.

Formed stools can usually be kept for one or more days, preferably in the ice-box, without loss of the diagnostic integrity of parasite objects which may be present. Unformed stools should be examined soon after they have been passed. For periods of several hours, sometimes longer, good preservation is obtained by refrigeration at 3° to 10°C. For reliable and lasting preservation chemical fixation is required (page 425).

Processing of the Specimen

1. **Direct Unpreserved Fecal Film.**—Routinely the unpreserved specimen should first be examined grossly and then microscopically in coverglass preparations containing 1 to 2 mgm. of feces evenly suspended in one drop of physiologic saline. These films should be free of air bubbles and macroscopic débris. An unstained film of this type is useful for motile trophozoites of intestinal protozoa, helminth eggs and *Strongyloides* larvæ and has considerable diagnostic value for amebic cysts. For studying the internal

diagnostic characteristics of protozoan cysts, iodine stain (1% aq. sol. potassium iodide saturated with iodine crystals), is used. The stain may be placed at the edge of the coverglass and allowed to flow into the film, or added to a new preparation before the coverglass is applied. Only enough stain should be used to give the suspension a distinctly yellow hue.

2. **Preserved Stained Film.**—If it is desired to make a permanent, stained film of fresh feces for study of intestinal protozoa, a representative fleck of the material is smeared as evenly as possible in a thin film on an absolutely clean slide and is treated with a liquid fixative. Before the material has dried it is immersed in Schaudinn's solution (sat. sol. mercuric chloride in distilled water, 200 cc.; 95% ethyl alcohol, 100 cc.), to which glacial acetic acid, 15 cc. is added just before the fixative is to be used.

A number of different stains may be used but iron-hematoxylin is usually employed. In following the steps described below, the film must not be permitted to dry and the time schedule must be adhered to except where smears are in 70% alcohol, when over-night or longer delay is allowable.

Iron-Hematoxylin Stain.—1. Fix smears in Schaudinn's solution 15 minutes at room temperature.
   2. Immerse smears in 70% alcohol; 70% alcohol to which enough iodine has been added to give a pale urine color; 70 and 50% alcohol, leaving in each 2 to 5 minutes.
   3. Wash in running water for 2 to 10 minutes.
   4. Immerse smears in 2% aqueous iron-alum solution for 5 minutes.
   5. Wash in running water 3 minutes.
   6. Stain in 0.5% aqueous hematoxylin for 5 minutes.
   7. Wash in running water 2 minutes.
   8. Differentiate for 10 to 15 minutes in saturated aqueous picric acid.
   9. Wash in running water 10 to 15 minutes.
   10. Immerse smears 2 minutes each in 70, 80, 90% and absolute alcohol.
   11. Clear smears with xylol.
   12. Mount in a standard neutral resin.

Brooke and Goldman's PVA (Polyvinyl Alcohol) Fixative (1949).—This is a convenient method for fixing fecal films on microscopic slides. The fixative-preservative solution consists of: Schaudinn's sol., 93.5 cc.; glycerol, 1.5 cc.; glacial acetic acid, 5.0 cc. and powdered polyvinyl alcohol, 5 Gm. The polyvinyl alcohol is added by constant stirring when the other ingredients have been heated to 75° C. For use, 1 drop of well comminuted fecal suspension and 3 drops of the fixative are spread over the middle third of the microscopic slide, which is then dried overnight at 37° C. At a convenient time, the dry film is then placed in 70% alcohol containing iodine to remove excess mercuric chloride, then stained by the iron-hematoxylin technic.

MIF (Merthiolate-Iodine-Formaldehyde) Fixative-Stain of Sapero and Lawless (1953).—The stock solution consists of distilled water, 250 cc.; tincture of merthiolate No. 99 Lilly (1:1000), 200 cc., formaldehyde U.S.P., 25 cc., and glycerol, 5 cc., to which 10 to 15 parts of freshly prepared Lugol's solution (5% iodine in 10% potassium iodide in distilled water) is added. This may be used (*a*) in making direct fecal smears or (*b*) for collection and preservation of bulk stool specimens.

(a) *Direct Fecal Smears.*—Place 1 drop each of distilled water and 1 drop of MIF fixative-stain together on the slide, then add a small fleck of feces and mix thoroughly. Mount with a coverglass and examine.

(*b*) *Collection and Preservation of Bulk Specimen.*—For approximately each 0.25 Gm. of stool to be processed first introduce 0.15 cc. of Lugol's solution followed by 2.35 cc. of the MIF stock solution into a convenient-sized test-tube or other glass container, then add the stool specimen and mix thoroughly until there is a homogeneous suspension. This method is particularly adapted to field collections. All microscopic parasite objects are well preserved in a natural state and adequately stained for diagnostic reliability. Once preserved the material keeps well in a tightly-stoppered bottle for a year or more.

3. **Concentration Technics.**—Microscopic parasite objects may be concentrated and separated from other objects in the feces by sedimentation, flotation, or a combination of the two.

I. SEDIMENTATION.—This is accomplished by suspending the stool in tap water and allowing natural settling to take place, or by accelerating the process mechanically through centrifugation. This technic is primarily useful for concentration of protozoan cysts and helminth eggs, but by substituting physiologic salt solution amebic trophozoites may be concentrated by centrifugation and retain their viability.

(*a*) *Simple Sedimentation.*—For the intestinal protozoa this method is tedious and provides little if any concentration over the direct fecal film (Faust *et al.*, 1938). On the other hand, for helminth eggs it has several advantages over other methods of concentration, since the eggs of all species settle to the bottom of the container in a viable, undistorted condition. It is especially recommended for eggs of *Schistosoma, Clonorchis, Opisthorchis*, and heterophyid flukes. Although the technic is relatively slow, there is ample compensation in the much larger amount of material which can be processed in a single container.

A 10-Gm. portion of the fecal specimen is thoroughly comminuted in 10 to 20 times its volume of tap water, poured into a sedimentation glass and the sediment allowed to settle out. After an hour, the top two-thirds with the floating débris is either carefully poured off or siphoned off, water is added to near the top of the container and the fecal material thoroughly resuspended in it. This procedure is repeated until the supernatant fluid is relatively clear. After final removal of water a small portion of bottom sediment is removed with a long pipette to a broad (fecal) slide (37 × 75 mm.) and examined for eggs.

Faust and Ingalls (1946) confirmed for *Schistosoma japonicum* the earlier observations of Faust and Hoffman (1934), that 0.5% glycerol added to tap water causes increased "wetting" and more rapid sedimentation, minimizes the number of eggs decanted and provides a yield up to about 25-fold that of the unprocessed stool. It is desirable to strain out the larger detritus in the stool through surgical gauze having about 22 meshes to the linear inch, using 2 to 4 thicknesses which have been previously soaked in water and the excess of water squeezed out. The gauze is then stretched loosely over a funnel of appropriate size and the emulsified feces poured through into the sedimentation glass. Very few eggs are trapped in the gauze unless there is considerable mucus in the stool. After 1 hour, the first decantation is made, 45 minutes later a second, and 30 minutes later a third and last one. Measured amounts of the sediment in the bottom are then removed to a microscopic slide and mounted with a 40 × 22 mm. cover-glass. Eggs of all types in the stool without loss of viability due to the technic are present in unusually high concentrates in the sediment (Maldonado and Acosta-Matienzo, 1953). It is probably the most practical method for obtaining immature, fully mature and degenerate eggs of *Schistosoma japonicum* and *S. mansoni* for diagnosis in the same proportion in which they occur in the stool.

(b) *Centrifugation.*—This method is fairly useful for concentration of protozoan cysts and helminth eggs in the stool, and if isotonic salt solution is substituted for tap water amebic trophozoites concentrate in a living state from 15- to 40-fold.

A 2- to 3-Gm. fecal specimen is thoroughly mixed with about 10 parts by volume of tap water, and is then strained through 2 layers of 16- to 20-mesh cheesecloth (to remove débris) into a 13 × 100 mm. serological pyrex glass tube. These tubes are cheap, are not easily broken and fit into the 9.5-cm. metal carrying tubes of the smaller electric-powered centrifuges of the International clinical centrifuge type. Because of their rounded bottoms they are better for fecal concentrates than the conventional 15-cc. centrifuge tubes, since the material does not easily pack in the base of the tube. The tubes are revolved in the centrifuge at a moderate speed (*ca.* 1500 to 2300 rpm.) for 1 to 2 minutes, are then removed, the supernatant liquid poured off, the tubes filled with water which is mixed with the fecal sediment, and are again centrifuged. Theoretically, the centrifugation should be repeated until the supernatant fluid is clear, but in practice 2 to 3 spinnings are usually satisfactory.

For the diagnosis of *Schistosoma* eggs in the stool, Baroody and Most (1946) developed a *macro-centrifugation technic*, comparable in the quantity of feces processed to sedimentation but more rapid. The steps are as follows: (1) 10 to 15 Gm. feces is shaken up thoroughly for 1 or 2 minutes in a 125 cc. Erlenmeyer flask containing about 100 cc. tepid tap water; (2) the suspension is strained through two layers of wet gauze into a 50 cc. centrifuge tube with a teated bottom; (3) this is spun in the centrifuge for 30 seconds at 1500 rpm; (4) the supernatant fluid is poured off, 40° C. water is added and centrifugation is repeated; (5) repeat step (4) until supernatant fluid is clear; (6) 4 drops of sediment are examined under a 22 × 40 mm. coverglass; (7) if not positive for *Schistosoma* eggs, add 10 drops of water to the sediment and allow to stand until morning, then look for hatched miracidia.

Ritchie (1948) adds formalin for fixation and preservation of the parasite objects, and ether to remove fats and oils. The stool specimen is first comminuted in sufficient physiologic salt solution to provide 10 to 12 cc. of stool suspension, which is strained through 2 layers of surgical gauze into a 15 cc. centrifuge tube. The suspension is then centrifuged, the supernate decanted and the particulate matter resuspended repeatedly until the supernate is clear. After an additional decantation the sediment is mixed with 10 cc. of 4% formaldehyde U.S.P. and allowed to stand for 5 minutes, after which 3 cc. of ether is added and the suspension is shaken vigorously. Following an additional period of centrifugation at about 1500 rpm for 2 minutes, the entire supernate is poured off. A thin film of the sediment is placed on a microscopic slide, a drop of iodine stain is mixed with it and the preparation mounted with a coverglass for examination. This method provides a good concentrate of protozoan cysts and helminth eggs which are diagnostically satisfactory.

II. GRAVITY FLOTATION.—In contrast to sedimentation, in which microscopic parasites that are heavier than bacteria and undigested food particles in the stool sink to the bottom of a container, flotation utilizes a liquid suspending medium heavier than the parasite objects so that they rise to the surface and can be skimmed out of the surface film. For diagnostic usefulness, the suspending medium must not only be heavier than the object to be floated; it must not produce shrinkage sufficient to render the object undiagnosable.

The floating medium generally employed is brine, *e.g.*, saturated solution of NaCl, having a specific gravity of approximately 1.200. Eggs of the common intestinal helminths, such as the hookworms, *Ascaris* and *Trichuris*, are not damaged by this process, but those of *Schistosoma*, hookworm and *Strongyloides* larvæ, and protozoan cysts become badly shrunken; furthermore, eggs of *Clonorchis*, *Opisthorchis* and heterophyid species have a specific gravity higher than 1.200 and do not float in brine.

The procedure is simple. A sample of feces is thoroughly mixed with 10 times its volume of brine, strained through gauze to remove coarse elements, transferred to a test tube, and allowed to stand undisturbed for 20 to 30 minutes. The tube may be filled to near the brim and the eggs removed by means of a wire loop (about 5 mm. diameter) for examination under a microscope (usually without a coverglass), or the tube may be filled completely, so that a clean slide placed over the mouth closes the tube without trapping air between the slide and the suspension. After standing for 20 to 30 minutes the slide is lifted without tilting, reversed in a gentle but rapid movement to bring the wet side on top, and examined under a microscope. If examined promptly a coverglass is not required.

III. CENTRIFUGAL-FLOTATION.—This method is based on essentially the same principles as gravitation and flotation. A sample of stool is suspended in approximately 10 times its volume of water, strained through gauze to remove the larger objects, placed in a centrifuge tube and by means of 2 or 3 successive centrifugations, decantations of the supernate and resuspensions, is cleared of the fine particulate material. After the last centrifugation the entire supernate is drained off, the sediment is then resuspended in the floating medium, recentrifuged and after the centrifuge tube has been at rest for approximately 1 minute, the surface film is removed with a wire loop or a superimposed microscope slide. This technic provides high concentration of parasite objects practically free of detritus. The floating medium generally employed is zinc sulfate solution having a specific gravity of 1.18.

The *zinc sulfate flotation* technic was developed by Faust *et al.* (1938, 1939) to meet the needs of the clinical laboratory for heavy concentration of protozoan cysts, helminth eggs and larvæ present in the stool, in a readily diagnosable condition. All of these parasite objects, except for operculate eggs, those of blood flukes and eggs heavier than the floating medium, are recovered in good concentration and in a viable condition.

The steps in the original technic are as follows:

(*a*) Prepare a fecal suspension by comminuting about 10 parts of tapwater with 1 part of the stool specimen.

(*b*) The suspension is strained through gauze and a Wassermann tube is filled with the strained suspension.

(*c*) The preparation in the tube is then centrifuged for 45 to 60 seconds at top speed of an International clinical centrifuge (*ca.* 2300 rpm.). The supernatant fluid is poured off, 2 or 3 ml. of water added, the sediment broken up by shaking or tapping, and additional water added to fill the tube.

(*d*) Repeat "*c*" once or twice until the supernatant fluid is clear.

(*e*) The last supernatant fluid is poured off, 1 or 2 ml. of zinc sulfate solution added, the packed sediment broken up and enough zinc sulfate solution added to fill the tube to 3 or 4 mm. of the rim.

(*f*) The tube is centrifuged for 45 to 60 seconds at top speed and is allowed to stop without interference.

(*g*) After 15 to 20 seconds and without removing the tube from the centrifuge, several loopfuls of diagnostic material floating in the surface film are removed by means of a wire loop onto a clean slide, 1 drop of iodine stain (saturated iodine in 1% KI) is added and the preparation agitated manually to insure uniform staining.

(*h*) The preparation is mounted with a coverglass and is now ready for examination.

Numerous modifications and simplifications of the zinc sulfate centrifugal flotation technic have been introduced (Beaver, 1952).

QUANTITATIVE EGG-COUNT TECHNICS.—While the several technics described above provide opportunity for efficient recovery and accurate identification of most parasite objects in the stool, there is need for estimating the parasite burden of the patient, to determine the degree of infection, whether incidental, moderate or heavy. Methods have been developed for relatively accurate calculation of hookworm, *Ascaris* and *Trichuris* worm burden by eggs present in the stool.

Direct Egg-Count Technic (Beaver, 1950).—The method of making egg-counts by direct smear is based on the observations that eggs of hookworms, and probably those of other species which inhabit the small intestine or upper colon, have random distribution in the stool, and that any series of direct smears of equal density taken from the same stool contain equal quantities of fecal solids and statistically equal numbers of eggs. A method of making uniform smears has been devised and the factor for converting eggs per slide to eggs per cc. of formed stool has been determined for the type of smear which is regarded as being of ideal density. This involves the use of a photo-electric type of light meter which is adapted to measuring the turbidity of the fecal smear. A wooden block 18 mm. in thickness and of any convenient diameter is fitted to the light meter's window and a 16 mm. hole is drilled into the center of the block. This serves as a platform for the microscope slide on which the smear is made and provides a mask which reduces the window to a convenient size for preparing and spreading the smear. An electric lamp is suspended directly over the reduced window and made adjustable so that arbitrary whole number readings can be obtained.

When the original light meter reading is adjusted to 20 the interference readings of 7.5, 10, 11.5, 13 and 16 correspond to uniform fecal smears containing respectively 1/200, 1/300, 1/400, 1/500 and 1/1000 cc. For standardization 1 drop (0.05 cc.) of a mixture of N/1 $BaCl_2$, + 2N Na_2SO_4 each previously mixed with $\frac{1}{2}$ part pure glycerol, in the following proportions, provides density readings equivalent to the fecal smears: 3:2, 1:200 cc.; 2:3, 1/300 cc.; 1:2, 1/400 cc.; 1:3, 1/500 cc., and 1:6, 1/1000 cc. For routine smears 1/500 cc. (2 mg.) amounts of suspension are most useful; for stools with large numbers of eggs, 1/1000 cc. smears are more satisfactory. For the number of eggs per cc. of stool the egg count is multiplied by the denominator *viz.*, when the smear contains 1/500 cc. the factor is 500, etc. Calculation of hookworm burden is similar to that described immediately below, and the accuracy of the calculation is approximately the same.

Ordinary direct fecal smears made by experienced technicians for routine diagnosis of parasitic infections almost invariably contain the equivalent of about 2 mg. (1/500 Gm.) of formed feces. For rough approximation of worm burden, counts of "eggs per smear" are therefore as useful as the more complicated, time-consuming methods.

Dilution Egg-Count Technic (Stoll and Hausheer, 1926).—The technic is as follows: Four grams (cc.) of feces is measured by displacement while being placed in a small Erlenmeyer flask or large test-tube having marks indicating 56 and 60 cc.

levels, and into which decinormal sodium hydroxide was poured in up to the 56 cc. mark. Several small glass beads are now added, the container closed with a rubber stopper and the contents shaken until the feces are thoroughly comminuted. A hard fecal specimen should be left in the liquid over night to secure adequate disintegration. When proper comminution has been obtained, the mixture is throughly shaken up and 0.075 cc. of the suspension is drawn up into a calibrated pipette, discharged onto a clean fecal slide and covered with a 22 × 30 mm. coverglass. The number of eggs of the particular species of helminth under observation is then counted, and this number multiplied by 200 to obtain the number of eggs per gram of feces. The estimate obtained depends on the consistency of the feces. Correction factors must therefore be used to convert the estimate to the formed stool basis (fsb). Failure to take this variable into account will result in very wide errors in the estimates. Counts on mushy-formed feces must be multiplied by 1.5, mushy by 2, mushy-diarrheic by 3, flowing-diarrheic by 4, and watery by 5 or more. Thus an egg count of 5,000/Gm. of mushy feces is equivalent to 10,000/Gm. of formed feces from the same individual. *Note*: These conversion factors are not needed for counts made by direct smear.

Worms Migrating Out of the Anus

In the case of *Enterobius* infection, it is not usual for the gravid female worms to oviposit within the bowel. Adult females habitually migrate out of the anus and their eggs commonly are shed onto the perianal and perineal skin. The worms may be passed in the feces but more commonly crawl out of the anus at night. Mature and immature *Ascaris* are frequently passed spontaneously by the host. They should be preserved in alcohol or formalin and properly identified. Tapeworm proglottids (species of *Tænia* or *Dipylidium caninum*) singly or in chains, are usually discharged periodically in the stools of infected patients. Specific identification of these worms can most readily be made from the moist proglottids. Patients should be warned not to wrap them in toilet paper, which dries them out and usually renders identification difficult or impossible.

Anal Scrapings and Swabs

Amebiasis cutis of the perianal area may be diagnosed by scraping out the contents of suspected ulcers, removing the material to a slide in a drop or two of tepid physiologic salt solution, mounting with a coverglass and demonstrating typical *E. histolytica* motility.

Heller (1876) apparently first recommended the use of an anal scraper or swab to obtain material for microscopical examination for *Enterobius* eggs. Hall (1937) devised a much more convenient swab, which provides consistently high diagnostic yields. The applicator consists of a glass rod tipped with cellophane held in place with a rubber band, and is employed to swab the perianal area of the patient. The cellophane with adhering material is removed from the rod, is flattened between two glass slides and examined for eggs under low power of the microscope.

In 1941 Graham introduced a *Scotch cellulose tape technic* for obtaining eggs of *Enterobius* from the anal and perianal areas. A length of the tape is held adhesive-side-out on the end of a wooden tongue blade by the thumb and index finger, and after "swabbing" is placed adhesive-side-down, in a drop of toluene, on the slide for examination. Most workers regard this as considerably more efficient than the Hall technic (Beaver, 1949).

Scott and other workers claim that perianal swabbing has high efficiency in recovering eggs of *Schistosoma mansoni*, while Mazzotti regards it as the preferred technic in obtaining eggs of *Tænia solium*.

PURGED AND ENEMA SPECIMENS

The purpose of examining this type of material is to obtain diagnostic evidence of infection with *Entamœba histolytica*, usually in the cecal area of the intestine, when routine examination of the stools has been consistently negative and yet there is strong clinical suspicion of intestinal amebiasis. For diagnostic purposes, the purgative agent should be a salt solution. Although magnesium sulfate (Epsom salts) is usually employed, sodium sulfate (Glauber salts) or phospho-soda is probably better for delivering the amebic trophozoites in an undamaged, motile condition. For reliable diagnosis the examination must be made while the specimen is fresh. The material to be examined is the mucus and tissue detritus in the liquid portion following the evacuation of the fecal material. With a pipette, small amounts of the mucus or other sediment are transferred to microscope slides with as little water as possible, mounted with coverglasses and examined in the unstained condition. Typical pseudopodial activity and locomotion must be demonstrated in order to make a specific diagnosis of *E. histolytica* and care must be taken not to confuse trophozoites of *E. coli, Endolimax nana, Dientamœba fragilis* or host tissue macrophages with those of *E. histolytica* (See Plates I and II, pp. 23, 25).

Enema specimens should be obtained by high instillation of tepid physiologic salt solution, to irrigate the cecal area. As in purged material, the mucus settlings in the liquid portion of the evacuation will provide the greatest likelihood of obtaining positive evidence of *E. histolytica*.

EXAMINATION OF URINE

The pathogenic flagellate, *Trichomonas vaginalis*, is frequently recovered from urine sediment in both female and male patients who are infected. Rarely trophozoites of *Entamœba histolytica* may be present in urine of persons who have amebic ulceration of the genitalia.

Urine is the common excretion in which eggs of *Schistosoma hæmatobium* are discharged. Eggs of *Dioctophyma renale*, a rare parasite of man, are also recovered from the urine. In both of these infections the specimen of urine is collected in a urinalysis or sedimentation glass and the eggs allowed to sink to the bottom, together with erythrocytes and pus cells. The bottom sediment is then pipetted onto a fecal slide and examined microscopically. In Bancroft's filaria infection with chyluria the microfilariæ are discharged in the urine. They may readily be recovered from centrifuged specimens. There are rare occasions when *Strongyloides* larvæ have been identified in the urine.

EXAMINATION OF SPUTUM

In pleuropulmonary amebiasis, the rupture of the amebic abscess into a bronchus characteristically results in coughing up the contents containing blood, mucus, necrotic tissue cells and trophozoites of *Entamœba histolytica*. Similarly, rupture of a pulmonary hydatid cyst is followed by discharge of its contents, in which there will be fragments of the laminated membrane and germinal layer of the cyst wall, and usually many free scolices of *Echinococcus granulosus*. Sputum is the most common discharge from which eggs of the lung fluke, *Paragonimus westermani*, are recovered. Occasionally eggs of blood flukes are coughed up.

RECOVERY OF PARASITES IN THE BLOOD

Next to the feces, the blood provides the most common medium for recovery of various stages of animal parasites. From this source, diagnosis is routinely made of malaria, African trypanosomiasis and most types of filariasis, less frequently of Chagas' disease and rarely kala-azar and toxoplasmosis. It is necessary to remember that in a particular infection these etiologic agents are not consistently present, at least in high density.

Protozoa in the Blood.—The standard procedure to obtain material for diagnosis of protozoa in the circulating blood is to make microscope slide preparations. The older method consisted in obtaining only thin blood films but for rapid examination thick films are needed. Preferably a combined thin- and thick-film should be made on the outer thirds of the same slide. The slide should be smooth and free of all blemishes, oil, lint and finger marks. In making the thin film a small drop of blood from a finger, toe (of children) or ear lobe is brought in contact with one end of the slide and is immediately drawn out into a smooth film one-cell-thick with the smooth straight edge of another slide. In making the thick film a somewhat larger drop of blood is deposited near the other end of the slide and is spread out evenly to the size of about 20 mm. diameter. Both films must be allowed to dry thoroughly, without heating and without opportunity for contamination from dust or deposits of flies or roaches. Unless the slide is meticulously clean the thick film is likely to flake off. Freshly prepared films always stain best.

Giemsa's Stain.—The most valuable single stain for blood films which are to be examined for protozoa or microfilariæ is that developed by Giemsa, prepared from azure blue and eosin. The thin-filmed end of the slide must first be fixed in absolute ethyl alcohol or absolute methyl alcohol for 2 to 3 minutes to avoid dehemoglobinization. The thick film requires no fixation, since dehemoglobinization is necessary to see through the several layers of cells. When ready for staining the slide should be immersed for a period of 10 to 30 minutes in a mixture of 1 drop of the concentrated stain to each cc. of neutral distilled water, then washed off, and dried in the air or with non-linty blotting paper. It is now ready for examination with oil-immersion objective, but if it is to be preserved each portion should be covered with clarite and mounted with a No. 1 coverglass.

Wright's Stain.—Since blood films for differential white cell counts are usually stained by the Wright technic, in some laboratories it may be convenient to employ this stain in searching for protozoa in the blood. For the thin blood film enough of the undiluted stock solution is placed on the slide in sufficient amount to cover the film. This fixes the hemoglobin in the red cells. In 3 to 5 minutes, a sufficient amount of distilled water is added to produce a greenish metallic surface. After 5 to 20 minutes, the stain is thoroughly washed off in running water, the film is dried and is ready for oil-immersion examination. For the thick film Wright's stain may be diluted with distilled water 1:30, but most modern workers prefer Giemsa's or Field's stain.

Field's Stain.—This stain was developed by Field (1941) for thick blood films in the diagnosis of malaria. As in the Giemsa method for staining thick-blood films, no preliminary fixation is required but the films must be completely dry and should be freshly prepared.

Preparation of Stain.—Two solutions are utilized, both isotonic and adjusted to a pH of 6.6.

Solution 1:

Methylene blue	0.8 Gm.
Azure B	0.5 "
Disodium hydrogen phosphate (anhydrous) .	5.0 "
Potassium dihydrogen phosphate (anhydrous)	6.25 "
Distilled water	500 cc.

Solution 2:

Eosin	1.0 Gm.
Disodium hydrogen phosphate (anhydrous) .	5.0 "
Potassium dihydrogen phosphate (anhydrous)	6.25 "
Distilled water	500 cc.

The phosphate salts are first made up in solution in the distilled water and the respective stains added. (The azure B is first ground in a mortar with a little of the phosphate solution.) Let each dye solution stand for twenty-four hours, then filter. If scum or precipitate forms later, refiltration is required. The stains may be kept for several weeks and used over and over, if they are in covered staining jars. When the eosin solution becomes greenish, it should be renewed.

Technic of staining:

(1) Dip film for one second in Solution 1.
(2) Rinse immediately in clean water until stain ceases to flow from film.
(3) Dip for one second in Solution 2.
(4) Rinse in clear water.
(5) Place in vertical position to dry.

Microfilariæ in Blood and Cutaneous Tissue Juice.—In most instances microfilariæ circulating in the peripheral blood (or in cutaneous tissue juices, *viz.*, those of *Onchocerca volvulus*) are satisfactorily stained by the Giemsa technic. The thick film is recommended. After the material has been flattened into a circular area about 20 mm. in diameter on an absolutely clean microscope slide and has been thoroughly dried, the slide is placed vertically in the diluted Giemsa stain (see above). In approximately 30 minutes the staining is completed, the slide is removed, washed gently in tap water and dried. Overstaining is not likely to occur.

28

Hematoxylin Stains.—Some workers prefer hematoxylin to the Giemsa stain. The dried thick film is dehemoglobinized in 0.5% HCl, washed in 1% lithium carbonate solution and then stained by the iron-hematoxylin technic (see page 425), or by the Bullard technic. Bullard's hematoxylin is prepared as follows:

1. Fifty % alcohol, 144 cc.; glacial acetic acid, 16 cc.; hematoxylin crystals, 8 Gm.
2. Heat the above and add: distilled water, 250 cc.; ammonium alum, 20 Gm.
3. Heat to boiling and add slowly: red mercuric oxide, 8 Gm.
4. Cool quickly, filter and add: 95% alcohol, 275 cc.; glycerol, 330 cc.; glacial acetic acid, 18 cc.; ammonium alum, 40 Gm.
5 Keep in bright light for about one week for ripening and filter again before using.

The staining process is similar to that employing Harris' hematoxylin, *viz.*, immerse in the full-strength staining solution for 12 to 15 minutes, wash in tap water or 1% lithium carbonate solution until the film is distinctly blue, then dry.

Concentration of Microfilariæ.—Defibrinated and dehemoglobinized blood, lymph or chylous urine is concentrated by centrifuging for about one minute at 1000 or more revolutions per minute, the supernatant fluid decanted and the sediment examined for microfilariæ. These may be vitally stained or the film air-dried, fixed and permanently stained.

Knott (1939) has modified this technic as follows: 2 cc. of blood is thoroughly shaken with 10 cc. of a 2% solution of formalin, centrifuged for 5 minutes at 2,000 rpm., the supernatant fluid decanted and the sediment is ready to be stained in bulk, using iron-hematoxylin, then examined microscopically for microfilariæ.

RECOVERY OF PARASITES FROM ASPIRATES

Recovery of protozoa and helminths from aspirated material constitutes a very important part of the diagnostic problem.

Proctoscopic aspirates and scrapings are valuable in confirming suspicion of amebic ulcers in the lower sigmoid colon and rectum, but diagnosis of the cellular content of the aspirate is frequently a difficult problem, since host tissue cells are often confused with non-motile trophozoites or cysts of *Entamœba histolytica.*

Duodenal aspiration is employed in the demonstration of infections with *Giardia lamblia, Strongyloides stercoralis* (which may not be evident in stool examination), *Fasciolopsis buski* (eggs) and parasites located in the gall bladder or biliary tract. However, to avoid incorrect diagnosis or inference, when there is suspicion of biliary infection it is preferable to obtain samples of pure bile uncontaminated with duodenal juices.

Obtaining aspirates from lesions in the liver and lungs is particularly helpful for diagnosis of amebic liver abscess, as well as hydatid cyst. In the hepatic abscess, trophozoites of *Entamœba histolytica* are more likely to be demonstrated in aspirates obtained from the wall of the enlarging lesion than from the completely necrotic center of the abscess. Enzymatic liquefaction of viscous aspirates greatly facilitates search for amebæ (Lello, 1954). Streptodornase in sterile physiologic saline, 50 units/ml., is added to the fresh aspirate 1 to 5 parts. The mixture is incubated for 30 min. at 37°C., stirring 2 or 3 times. The liquified material is then transferred to tubes and centrifuged. Amebæ in the sediment are motile and can be cultured in preconditioned medium. Diagnostic evidence of hydatid cysts is found in the fluid content of the cyst, which usually contains numerous scolices.

Aspirates from lymph nodes, spleen, liver, bone marrow and spinal fluid frequently provide diagnostic evidence of African trypanosomiasis, visceral leishmaniasis (kala-azar), Chagas' disease and toxoplasmosis. The material obtained should be used in part for direct, unstained, coverglass preparations to demonstrate motile organisms (trypanosomes), in part for impression smears which are processed by the Giemsa technic (see above, page 432), and in part for culturing the organisms which may be present. (See Chapter 20, pages 441–447.)

BIOPSIED MATERIAL

Biopsy is becoming increasingly useful and common in the diagnosis of parasitic infections. This may be the most convenient and at times is the only method of confirming clinical suspicion of the infection.

Skin biopsies are employed for demonstration of amebiasis cutis, cutaneous leishmaniasis, and microfilariæ of *Onchocerca volvulus*. In the former two infections a representative portion or the entire lesion should be removed; this should be fixed in Zenker's solution and processed for serial, or at least several sections to be stained by the hematoxylin-eosin technic. For microfilariæ of *O. volvulus* only small, superficial biopsies are required. These thin samples of skin are each placed in a drop of tepid physiologic salt solution, mounted with a coverglass and examined for microfilariæ emerging from the tissue fragment. Occasionally in areas where other types of filariasis are endemic other microfilariæ may be present, particularly if the biopsy has been deep enough to rupture cutaneous blood vessels.

Superficial lymph node biopsies are designed for demonstration of the organisms of African trypanosomiasis, kala-azar, Chagas' disease and toxoplasmosis. While impression smears should be made for staining with the Giemsa technic, a representative portion should be fixed in Zenker's solution, sectioned and stained with hematoxylin-eosin.

Muscle biopsy is employed for demonstration of *Trichinella* larvæ and at times the cysticercus larvæ of *Tænia solium*. Some of the former material may be compressed between glass slides and examined directly for *Trichinella* cysts, but a portion should be digested in artificial gastric juice at 37° C. and the excysted larvæ concentrated by centrifugation. (If the specimen is adequate, a portion can be fed to a laboratory rat for evidence of the viability of the larvæ which may be present.) Usually muscle biopsy for demonstration of trichinosis is less common than immunologic technics. (See Chapter 21, pages 448–455.) If a cysticercus larva is present in the specimen, it should be carefully dissected out of its capsule, deflated with a needle and compressed between a slide and coverglass to demonstrate the characteristic scolex with four suckers and an anterior circlet of hooks.

Proctoscopic biopsy may be performed in an attempt to confirm suspicion of amebic colitis, but it is less commonly undertaken than proctoscopic aspiration. On the other hand, proctoscopic biopsy is a most valuable procedure for demonstrating eggs of *Schistosoma mansoni, S. japonicum* and *S. hæmatobium* which have been deposited in the lower mesenteric and rectal venules and have filtered into adjacent tissues of the sigmoid colon and rectum.

Meira and Soares (1948) state that biopsied rectal material taken from the level of the first valve of Houston, rendered transparent by KOH and examined microscopically under compression, provides a simple, harmless procedure. It is particularly valuable in chronic cases of intestinal schistosomiasis and as a follow-up of treatment, when stools are frequently negative for eggs of the parasite. It should always be employed as a check on immunologic tests. Similar technic, using the cystoscope to obtain biopsy of the bladder, is useful in diagnosing *S. hæmatobium* infection.

Visceral biopsy, particularly from the surface of the liver, provides the only practical clinical diagnostic procedure for demonstration of visceral larva migrans produced by dog and cat ascarids, *Toxocara canis* and *T. cati* (Beaver *et al.*, 1952).

SPECIMENS OBTAINED FOLLOWING CHEMOTHERAPEUSIS

The most common post-treatment examinations are made in helminthic infections of the intestinal tract, particularly those due to hookworms, *Ascaris*, *Trichuris*, the tapeworms, and intestinal trematodes. Depending on whether the anthelmintic is only anesthetizing or is lethal in its effect, the worms will be evacuated in an undamaged, living condition or may be badly damaged. Large worms are most easily recovered by dilution, sedimentation and decantation of the stools; smaller species are more readily found and their number counted by straining the diluted feces through wire gauze with appropriate-sized mesh (Beaver, 1952).

AUTOPSY MATERIAL

Protozoan Infections.—Since post-mortem tissue autolysis occurs rapidly and with it speedy degeneration of the parasites in the tissues, for good diagnostic evidence it is imperative that autopsy be obtained as soon as possible, preferably within four hours after death. Representative blocks of abnormal tissues should be fixed in formalin, or preferably in Zenker's solution, and then processed for sectioning and staining. Delayed autopsies may provide negative or equivocal information concerning any protozoön which may be involved. In the event the gross lesions strongly suggest amebic infection and necropsy has been delayed, routine sections first stained with hematoxylin-eosin and then with Best's carmine may allow identification of the amebæ by their strawberry pink staining reaction.

Helminthic Infections.—While it is always desirable to make necropsy examination for helminths as soon as possible after death, these parasites frequently survive for a considerable time in a diagnosable condition, especially if the body has been kept cold. A majority of helminths will be recovered from the intestinal tract and adjacent viscera, but filaria worms, *Paragonimus* and tapeworm larvæ will be located elsewhere.

Gastro-intestinal Infections.—After the gastro-intestinal tract has been removed from the body it should be opened along the line of lesser curvature and the contents from the several levels collected separately for subsequent examinations. Hookworms and whipworms should be removed by gentle traction from their attachment to the bowel wall. *Strongyloides* in the wall may be obtained by careful scraping of the mucosa, particularly of the duodenum and jejunum, but blocks of supposedly infected tissue should always be cut and fixed as soon as possible in Zenker's fluid, later sectioned and examined microscopically. Minute worms, as *Strongyloides* and heterophyoid flukes, are most readily obtained by placing the opened bowel in luke-warm physiologic salt solution, shaking vigorously and examining the liquid for the worms in a large flat petri dish, or by passing the liquid through a fine bronze screen or bolting cloth.   For *Clonorchis, Opisthorchis, Fasciola* and *Dicrocœlium* infections, the gall-bladder and biliary passages must be opened and carefully examined.

Helminthic Infections in Other Locations.—In *Schistosoma mansoni, S. japonicum* and *S. hæmatobium* infections, the liver should be removed intact with its connections to the entire intestinal tract, and the mesenteric and rectal venules carefully perfused.   Likewise, the intra-hepatic portal vein should be opened and search made there for the worms.   Representative blocks of intestine, mesenteric lymph nodes and liver should always be fixed and sectioned.   For *S. hæmatobium* and *S. mansoni,* the urinary bladder and other organs of the pelvic region together with their blood supply, should be removed and similarly examined.   All three species of *Schistosoma* may likewise be present at times in the pulmonary arterioles. *Paragonimus* is most commonly found within cystic tumors in the depth of the lungs but the worms may have developed in the abdominal viscera or even in the brain.   *Echinococcus* cysts most frequently occur in the liver but have been recovered from practically every organ and tissue of the body.   The adult Bancroft's filaria worms may develop in lymph nodes and lymphoid tissue in any portion of the body, but are most commonly located in the groin, medially above the testes or at the proximal end of obstructed lymph tracts.

Preservation of Helminths.—Most helminths do not require delicate technics for satisfactory preservation.   Tapeworms and trematodes usually fix well in steaming (not boiling) 2% formaldehyde (5% formalin), and nematodes may be fixed in the same medium to which glycerol (1 part to 10 by volume) has been added before the fixative is heated.   In case large tapeworms are desired for demonstration specimens, they should be chilled and should be placed in the desired position before fixation.

Sections of tissues containing helminths and their eggs or larvæ should be fixed in Zenker's fluid.   For museum specimens, in which it is desirable to retain the natural color of tissues, the Kaiserling technic may be employed.   For staining microscopic sections containing helminths, Delafield's hematoxylin with eosin is satisfactory.

For large tapeworms Roudabush (1947) recommends relaxation of the living worms in water in the icebox so that they will not move when touched.   Attached fecal débris should be removed, knots in the worms untangled and the worms wound around the outside of a cylinder in a relaxed state.   Then the fixative solution should be gently poured over the worm until complete killing of the tissues has been accomplished.   Roudabush (*l.c.*) uses the following fixative formula: Ethyl alcohol, 95%, 24 parts; commercial formalin, 15 parts; glacial acetic acid, 5 parts; glycerol, 10 parts; tap water, 46 parts.

Glycerogel Permanent Mounts for Helminths.—Yetwin (1944) has developed the following medium for making permanent mounts of small nematodes.

10% Bacto gelatin, granular (Difco) . .	150 cc.
Glycerol, reagent (Merck)	50 cc.
1% chromium and potassium sulfate, C. P.,	
granular (Merck)	100 cc.
Phenol, U. S. P., Liquid	1 cc.

The gelatin is dissolved in boiling water and the glycerol added and thoroughly mixed, after which the chrome solution and phenol are similarly introduced. The medium will jell at room temperature but liquefies in 15 minutes at 65° C. Specimens may be transferred directly from glycerol or formalin solutions to the mounting medium which hardens into a permanent mount. In 18 hours, the parasite objects are clear and ready for examination.

For delicate fixation of helminths, needed for study of the more detailed histology and cytology of the worms, Gilson's or Bouin's fluid is recommended. In the preparation of *in toto* mounts of trematodes, tapeworm proglottids or small nematodes, Bullard's hematoxylin may be used for staining, although good results are more difficult to obtain than with acid carmine solutions. Description of the methods will be found in any good manual on microtechnic. For studying the internal anatomy of nematode larvæ, a saturated solution of iodine in 1% potassium iodide provides a satisfactory stain for temporary mounts. Living miracidia and cercariæ of trematodes, and hexacanth embryos hatched from tapeworm eggs, may be studied to advantage in a 0.1% aqueous solution of brilliant cresyl blue.

Eggs of helminths obtained from centrifugation or sedimentation of feces or urine are satisfactorily fixed and preserved in steaming 4% formaldehyde. *Paragonimus* eggs in sputum may be preserved in a phenol-glycerol solution (phenol, 1%; glycerol, 5%; distilled water, 94%).

MATERIAL FROM THE ENVIRONMENT

Material obtained from the environment may be useful in providing evidence of specific causal relationship of an animal agent or vector to the disease in a particular patient, as, for example, recovery of an arthropod or vertebrate animal in connection with host venenation. In this connection, data concerning the presence of protozoan or helminth parasites in reservoir or alternate hosts may provide a clue with respect to the sources of these parasites in man.

Recovery of Parasite Objects from Fomites.—Protozoan parasites are rarely recovered from fomites. Gross fecal pollution of underclothing and furniture may furnish evidence of *Entamœba histolytica* cysts following immersion of these objects in water and concentration of the sediment by macro-centrifugation.

In contrast to the protozoan parasites, eggs of intestinal helminths are not uncommonly obtained from underclothing, household furniture, green vegetables, topsoil of potted house plants and from paper money. The most common of these eggs in the immediate environment are those of the seatworm, *Enterobius vermicularis*. Likewise it is frequently possible to obtain eggs of *Ascaris, Trichuris,* hunan hookworms, *Hymenolepis nana* and *Tænia* on the floors and in other locations within the homes of infected individuals.

Recovery of Parasite Objects from Water.—There is good circumstantial evidence that *Entamœba histolytica* may gain entry to the human digestive tract in drinking water grossly polluted with human excreta. Direct proof by isolation of amebic cysts from the water has been provided (Artigas, 1953). The recovery of eggs of *Ascaris, Trichuris* and *Tænia* by macrocentrifugation of sewage has been demonstrated both in natural and experimental studies.

Recovery of Parasite Objects from the Soil.—While it is possible and even probable that under certain conditions in moist tropical countries cysts of intestinal protozoa deposited on the soil in human excreta may survive and later get into the human digestive tract on contaminated objects, no eminently practical method has been developed for recovery of these organisms from the soil.

In epidemiologic investigations of intestinal helminthic infections, it is frequently necessary to obtain direct evidence of soil pollution by demonstration of the eggs or larvæ. When first deposited these parasite objects may be present in the fecal sump on top of the ground, but rain, coprophagous insects and other agents soon cause disintegration, with dissemination of the eggs, and the larvæ tend to migrate actively in the topsoil.

A satisfactory method of isolating helminth eggs from the soil is described by Headlee (1936) as an adaptation of the Caldwell and Caldwell technic, modified by Spindler (1929). A representative 5 to 10 Gm. sampling from a pint of suspected soil is first placed in a 50 cc. centrifuge tube and treated for an hour with 10 cc. of 30% antiformin solution. The mixture is stirred frequently, to bring the antiformin in contact with every particle of soil. The tube is then filled with sodium dichromate (1.35 specific gravity), the mixture thoroughly shaken, and then centrifuged at 1000 revolutions per minute for 2 minutes. After being allowed to rise to the surface film the eggs are looped from the film, transferred to a 15 cc. centrifuge tube with a conical bottom, and the tube nearly filled with distilled water. After shaking, the tube is centrifuged as before, the supernatant fluid pipetted off, and the sediment at the bottom of the tube, containing the eggs, is placed within a rectangular area on a fecal slide and examined microscopically.

Isolation of nematode larvæ from the soil is accomplished by the *Baermann technic*. The simple apparatus used consists of a glass filter funnel of 15 to 23 cm. diameter (preferably ribbed), placed in a convenient rack or ring stand, and connected at its lower end with a short rubber tube, provided with a pinch-cock. The soil sample to be tested is placed in a little basket made of 1 mm. mesh bronze or aluminum screening lined with cheesecloth. Luke-warm water is placed in the funnel and its height so adjusted that the soil will be immersed in the water. Within 10 to 15 minutes nematode larvæ in positive soils may be observed falling down the stem of the funnel. The maximum yield takes place within the first hour, after which the pinch-cock should be opened, about 10 to 15 cc. of water drawn off into a test-tube, the suspension centrifuged, the supernatant fluid pipetted off immediately and the sediment poured onto a slide for examination. The examiner needs considerable training to differentiate hookworm and *Strongyloides* larvæ from nematodes free-living in the soil. Improvements have been made in this technic (Beaver, 1953).

REFERENCES

ARTIGAS, J. J. 1953. Hallazgo de *"Entamœba histolytica"* en muestra de agua potable de Osorno. Nueva técnica de investigación. Bol. Inform. Parasit. Chilenas, *8*, 44.

BAROODY, B. J., and MOST, H. 1946. The Relative Efficiency of Water Centrifugal Sedimentation and Other Methods of Stool Examination for Diagnosis of Schistosomiasis Japonica. J. Lab. & Clin. Med., *31*, 815–823.

BEAVER, P. C. 1949. Methods of Pinworm Diagnosis. Am. J. Trop. Med., *29*, 577–587.

————. 1952. The Detection and Identification of Some Common Nematode Parasites of Man. Am. J. Clin. Path., *22*, 481–494.

————. 1953. Persistence of Hookworm Larvæ in Soil. Am. J. Trop. Med. & Hyg., *2*, 102–108.

—————. 1950. The Standardization of Fecal Smears for Estimating Egg Production and Worm Burden. J. Parasitol., *36*, 451–456.

BROOKE, M. M., and GOLDMAN, M. 1949. Polyvinyl Alcohol-fixative as a Preservative and Adhesive for Protozoa in Dysenteric Stools and Other Liquid Material. J. Lab. & Clin. Med., *34*, 1554–1560.

FAUST, E. C., D'ANTONI, J. S., ODOM, V., MILLER, M. J., PERES, C., SAWITZ, W., THOMEN, L. F., TOBIE, J., and WALKER, J. H. 1938. A Critical Study of Clinical Laboratory Technics for the Diagnosis of Protozoan Cysts and Helminth Eggs in Feces. Am. J. Trop. Med., *18*, 169–183.

FAUST, E. C., and INGALLS, J. W., JR. 1946. The Diagnosis of Schistosomiasis Japonica. III. Technics for the Recovery of the Eggs of *Schistosoma japonicum*. Am. J. Trop. Med., *26*, 559–584.

FAUST, E. C., SAWITZ, W., TOBIE, J., ODOM, V., PERES, C., and LINCICOME, D. R. 1939. Comparative Efficiencies of Various Technics for the Diagnosis of Protozoa and Helminths in Feces. J. Parasitol., *25*, 241–262.

FIELD, J. W. 1941. Further Note on a Method of Staining Malarial Parasites in Thick Blood Films. Trans. R. Soc. Trop. Med. & Hyg., *35*, 35–42.

HEADLEE, W. H. 1936. The Epidemiology of Human Ascariasis in the Metropolitan Area of New Orleans, Louisiana. Am. J. Hyg., *24*, 469–521.

KNOTT, J. I. 1939. A Method for Making Microfilarial Surveys on Day Blood. Trans. R. Soc. Trop. Med. & Hyg., *33*, 191–196.

LELLO, M. H. 1954. A Method for the Examination of Hepatic Abscess for *Entamœba histolytica*. Lab. News and Views. *3*, 107–108.

MEIRA, J. A., and SOARES, J. C. DE M. 1948. A biopsia retal no diagnostico da Esquistosomiase Mansoni. Arq. Fac. Hig. e Saude Pub., Univ. São Paulo, 2, 45–90.

RITCHIE, L. S. 1948. An Ether Sedimentation Technique for Routine Stool Examinations. Bull. U. S. Army Med. Dept., *8*, 326.

ROUDABUSH, R. L. 1947. A Method for Relaxing and Fixing Large Tapeworms. J. Parasitol., *33* (2nd Sec.), 17.

SAPERO, J. J., and LAWLESS, D. K. 1953. The "MIF" Stain-preservation Technic for the Identification of Intestinal Protozoa. Am. J. Trop. Med., and Hyg., *2*, 613–619.

STOLL, N. R., and HAUSHEER, W. C. 1926. Concerning Two Options in Dilution Egg Counting: Small Drop and Displacement. Am. J. Hyg., *6* (March Suppl.), 134–145.

Chapter 20

Culture Technics

THE cultivation of animal agents or vectors of human disease serves a threefold purpose *viz.*, (1) to supplement other methods of laboratory diagnosis, (2) for use in teaching and (3) to provide organisms in quantity for investigation. Diagnostically, it is sometimes possible to obtain the parasite or its vector in culture in an identifiable stage when other material for diagnosis may fail to furnish specific evidence. Culture technics are available for protozoan and helminthic parasites and many of the arthropods.

In Vitro Cultivation of Protozoan Parasites

Intestinal Protozoa.—Numerous media have been developed for the cultivation of intestinal amebæ, flagellates and the ciliate *Balantidium coli*. To initiate a culture fresh stools uncontaminated with urine are required. Formed stools containing the cysts may be employed, or liquid specimens with trophozoites. In the latter case elements of mucus and tissue detritus are more likely to contain the pathogen than the diluted fecal portion. To prevent rapid overgrowth of enteric bacteria it is frequently helpful to add penicillin when the stool sample is inoculated into the culture medium, and it is necessary to introduce considerably more inoculum than in bacteriologic cultures.

In general, the inoculum should consist of representative portions of the several components of the stool, saline-purged specimen, enema specimen, proctoscopic aspirate, liver aspirate or other material obtained from the patient. About $\frac{1}{2}$ cc. of the material is inoculated into the medium and the culture is incubated at 37° C. Aseptic technic is recommended. Subcultures usually are made at 48-hour intervals. At times no evidence of the suspected organism is found in samplings of the original culture but subcultures may be positive. The following media are selected from the many good ones which have been developed. (For other technics please consult Craig's *Laboratory Diagnosis of Protozoan Diseases*, 2nd ed., 1948.)

CULTURE MEDIA

Balamuth's Monophasic Medium (1946)

A. *Preparation*
1. Weigh 288 Gm. dehydrated egg yolk.
2. Add 288 cc. distilled water and 1000 cc. 0.85% saline, and with an electric mixer (or similar instrument) emulsify until suspension is smooth.
3. Heat over an open flame in the top part of a double boiler, stirring constantly until coagulation begins (5–10 min.).

(441)

4. Heat the mixture over boiling water, stirring occasionally until coagulation is complete (about 20 min.). Add 160 cc. distilled water to offset loss from evaporation.
5. Filter the mixture through a muslin bag. When the bag cools its may be squeezed gently to obtain the maximum volume of filtrate.
6. Measure filtrate and add 0.85% saline to bring volume to 1000 cc.
7. Dispense the filtrate into 2 one-liter Erlenmeyer flasks. Autoclave for 20 min. at 15 lbs. (121° C.).
8. Place the flasks in the refrigerator overnight or until the solution is thoroughly chilled.
9. Filter while cold through a Buchner funnel, preferably using negative pressure to facilitate filtration. Use 2 pieces of Whatman qualitative filter paper of suitable size and pour the mixture in small amounts through the funnel, replacing the papers frequently.
10. Measure the filtrate. Add an equal volume of Balamuth's buffer solution.
11. Add 0.5% crude liver extract (Lilly, No, 408) (5 cc. per liter of medium).
12. Dispense in 5–7 cc. amounts in tubes; autoclave for 20 minutes at 15 lbs. (121° C.). Add sterile rice powder and incubate for 24 hours at 37° C. before using. The medium may be left in flasks in large amounts, autoclaved, and stored in the refrigerator. It can be kept for a month or more without deterioration, though there may be an accumulation of sediment which should be removed by filtration. Re-autoclaving produces no harmful effects, and may even be beneficial.

B. *Solutions*

1. Balamuth buffer solution

(a) $1M$ K$_2$HPO$_4$	174.180	Gm.
Distilled water to make . .	1000.0	cc.
(b) $1M$ KH$_2$PO$_4$	136.092	Gm.
Distilled water to make . .	1000.0	cc.

2. Mix these solutions in a ratio of 4.3 parts $1M$ K$_2$HPO$_4$ to 0.7 parts $1M$ KH$_2$PO$_4$. To one part of this mixture add 14 parts of distilled water to prepare the $M/15$ buffer. This final solution is the one used in (10) above in the directions for preparation of the medium.

Boeck and Drbohlav's Diphasic (L.E.S.) Medium (1925)

Preparation.—Four eggs are washed, brushed with alcohol, and broken into a sterile flask containing glass beads. Fifty cc. of Locke's solution (see below) are then added and the mixture broken up by shaking. Test tubes are then filled with enough of the mixture to produce slants about 1 to 1.5 inches in length upon coagulating by heat. The tubes are slanted in an inspissator and heated at 70° C. (158° F.) until the mixture is solidified, after which they are autoclaved at 15 lb. pressure for twenty minutes. The tubes are then covered to a depth of about 1 cm. with a mixture of equal parts of sterile Locke's solution and 1 part of sterile inactivated human blood serum after the mixture has been passed through a Berkefeld filter and incubated to determine sterility.

Medium No. 2. Locke-egg-albumin (L.E.A.) Medium.—The above medium was modified by Drbohlav by using crystallized egg albumin instead of human blood serum. A 1% solution of crystallized egg albumin in Locke's solution was sterilized by passage through a Berkefeld filter, and then added to the tubes containing the egg slants as described for the L.E.S. medium.

The initial reaction of these media varies from *p*H 7.2 to *p*H 7.8 and requires no adjustment.

Locke's Solution.—The Locke solution used in the above media has the following formula:

NaCl	9.0 Gm.
CaCl₂	0.2 ”
KCl	0.4 ”
NaHCO₂	0.2 ”
Glucose	2.5 ”
Distilled water	1000 cc.

The solution is sterilized in the Arnold sterilizer or the autoclave.

Modified Diphasic Medium (As utilized in the Dept.
of Trop. Med. & Pub. Health, Tulane Univ.)

A. Preparation

1. Emulsify 4 whole hen's eggs with 50 cc. of Ringer's Solution.
2. Filter the emulsion through several thicknesses of cheesecloth or surgical gauze.
3. Dispense 2–3 cc. amounts into 16×150 mm. Pyrex test tubes.
4. Place several layers of paper in the bottom of the autoclave and slant the tubes at an angle of 30°. (Place the tubes in baskets so that the rows are not more than 2–3 deep.)
5. Inspissate for 10 minutes at 15 lb. in the autoclave. (Set valves according to directions which accompany the machine.) Cool.
6. Overlay each slant with approximately 5 cc. of buffered saline (*p*H 7.0), or normal saline containing 0.5% crude liver extract (Lilly, No. 408).
7. Sterilize slants in the autoclave for 20 minutes at 15 lb. (121° C.). (Wrap the baskets in paper to minimize breaking of the slants during sterilization.)
8. Add about one loopful of sterile rice powder to each sterile overlayed slant.
9. Incubate medium for 24 hrs. at 37° C. just prior to use, to demonstrate sterility.

B. Solutions.

1. Stock Ringer's Solution

NaCl	70.0 Gm.
CaCl	3.0 ”
KCl	2.5 ”
Distilled water	1000 cc.

Dilute the stock solution 1:10 with neutral distilled water for use.

2. Buffered Saline (*p*H 7.0)

0.85% Saline	450.0 cc.
$M/15$ KH₂PO₄	19.0 cc.
$M/15$ Na₂HPO₄	31.0 cc.
$M/15$ KH₂PO₄, prepared as follows:	
KH₂PO₄	0.07 Gm.
Distilled water to make	1000 cc.
$M/15$ Na₂HPO₄, prepared as follows:	
Na₂HPO₄	9.46 Gm.
Distilled water to make	1000 cc.

Nelson's Medium (1947)

Preparation.—The material consists of human, calf, beef or guinea-pig liver, cat intestine, or egg yolk; all give about the same result when extracted.

The extraction of the selected tissue is made with 95% ethyl alcohol by adding 10 parts of the tissue or egg yolk to 90 parts of the alcohol. The tissue used is cut into small pieces and placed in the alcohol; if egg yolk is used the yolk is separated from the white which gives an inert extract.

The flask or bottle containing the alcohol and tissue is shaken several times a day and is ready for use in 48 hours. At the time of use place 10 cc. of the stock alcoholic extract in a small flask and drive off the alcohol by heating in a water bath; then add 20 cc. of a melted 2% agar in buffered 0.5% saline, tube the mixture in 2 cc. quantities and slant. No serum supplement is required. Cover the agar slants with buffered 0.5% saline, inoculate and incubate. (The agar mixture can be autoclaved before slanting if desired.) The pH of the medium should be 7.4 if tissue extracts are used and 7.6 if egg-yolk extract is used. Rice flour sterilized at 150° C. is added to the medium at the time of inoculation.

Phillips' Medium (1950)

This differs from all other *in vitro* culture media for *Entamœba histolytica* in the substitution of *Trypanosoma cruzi* as the metabolic associate. The amebæ previously grown in a Shaffer-Ryden-Frye (1948) type of medium are inoculated into a thioglycollate preparation with horse serum and a rich suspension of *T. cruzi* which has been grown on diphasic blood agar. Penicillin is added to provide bacterial sterility, and petrolatum overlay to reduce O_2 tension. Transfers are made at 48-hour periods.

STS Medium for Trichomonas vaginalis (Kupferberg *et al.* 1948)

This medium is suitable for isolation of *T. vaginalis* from vaginal exudates and also for the maintenance of bacteria-free cultures for teaching or research. Bacteria can be eliminated by serial transfers in medium containing 500 units of penicillin and 500 mg. of dihydrostreptomycin sulfate per ml.

MATERIALS

Trypticase (BBL) . .	20.0 Gm.
Cysteine HCl . . .	1.5 Gm.
Maltose	1.0 Gm.
Agar (Difco) . . .	1.0 Gm.
Distilled water, *q.s.* .	950.0 ml.

The above ingredients are mixed and the pH adjusted to 6.0 with HCl or NaOH. Heat the mixture to boiling to dissolve the agar and filter while hot through porous Reeves-Angel filter paper No. 845. If desired, add 0.6 ml. of 0.5% methylene blue as an indicator for oxygen tension. Cool to 46° C, adjust pH to 6.0 if necessary, dilute to 950 ml. and tube in amounts of 9.5 ml. Autoclave the tubed medium for 15 minutes at 15 lb. pressure. Store in refrigerator and prior to inoculation add 0.5 ml. of sterile human or rabbit serum.

Rees' Medium for Balantidium coli (1927)

Preparation.—A modified Ringer's Solution is made up as follows:

NaCl	6.50 Gm.
KCl	0.14 "
CaCl₂	0.12 "
NaHCO₃	0.20 "
Na₂HPO₄	0.01 "
Distilled water . . .	1000 cc.

To each 18 cc. of this solution placed in a test tube and autoclaved at 15 lb. pressure for 10 minutes, 2 cc. of sterile human or horse serum and a small sprinkling of sterile rice powder are added. The inoculum is then introduced, the culture incubated at 36° C., and transfers made every 72 hours.

Blood and Tissue Flagellates.—The inoculum consists of blood, aspirates or small amounts of biopsied or post-mortem samples from glands, spleen, liver or bone marrow, obtained aseptically from patients suspected of having infection of *Leishmania donovani, L. braziliensis, L. tropica, Trypanosoma gambiense, T. rhodesiense, T. cruzi* or other hemoflagellates. To insure bacterial sterility it is desirable to introduce 500 units of penicillin plus 500 mgm. of dihydrostreptomycin sulfate into each tube at the time of inoculation.

Novy, MacNeal and Nicolle's (NNN) Medium (1904–1908)

This method was developed for cultivation of the leishmanias but is equally satisfactory for *Trypanosoma cruzi*.

Preparation.—The formula is as follows:

Agar	14 Gm.
Sodium chloride . . .	6 "
Distilled water . . .	900 cc.

Mix and bring to the boiling-point, then distribute in tubes and sterilize in the autoclave.

In using the tubed medium, it is melted and then cooled to 48° C. and to each tube of medium one-third of its volume of sterile defibrinated rabbit blood is added. This is well mixed with the medium by rotating the tube, after which the tubes are slanted and allowed to cool. This is best done on ice, as more water of condensation is obtained, and it is in this supernate at the bottom of the tubes that the organisms develop most rapidly and in greatest numbers. Before using, the tubes should be tested for sterility by placing them in the incubator at 37° C. for twenty-four hours.

Tobie's Diphasic Medium (Tobie *et al.*, 1950).

This medium is satisfactory for *Trypanosoma cruzi, T. rangeli, T. gambiense T. rhodesiense, Leishmania tropica, L. braziliensis, L. donovani*, and many non-human species of hemoflagellates. It is a diphasic medium.

Solid phase: Dissolve 1.5 Gm. Bacto-beef (Difco); 2.5 Gm. Bacto-peptone (Difco); 4.0 Gm. sodium chloride; and 7.5 Gm. Bacto-agar (Difco) in 500 ml. distilled water. Adjust the *p*H to 7.2–7.4 with NaOH and autoclave at 15 lbs. pressure for 20 minutes. Cool this mixture until it can be comfortably held in the hand (about 45° C.), then add whole rabbit blood, which has been inactivated at 56° C. for 30 minutes, in the proportion of 25 ml. blood to 75 ml. base. Coagulation of the whole blood is prevented by using 0.5 percent sterile sodium citrate.

Liquid phase: Sterile Locke's solution of the following composition: NaCl, 8 Gm.; KCl, 0.2 Gm.; CaCl₂, 0.2 Gm.; KH₂PO₄, 0.3 Gm.; dextrose, 2.5 Gm., and distilled water, 1,000 ml. is used.

The base is dispensed in amounts of 5 ml. or 25 ml. into test tubes or flasks respectively. The test tubes are kept in a slanted position and the flasks upright until the base has solidified. Then the liquid phase is added in amounts of 2 ml. and 10 to 15 ml. respectively. The tubes and flasks are closed with cotton plugs which need not be capped since subcultures must be made before evaporation becomes serious. There is, however, no objection to screw-caps.

Weinman's Medium (1960)

The isolation of *Trypanosoma gambiense* and *T. rhodesiense* is often difficult. The following method was developed to insure greater success in the cultivation of the African sleeping-sickness trypanosomes from blood and spinal fluid.

Preparation.—The medium is made up in two portions, an autoclaved base and a non-heated portion.

1. *Base*: Nutrient agar, Difco   31 Gm.
        Agar   5 Gm.
        Distilled water   1000 ml.

Dissolve by heating, cool to 45° C, adjust pH to 7.3, distribute in known volumes as convenient, autoclave, store in refrigerator.

2. *Non-autoclaved portion*: Centrifuge citrated human blood or allow cells to sediment by gravity. Remove the plasma and inactivate at 56° C. for 30 minutes in a water bath. Wash the blood cells three times by suspension and centrifugation in sterile saline (0.9%).

3. *Preparation of slants*: Mix equal volumes of inactivated plasma and packed, washed blood cells. Melt sterile agar base in a water bath and cool to 45° C. Add one part reconstituted blood to 3 parts base, mix well, dispense in 5 ml. amounts into sterile, 150 × 15 mm. screw-cap culture tubes, and allow to set in a slanted postion for 2 to 3 days. If desired, after several hours at room temperatures the slants may be refrigerated overnight in baskets in a slanted position to hasten setting. Incubate slants at 37° C. for 25 hours to test sterility. Store in refrigerator at 4° to 8° C; the medium remains satisfactory for about 6 months.

4. *Use of medium*: Small amounts of blood (0.1 ml.) may be inoculated directly into slants. The use of polyvinyl sulfuric acid (PVSA) is recommended for larger blood inocula as an anticoagulant and anticomplementary agent. The PVSA prepared by the method of Chargaff, Bancroft and Stanley-Brown (1936) is prepared as a 0.5% solution in saline, pH 7.5, and sterilized by filtration. Use 0.1 ml. PVSA per ml. of blood, mix thoroughly and inoculate promptly up to 2 ml. per tube of medium.

It is recommended that dihydrostreptomycin sulfate, 0.5 mgm. per ml. of blood, or penicillin, 2000 units per ml. of blood, be added to control contamination.

The slants are tilted to spread the inoculum over the surface and incubated in darkness at 25° C. For examination, fluid from the tube is run over slant with a Pasteur pipette to wash down colonies and a drop then removed for examination. Cultures rarely become positive earlier than 5 days, or after 30 days.

Malaria Parasites.—*No simple, satisfactory culture method has been developed* for the *in vitro* cultivation of malaria parasites. Relatively complicated media, apparatus and technics have led to success in survival and asexual mutliplication of *Plasmodium vivax*, *P. falciparum*, *P. knowlesi* and *P. cynomolgi* in a medium consisting of inorganic salts, carbohydrates, liver extract, ascorbic acid, and whole-blood mixtures containing the parasites (Geiman, 1951).

Toxoplasma.—*T. gondii* has been cultured in roller tube cultures of mouse and human tissues by Chernin and Weller (1957). However, this parasite has not been cultured in the absence of living tissue cells.

In Vitro Cultivation of Parasitic Helminths

Attempts have been made to culture parasitic helminths in nutrient media, in some instances attended with partial success. In general, aseptic technics in bacteria-free media have prolonged the life of the worms and in some species have resulted in development from a larva to a more mature larval stage or to sexual maturity. *Nippostrongylus muris*, a nematode parasite of the rat, has been grown from the egg to the adult stage in axenic cultures (Weinstein and Jones, 1956).

In contrast to the above-mentioned parasitic helminths, it is relatively easy to obtain the complete extrinsic, *e.g.*, free-living stages, of strains of *Strongyloides stercoralis* or of other species of this genus exhibiting indirect development. Rhabditoid larvæ (or eggs) of these strains, recovered from the stools of the natural hosts, provide the inoculum. The media consist of host's feces or other suitable nutriment, containing the associated enteric bacteria or free of bacteria.

REFERENCES

BALAMUTH, W. 1946. Improved Egg Yolk Infusion for Cultivation of *Entamœba histolytica* and Other Intestinal Protozoa. Am. J. Clin. Path., *16*, 380–384.

BOECK, W. C., and DRHBOLAV, J. 1925. The Cultivation of *Endamœba histolytica*. Am. J. Hyg., *5*, 371–407.

CHARGAFF, E., BANCROFT, F. W., and STANLEY-BROWN, M. 1936. Studies on the Chemistry of Blood Coagulation. II. On the Inhibition of Blood Clotting by Substances of High Molecular Weight. J. Biol. Chem., *115*, 155–161.

CHERNIN, E., and WELLER, T. H. 1957. Further Observations on the Growth of *Toxoplasma gondii* in Roller Tube Cultures of Mouse and Primate Tissues. J. Parasitol., *43*, 33–39.

GEIMAN, Q. M. 1951. The Cultivation of Malarial Parasites, in *Parasitic Infections in Man*, edited by Harry Most, pages 130–149. Columbia University Press, New York.

KUPFERBERG, A. B., JOHNSON, G., and SPRINCE, H. 1948. Nutritional Requirements of *Trichomonas vaginalis*. Proc. Soc. Exp. Biol. & Med., *67*, 304–308.

NELSON, E. C. 1947. Alcoholic Extract Medium for the Diagnosis and Cultivation of *Endamœba histolytica*. Am. J. Trop. Med., *27*, 545–552.

NOVY, F. G., and MacNEAL, W. J. 1904. On the Cultivation of *Trypanosoma brucei*. J. Infect. Dis., *1*, 1–30.

PHILLIPS, B. P. 1950. Cultivation of *Endamœba histolytica* with *Trypanosoma cruzi*. Science, *111*, 8–9.

REES, C. W. 1927. Balantidia from Pigs and Guinea-pigs: Their Viability, Cyst Production and Cultivation. Science, *66*, 89–91.

TOBIE, E., VON BRAND, T., and MEHLMAN, B. 1950. Cultural and Physiological Observations on *Trypanosoma rhodesiense* and *Trypanosoma gambiense*. J. Parasitol., *36*, 48–54.

WEINMAN, D. 1960. Cultivation of African Sleeping Sickness Trypanosomes from the Blood and Cerebrospinal Fluid of Patients and Suspects. Trans. R. Soc. Trop. Med. & Hyg., *54*, 180–190.

WEINSTEIN, P. P., and JONES, M. F. 1956. The *in vitro* Cultivation of *Nippostrongylus muris* to the Adult Stage, J. Parasitol., *42*, 215–236.

Chapter 21

Immunologic Diagnosis

Introduction

INFECTION with parasites belonging to any of the major groups may stimulate the production of antibodies in a given host. An antibody response is more likely to occur when the offending parasite is in intimate contact with host tissues than when it is a lumen dweller or an ectoparasite. Sero-immunologic tests have been devised for detection of antibodies in many parasitic infections. Some of these procedures are of academic interest only, others are useful for teaching or research, but only a few are of value to the clinician as aids in diagnosis. Immunologic tests are of greatest value in those infections that cannot be readily diagnosed by the demonstration of some stage of the parasite in host tissues or excreta. This is true during the prepatent period of many infections, the chronic phase of some, and in those in which the insulting parasite is at no time detectable by ordinary means.

Although in some instances extracts of a whole parasite are adequate for use in an immunological test, these extracts usually must be fractionated by chemical or physical means so as to reduce the number of cross reacting components. Moreover, as in bacterial and viral diseases, the interpretation placed on a given test will depend on the stage of the disease. The types of serologic tests used for the detection of parasitic infections are standard procedures involving routine technics.

Immunologic Tests for Protozoa

Intestinal Protozoa.—The only intestinal protozoön for which immunologic tests may have significance is *Entamœba histolytica* and even for this species no dependable immunologic technic of practical diagnostic value has been developed (Bozicevich, 1950).

Blood and Tissue Flagellates. — *The Leishmanias.*—Although *Leishmania donovani*, *L. tropica* and *L. braziliensis* are morphologically indistinguishable from one another, they may be differentiated by agglutination tests, employing the leptomonas stage of the respective organisms grown in blood-agar culture and sera from immunized rabbits.

Practical diagnosis of leishmaniasis may be obtained by agglutination, precipitin or complement-fixation reactions.

Nonspecific Tests.—In kala-azar there is characteristically a notable increase in serum globulin, so that the addition of a small amount of distilled water, antimony or formalin to patient's serum produces precipitation or cloudiness of the serum. The test is performed in a serologic tube, into which approximately 1 cc. of patient's

(448)

serum is introduced. If 2 or 3 volumes of distilled water are then introduced, a white precipitation occurs in a half hour or less in positive cases. This is the *serum-euglobulin test* of Bramachari and of Sia. A similar precipitate is formed (*antimony test*) in the sera of positive cases when urea stibamine (4% sol.) or stibosan is allowed to trickle down the side of the tube (Chopra, das Gupta and David, 1927). Likewise, if 1 drop of commercial formaldehyde is added to 1 cc. of positive serum in the tube and the mixture is shaken well, an opaque opalescent whitish gel is soon formed. This is the *formol-gel test* or *aldehyde test* of Napier (1921).

Complement fixation has also become a very efficient method of diagnosis in kala-azar. Sen Gupta (1943), who made extensive clinical trial of the tubercle-antigen complement-fixation test developed by Greval, Sen Gupta and Napier (1939), states that this test is of high diagnostic significance.

More recently it has been demonstrated by several observers that complement fixation with the antigen devised by Witebsky, Klingenstein and Kuhn, prepared from the acid-fast bacillus of Kedrowsky, gives a very high percentage of positive results with the blood serum in early cases of kala-azar. Sen Gupta (1944) has reported that in 900 cases of kala-azar and other diseases, 93% of the 240 cases of kala-azar gave a positive reaction, while in 664 patients suffering from other diseases liable to be confused with kala-azar 99% gave a negative reaction. He concluded that this test is even superior to sternal puncture in the early diagnosis of kala-azar.

Attempts should always be made to support positive serologic reactions by recovery of the leishmania in material obtained by aspiration from enlarged glands, bone marrow or spleen, either by demonstration of the organism in Giemsa-stained smears or after culture in blood agar media.

The *intradermal reaction* has been tested in all three types of leishmaniasis and has potential diagnostic usefulness. The antigen is obtained by physiologic saline extraction of cultured leishmanias. Positive diagnosis may be obtained before the organisms themselves are demonstrable in the patient's tissues. The reaction is of the delayed type but usually appears within 24 hours following the introduction of antigen into the skin. In 1926, Montenegro demonstrated the diagnostic value of this test, with confirmation by Gomes (1939), Pessôa and Pestana (1940) and Battistini and Herrer (1945) for *L. braziliensis* and Dostrovsky and Sagher (1946) for *L. tropica*. Its particular diagnostic value in *L. braziliensis* infection is after extension of the primary lesion to the muco-cutaneous junctions, in which the leishmanias may be difficult to demonstrate.

Trypanosoma cruzi.—The complement fixation test as described by de Freitas (1951) is widely used and constitutes the most valuable diagnostic method, particularly in chronic infections which are by far the most common. This is a quantitative technic in which titers are determined by employing different amounts of complement. In acute and subacute cases, a precipitin test with a polysaccharide antigen is sometimes useful (Muñiz, 1948).

Toxoplasma.—In detection of *Toxoplasma* in experimental animals and human cases, Sabin (1949) developed a highly specific *complement-fixation test* in which antigen is obtained from centrifuged concentrates of the organism grown on the chorioallantoic membranes of chick embryos. However, the *Sabin-Feldman dye test* (1948) is equally satisfactory and is much easier to perform. It is carried out as follows: Living toxoplasmas from peritoneal exudate of an experimentally infected laboratory mouse are placed as a thin wet film on a test plate in a small amount of normal human serum, and a similar test plate is prepared with serum of a suspected case of toxoplasmosis. A drop or two of alkaline methylene blue stain are now mixed with the film on each plate. In the control plate the cytoplasm and nuclear material of all cells are rather deeply stained. If the second plate is from a *Toxoplasma* patient (either with active, chronic or inapparent infection), the patient's serum

29

will contain neutralizing antibodies which will prevent the cytoplasm of the free parasites from taking the stain (although the cytoplasm of the parasites still within macrophages will be protected and will stain normally). In experimental animals, this test develops in three to five days after inoculation with *Toxoplasma*.

In *Toxoplasma* infection the dye test becomes positive earlier than the complement fixation reaction. High titers that may persist for several years develop by the second week. The complement fixation test is not positive until after one month of infection and becomes negative in a relatively short time. Thus a negative complement fixation test does not exclude past contacts with *Toxoplasma*. Jacobs and Lunde (1957) described an indirect hemagglutination test which was satisfactory for survey work (Lunde and Jacobs, 1958). If this method proves to be as specific as the dye test, it will be most useful because the antigen is prepared from lysed organisms.

Immunologic Tests for Helminths

Trichinella spiralis.—Antigens for intradermal and serologic tests are generally prepared from larvæ digested from the tissues of infected rats or rabbits. The washed larvæ are lyophilized and used as whole worm extracts or, more often fractionated by standard procedures.

Intradermal Tests for trichinosis, using a fat-free antigen (Bachman, 1929) in a dilution of approximately 1:10,000, are useful primarily for epidemiologic studies. In the test, 0.1 cc. of antigen is introduced intracutaneously on one forearm and and equal amount of the diluent is injected intracutaneously on the other forearm. In positive cases (whether clinical or subclinical), a small white swelling appears immediately around the injected site, surrounded by an unraised irregular erythematous area of about 5 cm. diameter. The reaction reaches its maximum in about 10 minutes and begins to fade in 15 to 20 minutes. This test is rarely positive earlier than the 3rd week of infection. Although, under carefully controlled technic, false positives do not commonly occur, it is always desirable to supplement the intradermal test with one of the serologic tests (*see below*), especially to determine if the infection has been of recent origin.

Precipitin Test.—Oliver Gonzalez (1941) discovered that there are two types of antibody reaction in trichinosis, one which is anti-larval and one anti-adult. The latter forms a precipitate *in vitro* around the mouth, vulva and anus of adult trichinas, is detectable 15 days after infection, reaches its maximum about the 25th to 35th day and terminates on the 50th day. The anti-larval type of antibody produces a precipitate which reaches a maximum between the 45th and 60th day.

Suessenguth and Kline (1944) have adapted the Kline test for syphilis to trichinosis. They report early, accurate diagnosis.

Agglutination.—Sadun and Norman (1955) demonstrated that a bentonite flocculation test, using an acid-soluble protein fraction of lyophlized larvæ, was sensitive and satisfactorily specific. The same antigen was used by Kagan (1956) in an indirect *hemagglutination test*, which was shown to be sensitive to antibodies that were demonstrable as early as the 6th day of infection in experimental animals.

Filarial Worms.—Because human filarial worms are difficult to recover from host tissues, most immunologic studies to date have used non-human filariæ, particularly *Dirofilaria immitis*, as a source of antigens. Consequently, serologic tests have reflected group relationships rather than species specificity.

Intradermal Tests.—Saline extracts of non-human filariæ have been used for intradermal testing in dilutions of 1:8000 or more. The reactions are of the immediate type. Reactivity appears within two months of infection. However, the amount of cross reactivity noted with other helminthic infections (Bozicevich *et al.*, 1947) precludes the use of this test in regions where ascariasis, hookworm infection, strongyloidiasis etc. may be present.

Serologic Tests.—A complement fixation reaction using an alcohol extract of *D. immitis* (Fairley, 1931) shows greater specificity than the intradermal test. However, the test has a relatively low sensitivity. Thus, although a positive reaction may indicate infection with filarial worms the reverse does not eliminate the possibility of infection.

Tropical Eosinophilia.—Studies by Danaraj *et al.* (1959) have indicated that some cases of tropical pulmonary eosinophilia may be due to cryptic filariasis. Sera from these patients provided high titers in a complement fixation test using an alcohol extract of *D. immitis.*

Strongyloides stercoralis.—Because of difficulties frequently encountered in recovering larvæ of *S. stercoralis*, immunologic tests would be useful as aids in diagnosis of these infections. Skin sensitivity to *Strongyloides* extracts was demonstrated by Fülleborn as early as 1926, but to date there is no specific intradermal test available. Serologic tests for strongyloidiasis have only been used on occasion (Brannon and Faust, 1949). At present there is no specific serologic test available for practical use.

Ascaris lumbricoides.—Although *A. lumbricoides* is known to be highly allergenic, immunologic tests for intestinal ascariasis have no practical value (see *Toxocara*, visceral larva migrans).

Toxocara species (Visceral Larva Migrans).—Until recently the diagnosis of larval helminthiases has depended on clinical signs and symptoms or on recognition of larvæ in histopathological studies of biopsy or necropsy material. These infections require the development of immunologic tests that can aid in diagnosis. Studies by Kagan (1959) and by Jung and Pacheco (1960) have shown that an indirect hemagglutination test using protein-polysaccharide fractions of adult ascarids may be of value as an aid in diagnosis despite the fact that there is cross reactivity with some other helminthiases.

Schistosoma species.—Since clinicians will usually depend on the demonstration of eggs in excreta or tissue as a diagnostic criterion, immunologic tests for schistosomiasis are of interest mainly as epidemiologic tools. Almost all stages of the parasites have been used as sources of antigenic materials, and in some of the tests the living organisms have been used.

Intradermal Tests.—The use of purified extracts of adults or cercariæ in intradermal tests has proved quite sensitive as well as specific. The advantage of this test is that it will be positive during all but the earliest phases of the disease (Pellegrino *et al.* 1959).

Complement Fixation.—Complement fixation tests performed with fat-free extracts of adults or cercariæ have been found useful in detecting infections during the first three years of the disease (Chaffee *et al.*, 1954). The same type of response has been observed using alcohol extracts of snail livers in a complement fixation test (Schofield, 1959).

Circumoval Precipitin.—The circumoval precipitin test (Oliver-González, 1954) has been shown to be sensitive and species-specific (Newsome, 1958); it is of greatest value in those cases in which eggs are no longer being passed. The test does not become positive until oviposition has begun and there is some indication that it may become negative following treatment (Oliver-González *et al.*, 1955).

Cercarienhüllenreaktion and *Miracidial Immobilization Test.*—The Cercarienhüllenreaktion (Vogel and Minning, 1948) and the miracidial immobilization test (Senterfit, 1958) have been shown to be early responses of the host that may be diminished or absent in the chronic phase. Both of these responses are sensitive and relatively specific.

Other Serologic Tests.—Bentonite flocculation (Sadun *et al.*, 1959) and indirect hemagglutination have been shown to be very sensitive tests when used with fractionated extracts of adult worms or cercariæ.

Paragonimus westermani.—Immunologic tests for the detection of infection with *P. westermani* are valuable to the clinician as well as to the epidemiologist, since a large percentage of infected individuals do not pass eggs in their feces or sputum. Using purified extracts of adult worms, Sadun (1960) was able to demonstrate complement fixation and intradermal tests for effective diagnosis in surveys and in individual infections.

Echinococcus granulosus.—*Intradermal Test.*—Since 1911, when Casoni first described the specificity of the intradermal test in persons parasitized by the hydatid cyst, it has been used as a clinical diagnostic procedure, and became a particularly valuable test after it was refined by Dew, Kellaway and Williams (1925). The antigen employed consists of sterile hydatid fluid obtained by puncture of unilocular hydatid cysts of sheep, pigs, oxen or human cases. The liquid antigen is filtered, incubated to test its sterility, and placed in sealed ampules on ice. With these precautions it is potent up to 6 months. For the test, 0.2 cc. of the antigen is introduced intradermally on the upper arm after sterilization of the area with alcohol, and is controlled by the injection of a like amount of sterile physiologic salt solution into the skin several centimeters distant or on the opposite arm. The control fades almost immediately, while the tested site of positive cases develops a typical wheal within $\frac{1}{2}$ hour. This test is particularly useful preoperatively. In postoperative tests, an intense skin reaction may result even though the cyst may have been removed many months previously.

The most potent hydatid antigen is that provided by the Dennis (1937) technic for fractionating hydatid fluid.

For intradermal tests the purified powdered Dennis antigen is diluted 1 to 10,000 in physiologic salt solution and 0.2 cc. of this solution employed.

Complement fixation.—The antigen consists of hydatid fluid removed aseptically from known infected human cases or from infected domestic mammals. Fairley (1922) found antigen obtained from sheep having cysts with viable scolices to be most satisfactory. Contaminated antigen must not be used. For this test the Dennis purified powdered antigen is diluted 1 to 5000 and is utilized as in the Kolmer modification of the Wassermann test. This antigen is sensitive, specific, not anticomplementary and apparently gives no false positive tests.

Indirect Hemagglutination.—The indirect hemagglutination test has been compared with complement fixation and with bentonite flocculation (Garabedian *et al.*, 1957; Kagan *et al.*, 1959) and has been found to be more sensitive and just as specific when used with dialyzed hydatid fluid. More recently a modification of the Dennis antigen (*loc. cit.*) has been found to be more sensitive than unfractionated hydatid fluid for use in the hemagglutination test (Kagan, 1960).

Cysticercus cellulosæ.—*Intradermal Test.*—This is a group-specific test. In testing for *C. cellulosæ* in man, antigen may be obtained from fluid of various species of cysticerci in domestic animals.

Precipitin Test.—The reaction is carried out as in testing hydatid infection. Antigen fluid is obtained from cysticerci from previous human cases, or, more practically, from the bladder worms of *Tænia solium* or other species of *Tænia*, the larvæ of which develop in hogs, rabbits and other intermediate hosts.

Immunologic Tests Involving Arthropods

Although Blacklock and Thompson (1923) demonstrated that invasion of the tissues of experimental laboratory animals by the larvæ (maggots) of the tumbu-fly, *Cordylobia anthropophaga*, calls forth notable immune response to subsequent attack, this phenomenon has not been employed as a clinical laboratory test in this or other arthropod infestations. The only practical use which has been made of the sensitization reaction to arthropod metabolites concerns the venom of the honey bee. Persons who develop hypersensitivity to bee sting may be desensitized and thus freed of the liability of fatal anaphylactic shock.

Precipitin Tests for Blood Ingested by Arthropods.—Malariologists and other workers frequently need to know whether a mosquito or other blood-sucking arthropod is selective in animals on which it feeds, to determine whether a particular species is dangerous as a transmitter of infectious agents from person to person. Precipitin tests and other standard methods of blood sampling provide the methods for obtaining this information.

Additional application of the precipitin test has been made by Weitz and Buxton (1953), to determine the period of digestion of blood meals by various arthropods. Mosquitoes and the midge *Culicoides* usually gave positive tests up to 24 hours; some tsetse flies (*Glossina morsitans*) up to 3 days but another species (*G. swynnertoni*) only within a much shorter time; the soft-bodied tick, *Ornithodoros moubata*, more than 6 months, and the rat mite, *Bdellonyssus bacoti*, only 1 day.

Tests for Virus Neutralizing Antibodies in Mosquitoes.—In the study of arthropod-borne viruses, it is important to know how long species which have fed on immune vertebrate hosts retain the specific antibodies and what effect this may have on subsequent blood meals containing active virus of the same kind. Scrivani *et al.* (1953) studied this problem with *Aëdes nigromaculis* and *Culex tarsalis*, which are natural transmitters of Western equine encephalomyelitis. They found that immune antibodies do not remain active beyond a 24-hour period. This indicates that these mosquitoes collected in the field should be kept in the laboratory at room temperature for that period before they are pooled and frozen to test whether they are carrying the live virus.

REFERENCES

BACHMAN, G. W. 1929. An Intradermal Reaction in Experimental Trichinosis. J. Prev. Med., *2*, 513–523.

BLACKLOCK, D. B., and THOMPSON, M. G. 1923. A Study of the Tumbu-fly, *Cordylobia anthropophaga* Grünberg, in Sierre Leone. Ann. Trop. Med. & Parasitol., *17*, 443–510.

BOZICEVICH, J. 1950. Discussion of "The Complement Fixation Test for Hepatic Amebiasis." Am. J. Trop. Med., *30*, 154–157.

BOZICEVICH, J., DONOVAN, A., MAZZOTTI, L., DIAZ, T. A. and PADILLA, E. 1947. Intradermal and Complement Fixation Reactions Elicited by Various Antigens in Persons Infected with *Onchocerca volvulus*. Am. J. Trop. Med., *27*, 51–62.

BRANNON, M. J. C., and FAUST, E. C. 1949. Preparation and Testing of Specific Antigen for Diagnosis of Human Strongyloidiasis. Am. J. Trop. Med., *29*, 229–239.

CHAFFEE, E. T., BAUMAN, P. M., and SHAPILO, J. J. 1954. Diagnosis of Schistosomiasis by Complement Fixation. Am. J. Trop. Med. and Hyg., *3*, 905–913.

CHOPRA, R. N., DAS GUPTA, J. C., and DAVID, J. C. 1927. The Antimony Test in the Diagnosis of Kala-azar. Indian Med. Gaz., *62*, 688–691.

DANARAJ, T. J., DA SILVA, L., and SCHACHER, J. F. 1959. The Serological Diagnosis of Eosinophilic Lung (Tropical Eosinophilia) and its Etiological Implications. Am. J. Trop. Med. and Hyg., *8*, 151–159.

DENNIS, E. W. 1937. A Stable Concentrated Purified Antigen for the Immunological Study of Hydatid Disease. J. Parasitol., *23*, 62–67.

DEW, H. R., KELLAWAY, C. H., and WILLIAMS, F. E. 1925. The Intradermal Reaction in Hydatid Disease and Its Clinical Value. Med. J. Australia, *i*, 471–478.

DOSTROVSKY, A., and SAGHER, F. 1946. The Intracutaneous Test in Cutaneous Leishmaniasis. Ann. Trop. Med. & Parasitol., *40*, 265–269.

FAIRLEY, N. H. 1922. The Complement-Fixation Test for Hydatid Disease and Its Clinical Value. Med. J. Australia, *i*, 341–346.

—————. 1931. Serological and Intradermal Tests in Filariasis. Trans. R. Soc. Trop. Med. & Hyg., *24*, 635–648.

DE FREITAS, J. L. P. 1951. Reacão de fixacção do complemento para diagnóstico da molestia de Chagas pela técnica quantitativa. Arq. de Hig. e Saúde Púb., *16*, 55–94.

GARABEDIAN, G. A., MATOSSIAN, R. M. and DJANIAN, A. Y. 1957. An Indirect Hemagglutination Test for Hydatid Disease. J. Immunol., *78*, 269–272.

JACOBS, L., and LUNDE, M. H. 1957. A Hemagglutination Test for Toxoplasmosis. J. Parasitol., *43*, 308–314.

JUNG, R. C. and PACHECO, G. 1960. Use of a Hemagglutination Test in Visceral Larva Migrans. Am. J. Trop. Med. and Hyg., *9*, 185–191.

KAGAN, I. G. 1956. Studies on the Serology of Trichinosis with Hemagglutination, Agar Diffusion Tests and Precipitin Ring Tests. J. Parasitol., *42*, 237–245.

KAGAN, I. G., ALLAIN, D. S., and NORMAN, L. 1959. An Evaluation of the Hemagglutination and Flocculation Tests in the Diagnosis of Echinococcus Disease. Am. J. Trop. Med. and Hyg., *8*, 15–55.

KAGAN, I. G., NORMAN, L., and ALLAIN, D. 1959. Studies in the Serology of Visceral Larva Migrans. I. Hemagglutination and Flocculation Tests with Purified *Ascaris* Antigens. J. Immunol., *83*, 297–301.

—————. 1960. Studies on Echinococcosis: Serology of Crude Fractionated Antigens Prepared from *Echinococcus granulosus* and *Echinococcus multilocularis*. Am. J. Trop. Med. and Hyg., *9*, 248–261.

LUNDE, M. H., and JACOBS, L. 1958. A Comparison of Results of Hemagglutination and Dye Tests for Toxoplasmosis in a Survey of Trinidad Natives. Am. J. Trop. Med. and Hyg., *7*, 523–525.

MUÑIZ, J. 1948. Do valor da reacção de precipitina no diagnóstico das formas agudas e sub-agudas de "doença de Chagas" (("trypanosomiasis americana"). Mem. Inst. Oswaldo Cruz, *45*, 537–549.

NAPIER, L. E. 1921. Kala-azar. Indian Med. Gaz., *56*, 401–404.

NEWSOME, J. 1958. Species Specific Serological Tests for Bilharzia. Ann. Trop. Med. and Parasit., *52*, 82–86.

OLIVER-GONZÁLEZ, J. 1954. Anti-egg Precipitin in the Serum of Humans Infected with *S. mansoni*. J. Infect. Dis., *95*, 86–91.

—————. 1941. The Dual Antibody Basis of Acquired Immunity in Trichinosis. J. Infect. Dis., *69*, 254–270.

OLIVER-GONZÁLEZ, J., BAUMAN, P. M., and BENENSON, A. S. 1955. Immunological Aspects of Infections with *Schistosoma mansoni*. Am. J. Trop. Med. and Hyg., *4*, 443–452.

PELLEGRINO, J., BRENER, Z., and POMPEU MEMORIA, S. M. 1959. A Comparative Study of Intradermal Tests and Stool Examinations in Epidemiological Surveys on Schistosomiasis Mansoni. Am. J. Trop. Med. and Hyg., *8*, 307–311.

SABIN, A. B. 1949. Complement Fixation Test in Toxoplasmosis and Persistence of the Antibody in Human Beings. Pediatrics, *4*, 443–453.

SABIN, A. B., and FELDMAN, H. A. 1948. Dyes as Microchemical Indicators of a New Immunity Phenomenon Affecting a Protozoön Parasite. Science, *108*, 660–663.

SADUN, E. H., and BUCK, A. A. 1960. Paragonimiasis in South Korea—Immunodiagnostic, Epidemiologic, Clinical, Roentgenological and Therapeutic Studies. Am. J. Trop. Med. and Hyg., *9*, 562–599.

SADUN, E. H., LIN, S. S., and WALTON, B. C. 1959. Studies on the Host Parasite Relationships to *Schistosoma japonicum*. III. The Use of Purified Antigens in the Diagnosis of Infections in Humans and Experimental Animals. Mil. Med., *124*, 428–436.

SADUN, E. H., and NORMAN, L. 1955. The Use of an Acid Soluble Protein Fraction in the Flocculation Tests for the Diagnosis of Trichinosis. J. Parasitol., *41*, 476–482.

SCRIVANI, R. P., REEVES, W. C., and BROOKMAN, B. 1953. Duration of Activity of Western Equine Encephalomyelitis Neutralizing Bodies in *Aëdes nigromaculis* and *Culex tarsalis*. Am. J. Trop. Med. & Hyg., *2*, 457–463.

SENTERFIT, L. 1958. Immobilization of the Miracidia of *Schistosoma mansoni* by Immune Sera. I. The Nature of the Reaction as Studied in Hamster Sera. Am. J. Hyg., *68*, 140–155.

SCHOFIELD, F. D. 1959. The Schistosomal Complement-Fixation Test. Trans. Roy. Soc. Trop. Med. & Hyg., *53*, 64–74.

SUESSENGUTH, H. and KLINE, B. S. 1944. A Simple Rapid Flocculation Slide Test for Trichinosis. Am. J. Clin. Path., *14*, 471–484.

VOGEL, H., and MINNING, W. 1948. Hüllenbildung bei Bilharzia-Cercaria im Serum Bilharzia infizierter Tiere und Menschen. Zentralbl. f. Bakt. I Orig., *153*, 99–105.

WEITZ, B., and BUXTON, P. A. 1953. The Rate of Digestion of Blood Meals of Various Hematophagous Arthropods as Determined by the Precipitin Test. Bull. Ent. Research, *44*, 445–450.

Chapter 22

Entomological Material, Intermediate and Reservoir Hosts

Introduction.—The usefulness of this material is threefold. The organism may be the causative agent, the suspected transmitter or an important host harboring the agent of human disease. It may prove to be a valuable demonstration for teaching medical students, sanitary officers or technicians. And it may provide opportunity for carrying out a research problem. In spite of the fact that much is known about the epidemiologic aspects of infections produced by animal parasites, a great deal remains to be learned. Specimens obtained in the hospital, brought in by patients to the clinic or collected in the field should be given careful examination, even though many of them are plentiful and have no particular medical interest; a few may be important.

First of all, it is necessary to distinguish between living and dead specimens. In the former case it may be desirable to keep the material alive or to culture it to a more mature stage. If the specimens are dead and there is need to preserve them, it will be helpful to know whether they keep well as dry objects or should be preserved in liquid media such as alcohol or formalin. If the specimens are captured alive and are to be preserved, then it is necessary to know the most satisfactory methods of anesthetizing them so that their exhibit value will be retained.

Collection and Preservation of Arthropods.—The technic of collecting arthropods varies, depending on the type or group concerned. Centipedes, scorpions, ticks, spiders and assassin-bugs are brought into the laboratory by interested persons for identification. If placed in a dry container they are usually not damaged when they arrive. Trombiculid mites (*i.e.*, "red bugs"), sarcoptoid mites and human lice may be preserved in small vials containing alcohol. Bed-bugs can be obtained by careful search in infested homes. Adult fleas can be removed from dogs and cats by touching them with a camel's hair brush moistened with xylol or chloroform and removing them with fine forceps to a vial or jar. Rats caught in traps may be placed in an air-tight chloroform chamber for removal of their fleas, mites and lice. Flea larvæ are readily obtained by sieving the sweepings from the floors of dwellings occupied by infested persons, dogs or cats.

The aquatic forms are collected with a dipper and transferred to bottles with a pipette. Adult insects in the open may be captured with a collecting net, taken from resting surfaces by means of a suction tube, or collected in appropriate traps which utilize shelter, food or light as the attractant. The eggs, larvæ or pupæ of mosquitoes, sand-flies or *Culicoides* may be collected as indicated above and brought into the laboratory for completing the developmental stages. *Culex* and *Aëdes* mosquitoes may usually be bred through several generations in the laboratory, so that students may have complete demonstration of their life cycles, but most species of *Anopheles* require larger, better controlled breeding quarters than the average laboratory is able to provide.

Filth flies which breed in garbage, human feces and animal manure, or decaying meat, may be obtained as adults from unprotected latrines, garbage piles and dead animals lying on the ground, or the gravid females may be induced to oviposit or larviposit in the laboratory on decaying food or manure as culture media.

Soft-bodied larvæ should be killed in hot water and preserved in 70% alcohol. Ticks, mites, lice, fleas, and other arthropods with hard exoskeletons may be placed directly in the alcohol. Arthropods should not be stored in formaldehyde solution because this causes excessive shrinkage and hardening, and alcohol ruins adult mosquitoes for purposes of identification.

Winged adult insects are best preserved as dry specimens mounted on insect pins. Killing jars of any desired size are prepared by placing granular potassium or sodium cyanide in a wide-mouth bottle and covering it with a layer of sawdust held in place by a disc of cardboard or plaster of Paris. A chloroform tube, most generally used for mosquitoes, consists of a corked test tube containing rubber bands which are soaked with chloroform and covered with a layer of cotton and a tightly fitted disc of blotting paper. Larger specimens are mounted on pins thrust through the thorax, while mosquitoes and other small species are placed on a minute pin carried on a small block of cork or balsa wood on the larger pin. Small specimens may also be glued to the side of a pin or to the point of a slender triangle of paper borne on the pin. Pinned specimens are not treated with a preservative but are simply allowed to dry. To protect them from dust, air currents, and museum pests, they must be stored in tight boxes lined with a pinning surface of sheet cork, balsa wood, or two layers of corrugated carton paper. Individual specimens may be pinned on a cork inserted in a vial. For transportation to specialists for identification, unmounted flies and mosquitoes should be placed between layers of soft paper in a well-buffered pill box. Dry specimens may be pinned after softening them in a moist chamber containing phenol to inhibit molds.

Collection and Preservation of Molluscs.—While the clinical laboratory has no special need for preserving snails or other molluscs, the laboratory may be called on to make identification of the specimens. This is a task for specialists, frequently at a distance from the laboratory, and molluscs do not ordinarily survive shipment in a living condition. Snails should be relaxed by slowly adding menthol crystals or Nembutal solution to the water in which they are placed, then killed in hot water and preserved in 70% alcohol.

Collection and Preservation of Vertebrate Animals.—Fishes and reptiles may be preserved either in 4% formaldehyde or 70% alcohol and will keep well, provided slits have been made beforehand into the animal's body cavities so that the viscera will be adequately fixed. Although it is not usual to preserve the entire bird or mammal, this may be done and the animal mounted if the technician is a good taxidermist. More frequently only the "skins" of birds and the pelts and skulls of mammals are kept. These, too, require some skill to prevent their deterioration and considerable care that they do not become infested with maggots before they are "cured."

Identification of Specimens.—The time has long since passed when it is sufficient to identify an arthropod as a tick, mite, fly or mosquito. Similarly there is need for adequate identification of molluscs and vertebrate animals, especially if they have a connection with disease in man or domestic animals. In case such expert service is not available in the immediate vicinity and the specimen seems worthy of diagnosis, it should be shipped to a specialist. The one institution in the United States, in which there is a corps of experts always willing to make identification of adequately preserved specimens, is the U. S. National Museum, Washington, D. C. It will be well first to address a letter to "The Curator of [Arthropods, Molluscs, Fishes Reptiles, Birds, Mammals, etc.]," at the U.S. National Museum, advising him of the need for identification and requesting instructions for packaging and prepaid shipment. Although several weeks may be required before the identification has been made, it can be depended on as being accurate, provided the material sent is in identifiable condition and arrives in an undamaged state.

The Mounting of Arthropods as Permanent Preparations.—Some of the smaller arthropods and early larval stages of larger ones are sufficiently clear and transparent so that *in toto* mounts may be made by passing them through dehydrating and clearing agents into balsam or clarite. Others, which have tissues that are too dense for satisfactory slide preparations without special treatment, should be placed in 10% cold aqueous potassium hydroxide solution for 24 hours. If rapid diagnosis is essential, the specimens may be punctured with finely pointed needles, placed in the caustic solution and heated to steaming for a few minutes, care being exercised not to cause their disintegration. After thorough washing they are ready for dehydration and clearing. For sectioning of arthropods or arthropod parts, the organism should be carefully punctured to allow rapid penetration of the fixing fluid. Bles' fixative (225 parts 70% alcohol, 18 parts formalin, and 7 parts glacial acetic acid) is recommended.

Chloral Hydrate Mounting Medium.—Probably the simplest practical method for killing, fixing, dehydrating, staining, clearing and mounting small arthropods (as *Cyclops* and *Diaptomus*, mites, unfed stages of ticks, fleas, lice, bedbugs, mosquito larvæ, pupæ and adults, other small blood-sucking or filth flies, as well as their dissected diagnostic parts) consists in using Doetschman's modification of the Berlese technic (Doetschman, 1944). The formula is as follows:

Distilled water	35 cc.
Chloral hydrate	20 Gm.
Gum arabic	20 Gm.
Glycerol	20 cc.
Glucose syrup	3 cc.
Basic fuchsin	10 drops or more

The gum arabic will dissolve readily if the solution is heated in a water bath. This method likewise prevents carbonization of the chloral hydrate and caramelization of the glucose. The water in the solution should be evaporated until a desired viscosity has been obtained. Living specimens or those previously fixed and preserved in 70% alcohol may be utilized. The mounts should have little slivers of glass between the slide and coverglass to prevent too much compression of the mounted object. The preparation clears almost immediately and may be utilized as a temporary mount, or it may be heated in a drying oven at 37° to 40° C. for permanency. Air bubbles in the preparation will be minimized if 1 drop of the medium is placed on the slide, the object to be mounted centered therein and a second drop of the medium placed on the lower side of the coverglass to be superimposed on the object. Polyvinyl alcohol mounting medium may be used in a similar manner for mounting small specimens. This is prepared by dissolving 10 Gm. of polyvinyl alcohol in 100 to 150 cc. of water at 70° C. and adding 40 cc. of lactic acid to form a clear solution of the desired viscosity.

Larger arthropods which remain in good condition as demonstration objects following dehydration may be successfully mounted in clear plastic medium. Instructions and material for plastic mounts may be obtained from several biological supply houses, including General Biological Supply House, Chicago, Illinois and Ward's Natural Science Establishment, Rochester, N.Y.

Care of Demonstration Collections.—Demonstrations and mounted specimens which are preserved as dry mounts must be kept in tight boxes away from dust and breeze. Precautions must be constantly taken to prevent the small, plump, hairy larvæ of *Anthrenus museorum* and *A. verbasci* (dermestid beetles) from eating the specimens. Crystals of paradichlorobenzene, placed in a little cardboard or paper cup in one corner of each box and renewed 3 to 4 times a year, will guard against such danger.

REFERENCES

Abbott, R. T. 1948. Handbook of Medically Important Mollusks of the Orient and Western Pacific. Bull. Mus. Comp. Zoöl., Harvard Coll., *100*, 246–328.

Doetschman, W. H. 1944. Some Suggestions in Microtechnique Particularly Useful in Microëntomology and Parasitology. Trans. Am. Micr. Soc., *63*, 175–178.

Eltringham, H. 1930. *Histological and Illustrative Methods for Entomologists.* Clarendon Press, Oxford (England), 139 pp.

Fox, C. 1925. *Insects and Diseases of Man.* Chap. 22, "A Few Notes on Technique." P. Blakiston's Son & Co., Philadelphia.

Frings, H. 1947. A Simple Method for Rearing Blowflies without Meat. Science, *105*, 482.

Smart, J. 1940. Instructions for Collectors. No. 4a. Brit. Museum of Nat. Hist., London. 164 pp.

Index of Authors

A

Abadie, 290, 292
Abbott, 459
Abdel Aziz Salah, 395, 414
Acosta-Matienzo, 426
Addario, 314
Adler, 41, 45
Adrouny, 365, 395
Africa, 144, 159, 265
Agosín, 319
Aldridge, 275
Alexeieff, 35
Alford, 405, 414
Alicata, 148, 159, 279, 288
Allain, 454
Allen, R. W., 193, 220
Altenkamp, 192, 220
Alving, 124
Amaral, 258, 288
Amberson, 257, 288
Anderson, H. H., 15, 19
Anderson, W. B., 391, 395
Andrade, 206, 220
Andrade Lima, 258, 288
Andrews, J. M., 17, 20
Andrews, W. H., 268
Andrews, W. H. H., 20, 112, 125
Anond, 200, 220
Antell, 289
Anthony, 292
Apablaza, 124
Arnold, 118, 124
Arru, 354, 357
Artigas, 438, 439
Asenjo, 206, 207, 220
Ash, 6, 15, 20, 112, 114, 124, 165
Ashburn, L. L., 308, 319
Ashburn, P. M., 402, 413
Ashford, 253
Ashton, 283, 288, 292
Askanazy, 260
Atencio, 174
Atkins, 343, 357
Audy, 332, 333, 407, 413
Augustine, 279, 288
Austin, 358
Azar, 178, 184

B

Bachman, 450, 453

Baelz, 154
Baer, 7, 19
Baerg, 338
Baker, E. W., 357
Baker, J. R., 59, 68
Balamuth, 441, 447
Bambridge, 320
Bancroft, F. W., 446, 447
Bancroft, J., 236, 293
Barlow, 136, 138, 159, 177, 184
Barnett, 368, 395, 407, 413
Baroody, 427, 439
Barrett, 83, 214, 220
Barretto, 46, 47, 68
Basnuevo, 137
Bastianelli, 99
Batsch, 210
Battistini, 449
Bauman, 164, 185, 453, 454
Bautier, 409
Bavay, 260
Baylis, 268, 270, 325, 327
Beadle, 403, 413
Beard, 290
Beattie, 127, 129
Beaver, 16, 20, 74, 82, 83, 88, 89, 180, 182,
    185, 197, 198, 220, 228, 230, 234, 235,
    239, 242, 252, 254, 256, 280, 281, 282,
    283, 284, 288, 289, 290, 429, 436, 439
Beck, 231, 289, 324, 326
Becker, 344, 357
Belding, 6, 131
Bell, 157, 160, 320
Benenson, 164, 185, 454
Bengtson, 405, 407, 413
Bennett, 221
Bennington, 141, 159
Ber, 41
Berberian, 45, 51, 67, 83, 88, 191, 195
Berry, 166, 185
Besa, 185
Beye, 18, 20
Beyer, 363
Biagi, 160
Bicalho, 358
Bickerstaff, 206, 220
Bierstein, 185
Bignami, 99
Bilharz, 142, 172, 175, 196
Biocca, 181, 184, 252, 289
Blacklock, 304, 307, 452, 453
Blanchard, 153, 179, 196, 197, 198, 329

(461)

Subject Index

A